THE LIFE OF
MAMMALS

THE LIFE OF
MAMMALS

BY

J. Z. YOUNG
M.A., F.R.S.
PROFESSOR OF ANATOMY
AT UNIVERSITY COLLEGE
LONDON

OXFORD UNIVERSITY PRESS
NEW YORK & OXFORD
1957

PRINTED IN THE UNITED STATES OF AMERICA

PREFACE

WHEN presenting any subject it has to be decided whether to accept a conventional method, known and widely accepted, or to try to invent a better one. The latter is the more exciting course, but a compromise is safer for the author and kinder to his readers, who want to learn the subject as it is. This book attempts to have the best of both methods. It presents mammalian anatomy, physiology, histology, and embryology as they are, and at the same time tries to show what in the future they may be. It begins with a discussion of biological method, which may seem to be a strange and difficult subject to the scientist, who is apt to leave these matters to philosophers. I recommend even the beginner to read it before he passes to the detailed work of the rest of the book. It may show him how many parts of the subject are imperfect and how they can be illuminated by use of a new language that considers the body as a self-controlling machine. This idea is not new but in developing it I have been pleased to find how interesting it makes the consideration of the structure and function of many parts of the body. I have not been able to apply the methods of information theory fully or exactly, but I hope that others may come to do so and to find in the study of control the clue that unifies many parts of Biology.

As one tries to treat the whole organization of life in this way it seems that a new science is growing with every word. This is very exciting, but the average student of biology or medicine cannot wait for a new science to be born. He must learn now, and the book attempts to give an orthodox presentation that will be acceptable by the most conventional, while yet showing how new approaches can be incorporated.

The book is meant to be used as a systematic aid to the student of mammals and man who has already some general familiarity with biology. It should serve as a companion to a course of practical study of dissection and of histology and embryology. Drawings of dissections and sections are included with the hope that they will be found useful in the laboratory. The book was first drafted some years ago when I was writing the *Life of Vertebrates* and in a sense it forms part of that work. But it became clear that a Life of Mammals of somewhat different scope might be useful not only to zoologists beginning their course but to others as well.

Most students first learn about mammals through dissecting the rabbit or the rat and the book therefore gives special attention to these species. For the medical student these mammals are an introduction to the study of man and I have tried to present their biology in a way that will be useful for this purpose. In particular the sections on the skeletal and muscular systems and on neurology are meant to provide an introduction to those subjects as they are treated by human anatomists and physiologists. Too often the zoologist who trains future medical students is unfamiliar with the methods and terminology that his pupils will meet later. One aim of this book is to bridge the gaps between the basic and the medical aspects of biology. Unfortunately the book ignores altogether many aspects of mammalian life that many would wish to study, for example ecology. It provides only a framework or scheme for the study of mammalian life, within which much else could be incorporated.

It is impossible for any work of this sort to be authoritative and original as well as comprehensive. I have tried to cover the ground but have had no hesitation in lingering longer in the fields that have interested me especially. I doubt whether anyone suffers by learning from a book in which he can discern the personality, interests, and foibles of the author. Perhaps some of the complaints about the aridity of science come from the attempt to produce giant comprehensive textbooks written by collections of depersonalized authors. One of the chief lessons for any intending scientist is that the facts that he is told may be wrong and that points of view differ and change. This is no excuse for making mistakes, as I have no doubt often done; but let a critic realize that the anxiety involved in uttering such a work is formidable. References appropriate to each chapter are given at the end of the book. Recent references have generally been preferred and this has meant omitting classical ones. A contemporary survey, even if of little originality or critical worth, is often the most useful reference from which to work backwards through the literature.

Any system of arrangement of so vast a subject-matter will seem to be in some way illogical. The plan adopted assumes that the student will first dissect the parts of the mammalian body and learn the microscopic appearance of the tissues at the same time. Having dealt with the skeletal and vascular systems he will study the individual organs, and last the nervous system, receptor organs, and endocrines. During this work he will often want to know about development, but in practice the study of embryology is distinct and is here treated separately at the end.

In due time we shall learn how to combine macroscopic and microscopic studies with those of biochemistry and biophysics. All that I have been able to do here is to issue reminders that there is a connexion and to suggest possible means of unification.

Preparation of such a treatise involves collaboration by many people. I should like to thank most warmly all those who have given help, directly or indirectly. Many have read sections dealing with their own specialities and are mentioned separately below. Others have allowed their illustrations to be copied or have provided the material for new pictures. The figures have been drawn from life or redrawn from other figures by Miss E. R. Turlington and Miss J. I. D. de Vere. Their faculties of observation, care, and skill have been disciplined continually by a consideration of the needs of the user. The production of such representations is an integral part of the work of biology, for which we cannot be too grateful. Mr. J. P. Stanier and Dr. E. G. Gray have helped with innumerable tasks of editing, assembling of figures, and of bibliography. Finally, it is a pleasure to record my thanks to the Secretary and Staff of the Clarendon Press for their skilful and willing collaboration in the preparation of the book.

J. Z. Y.

January 1957

ACKNOWLEDGEMENTS

My grateful thanks are due to the following, who spent much time reading and criticizing various parts of the manuscripts and proofs:

J. T. Aitken	D. Mackay
L. E. Bayliss	D. R. Newth
A. d'A. Bellairs	R. J. Pumphrey
R. Bellairs	K. C. Richardson
E. C. Cherry	A. Shefford
B. G. Cragg	D. A. Sholl
J. A. B. Gray	M. Smith
R. J. Harrison	W. K. Taylor
A. F. Huxley	D. R. Wilkie

F. G. Young

Dr. W. Hedley Jones helped with the dissections upon which the figures of the rabbit are based. Professor M. Maizels and Miss E. M. Graves kindly helped with the figures of blood cells, Dr. E. A. Fraser with those of the development of the kidney, and Dr. D. R. Newth with the development of the frog.

CONTENTS

XII. DIGESTION

XIII. THE INTERNAL ENVIRONMENT AND COMPOSITION OF THE BODY FLUIDS

XIV. THE HEART AND CIRCULATION

XV. RESPIRATION

XVI. EXCRETION AND THE CONTROL OF WATER BALANCE

XVII. THE NERVOUS SYSTEM

XVIII. THE SPINAL CORD

XIX. THE ORGANIZATION OF THE BRAIN

I

THE CONTROL OF LIVING SYSTEMS

1. The methods of biology

It is easy to say that the purpose of any biological inquiry is to study the life of the organisms concerned, but this implies that we must begin by discussing what we mean by 'life' and by examining the methods that are available for investigating it. In an earlier time it would have been enough to say that this book about the life of mammals is an account of the structure, function, and development of the mammalian body; but a description like this in terms of the old and apparently obvious sciences of anatomy and physiology is no longer adequate. In order to make full use of recent advances we must inquire more closely into what is involved in the use of such terms as 'structure' and 'function'.

2. The development of the language of biology

No investigation of this sort can begin without making decisions about the terminology that is to be used, and this introduces questions that are usually dealt with by logicians and philosophers. It is not satisfactory for anyone to say that being a scientist he is not interested in such matters; if he does not discuss them the result will be that he proceeds to use uncritically the words he has learned. Adequate representation by one person to another about any subject-matter depends upon agreement about the use of symbols.

For our present purpose we have to make a brief study of the words that are used for the description of living activities. Words have many functions and it would be impossible here to give a proper account even of the sorts of words that are commonly used by biologists. Nevertheless some consideration of the problem helps to show the significance of recent changes in biological terminology and allows us to reorganize our knowledge more satisfactorily.

Animals may be said to remain alive by taking action that foreshadows or predicts the probable course of events (p. 18). They can do this because the body, and especially the brain, contains a record of past sequences and associations. Use is made of this record by comparing each new situation with it so that, if the comparison is sound, an accurate forecast results. As each individual life proceeds an increasing store of 'knowledge' about probable sequences of events is built up and this is drawn upon in each new situation, so that actions that ensure survival can be made in circumstances that resemble those of the past.

In man the individual is able to improve his store of knowledge by drawing upon the experience of others, and one of the functions of words is to ensure this transmission of information. One individual can tell another about the probable outcome of a situation by showing him that it is like some other one that is already familiar to the receiver.

The process of description thus consists in one person adding his experience to that of another. A basic problem for any developing science, therefore, is to decide what comparisons are likely to prove effective for conveying information about the subject-matter.

Certain principles controlling the efficiency of such communication can be recognized. The effectiveness of comparison of a new situation with a given object or process depends upon the familiarity of the recipient with that object. If I say that an animal or a river is raging or acting fiercely this conveys to the listener much about the probability of its future behaviour, because he has studied fierceness in human behaviour and is able to forecast what a fierce system will do. The accuracy of his forecasts will also depend, however, upon the adequacy of the comparison. He may, for example, be led to act as if it was more complete than it is, as if he tries to placate the fierceness of the weather with an offering that would appease a man. Effective description, therefore, requires to be made by comparisons that are understood by all people and yet are exact, including neither too much nor too little.

Fully effective comparisons have hitherto only been available for some of the simpler phenomena of the physical world but they present an ideal to which biological science can strive. In trying to provide a system that enables others to learn how living organisms behave we need to use terms that relate to a wide range of human experience and yet are adequate to describe all the many complexities of living systems. This is not an easy task. The language of the physical sciences is exact and general and biology uses it where possible, but where physical language is not able to describe some aspect of living other words may have to be called in. Some scientists would say that unless the language of physical science can be used by biology no progress can be made. Apart from the compromise with honesty that would be involved in leaving out many of the observations, biologists who have to make practical application of their science clearly cannot adopt this view. A doctor cannot neglect to treat a diseased brain because language for speaking about that organ is inexact.

A more profitable approach is to consider so far as we are able the types of comparison that have been made in the description of aspects of living, in order to discover the principles of the growth of biological language. Then we can apply these principles in the attempt to make further improvements in methods of description. Anyone who does not find new words such as those adopted in this book to his taste can of course suggest others that he thinks will describe the phenomena more fully. Criticism of the use of the new categories here suggested, such as 'information' and 'representation', is only justified if others are provided that will cover the same data.

The history of the origin of language is obscure and will perhaps never be discovered. Many animals produce signs or sounds that 'release' particular patterns of sexual or avoidance behaviour in others. Communication about events in the world around presumably depended at first on the transmitter's producing behaviour that in some way represented an external situation and elicited in the recipient behaviour appropriate to those events. A parallel can be seen in the 'language' of bees, where the 'dance' of a worker returning to the hive is so related to the direction of the honey found that other bees, following the dance, move off in the right direction (v. Frisch; Haldane, and Spurway, 1954). We do not know how signs and sounds were first used by men to indicate external situations. Onomatapoeic sounds and gestures with the hands and face still serve to make representations in this way, arousing appropriate responses in the receiver. But it is a long way from those signs to communication by our elaborate set of symbols.

It is impossible to discuss here the whole question of the development of language. We cannot even hope to follow adequately the complicated question of the evolution of biological terminology. Johannesen (1950) has shown that in languages as distinct as Arabic and Old Indo-European there are certain common features in the terms used for parts of the body. Thus in such languages many of the words for the head refer either to the direction upwards, or to the curve of the vault of the cranium, or to the act of slaughter for butchery, or augury. The fact that so much of early language centres around terms of direction had led Paget and Johannesen to the theory that the basic activity involved is gesturing with the tongue and hands. Today, even in arguments about complicated mathematical matters, a speaker will often use his hands in the attempt to arouse an appropriate response in the brains of the listeners.

The point for our present discussion is to recognize that communication about some object or situation new to the receiver involves the making of comparison with one that is familiar. We see many examples in anatomy of comparisons that are made to call attention to the shape of organisms or their parts. These comparisons are not necessarily of much relevance to the study of the whole life of the organism concerned. For example, many anatomical terms indicate comparison with familiar objects of everyday life—the neopallium (new cloak) of the brain or the navicular (boatlike) bone of the foot.

3. Person language

A very powerful means for describing any system is to compare it with the face and its gestures, that is to say with a chief part of the human communication system itself. Every child learns in its early life the significance and names of the expressions of the face and the words that go with these. To react correctly to these expressions is the first essential of social life, to which the child is bound in order to obtain the means of subsistence. All normal human beings therefore can react appropriately when they hear, for example, that a fire or an animal is acting gently. This comparison with human features and human behaviour is the basis of a whole system of language in which the behaviour of entities is described by speaking as if they contain agents that act like human beings. We may call such a system *person language* and it has given rise to the most elaborate structures of animism and religion. It has been used extensively in biology, for example in the medicine of the Middle Ages, which attributed humours and spirits to each organ, speaking as if each contained a resident creature with properties resembling those of a person.

Such language has considerable descriptive power but it lacks generality. We can describe a disturbed condition of the liver as due to excess of its depressing humour but this tells us little or nothing further about this humour or its relationship to others except that they all produce actions that are in some way like those of whole men. As a system of biology, therefore, the method is circular (tautologous); it describes actions of the parts only in terms of those of the whole.

4. Language and tools

The language of science has been developed by making comparisons of events not only with human beings but with other aspects of nature and in particular with the tools that man has evolved. It is obvious that the most powerful and widely understood descriptive language in any generation will consist of words that refer to the means by which men at that time get their living. These will be the words that produce in others the most effective reactions. At a time when systems for ensuring co-operation between men were even less perfect than they are now, person language, based on attention to the human face and communication, held greater power than any other. Now that we operate by the use of a variety of tools and machines it is by reference to these, as well as to human co-operation, that the greatest effect can be achieved.

5. Tool language in biology

The development of the terminology of biology in the modern period has therefore involved the gradual introduction of methods of representation and description of living things in terms of tools and machines, rather than by comparison with human beings. At the same time the new tools themselves have been used for the investigation of living bodies, revealing aspects of them that were completely hidden to the unaided senses. We cannot now trace this history in detail but endless examples come to mind. After the taming of fire and understanding of its properties the actions of parts of the body came to be described in terms of inner fires. When cooking had developed the organs were said to produce various concoctions (Lat. *coquere*, to cook). With the development of windmills and clocks the body was likened to a machine, built with a certain 'structure' and with parts having 'functions'. When chemistry developed, men recognized the presence of elements and compounds in the body and applied chemical techniques to find out more about them. The discovery of electricity and of electrical machines led to analysis of the electrical properties of the body. Finally we shall have much to say about the effect upon biological description of the invention of machines that control themselves, performing calculations and storing information in their memory systems.

The process of development of tools and language for them is obviously a complicated one, which cannot be adequately described in a few sentences. Human populations seem to produce continual cycles of inventions. Tools are framed in order to imitate some function previously performed by the body. Familiarity with these tools leads to description of actions of the body in terms of some of them, and application of the tools themselves to biological study then produces further discoveries about the living organism. More elaborate tools are devised to imitate the newly discovered actions and the cycle repeats.

As our language and tools have evolved they have produced continually more perfect ways of forecasting the general course and the details of the future and providing means to meet it. It is characteristic of science that it has learned to extract certain general rules that apply to all phenomena and enable very exact forecasts to be made. Alchemists acquired a wide knowledge of the special properties of materials, but their general comparisons and theories were defective and of little power compared to the generalizations of modern chemistry, such as the laws of mass action and the periodic system.

Biology today has a great mass of information about particulars, but it is still provided with few generalizations that have power to forecast the characteristics of the behaviour of all living material. In the attempt to see how such generality may be achieved we may look briefly at some aspects of the history of biology in the recent past. Even a superficial study may show us how we can build upon existing knowledge and organize it around general principles. Inevitably our view will be limited by the terminology at present available. Study of the history of the subject should at least show that terms are valid only in their own day and context, and that this validity can be measured only by their effectiveness in forecasting—ultimately by whether the terms enable the race that uses them to make predictions by which it survives.

6. Naturalists' language

One very good way to study the life of any type of organism is to watch the behaviour of the creatures, to describe what they do under various circumstances. This is essentially the method used by naturalists and psychologists, and it is certainly useful in providing forecasts. If you have watched a rabbit warren or a household carefully you will be able to say rather exactly what the inhabitants are likely to do. Yet to restrict biology in this way to natural history and the observation of whole animals would be to ignore the method of analysis that has been developed by science during the past three or four hundred years. Some tremendous generalizations have been discovered by naturalists, notably the fact of evolution, but in recent times most of the advances in biology have been achieved by examining the many parts into which organisms can be divided and comparing the actions of these parts with those performed by man-made tools. The development of the subject has depended upon the application of new technical methods for revealing these parts and of new verbal methods for describing them. This method of analysis of what goes on inside the body has provided more powerful means of forecasting and controlling the actions of men, animals, and plants than was possible by observation only of the behaviour of whole organisms.

7. Classification and visual language

In this way the various sciences that comprise biology today have grown up. Anatomy achieved the first great successes. Man, like other primates, depends largely upon the eyes for information (p. 481), and in the modern period the first attempts to represent the contents of organisms consisted mostly in naming their visible parts. By the end of the sixteenth century the work of Vesalius and his successors had provided good descriptions of the parts of the body that are visible to the naked eye after dissections.

8. The growth of machine language

Then in the seventeenth century the successes of the physicists and early engineers led to the comparison of organisms with man-made machines. The actions of the parts that had been revealed by dissections were represented by saying that they had 'functions' and thus the science of 'physiology' grew up, especially following Harvey's demonstration of the circulation of blood and the action of the heart as a pump, and Descartes' attempt to treat the nervous, muscular, and other systems as parts of a 'machine'. We shall discuss the implications of the analogy between living bodies and machines again later; it has been the main basis of the attempt to separate the study of the activity of the parts ('physiology') from study of their visible structure ('anatomy'). A moment's thought will show that if we are considering the living body this distinction cannot be maintained. The apparently stable visible parts are the site of continual activity and change; if these actions stop, life ends. We need, therefore, to try to find some better comparison that will allow us to speak about these actions that maintain the body.

Anatomy and physiology arose as distinct sciences because men could name visible parts by comparison with other objects long before there were any machines available that acted in ways sufficiently complicated to allow useful comparison with living things. The drawing of successful new analogies is one of the most difficult of creative human activities. It took a Leonardo or a Descartes to see the possibility for human development that lay in what must then have seemed to be crude comparisons between men and machines. The sophisticated practitioners of any current technique will often scoff

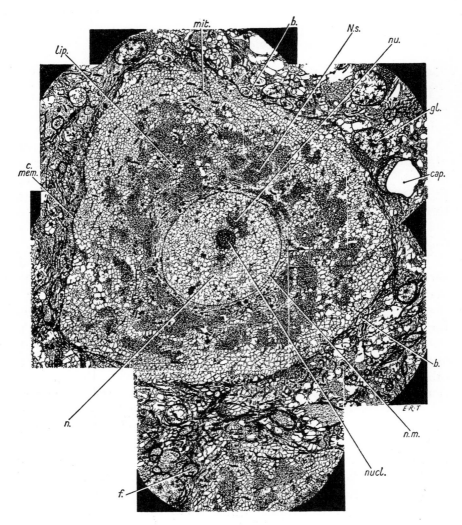

FIG. I. Drawing made from a set of electron microscope photographs of a nerve-cell from the spinal cord of the cat. Fixed in osmium tetroxide and sectioned at about o·I μ thickness.

b. terminal bouton; *cap.* capillary (with its nucleus); *c.mem.* outer membrane of the cell; *f.* nerve-fibre with thick myelin sheath; *gl.* glia cell; *lip.* opaque spheres ('lipochondria') corresponding in part to the Golgi material; *mit.* mitochondria; *n.* nuclear 'sap'; *n.m.* nuclear membrane; *N.s.* Nisal substance, containing nucleic acid and showing various types of organization, especially near to the nucleus; *nucl.* nucleolus, opaque because of high content of nucleic acid; *nu.* somewhat less dense nucleolar material.

at the simplicity and inadequacy of new comparisons, not realizing that their own language is different only in that its comparisons are even less effective.

In order to find methods by which living organization can be further described we must be prepared to explore the advantages of comparison with new types of machine and to apply to biology the language that goes with these machines. This process has indeed been going on continually throughout recorded human history, and with increasing activity since the seventeenth century.

9. Microscopy and the recognition of small parts

The invention of the microscope soon led to its use by Leeuwenhoek, Malphigi, and others for study of living things; it provided further powerful means for revealing the parts into which an organism can be divided. The process of looking at smaller and smaller parts of animals or plants has continued until the present day. For Hooke in the eighteenth century and Schleiden and Schwann in their cell theory of 1839, the cell was the unit of microscopical structure and was almost the smallest object that they could distinguish. By the end of the nineteenth century much smaller parts had been described in nucleus and cytoplasm. During the twentieth century improvements in visual microscopy and the invention of the electron microscope have revealed a range of still more minute 'structures' (Fig. 1).

10. The language of biochemistry

Meanwhile the development of chemistry provided a different method by which the constituent parts of organisms could be described. As the science of chemistry became perfected through the first part of the nineteenth century the biochemists' knowledge of the properties of the 'substances' that make up a living organism developed and now forms a collection of information as imposing as that provided by the anatomist. Like the latter the biochemist at first spent most of his time investigating the parts (substances) that can be separated from the body after death, but he is now beginning to find means of investigating the complicated system into which the substances weave themselves during life. Yet up to the present biochemistry has not succeeded in providing a general terminology by which we can show how the activities of the organism ensure its survival.

11. Biophysics

The fact that such aspects of living organisms as mass, temperature, energy change, and movement can be described in the language of physics has long been evident. Detailed application has been slow because the precise definitions of the physicist are hard to apply to the complicated situations in organisms. As electrical machines have been developed during the past century they have been applied to the study of living things and conversely the language of physicists and electrical engineers has been used to describe actions in the body. In the nineteenth century electrical engineering was chiefly concerned with problems of transmission of energy and biophysics dealt mainly with the energy changes in the body. In recent years physics and engineering have turned to the study of communication and control. This interest has led to such developments as radio communication and the study of machines that make 'predictions' and control themselves. The importance of this development for our purpose is that it is turning the attention of biologists to the study of problems of communication and control in organisms. As has happened so often before, we find it useful to compare ourselves with the new machines that have been produced to help us, such as calculating-machines, automatic factories, and guided missiles. The only thing that is new about this situation is that the comparisons are especially helpful in enabling us to describe the system that ensures that life goes on. We shall use them often throughout this book.

12. The divisions of biology

During recent centuries, therefore, man has learned to represent organisms by speaking of their visible structure, microscopic structure, and physico-chemical properties. These representations constitute the sciences of anatomy, physiology, histology, biochemistry, and biophysics, which provide the symbols that we use for describing and influencing adult living organisms.

The method of all these sciences has been essentially analytical in the sense that they have divided up the organism in some way, describing the parts separately. This method gives a great gain. In order to talk effectively about a complicated organization it is well to describe separately what happens in its various parts. In this way man has achieved considerable powers of control over himself and other creatures. Most of us, if we had a disordered stomach, would be glad of the attentions of men who are familiar with the anatomical and chemical representations of that organ. Biological and medical science certainly cannot afford to abandon this analytical approach; indeed we should go farther forward with it. Only by concentrating attention on parts can we make proper use of the methods of exact observation and measurement that the growth of science has made available.

13. A language that describes the whole of living organization

Nevertheless, it is a considerable disadvantage that our analytical approach fails to consider the whole organism and its organization. This omission is so obvious that it is often dismissed as unimportant. Indeed the omission is often denied; biologists claim that they put the organism together again in their minds after they have divided it into its cells or its molecules. No doubt the wish to do so is there, but a learner, looking at the numerous branches of biology, will soon begin to suffer from the fact that the biological specialist fails in practice to produce any complete representation of organisms from the fragments of his knowledge about them. It may seem to the beginner, groping among a mass of new facts, that the various branches of biological science have no common system of reference or framework of words with which to say how a living organism lives. Indeed, the bewildered novice may wonder sombrely how one human brain could possibly synthesize so much information. As he turns the thousands of pages of the great textbooks of anatomy, physiology, genetics, embryology, histology, and biochemistry he may well think that if the organization of a mammal contains so many parts as this then neither he himself nor anyone else can ever come to envisage such a complicated affair as a whole. It is difficult enough, he may feel, to describe the patterns of behaviour of objects with which he is familiar—his family or his motor-car. Can it ever be possible to have an exact idea of the combined actions of these hundreds of organs in the body, thousands of chemical substances, and millions of cells?

It must be admitted that biology has not yet proceeded far with the important business of describing the characteristics of the organization of a species as a whole. Each of the sciences that together make up biology has grown mainly independently, without much pause for thought about providing principles for the complete science. The result has been that each branch of biology has produced its own words for descriptions of facts and these are the statements that inevitably we must learn as biologists today. Yet it is obvious that the scientists in question, in spite of their differences of language, are all dealing with the same organism. No doubt in so far as each studies it in his own way he gives a different picture, and this variety is desirable. We want as many useful representations or views of the organism as we can get; the anatomist's vision is no more or less 'real' than the histologist's or the biochemist's. It may be profitable, however, to spend a little while in trying to see whether there is any unifying principle that could bring all these distinct approaches together.

It is beginning to be technically possible to do this at the present time because developments in statistics and in the methods for designing machines for handling and processing information have given us new ways of talking about elaborate self-controlled systems. The new approach allows the more ambitious attempt to frame an exact language for speaking about the interrelationship of all these parts, bringing together the various existing divisions of biological science, including not only those that deal with the daily life of organisms but also embryology and palaeontology, with their studies of past history. We can thus begin to see the outlines of a science of biology that covers all the aspects of life that we can yet understand.

The difficulty in doing this arises from the fact that every living creature contains many parts and is influenced by a great variety of agencies past and present, so that it is correspondingly hard to foretell what it will do. In the exact sciences, such as physics and chemistry, forecasts are accurate because the situations studied are relatively simple. Biochemistry has so far also dealt with isolated reactions or with rather short sequences of them. As biochemical knowledge develops longer sequences become understood and we need means for describing how these sequences are related to each other and to the behaviour of the whole organism.

This is, of course, a gigantic task and it must be appreciated that it is not likely that any system that is suggested will immediately be perfectly successful. The method adopted here is to use the terminology by which we speak of the control of human behaviour, saying that an individual acts because of the *information* that he has received. In daily life this method of speaking allows us to describe with some accuracy the 'causes' of the varied actions even of complex human characters. Moreover, in recent years engineers concerned with the problems of transmission of speech by telephone, radio, &c., have devised methods by which rates of transmission of information can be measured. With suitable modification it may be possible to use these statistical methods to describe the contributions of 'information' from various sources by which living processes are controlled. Yet it is important not to be deceived into thinking that a neat system of words solves the problem. Logicians and mathematicians have not yet succeeded in devising means by which amounts of information can be exactly defined and measured under various conditions, though they are actively seeking to do so (see Mackay, 1950; Jackson, 1953). What they have achieved is a means of measuring amount of information when the context in which the information is received is accurately known.

It is important also to recognize that the purpose for which this or any other comparison is used is only to allow description to others of an obscure set of events by noting its similarity with events that are already well understood. Classical physics developed by use of just such comparisons, for example those of 'force' and 'energy', borrowed from the daily words that are used to describe simple human actions. These words are very effective in describing the changes in simple systems, where one or a few agents act upon others. Similarly there is reason to hope that the complicated actions of whole living organisms, influenced by many factors, can be described by saying that they are controlled by 'information', as a whole man might be. This method may be useful for a while, no better being available; later it may be discarded.

We know that someone is receiving information by observing the decisions that he makes. We say that he has received information from this source or that by studying the actions that he takes after various preceding events have occurred. The concept of information is thus related to that of causality but its special characteristic is that the greater part of a man's information is received in the form of a code of words and other signals, which has been learned beforehand by the transmitter and receiver. This code is related to the events that occur around the men and to the acts that they perform. Information transmitted by selecting words from the language ensures that the receiver selects appropriate responses from the many that he could give. *Information theory* is the branch of statistical science that deals, among other things, with communication by transmission of signals selected from a code. Its terminology therefore gives us a possibility of describing the adaptive character of living actions, which, it must be stressed again, is not allowed for in the classical terminology of biochemistry and biophysics. Information theory does not, of course, replace these studies, but supplements them by allowing description of how sets of physical processes are selected in living organisms.

In order to apply to organisms the words that are used to describe information transfer we must therefore be able to recognize some form of communication channel, with at one end a transmitter and at the other a receiver or agent, the two being separated by a series of events in a transmission line, which events can be said to constitute a code. The amount of information received per unit time is measured in terms of the number of possible alternatives between which decision is made by the receiver.

Although we are not yet in a position to apply this method in detail and quantitatively to biology it is already clear that it has considerable value in unifying our description of the various factors that control life. It can be applied wherever we find that the organism makes 'choices' between one of several possible paths and we shall find that it is by repeatedly making such 'decisions' that the organism maintains its integrity. For example, the genes can be said to carry information that decides which of a large set of characters an individual shall develop. The receptors of the nervous system provide the information by which decision is reached among the numerous possible courses of behaviour. Again, each molecule that is taken into the body may become incorporated into one of many chemical compounds and we can try to describe the organization of biochemical events in terms of the 'information' by which decision is made among the various possible courses of metabolism.

These are only a few examples of the parts of biology in which the organization of the actions cannot be described in the terms of ordinary physics and chemistry, because they are all so directed as to ensure maintenance of the whole. This property can be shown, however, to result from the selection of certain sets of actions from among large sets of possible alternatives (p. 16). Only a very general beginning can be made in this book, mainly by suggesting lines of approach, without quantitative treatment. But by treating the behaviour of living systems in this way we should be able to measure and compare the contributions that are made by different influences to the operations. For example, it has long been an aim of biologists to assess the relative contributions of heredity and environment during development of the structure, say, of a bone, but no one has suggested how these contributions may be measured. In this system we can say that both provide information and we can try to measure the amounts of information that are due to each.

This ideal is very far from realization but one advantage of trying to reach it is to emphasize that these general biological problems may be said to resolve themselves into studies of *control*, by selection among alternatives in the light of information that depends upon past associations of events. In this way we can speak of the difficult problems of adaptation of an organism to its environment, saying that the former has gradually built up a *representation* of the latter. This leads to the concept of *memories*, or *information stores*, not only in the nervous system (p. 23). The whole stability of the organism can be treated in the language that is used by the engineer to describe the control of machines. We can even deal with some of the most difficult problems of embryogenesis by considering the characteristics of machines that control their own structure.

It is perhaps important not to be dazzled by the considerable prospects of unification held out by these wide uses of words centring round the concept of information. They are valuable in proportion as they are used with caution to describe aspects of life that elude more conventional scientific description. We may now explore the extent of these possibilities by examining in ordinary language the characteristics of living things and then attempting to express these in the new terminology.

14. Characteristics of living organization

What are the characteristics by which we recognize an organism as living? Are there any general statements about living things, describing conditions that everyone can recognize as being typical of them all?

1. *Distinctness from environment*

One outstanding feature, so obvious that we are apt to overlook it, is that living organisms hold themselves distinct and separate from their surroundings. Usually we are not in serious doubt where an animal or plant begins or ends—it has boundaries; indeed they are often very clearly marked; it is a system bounded off from the world in which it lives. After death this separation gradually becomes obscured. Around each organism is found an 'environment' or set of surroundings that is appropriate, indeed necessary, for it, but with which it does not merge. We say that the whale is adapted to live in water, man on the ground, and birds in the air; these are their environments. Evidently any system that describes whole living organisms must show how the actions of the parts serve to keep each creature intact and distinct from its particular environment.

2. *Interchange with environment*

Although the organism remains distinct it is not cut off from the environment but continually exchanges material with it. Indeed we commonly use the persistence of these interchanges as the means of deciding whether an organism is 'alive'; we ask, 'Is it still breathing?' If the intake of oxygen and food stops, the integrity of the organism is not long maintained. Clearly, therefore, the living system is not in equilibrium with the environment but maintains a steady state. This has become especially clear in recent years with the use of radioactive isotopes. These reveal that no atom stays indefinitely within the body and conversely no part remains composed of the same atoms. Even the hard parts such as the bones, and the inner parts, such as the nuclei of the cells, are continually taking in and giving out material (Schoenheimer, 1946; Baldwin, 1952).

The problem of describing living organization is thus to find ways of showing how exchanges are controlled so that the whole maintains a steady state of living. Obviously since each individual sooner or later dies the organization to be described is that of the community, persisting through millions of years.

3. *Internal divisions*

Even the simplest organisms do not consist of homogeneous chemical systems but show internal division into many parts, such as organs, cells, nuclei, mitochondria, and other granules (Fig. 1). This multiplicity of internal divisions is probably one of the chief factors responsible for giving to organisms their remarkable powers. In higher organisms there is a whole hierarchy of intracellular bodies, cells, and organs of various types, making possible the performance of many specialized activities, those of the glands, muscles, nerves, and so on. The properties of living systems depend largely upon the capacity of the carbon atom to provide a great variety of compounds that have slightly different properties. This property makes possible the development of the many differences within the various cells. Moreover, each species of organism contains individuals that differ from each other. This fact of variation is the basis of the properties of 'adaptation', 'prediction', and 'homeostasis', which seem to mark off living from non-living systems. In each species and each individual there is a large set of parts with slightly different properties. Within each organ as within the species sets that ensure survival persist and thus constitute a store of information, recording the variables that have been associated with survival in the past.

The study of the sets of substances and parts into which organisms and cells are divided, and of the surfaces and combinations that are thus presented is therefore of central importance. Biology might be said to be the study of reactions and combinations at complicated systems of surfaces. One of our chief tasks is therefore to find exact ways of describing these arrangements and their variations. The unified picture of the organism that we are seeking must represent all these parts in their proper relations to each other and to the whole. This is the special task of anatomists and histologists. Yet all these parts that are seen must not be thought of as isolated or static. Each is the site of continued change, new molecules arriving and the old ones leaving.

4. *Maintenance of a steady state. Homeostasis*

Any physical system that differs from its surroundings will tend to merge by diffusion into those surroundings. Living organisms are not exempt from the operation of this tendency; the matter and energy that they contain tend to spread away into the environment. But it is characteristic of organisms that they resist this tendency to dissipation; indeed they take in materials from the environment against the concentration gradients. A man is a watery system and tends to lose water to the drier air around him, but in compensation he has elaborate means for seeking and taking water from an environment that contains little of it. Organisms show a great number of such devices by means of which they maintain themselves intact in spite of the tendency to diffuse into the surroundings.

This is another way of expressing a further characteristic of living organisms, namely, that they act; within them there is continual change. Moreover these activities are so directed that they expend energy in ways that ensure that the organism maintains the independence from the environment that we have seen as its first characteristic.

This concept of the 'direction' of living activities has been one of the most difficult in biology to make precise. Yet without it no adequate description of a living organism can be achieved. We can express it by saying that in each situation the selection between possible actions of the living system is determined not only by the conditions obtaining at the moment but also by an information store or record of the actions that have ensured survival in the past under various sets of circumstances. In each further situation the organism then proceeds to take actions that resemble those that have previously been effective. More exact formulation of the nature of the information stores of organisms and the predictive powers that they give is of first importance for biology (see Sommerhoff, 1950). We shall attempt to make some progress in this book by comparing the organism with man-made machines that make predictions, although the particular method that is used for this purpose in living systems depends upon the selection of some among a very large number of units, a principle that is not easily adapted to the design of human artefacts.

In the animals that we call 'higher', such as the mammals, this tendency to make predictions that ensure maintenance of an improbable state appears in a marked degree. These animals differ widely in composition from the medium in which they live. Thus a human being only remains as a distinct entity by virtue of the expenditure of much energy, by an elaborate control system with an extensive information store. In this way he obtains the materials necessary to prevent the dispersal of his system.

Physiologists have paid special attention to one aspect of the process of self-maintenance—namely, the composition of the blood. Claude Bernard noticed that in animals the blood constitutes a kind of 'internal environment' around the separate cells and that in mammals there are elaborate processes of regulation, or 'homeostasis' as it has been called by Cannon (1932), which tend to keep the composition of the blood constant. On this fact Bernard based his famous dictum (1878): 'la fixité du milieu intérieur c'est la condition de la vie libre.' The phrase reads well and is still often quoted, but it only partly meets the need we feel today for a general principle in physiological studies. All organisms keep themselves more or less constant and distinct from their environment; in this sense all animals are free, whether they have an 'internal environment' or not. The concept of a process of homeostasis can be extremely valuable if we recognize that it implies control by the use of an information store and if we generalize this idea to cover all life. It expresses in a word the tendency to self-maintenance that is the characteristic of all living activities.

A summary of the more obvious features of living things thus shows that they are complicated polyphasic systems, composed of series of sets of carbon compounds, differently grouped in each organism and part. The particular set present in any part of a living organization depends upon the influences that have borne upon it in the past. The interchanges of each organism with the environment are such that it maintains itself distinct from its surroundings, provided that these approximately resemble those that have been already experienced. The particular association of features that each organism inherits thus controls the interchange and expenditure of energy in such a way as to ensure survival. We can therefore attempt to describe the operation of a whole living system by comparing it with a machine so organized that its activities tend to homeostasis—the maintenance of a steady state in spite of changes in the surroundings.

15. Characteristics of homeostatic machines

Engineering science has not produced any self-regulating machines that remotely approach a living body in the number and delicacy of their adjustments, but a beginning has been made of the study of the principles on which machines that control themselves may be constructed. These principles provide us with a language that is proving to be of value for talking about the organization of living things.

The machines that were first developed by man performed their work under manual guidance. They provided substitutes for the energy-releasing mechanisms of the body, but the *control* was still exercised by the human brain. Self-adjusting windmills and governors for steam-engines were early examples of machines capable of some degree of self-regulation. In modern automatic machines and guided missiles the machine is able to take into account a variety of circumstances in regulating its actions. Correspondingly the number of adjustments that the machine can make has increased.

Human operations of the type that we call control imply action by a man, who is often directed by *instructions*, selecting some out of the many things he could do so as to ensure the achievement of some aim. Control operations thus consist in making decisions as to which of two (or more) actions shall be performed by ourselves or our machines. Such decisions are reached on a basis of *information* received from the environment about occurrences that are relevant to the pursuit of whatever aim the instructions indicate. The rate at which information is received can be measured in terms of the number of alternative courses between which decision is made, the unit being that which determines the decision between two equiprobable courses.

A person who exerts control of a given situation must carry within himself a system that is a *representation* or replica of certain aspects that are relevant. Similarly the thermometer of a thermostat 'represents' temperature and receives information that allows comparison between its own temperature and that of the surroundings. The

difference between the external conditions and the internal representation is measured and made to operate a control system that adjusts the
machine to maintain a particular steady state. The machine must
therefore have means for detecting changes in its surroundings that
threaten the continuance of its operations. It must make comparison
between the environment and the representation that indicates its
instructions and take action that ensures the required conditions.

The essence of a self-controlling machine is thus that it contains
some system that is a representation of the conditions that are likely
to be met with in the surroundings. Its detectors inform it when any
condition changes. They provide information that determines the
appropriate response among the repertoire of possible actions. The
characteristics of such a machine provide a useful way of describing
the actions of living organisms, for the maintenance of the integrity of
an animal or plant depends upon a series of 'decisions' as to the action
to be taken from moment to moment. The alternatives may be between
two possible actions of the whole body, for example whether to attack
or to retreat, or as to how a given molecule, say of oxygen or sugar, is
to be combined with the existing substance of the body. The immensely
difficult task of describing how organisms maintain their organization
may be approached by considering that the decisions between alternative courses are made in the light of information received from three
sources: (1) from heredity, (2) from the environment, and (3) from the
information store that has been acquired during the lifetime of the
individual.

In any man-made machine the method of operating is obviously
determined by the way it has been made. This seems at first to distinguish machines sharply from organisms, since the latter construct
themselves. However, self-controlling machines are able to modify
their actions according to the information they receive and there is no
reason why they should not also modify their own structure. The
suggestion is that we may speak about living systems as machines that
continually modify their own structure and operations, in such a way
as to remain alive in spite of changes in the environment.

Of course the question how such systems first arose obtrudes itself,
but is too large to discuss fully here. The capacity to build up a
homeostatic organization depends upon selection of those associations
of actions that have survived in the past and it is possible because of
the varied properties of carbon compounds. These properties may first
have been manifested in quite simple systems, later gradually increasing in complexity by continually building up further associations.

If a self-controlling machine is to function adequately it must be so constituted that it adequately represents its environment. That is to say it must 'match' the latter in the sense of being able to take the appropriate materials and information from it. We may say that the genes provide a system that has correspondence with the environment and provides a coded representation of it. This representation corresponds adequately to the environment because the processes of variation and natural selection have operated to ensure that it shall do so. By this laborious statistical process of elimination each population comes to contain genes that produce adult organisms that are able to make appropriate adjustments to all likely changes in the environment.

As development unfolds in each generation the representation included in the genes is transmuted into another representation of the environment, namely, the adult. We can consider this process of embryological development as one of communication. Communication theory deals with the transmission of representations and it provides methods that may be used to make more exact our description of how the genes control the processes of development in such a way as to produce an effective adult (Chapter XXXVII).

The adult organism can thus be considered as containing a representation of the environment, transmitted to it from the genes by the processes of development. But the organism is not limited to receiving only this representation. It is able to improve the representation by receiving information direct from the environment. Throughout the later stages of embryological development, and in the adult, the representation that is used for predicting appropriate responses is continually improved in this way. The animal is able to acquire 'memories', stores of information that improve its representations of past sets of events and thus enable it to make correct predictions, that is to say, to act in ways that are likely to ensure homeostasis.

Such an analysis is not limited only to more complicated organisms with nervous systems that store memories. Even the simplest bacterium has its characteristic way of reacting to substances present in its environment and it may adapt its enzyme system to enable it to metabolize them. We can say that its inherited information store allows it to react appropriately to the information provided by the environment.

16. Double dependence

This analysis focuses attention on the fact that living activities are devoted to the maintenance of a stable pattern of organization and the transmission of this pattern to the future. In order to find words with which to describe the transmission of patterns we turn to the study of human communication by words and other symbols. For any pattern to be copied and transmitted correctly in the presence of noise it is necessary that it be represented by a series of discrete units whose magnitude is comparable to that of the error allowed and each of which is transmitted as a whole. Any attempt to make repeated *exact* copies without breaking up into units is bound to fail because divergences will occur on account of inevitable fluctuations. The resulting deviations must lead to progressive divergence from the original pattern. It is for this reason that human communication makes use of conventional units such as words or the symbols of the Morse code. It is therefore of the greatest interest to find that organisms also make use of units to transmit a stable pattern. The particulate genes, arranged in a regular manner on the chromosomes, are the central example. The cytoplasm of cells also contains several different sorts of particle, the mitochondria, lipochondria, microsomes, and endoplasmic reticulum (Fig. 1). These are all complex aggregates of molecules carrying the enzymes that control metabolism. They can be considered as 'signals', preselected units comparable to words, with which the cells operate to transmit a stable pattern.

We can even go farther and consider that every cell constitutes a two-way communication system. Following a change at its surface changes occur in the cytoplasm, which may thus be considered to transmit information inwards to the nucleus. The latter, constituting the fundamental control centre of the cell, sends out substances that regulate the operations of the cytoplasm, ultimately causing it to act upon the environment. We know all too little about this intracellular communication system but it is useful to keep it in mind when considering the organization of cells. It is another way of expressing the fact that the composition of every part of the body varies continually under a double system of control. The information of heredity, operating from within, provides the system with certain tendencies that have been selected by past history. On the other hand, the events occurring in the environment constantly modify the operations of this system within the tissues. We shall find many examples of this *double dependence* of tissues. The composition of every cell depends upon the interaction of influences from within and from without. No tissue maintains a constant state of development for long, if used more it hypertrophies but if left without use it undergoes atrophy (see Young, 1946).

17. The acquisition of information stores

Higher organisms have great capacity to learn from their own past individual experience. In mammals this information that is stored during the individual's own lifetime is of special importance in determining the course of action. The store is mainly within the nervous system, but the characteristics acquired in many tissues during life constitute information stores, providing means to meet future eventualities. When an animal lives in an environment that is poor in oxygen the oxygen-carrying power of its blood is increased (p. 279). If it is called upon to use one set of muscles more than others these undergo hypertrophy (p. 123). The bones may be said to carry stores of information about the stresses imposed upon them (p. 97). When an animal meets a particular set of bacteria or other infective agents antibodies capable of neutralizing these are produced (p. 265). Such 'adaptations' by the organism can all be regarded as 'memories', stores of information that improve its representation of the environment and provide powers of action likely to be useful if the future resembles the past. Little is known about the means by which these 'adaptive' actions of the organs are produced. They can be regarded as the result of selection, by the influence of the environment, among the set of reactions that are possible within the cells. This set of reactions includes those that are likely to be appropriate for the organism because of the past operation of natural selection upon the genes of the population. The events occurring in the environment then select appropriate combinations of actions from the 'code' that is provided by heredity, and this enables the organism to produce a representation that allows it to take such actions that it remains in a steady state in its environment. There is thus a two-way communication between the hereditary system and the environment, along the channel provided by the body.

18. Methods of control

The making of artefacts to assist in the control of machines has led to considerable clarification of the concept of control and extension of the terminology available for describing its variables. When a human operator wishes a machine to function at a given level he usually does not set a lever once for all at a fixed place but adjusts the output of the machine so that it is appropriate to the resistance that is met at each phase of starting and operation. If this adjustment were not made the resulting operations would be jerky and would throw impossible strains upon the machine.

The human controller of a machine is able to regulate the flow of power so as to produce smooth action because he can follow the course of the operation with his sense organs. He can see or feel whether the machine is accelerating smoothly and can adjust the flow of power

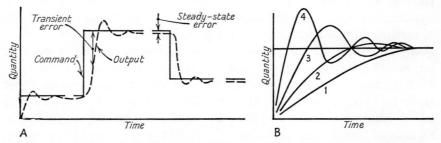

Fig. 2. A. Diagram to show the errors liable to occur between a command (solid line) and the response (dashed line) during a sudden change in command. There is a lag in initial response (transient error), followed by some oscillation and then a divergence between the maintained response and the command (steady state error). B shows that the transient errors and oscillation vary with degree of damping. Curves 1, 2, 3, and 4 show the response in systems with decreasing degrees of damping. Curve 1 is over-damped and shows a large transient error but little oscillation. Curve 4, the least damped, has a small transient error but a large oscillation. (After Brown and Campbell, 1948.)

accordingly. Such return information of the effects of any controlling action is called by engineers a *feed-back*, and careful study has been made of the characteristics of the feed-back that are needed to ensure smooth operation. This problem has become especially prominent for engineers with the development of remote control systems, in which a human operator, instead of actuating a machine directly, does so by sending a pattern of signals along a communication line. These signals then control a special motor that operates the control device. The motor is called a servo- or slave-motor and such *servo-mechanisms* are used in a wide variety of situations to enable a distant operator to control a powerful engine precisely, without himself exerting great force; a good example is the steering system of a large ship.

The operation of servo-mechanisms is obviously analogous in several ways to that of the nervous system and indeed of other controlling mechanisms in the body, and it is worthwhile to consider briefly the principles that are involved. The essential feature is the presence of a receptor that records the state of the output system. Signals from this receptor are then compared with the signals that constitute the instruction. The output of the comparator, if necessary after amplification, is made to control the power output ('negative feed-back'). The whole device is in effect a monitoring system, which ensures that the actual performance of the machine corresponds to that called for by the instruction.

Obviously the study of servo-systems involves investigation of the concepts of instruction, information, coding, and representation, briefly considered above. The instruction is a coded representation of a pattern of action for the machine. The receptor provides a representation of the course that the machine output actually follows. The comparator measures the difference between the two representations and provides a controlling output that reduces the mismatch.

Such systems are liable to three main types of error, which are also seen in the control systems of living organisms (Fig. 2). If there is a considerable delay or damping in the operation of the system the output may not follow the command closely. It may produce a large *transient error* during adjustment to any change, though a small *steady-state error*. Conversely if the feed-back system is oversensitive and produces large changes in the servomotor control there may be overcorrection and *oscillation* in response to even the smallest changes. One means of preventing oscillatory behaviour is to make the correction dependent upon rate of change of error as well as upon its magnitude. (For further details see Ruch in Stevens, 1951.)

19. Control in living systems

A living thing maintains an improbable steady state, by which it is prevented from diffusing into its surroundings. It does this because its past history enables it to receive information and to build up a representation of environmental conditions. It uses this representation to make a measure of any mismatch that is likely to upset the steady state, and thus sets in operation controls that ensure stability, essentially by a mechanism of negative feed-back.

The controls operated by living systems are numerous and varied, and they proceed with time scales differing between the rapid adjustments mediated by the nervous system and the very slow ones involved in evolution. Processes analogous to negative feed-back are involved in many of these controls, especially in higher organisms. Some of these adjustments are operated by statistical processes, such as those of natural selection, stability being ensured simply by eliminating those processes that do not match. Organisms are able to proceed in this way because of the great number of individuals and parts that are involved and the presence of minute variations among these. Very subtle adjustments can be made in this way in the composition of a population or of a part of the body, but such adjustments are rather slow. Where adjustments are rapid, as in the nervous system there are means for preventing errors. Thus the cerebellum provides, among other things, a mechanism for the prevention of oscillation (p. 410).

In dealing with any part of the body we have therefore to ask what are the controls that regulate its action. Some tissues adjust very quickly. The nervous system in particular is so organized that, following a small change in the environment, information is communicated to the brain and compared with the appropriate representation stored there. The brain region in question then emits an output that quickly adjusts the activity to suit the new conditions, and a feed-back system ensures that the muscles are brought smoothly into action (p. 364). Control of the operations of the respiratory system is another example of rapid adjustment, the representation used for matching being located in the medulla oblongata (details on p. 307). Instances of such rapid control occur endlessly throughout the animal body. The most elaborate forms of human behaviour depend upon comparing the input from the receptors with a detailed representation of the environment that is gradually built up in the cerebral cortex (p. 429).

The secretions of the endocrine glands provide a set of signals controlling the slower changes in the body, such as these concerned with nutrition, excretion, growth, and reproduction. Presumably such chemical agents provide a more effective means for regulation of such long-lasting processes than would the brief signals of the nervous system (p. 575).

Still slower adjustments are made by changes in the composition of parts of the body. No tissue is in equilibrium with its surroundings; all are continually changing their materials. As molecules break down and are replaced by others there are small but important alterations in the fabric of the body. These 'adaptations' ensure that each tissue is suited to represent the conditions that fall upon it. Such growth changes are influenced by the information that is provided by surrounding events; they thus provide a record of this information. This slow control by growth changes is found in all tissues and probably plays a part in the setting up of the information store of the nervous system.

On a still longer time-scale living organization is regulated by the process of evolutionary change. The representation that controls all the operations of more rapid control that we have been considering is coded into the hereditary material of the genes. This hereditary information store includes elaborate provisions ensuring that it shall itself be subject to continual change. Each new version is compared with the environment and control is produced by the slow process of natural selection.

This method of speaking about animals may seem at first to be unnecessarily complicated and laboured. Yet as each aspect of life is considered, the language will be found to be illuminating and stimulating. It provides the possibility of unifying the different treatments that are adopted by anatomy, physiology, embryology, biochemistry and biophysics, ecology, psychology, genetics, and evolution. Such unification is itself a great gain and it has the special advantage that it brings into focus important aspects of living organization that are at present neglected or obscure. In particular it allows description of the control of the interchanges that go on continually in the tissues. Revelation of the extent of this turnover is one of the largest changes produced by recent biological research. If the substance of the body is continually changing then the old analogy of a simple machine having 'structure' and 'function' is no longer adequate. Comparison with machines that control themselves is much more helpful, especially if we can find ways of describing how the control system itself changes with time. The methods used by information theory may be able to do this because they tell us how to deal with situations that are controlled by the accumulated effects of associated events, some of them occurring long ago. By comparing the events in organisms with the selection of words in a language or other code we obtain a means of speaking about 'organization' and 'adaptation', which will at least serve until some better method is found to provide a more exact science of the study of living organization.

20. The mammalian homeostatic system

The approach suggested for the study of living organization can be summarized by describing the characteristics of a homeostatic machine that would be able to maintain a steady state under conditions similar to those encountered by mammals. This account amounts to a description of mammalian organization given in the terms that might be used for describing a man-made machine. The various headings mentioned therefore correspond to the separate parts of the body and its activities as they are usually considered. Such a system of description is not fundamentally novel; its advantage over that usually adopted is that it uses the recent developments in the language and methods of engineers to give a more complete and consistent account of living activities.

The machines are heterogeneous (polyphasic) chemical systems operating by virtue of the properties of carbon compounds, arranged into a hierarchy of sub-systems. They have the characteristic that their actions are so controlled that they maintain a steady state of interchange with the surroundings in spite of variations in the environment. The regulation depends upon the fact that the organism contains representations of the features of its environment that are relevant for its existence. These representations are matched against environmental conditions, and when deviations occur processes are set up that so alter the organism (or the environment) that the mismatch is corrected.

The persistence of a stable set of the machines (the 'race') is ensured by elimination (death) of the old and replacement by new ones. This is achieved by the presence of a coded version of the representation, the genes, mainly nucleo-proteins. These have been selected over a long period to include units that represent various probable environmental conditions. Out of this code at intervals new combinations are chosen and then transmuted into the control systems of a varied set of adults.

The fundamental property of the system is that the nucleo-proteins of the genes replicate themselves when in suitable surroundings. Then by natural selection it is ensured that the code includes elements which when suitably combined allow the organisms to react appropriately if future conditions resemble those of the past. The gene representations thus enable the organisms to receive information from the environment. In highly developed forms of the machines, such as those of mammals, the long history of past associations of events provides most elaborate control systems that are able to maintain stability in spite of the fact that they differ widely from the environment and that the latter fluctuates considerably.

The detailed controls of each organism are very numerous. It is able to take in the necessary materials, including sources of free energy, and to maintain itself in surroundings in which they are available; it also eliminates waste. These are the metabolic activities, commonly considered as the subject-matter of physiology. The whole organism is surrounded by a covering that separates it from the surroundings but allows regulated exchanges at certain points (Ch. II). It is supported by a framework (Chs. II–VII) but this permits movement of the parts in relation to each other and of the whole in relation to the surroundings (Ch. VI).

For taking in materials the machine has a number of effector systems such as the mouth, digestive apparatus, and lungs (Chs. XI and XII). These are arranged to operate with a periodicity that is regulated by the rate of demand. The system is physically large and transportation of materials between its parts is ensured by a suitable circulatory mechanism (Chs. XIII and XIV).

Maintenance of the whole in situations where materials are available is ensured by a special system of effectors that moves the whole structure. Detection of suitable conditions is ensured by a variety of receptors (Chs. XXIV–XXVIII). There is an elaborate communication system by which the information collected by the receptors is made appropriately to operate the effectors (Ch. XVII–XXIII). This communication system includes a variety of predictors. Some of these are 'reflex systems' built so that they operate alike in all machines of each type on receipt of certain signals (Ch. XVIII). Other predictors operate by storing information as to the relation between certain sets of signals from the receptors and the presence of suitable or unsuitable external conditions. These are the parts that learn and continually change the representation that they contain of surrounding conditions (Chs. XXII, XXIII). Stability is partly ensured by feed-backs operated by receptors within the machine, which signal deficiency or excess of some component or activity. A system of chemical signalling by the liberation of substances into the circulatory system is used for the slower regulation of some of the fundamental chemical processes on which the whole system depends (Ch. XXIX–XXXIII). Mechanisms are present that are set into operation to counteract many of the deleterious influences that are likely to destroy the system. Some of these operate through the nervous system to produce attack or retreat. Others provide chemical defence against the intrusion of living parasites and toxic substances. After each defensive action the system is usually so modified as to be better able to meet a similar danger in the future.

The activities of the genes also provide that the whole system shall ultimately cease to operate but shall set up a new set of genes (reproduction, Ch. XXXIV). This new set then proceeds to provide a system that is similar to but not identical with the parent (embryogenesis, Chs. XXXV–XLIII). Thus each type of organization exists in a sufficiently large variety of forms to ensure homeostasis in spite of slow changes in the surroundings.

In this manner we can give an account of all the various operations that an organism performs and of the ways in which they are regulated to ensure homeostasis. We use as the central concept the description of the sets of nucleo-proteins of the genes and the capacities for performing actions that ensure self-maintenance that are conferred by selection of groups of these that have proved effective in the past. The account cannot be a simple one, for the living machine performs a range of adjustments vastly greater than that of any man-made machine. We must not expect the study of biology to be simpler than that of engineering. The amateur who wishes to enjoy a superficial study of the actions of living things will not wish to be troubled with so complicated an analysis. But the professional biologist or medical man will find in it the basis of a method by which he can describe and control living processes. The system is far from perfect but we may be amazed that after investigation extending in its present form over a few years it is possible to see the outlines of a unified terminology for description of man, animals, and plants.

II

THE SKIN, CONTROL OF TEMPERATURE AND APPEARANCE

1. The boundary of the body

THE skin marks the boundary between the organism and its environment and is largely responsible for the retention of the characteristic shape of the individual. In the fully terrestrial mode of life adopted by most mammals the properties of the surface layers are obviously of first importance and the skin is an elaborate structure, showing special features not found in lower vertebrates. These features are connected with temperature control and with the formation of an impermeable yet sensitive surface, able to resist tensile forces and to prevent the access of bacteria.

The skin and its derivatives therefore play a very important part in the life of a mammal. Study of the differences between the skins of various mammals shows how closely the activities of the body are related to the conditions of the environment. In this chapter besides describing the histological structure of the skin we shall see how some of its many derivatives play their part in the life of the species and also how this part may vary in different sorts of mammals.

Although the skin is a resistant, relatively inert material it does not persist unchanged throughout life but is continually renewed by the activity of the cells below. Even the outer boundary of the organism is therefore not in static equilibrium but is in a steady state, continually changing its material.

Control of the metabolic interchanges in the skin is largely a matter of the operation of hereditary morphogenetic factors, serving to maintain different sorts of skin on the various parts of the body (p. 33). Yet there are also changes in the skin in relation to changes in the environment. These changes may be fast, such as those concerned with temperature control, or slow, for example the hardening of the palms of the hands.

Being the boundary of the body the skin 'represents' the environment in a particularly clear sense. It is enabled to conform to the outside conditions by its texture, colour, scent, temperature, and many other features. This conformity is maintained by control on all time scales between the few seconds required for temperature regulation and the many generations for selection of a new set of genes controlling the coat colour.

2. The epidermis

The skin consists of two chief layers (Fig. 3), an outer, non-vascular, stratified squamous epithelium, the *epidermis*, and below this

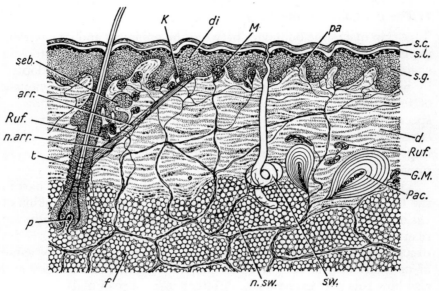

Fig. 3. Composite diagrammatic section of the human skin.

arr. arrector pili muscle; *d.* dermis; *di.* Merckel's disks; *f.* fat; *G.M.* Golgi-Mazzoni corpuscles; *K.* end-bulbs of Krause; *M.* Meissner's corpuscles; *n.arr.* nerves for arrector muscles; *n.sw.* nerves for sweat gland; *p.* papilla of hair; *pa.* pain fibres; *Pac.* Pacinian corpuscle; *Ruf.* endings of Ruffini; *s.c.* stratum corneum; *seb.* sebaceous gland; *s.g.* stratum granulosum; *s.l.* stratum lucidum; *sw.* sweat gland; *t.* touch fibres of hair follicle.

(After Woollard, Weddell, and Harpmann, *J. Anat. Lond.* **74**, 1940.)

a layer of vascular connective tissue, the *corium* or *dermis*, projecting outwards by papillae, which are vascular and sensitive, into the epidermis. The sweat glands, sebaceous glands, and hair follicles are derivatives of the epidermis that project inwards into the dermis.

The epidermis is a stratified squamous epithelium. It consists of many layers of cells the inner of which are active and protoplasmic and are continually producing cells that pass outwards and gradually undergo a process of cornification, by which they are converted to masses of the protein keratin. This substance is the distinctive component of the epidermis and its derivatives, hairs, hooves, nails, and horns. Keratin contains large amounts of the sulphur-containing amino-acids cystine and methionine and its most interesting property is that it has a very low solubility in water and therefore makes an ideal protective outer covering for the body. The arrangement of the keratin molecules determines the physical properties of the tissue and the various epidermal derivatives show different molecular arrangements, with characteristic X-ray diffraction patterns.

The process of keratin formation is continuous from within outwards but the conditions at certain levels give characteristic appearances to the cells and thus several layers can be named. The innermost part of the epidermis, the *stratum germinativum* or *stratum Malpighii*, contains the active cells, among which mitotic figures appear. Outside these begins the horny layer, the innermost cells of which (*stratum granulosum*) contain granules of a substance known as keratohyalin. Outside this the cells come to contain the clear substance eleidin in the *stratum lucidum* and then finally become keratinized and non-nucleated in the many layers of the *stratum corneum*.

The keratinizing process is, of course, not peculiar to mammals but it is highly developed in them and is specialized for appropriate purposes in various parts of the body. The thickness of the epidermis varies, being greatest on regions such as the foot-pads that suffer special friction. Mechanical influences are known to stimulate mitosis in the Malpighian layer but the skin of the soles of the feet of man is thick before birth, showing that hereditary influences must be at work in controlling the regional characteristics of the skin. Pieces of skin transplanted to distant parts of the body retain their characteristic properties. Skin of the abdominal wall transplanted to the face of a man does not become more hairy, and skin of the sole of the foot grows thick wherever it is placed. We may say that the genus epidermis contains a number of distinct self-reproducing species, each with characteristics that are determined during development. The production of keratin is also made use of in special parts of the body to form the hairs, claws (or nails), and in some mammals, horns, spines, or scales.

Dark colour in the skin is due to melanin, produced by a system of branched melanophores (pigmentary dendritic cells), which lie among the cells of the stratum germinativum (p. 49).

3. Hairs

Each hair consists of a rod of elongated keratinized cells, forming a thread that is usually cylindrical but sometimes flattened, for example in the negro races of man. There is usually a central region in each hair, the medulla, consisting of cells that contain air. In the outer cortex there are often granules of pigment. Each hair develops as a thickening of the stratum germinativum of the epidermis, pushing inwards to the corium and becoming differentiated into a central shaft and an outer sheath. The mesenchyme at the base of the ingrowth forms a vascular papilla and the epidermal cells above this continue to produce keratin, thus providing the constantly growing base of the hair, whose activities soon push the tip out of the follicle and above the surface.

The hairs were probably developed originally to retain heat but they are associated with sebaceous glands, which keep them and the skin surface oily and hence waterproofed. They are also provided with nerve-fibres, which wrap around the base of the hair follicle (Fig. 3) and when they are moved provide nerve impulses that are recorded as the sensation of touch (p. 475). In nearly all mammals certain hairs on the snout, the *vibrissae*, have become elongated and stiffened for sensory purposes, and these make the animals sensitive to very light touch or even to small changes of air-pressure (p. 476). The rabbit possesses vibrissae above and below the eyes and on the nose.

4. Sebaceous glands and hair muscles

Each *sebaceous gland* consists of a few short sacks, the alveoli, opening into the hair follicle. The secretory cells are derived from the epidermis and at the centre of each alveolus they become converted into the substance *sebum*, formed mainly of esters of cholesterol, which keeps the hair greasy. Attached to each hair is a small bundle of unstriped muscle-fibres, the *arrector pili* muscle, whose contraction raises the hair, thus allowing for air movement and greater heat loss. The movements of the hairs probably also serve to press the sebum out of the follicles.

5. Temperature regulation

It is difficult to overestimate the importance of the advance in living organization that is made possible by the maintenance of a high and constant temperature (homothermy) (Robinson, 1952). Sir Joseph Barcroft pointed out that many refinements of organization can only operate under constant conditions. For instance, if there is a constant temperature, elaborate patterns of activity can be set up in the cerebral cortex, allowing for persistent and complicated memories (p. 457). Similarly, in various parts of the body, there are intricate sets of biochemical reactions that would be disturbed by large temperature fluctuations. At the same time achievement of a high temperature allows a greatly increased level of activity. The birds and mammals have been experimenting independently with high temperatures for probably more than 100 million years, but it may be that one or both groups will eventually make still more spectacular innovations of organization on this basis, including perhaps the use of still higher temperatures.

It is not known how the temperature-regulating mechanism first arose. The egg-laying mammals, platypus, and echidna, possess hair and they probably diverged from the other mammals not later than the early Jurassic Period, nearly 150 million years ago. Therefore it seems that the mammalian line began to be warm-blooded earlier than this date, as also did the line that was leading to the birds. This may have been a response to either cold or warm conditions; reptiles are severely limited in distribution by temperature. It is also possible that the condition did not follow any special climatic change but that the early avian and mammalian stocks were pioneers, driven by the competition of their many reptilian cousins to seek life in colder or hotter land regions, which were not yet inhabited by tetrapods.

Cold will make a reptile dormant unless the animal can be active enough to keep itself warm by the heat produced as a by-product of muscular activity. This will be made more easy if the animal is large (incidentally this may have been a reason for the great size of many reptiles) and, of course, especially if a heat-insulating mechanism is developed. It is not difficult to understand how a temperature above that of the surroundings could be achieved by sufficiently active reptilian animals. Even at the present day the heat of muscular work remains the chief source of heat in mammals. In the early stages of the evolution of high temperature, alteration of *heat production* was probably the main means of temperature regulation, as it still is today in monotremes and bats. In all mammals a fall of external temperature calls forth extra muscular activity by shivering. The higher mammals also possess a mechanism for the control of *heat loss* and they maintain a constant temperature largely by this downward regulation.

Control of the temperature-regulating mechanism is centred on the hypothalamic region of the forebrain (p. 419), especially in the *tuber cinereum*, which is large in birds and mammals. In this region there are cells that serve as detectors; when the blood is too hot or too cold nerve impulses are sent out to vary the rate of heat production or heat loss, and the temperature is kept steady with little oscillation. After removal of the tuber an animal no longer regulates properly, its temperature fluctuates with that of its surroundings. Other parts of the brain also play a large part in regulation and it has long been known that stimulation of the caudate nucleus of the corpus striatum (p. 426), for instance by puncture, causes a temporary rise in the temperature, which may reach as high as 42° C. It is not clear how these various heat-regulating centres are related.

If cooled blood reaches one of these regions the shivering mechanism is set in action; conversely perfusion of the carotid arteries with over-warm blood causes sweating or panting. Heat-producing systems other than the muscles may be called upon. The liver and other organs give out heat in the course of their work and it is possible that during periods of sleep they may be stimulated to increased activity and greater heat output. Thyroid secretion increases the basal metabolism and thus the amount of secretion produced by the thyroid affects the temperature: other endocrine organs are probably also involved.

6. Heat conservation

Hair tends to trap a layer of air, which insulates the body, reducing heat exchange with the environment. The air-retaining capacity is increased in some animals by a roughening of the surfaces of the hairs (e.g. in the wool of sheep and some rabbits), which causes them to stick together to make a *pelt*. The hairs are not of the same kind all over the surface of the body; often long stiff hairs are found mingled with the softer fur. In many mammals the hair changes according to the time of year so as to provide a thicker covering in winter than in summer.

The hairs do not grow straight out from the skin but are placed obliquely, so that they all 'set' in a particular direction, giving the coat its characteristic reaction to brushing. It has been suggested that the primary direction of the hairs provides a backward slope, which would prevent them from catching in grasses, &c. The reasons for the deviations from this direction, which occur in many mammals, are not understood.

Not all mammals use an air layer for the retention of heat. In the whales and sea-cows the body is covered with a thick layer of fat, developed in the dermis; the hairs are reduced to a few vibrissae. In man hairs are present over most parts of the body but their function is mainly tactile and heat is conserved by a layer of fat in the dermis. Very large mammals, such as the elephant or rhinoceros, have little need to minimize heat loss, since their surface area is small relative to the large heat-producing volume; the hairs are accordingly reduced.

Related species that existed during glacial periods had well developed hair (mammoths and the woolly rhinoceros).

7. Heat loss

Various agencies are responsible for control of heat loss. The convection from the surface of the body can be controlled by changing the position of the hairs. The skin contains devices for losing as well as for retaining heat. The *sweat glands* are derived from the epidermis

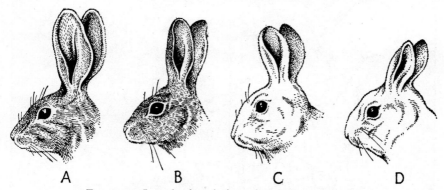

FIG. 4 A–D. Length of ear in hares in relation to latitude.

A, is Arizona jack-rabbit (*Lepus alleni*); B, is jack-rabbit from Oregon (*L. californicus*); C, is the varying hare (*L. arcticus*) from the Barren Grounds; D, *Lepus* sp. (From Hamilton, W. J., *American Mammals*, McGraw Hill Book Co., Fig. 41.)

but they lie deeply placed in the dermis. They are tubular glands, much coiled at their inner ends and surrounded by *myo-epithelial cells* that contain contractile fibrils and serve to expel the secretion. The sweat is a watery solution, whose evaporation serves to cool the body. The amount of liquid produced is controlled by the action of nerve-fibres of the sympathetic system (p. 392). Sweat glands are not well developed in all mammals, for instance in cats they are found only on the pads of the feet. In man they occur all over the body, most abundantly in the axilla and groin. They are altogether absent from the skin of whales and sea-cows and from the burrowing golden mole of South Africa.

The amount of heat lost from the surface is also controlled by regulating the flow of blood. When the whole capillary bed is used the skin becomes flushed and loses much heat, also the sweat glands receive more blood. In cold conditions a set of arterio-venous anastomoses is opened up so that the blood short circuits the capillaries and the skin becomes blue or white. These processes are influenced by the hypothalamus. The surface of the lungs also provides a means of heat loss. Animals such as the dog that have few sweat glands resort to panting.

Large animals use special means for losing heat, for instance the African elephant increases its total surface area by nearly one-sixth

FIG. 4 E. Length of ear in hares in relation to latitude.
Measurements of the length of the ears of hares in various regions of North America in relation to skull length.
(Data of Nelson, after Hesse, *Zeitschr. wiss. Zool.* **132**.)

when it raises its ears. The flapping movements of the ears are more frequent in large elephants than in small. The flow of blood to the ears is increased in hot weather. The ears are used for heat loss in smaller animals also; in North America the hares have longer ears in the warmer southern regions (Fig. 4 A–E).

8. Temperature regulation in various mammals

With such devices for control of heat production and heat loss most mammals maintain a constant temperature of about 39° C. There are none with a much greater temperature but several achieve only a lower and inconstant temperature. In the earlier types of mammal the temperature is lower (Martin, 1902). With an air temperature of 15° C. monotremes average 30° C., marsupials and hedgehog 35° C., man 37° C., cat and rabbit 39° C. Moreover, the lower forms are unable to regulate fully, either at high or low temperatures. The temperature of the spiny anteater (*Echidna*) falls to 25° C. at 5° C. external. This animal and the platypus rise in temperature with the environment above 30° C. and die of heat apoplexy at about 37° C. These imperfections of regulation greatly restrict the living conditions, especially of the echidna, which hibernates in winter and burrows in hot weather. The platypus has a few sweat glands, the spiny anteater none; neither of them increases the heat loss by panting at high temperatures or by vasodilatation in the

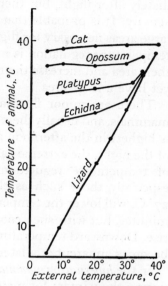

Fig. 5. Changes of body temperature with external change in lizards and various mammals. (After Martin, C. J., 'Thermal adjustment in monotremes and marsupials', *Phil. Trans. Roy. Soc. Lond.* **195**, 1902.)

skin. Temperature is therefore regulated in these animals mainly by variations of heat production and they have been observed to become warmer during periods of activity. Nevertheless the difference from the reptilian condition is striking (Fig. 5).

In the armadilloes and probably in other edentates the temperature remains fairly constant at 32° C. for as long as the surroundings are between 16 and 28° C. Above or below these limits the animal varies directly with external temperature. The case of the insectivorous bats is peculiar in that they have no mechanisms for control of the amount of heat produced. Every time a bat hangs up and goes to sleep its temperature falls and within an hour reaches that of the surroundings. On waking the bat is at first in a strangely 'reptilian' condition: its fur feels cold like that of a dead mouse. It can crawl, squeak, and bite but not fly. If left on its 'perch' it will perform a series of physical jerks, shivering and raising itself repeatedly by flexing the legs: since the wings are folded this produces a rise of temperature. Rapid and continuous movements of the head and ears begin at 25° C. and at about 30° C. flight may be attempted. Temperature is high immediately after flight, but then drops rapidly and thereafter varies with activity. It is probable that this condition is peculiar to the bats; the large areas necessary for flight involve such a great heat loss that strict temperature regulation is impossible. Other small animals minimize their area and increase their fur thickness. The bat must be small and yet have a large area.

There are minor fluctuations in temperature even in the higher mammals, and usually there is a daily rhythm. In man the temperature is highest in the afternoon and falls to a minimum in the small hours of the night, the extreme variations covering about 1·2° C. The power of temperature regulation is imperfect in new-born mammals, especially those such as the mouse that are very small. A bath at 27° C. will lower the temperature of a new-born baby by 2–3° C. in 10 minutes, but with such cooling the heat production and CO_2 output rise. Downward temperature regulation by sweating and panting only becomes apparent at a later age.

In the *hibernating mammals* the temperature regulation is abandoned during the winter; for many weeks or months the body remains at a temperature little above that of the surroundings. During this period the animal is inactive and takes no food; the small amount of energy necessary for breathing and circulation is provided from reserves of fat. The animals that behave in this way are mostly small and therefore present a relatively large surface for cooling. They would presumably not be able to produce enough heat to maintain a high temperature in winter. The hibernation is therefore a means for extending their distribution and is indeed a device also adopted by amphibia and reptiles. Hibernation is found among mammals living either in northerly regions or in high mountains. Familiar mammals that hibernate are the dormouse (*Myoxus*), marmot (*Arctomys*), hedgehog (*Erinaceus*), and the insectivorous bats.

9. Claws, nails, hooves, and horns

Besides producing hair the Malpighian layer also gives rise to special structures made of keratin on various parts of the body. The tips of the digits of mammals are nearly always covered with hardened plates of keratin. In their simplest form these are *claws*, similar to those of reptiles and birds; they partly embrace the tip of the digit, as in the rabbit or cat. There are transitions between this condition and the *hoof* of ungulates, which completely covers the digit, and the *nail* of primates, which is a flat plate found on one surface only. These are all products of the Malpighian layer, but it is not known what difference in the physical process of keratin deposition produces them.

The nail of man (Fig. 6) is usually considered to be a modified stratum lucidum and the underlying corium (*nail bed*) is very vascular, giving the pink appearance. At the base the epidermis is invaginated to form the *nail root*, so that the lucidum is here covered by a layer of stratum corneum, which projects for a short distance as a whitish fold,

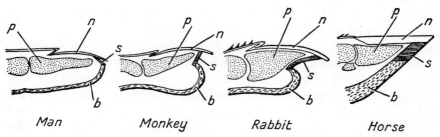

Man   Monkey   Rabbit   Horse

FIG. 6. Longitudinal section through the end of the digits of the manus of various mammals.

b. ball of finger; *n.* nail plate; *p.* terminal phalanx; *s.* sole plate.
(After Weber, *Die Saugetiere*, fig. 13.)

the *eponychium*, more extensive in the foetus. Under the nail root the corium is less vascular, producing the whitish *lunula*. The nail grows by proliferation of the cells of the nail root. In addition to this *nail plate* of horny epidermal cells mammals often have also a *sole plate*, a pad of somewhat less modified epidermis on the opposite side of the terminal phalanx (Fig. 6), and this is especially developed in the hoof of ungulate animals, where the weight is carried on the tip of the digit and the sensory functions of the leg are reduced.

The *horns* found in various mammals are also formed of keratin, produced by areas of skin overlying prolongations of the bones of the skull; the *antlers* of deer, however, are purely bony. Horns are either used for defence (and hence are found in both sexes) or as part of the sexual and social organization of species, usually where the males maintain their dominance by fighting. The horn of the rhinoceros is formed of a compact mass of keratin produced by the aggregation of a number of coarse threads; the process is apparently a modification of hair formation.

Various other special protective devices of the skin have been developed. Thus the pangolins, *Manis*, of Africa and Asia are covered with horny scales. Small scales occur on various mammals, for instance on the tail of rats. In hedgehogs and porcupines, and also in the monotreme *Echidna*, the epidermis produces sharp spines, usually considered to be modified hairs. It may be mentioned here that in armadilloes there is a dermal skeleton of bony plates.

10. Glands producing attractive or repellent scents

A further characteristic feature of the skin of mammals is the development of scent-producing glands, derived from sweat or sebaceous glands, or sometimes intermediate between the two. These play a large part in the life of the animals by providing the mechanism for recognition of members of the species, especially in social forms, and for bringing the sexes together. Most species of mammals have a characteristic smell, often different in the two sexes. Perhaps this condition has grown up in association with the development of sensitive chemoreceptors for hunting purposes (p. 521). Although many mammals have good eyes they rely for recognition mainly upon smell. Birds, on the other hand, which are microsmatic, have few scent glands but often show distinctive colours. In mobile animals, such as birds or primates, smell would evidently be of less use than sight for either recognition or hunting.

The characteristic smell of the rabbit is due to a pair of *inguinal glands*, opening between the anus and penis or vulva. Many other mammals have similar glands in this region, for instance the *civet-glands* of carnivora and the musk-glands of certain deer. Many antelopes have a special sub-orbital gland and the elephant has a gland on its forehead. The peccary has a large gland opening on its back. Marsupials commonly possess a complex scent gland at the base of the neck. Rhinoceros and other herbivores have scent glands on the feet and the callosities of the legs of the horse may be of similar nature. Scent glands are also prominent in primates, for instance the gentle lemur (*Hapalemur*) has a large one on the arm.

Scents have a highly 'emotional' quality in man and there is no doubt they act as important signals in both sexual and social organization. In animals with large scent glands there are probably characteristic differences of scent between individuals. These smells may be left upon trees and other objects and serve to mark the territory of an individual. No massive scent glands are present in man, but the characteristic smells of the secretions of the axilla and genital regions are due to modified sweat glands. Those in the axilla change in histological appearance during the menstrual cycle in women, being enlarged during the premenstrual period but reduced during menstruation.

Of the specifically repulsive smells developed the best known is that of the skunk (*Mephitis*) of America, a carnivore in which the perineal glands can emit a jet of secretion whose unpleasant smell is perceptible far away. Presumably in connexion with this habit the animals have a conspicuous sematic (warning) coloration of black and white.

11. Mammary glands

The glands that give the mammals their characteristic power of nourishing the young are products of the epidermis, resembling sweat glands in some respects. In the resting state they consist of a branching system of 'excretory ducts'. During pregnancy the epithelium of these ducts divides actively, producing secretory end sacks or alveoli. After birth of the young the alveoli produce the milk, the cells producing carbohydrates, proteins, fat, and water, and passing them to the lumen. The growth of the mammary glands is stimulated by the combined action of oestrogens and progesterone, and the release of the milk is elicited by substances produced by the pituitary (p. 556). All three endocrine secretions are necessary and each influences the secretion of the others.

The milk varies in composition in different mammals. In cows' milk the dry weight includes about 20 per cent. each of protein (mostly casein) and fat, and 60 per cent. of sugars (lactose). Salts and vitamins are present in the proportions in which they occur in the blood. It is usual to speak of milk as a 'nearly ideal food' for the young. Evidently the ideal varies in different species; the milk of whales and seals, for example, contains twelve times more fat and four times more protein than that of the cow, but no sugars. There is a relationship between the fat and protein content of the milk and the speed of growth after birth.

TABLE A

	Man	Horse	Cow	Pig	Sheep	Cat	Dog	Rabbit	Seal
Number of days in which weight of young is doubled after birth . .	180	60	47	18	10	9	8	6	5
Protein in milk (g/ 1,000) . .	19	20	33	37	70	95	97	104	119

Such differences show how complicated are the factors that determine the characteristics of each variety of living organization.

The mammary glands develop by thickening of the epidermis to form 'milk lines' extending along each side of the abdominal wall. The definitive mammae appear either dispersed along this line, as in the sow or bitch, or mainly at the hind end (ruminants) or front end (primates). The position and number of the mammae and nipples vary with the number of offspring and habit of the animal. The peculiar pectoral position in primates was probably first associated with arboreal life and carrying of the young.

Organs similar to mammary glands are found in the egg-laying monotremes. There has been some discussion whether these more closely resemble sebaceous or salivary glands, and it has been suggested that they represent a development parallel to that of 'true' mammary glands; the similarities to these latter are certainly striking. The gland of the echidna consists of numerous ducts, opening, without special nipples, on areas of skin on either side of the pouch in which the eggs and young are placed. The milk is a thick, yellow substance, which is licked rather than sucked by the young and contains proteins and fat but probably no lactose.

The mammary apparatus is well developed in marsupials, where the teat is placed in the mouth of the new born while it is in the pouch, before sucking is possible, and the milk is pumped in by the mother.

12. The dermis

Many of the structures derived from the epidermis are actually lodged in the underlying dermis (corium); in addition the tissues of the latter itself are of great importance for the properties of the skin as a whole and nearly all the nerve endings of the skin lie here. The dermis forms a tough, flexible, somewhat elastic covering over the whole surface of the body. Its function is to hold together, protect, and support the body, and to carry blood to the surface. It contains the nerve endings and in some mammals (whales and man) it carries much fat to serve as a heat-insulating layer. It plays a large part in the defence against bacterial invasion.

13. Musculature of the skin

The skin contains unstriped muscle-fibres and these permit a certain degree of movement, for instance in the nipples, penis, scrotum, and labia majora of man. In monotremes there is a well-developed layer of striped muscles below the skin over the whole surface of the body and these are innervated from the ventral roots of spinal nerves. This musculature appears to be a derivative of the myotomes that is peculiar to the early mammals but is reduced in later forms.

The skin musculature is often considered together with the striped musculature of the face under the title of *panniculus carnosus*. The

FIG. 7. The heads of various mammals.
(From Portmann, A., *Die Tiergestalt*, Rheinhardt, Basel.)

face muscles, however, found from the monotreme stage onwards, are lateral plate muscles (see p. 717), innervated from the facial nerve. It is possible that common morphogenetic influences operate to produce all these skin muscles, in spite of their 'morphological' differences; we know too little to be dogmatic on such subjects. The facial skin muscles have a special importance in the primates since they are the *muscles of expression*, which play such a large part in family and social organization. Paralysis of these muscles by injury to the facial nerve produces a distorted or dead-pan expression, which is a grave disability for its possessor.

14. Expression, body shape, and colour in mammals

Mammals are mostly less highly coloured than birds, the colour serving usually for concealment rather than for recognition or stimulation, which are accomplished by scent (p. 42). This dull colour is probably correlated with the fact that the early mammals were crepuscular or nocturnal animals, whose eyes lacked cones and were ill suited for detailed form discrimination or colour discrimination. Even today the majority of mammals are colour blind (p. 504).

Bright colours are found chiefly among primates; these, with their arboreal habit, have developed a predominantly visual sensory organization. Yet the external form of the body is probably significant in many mammals, perhaps more so in those that we recognize as 'higher' (Portmann, 1952). The heads of many small insectivores and rodents are almost exactly alike: they are, as we say, 'featureless'. On the other hand, in a lion or a monkey the muscles and other parts are developed to provide a means by which the creature exercises its influence on members of the same or other species (Fig. 7). These expressions are largely produced by actions of the musculature of the skin (p. 203) and are, of course, particularly developed in the face of man.

The shape of the body is often used as a means of communication in the social and sexual life of mammals, serving to produce appropriate responses in other individuals. Special shapes are often connected with recognition of the sexes (Fig. 8). The external form therefore does more than provide a 'physiological sack' for the organs: shape itself comes to have a significance for these types of animal organization that survive by co-operative action between individuals. Fig. 9 shows examples in which the front or hind end of the animal have characteristic shapes and colour patterns.

Coloration is brilliant only in a few mammals, for example the pink lower lip and pink and blue buttocks and thighs of the male mandrill. Another startling pattern is that of the gelada baboon, whose pink collar and chest, together with his white upper eyelids, give him a ferocious appearance when he bares his fangs by turning back the upper lip and showing the white inside. In this case the colour is made to 'change' suddenly by lowering the lids and turning back the lip, presumably to scare away an attacker by presentation of a startling pattern. Similar startling patterns are produced by several other types

FIG. 8. Secondary sex characters as seen in the drill (*Mandrillus*), sacred baboon (*Papio*), red park deer (*Cervus*), and lion (*Felis*). (From life.)

FIG. 9. Characteristic forms and postures.

A. Wild mountain ram showing well-developed appearance of both anterior and posterior ends. B. Postures adopted by wolves; the animal to the left ranks high and that on the right low in the social structure of the group. (From Portmann, B., after R. Schenkel.)

of animals, and such coloration may be called dymantic (startling) to distinguish it from concealing (cryptic) or warning (sematic) patterns.

A particular use is made of colour change as a means of communication in man by blushing. This is a sudden dilatation of the capillaries in the skin when social conditions become such as to make communication difficult, when the individual, as we say, feels embarrassed. Apart from these few special examples the colours do not change from moment to moment in mammals as they do in some cyclostomes, fishes, amphibians, and reptiles. Moreover, colour patterns are fairly

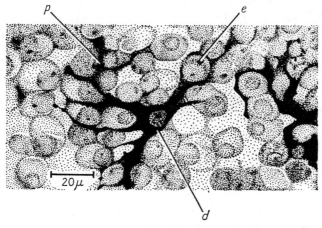

FIG. 10. Pigmentary dendritic cells seen in a preparation made by lightly squashing a piece of guinea-pig skin in Ringer's solution. The nucleated dendritic cells (*d*) have processes that twine around the epidermal cells (*e*) and transfer pigment (*p*) to the latter. (After Billingham and Medawar, *Heredity*, **2**, 29, 1948.)

constant in wild mammals among the various individual members of the species. They vary more in domestication, where selection is less strict or less uniform.

The colours are usually the result of various mixtures of black, due to the pigment melanin, with white, formed by the presence of air in the hairs. The pigment is produced by the *melanophores* (*pigmentary dendritic cells*) located in the basal layers of the epidermis. These are branched cells with long processes (Fig. 10), looking so like the neuroglia cells of the central nervous system (p. 379) that they have been called the 'epidermal glial system'. They are formed during development by migration from the neural crest (p. 769). Each branch of a dendritic cell ends as a cup-shaped button in contact either with an ordinary epidermal cell or with another dendritic cell, forming an elaborate branching system among the cells of the base of the epidermis. There is sometimes protoplasmic continuity between the branches of the dendritic cells. The pigment is manufactured in the dendritic cells and transferred to the epidermal cells.

The activities of the dendritic cells are influenced by environmental

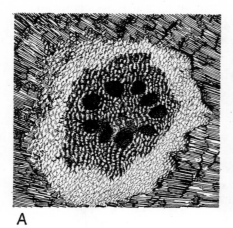

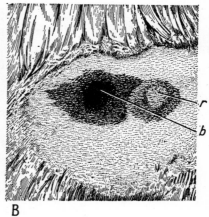

A   B

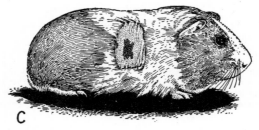

C

FIG. 11. The spread of 'infection' of skin from grafted dendritic cells.

A, Nine small pieces of black skin have been grafted 106 days before to a white area of the same guinea-pig. The skin around the grafts begins to form pigment. B, pieces of black (*b*) and red (*r*) skin grafted 138 days before to a white area of the same animal have produced 'infected' zones around them, the black advancing faster than the red. C, black area produced by inoculating white skin 267 days before with minute seeds of dark cells in the form of a suspension in Ringer from *another animal*. The foreign cells start the pigmentation but they then die and the dark colour is maintained by the spread of the 'infected' host cells. (Figures from photographs kindly supplied by Professor P. B. Medawar.)

factors. In the familiar case of the white human skin exposure to light produces increased synthesis of pigment. Exposure to cold will induce pigmentation of ears and other points of albino guinea-pigs, which, like white men, possess dendritic cells that produce melanin only under certain conditions.

The white patches that make up the pattern of spotted guinea-pigs and other mammals are due to the fact that the dendritic cells of these areas lack the power to produce melanin; they are therefore said to be *non-pigmentary dendritic cells* (Billingham and Medawar, 1948). This condition is presumably brought about by an inductive process during development that leads to absence of the necessary enzyme system (see p. 631). The cells can be made to acquire melanin-producing powers by transplanting black skin to a white area. Black coloration then spreads slowly away from the transplanted piece by a process of 'infection' of the dendritic cells with the melanin-producing system by contact with their new black neighbours (Fig. 11). Once infected the cells maintain their new character through all subsequent generations and can themselves infect another white area to which they are transplanted.

Many mammals wear coats of different colours at different seasons. Some arctic species become white in winter; deer become darker in winter, lighter and dappled in the summer. Sudden whitening of the hair in man is due to ingestion of the pigmented outer layer by phagocytes, allowing the air-filled medullary cells to produce the white colour.

15. Control of colour and expression

The appearance of the skin is maintained in an appropriate condition by regulation with time scales that vary according to the speed with which change is required. Blushing and the facial and other expressive movements of communication are under the immediate control of the nervous system. The colour of the sexual skin and other secondary sexual characters are controlled by chemical signals from the endocrine glands, producing effects that last for days or weeks. Changes in the whole shape of the body or of the basic colour patterns involve alteration of the hereditary make-up by variation and natural selection.

16. The skin and homeostasis

Evidently the skin is far more than a passive covering for the body. Study of even a few of its actions has led us to consider a variety of means by which homeostasis of the race is maintained. The skin plays a part in rapid adjustments such as those by which temperature is kept constant, as well as in the slow adjustments by which sexual and social organization are maintained and the race kept in balance with the environment by the production of varied new individuals. All these activities of the skin can be considered within one system of ideas by emphasizing the part that each organ plays in homeostasis.

The many actions of mammalian skin are made possible by the

multiplicity of morphogenetic processes that are at work in the embryo and the adult, producing the many types of cell, with their characteristic actions (Chapter XXXVII). These morphogenetic processes all operate under the instruction provided by the hereditary mechanism, and embryology shows that the genus skin becomes divided into its several species of cells by emphasis on particular types of enzyme action. Thus it is ensured that the skin provides a representation of the types of change in the surroundings that are likely to influence the animal. Its keratin gives it the qualities required to resist deformation, the dermis gives resistance to infection, hairs, and sweat glands provide a representation of the probable temperature changes. The colour and form of the outside of the body represent aspects of the activity of other individuals of the same and other species that the animal may meet. The receptor organs are sensitive to a certain range of the changes likely to occur around the skin.

Evidently the skin provides a very elaborate representation of conditions in its environment, which is another way of saying that mammals are 'higher' or 'well-developed' animals. The representation that the skin provides at any moment is mainly the result of the instructions of heredity, but information from the nervous system also arrives to enable the representation to be more complete—for example in relation to temperature. The skin of each individual also carries its own memory of conditions that have been encountered in the past—notably in the features of the human face.

Thus the outer layers of the body provide a mirror of the conditions both without and within, and of the conditions experienced in the remote and immediate past.

III

THE CONNECTIVE TISSUES

1. Consistency of the tissues

CONNECTIVE tissue, being dispersed throughout the body, is less conspicuous than the special tissues characteristic of the various organs, but its importance for the life of the whole individual is immense (Asboe-Hansen, 1954). Besides holding together and supporting the other cells it also provides a large part of the means of defence against infection.

The physical properties of the dermis are mostly those characteristic not of its muscles, described in the last chapter, but of connective tissue. Similar material is found throughout and around nearly all the organs. The protoplasm of cells is watery and soft; the firm consistency and resistance to stretch of the organs is a property of the connective tissue they contain, rather than of their own cells. This is well illustrated by the difference between a peripheral nerve, which contains much connective tissue and is therefore a relatively strong substance, and the matter of the brain or spinal cord, which has a minimum of connective tissue, is almost liquid, and can hardly be picked up with forceps.

2. Fibroblasts

The cells of connective tissue are always spaced at a distance from each other throughout the tissue, not aggregated to form epithelia or parenchyma. The characteristic cell type is the *fibroblast* (fibrocyte), which can assume a variety of shapes but is usually flattened, elongated, or branched (Fig. 12), often forming a sponge-work throughout the tissue. The nuclei are usually oval and sometimes have a slightly irregular outline, recalling the 'slipper' form of *Paramecium*. They often contain one or two nucleoli and fine granules of darkly staining chromatin. The tips of the separate cells may become fused, or so closely apposed as to appear so. Fibroblasts can multiply rapidly even in the adult, especially after injury, and they are then also able to migrate actively. In the embryo the spaces between the developing organs are occupied by *mesenchyme cells*, which may be regarded as embryonic fibroblasts. Some investigators claim that a reserve of mesenchyme cells remains in the adult, but there is little information about the processes that control the differentiation of fibroblasts nor whether there is a source from which they are recruited in the adult.

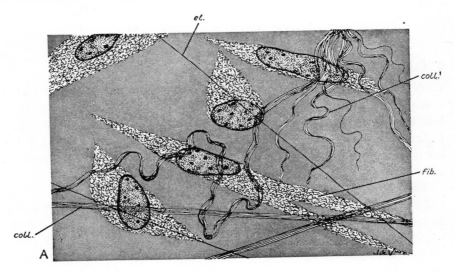

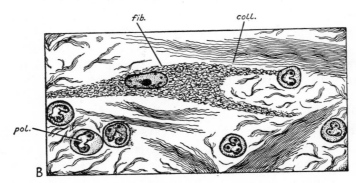

FIG. 12. Various forms of connective tissue.

A, Areolar tissue from the skin of a rabbit. B, fibroblast and young collagen fibres from a section of the skin of a monkey. *coll.* collagen fibres; *coll*[1]. same cut; *el.* elastic fibres; *fib.* fibroblast; *f.c.* fat cell; *pol.* polymorph.

(Figs. 12, 14, and 15 from preparations and photographs by Mr. K. C. Richardson.)

It is also not certain whether, as has often been held, fibroblasts can become converted into other types of cell, for example osteoblasts (p. 69) or endothelial cells (p. 257). Answers to these questions would be of great importance for the pathologist because fibroblasts play a leading part in the healing of wounds and the replacement of damaged tissues.

3. Ground substance

The fibroblasts are the cells that produce the structures that bind the parts of the body together. They do this by promoting the formation of various substances, of which the most ubiquitous is an intercellular matrix, the amorphous *ground substance*, which is found in all connective tissue. This matrix contains viscous polysaccharides of the hyaluronic acid type and their sulphuric esters, conjugated to form

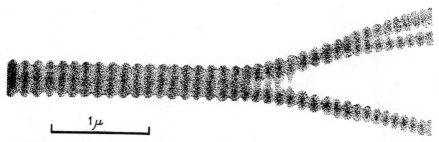

FIG. 13. Copy of electron microscope photograph of collagen fibrils from rat's tail. The fibrils have been obtained by dispersing trypsin-treated material in weak acid. Note that the cleavage plane at the frayed end is longitudinal.
(After Schmitt, Hall, and Jakus, *J. Cell. Comp. Physiol.* **20**.)

complex mucinous substances. The amorphous ground substance fills up all the interstices of an embryo or young mammal. *Wharton's jelly* of the umbilical cord is probably a pure form of this fundamental mucoid matrix protein; the substance of the vitreous humour of the eye may be similar. Electron microscopy shows that there may be submicroscopic fibrils in this matrix.

4. Collagen and tendon

Within the matrix there develop further supporting proteins, according to the particular function of the portion of connective tissue concerned. More is known of these than of the ground substances and they form visible fibrils. The chief of them is *collagen* (Randall, 1953), the sclero-protein that makes the sheets of *white fibrous tissue*, a material that is well able to resist stretch but has little resistance to compression and little elasticity. This substance occurs as fine fibres (less than $0.5\,\mu$ diameter), which do not branch or anastomose (Bear, 1952). Electron microscopic investigations show that these fibrils are cross-striated with a periodicity of 640 Å (Fig. 13). Collagen is a protein, whose characteristic amino acids are prolines (30 per cent.) and glycine (30 per cent.). The stereochemical arrangement of the polypeptide chains is not certainly known; arrangements of the molecules in sheets and as helical structures have been suggested. There is a slow turnover of the molecules of the collagen, say in a tendon, even in the adult.

The method by which collagen fibrils are produced is still unsettled.

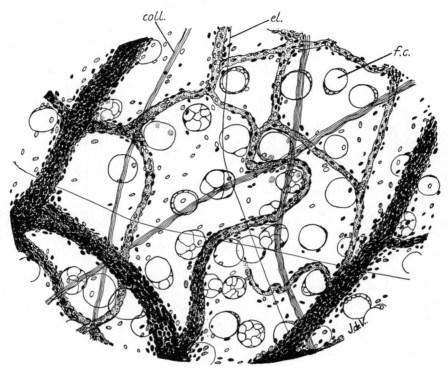

FIG. 14. Areolar tissue with fat cells and blood-vessels from the skin of a rabbit (lettering as in Fig. 12).

Fibroblasts must be present for the process to occur and fine fibrils have been described separating from the surfaces of the cells. Yet the completion of the fibres seems to occur in the matrix outside the cells, and collagen fibres can form in a clot of plasma that is separated from fibroblasts by a thin layer of porous glass filter. Evidently the fibre formation is a complicated process depending upon substances produced by the cells, but it continues in the matrix. The presence of ascorbic acid is necessary for collagen formation.

The fine collagen fibrils aggregate into bundles, $10\,\mu$ or more thick, making the characteristic wavy strands of white fibrous tissue, from which it derives its name of *fascia* (Latin *fascis*, a bundle). Collagen is recognized in histological preparations by the appearance of these wavy bundles. It stains readily with the dyes aniline blue and light green that are used in the staining methods of Mallory and Masson respectively and red with acid fuchsin in van Gieson's stain. The nature of these reactions is not understood chemically and the colours are not specific evidence of the presence of collagen. Collagen is found in almost pure form in the ligaments uniting the bones and in the tendons that join muscles to bones; also in such membranes as the *periosteum* around bones or *perimysium* around muscles. It forms the main component of *areolar tissue*, the sticky material that occupies the spaces between organs and gets its name from the fact that it readily takes up bubbles of air, assuming a white colour (Fig. 14).

Collagen fibres are so called because when boiled with water they dissolve to form gelatin or glue (Greek κόλλα, glue). Further characteristic properties are that the fibres swell in weak acids and alkalis and are dissolved by strong acids or alkalis, which are accordingly used in the process of *maceration* of tissues, when it is desired to allow the cells to fall apart. Collagen fibres are dissolved by peptic but not by tryptic enzymes; by this means they may be distinguished from other sorts of connective tissue (see below). Tannic acid and the salts of some heavy metals convert collagen to the substance *leather*, which is usually produced by tanning the collagen of the skin. The property that gives collagen its chief value to the organism is that while highly flexible it resists tension and thus gives to the tissues their power to resist deformation by stretching.

5. Reticular tissue

This is formed of fine networks of a protein similar to collagen, but the fibres always branch and are not arranged into bundles. As a result reticulin does not show the birefringence in polarized light that is characteristic of collagen. Moreover, among the fibres of reticulin there is much polysaccharide material, so that the substance forms sheets rather than fibres. These sheets make up the *basement membranes* lying below many epithelia and around many other types of cell, for instance fat cells. The sarcolemma around muscle-fibres and neurilemma around nerve-fibres are composed largely of reticulin. It also forms a framework for many organs, for instance when interspersed with lymph corpuscles in *lymphoid tissue*. Reticulin is best stained by certain special silver techniques and hence is sometimes known as *argyrophil tissue*.

6. Elastic tissue

The other main component of the intercellular substance of connective tissue is *elastin*, the substance of the yellow elastic fibres (Dempsey and Lansing, 1954). This is found mixed with white fibres in areolar and other connective tissues (Fig. 15). The elastic fibres are thin, optically refractile, and homogeneous in appearance. They branch at intervals. They curl up where they are cut, or if the tissue

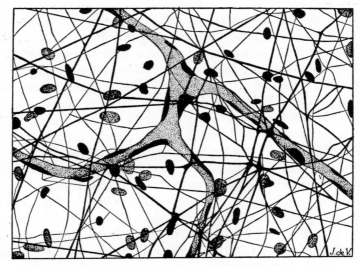

FIG. 15. Elastic fibres and capillaries from the mesentery of a rat.

is not stretched. Elastin differs from collagen in being insoluble in boiling water or strong acids but it is digested by trypsin as well as by pepsin. Elastic fibres are usually recognized by the fact that they stain with the dye orcein. A few tissues are composed mainly of elastic fibres, for instance the *ligamenta flava* uniting the vertebrae, and the coats of the larger arteries (p. 257). Such tissues are highly elastic, that is to say they return to their original length after being stretched.

7. Defensive functions of connective tissue

Connective tissue has a protective as well as a supporting function, and it contains a variety of cells that are concerned in the removal of foreign bodies and in resistance to infection. The most conspicuous of these are the *histiocytes* or *macrophages* (Fig. 16), which are often almost as numerous as the fibroblasts. They are flattened or spindle-shaped cells with a more definite outline than the fibroblasts. The nucleus is small, kidney-shaped, or irregular in outline and composed of coarse, dark-staining granules. Great variations occur, however, and it is often not easy to distinguish histiocytes from fibroblasts except by their characteristic property of taking up bacteria or other foreign particles and their power to store certain dyes, such as *trypan blue* or *lithium carmine*, after these have been injected into the animal. In conditions of infection or trauma the histiocytes become migratory

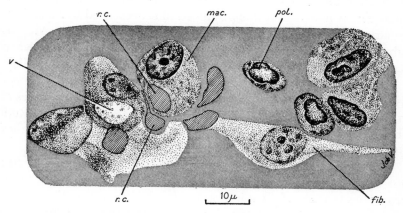

FIG. 16. Macrophages removing extravasated red cells in a wound of a guinea-pig's skin made one week previously.

fib. fibroblast; *mac.* macrophage; *pol.* polymorph; *r.c.* red cell; *v.* vacuole in macrophage. (From a preparation and photograph by Mr. K. C. Richardson.)

and ingest foreign bodies or degeneration products and their protoplasm is then seen to contain large vacuoles (Fig. 16); in this state they are known as *macrophages*. It is not clear whether they act by carrying away the debris or by dissolving it with enzymes on the spot.

The histiocytes thus provide a defensive system of cells dispersed throughout the tissues and sometimes known collectively as the *reticulo-endothelial system* (Chèvremont, 1948) or better as the *macrophage system*. The former name recalls the similarity of these cells to the reticular cells that line the sinuses of the lymph nodes and spleen (p. 267), which may be regarded as specialized macrophages. Other members of the macrophage group are the Kupffer cells of the liver (p. 252), the monocytes of the blood (p. 271), and the microglia cells of the central nervous system (p. 379).

Mast-cells (Asboe-Hansen, 1954) are found mainly in the connective tissues around the blood-vessels and they are characterized by the presence of numerous granules that stain supravitally with neutral red. The granules probably consist of the substance *heparin*, concerned in clotting of the blood (p. 271); they are dissolved out of the cells by the fixatives used in many routine histological methods, therefore special fixatives must be used to preserve them. *Plasma-cells* (p. 268), *eosinophil-cells*, and *pigment-cells* are other types sometimes found in connective tissue; *lymphocytes*, similar to those of the blood, may also be found there. There is evidently a close community of structure and function between the blood and blood-vessels and the connective tissues (see p. 256). The blood itself, like collagen, is an intercellular matrix and it is produced in spaces lined by cells that are remarkably similar to some of those in connective tissue. Moreover, substances usually reach the cells from the blood only after transport across the connective-tissue membranes that surround the cells.

In addition to its power of removing foreign bodies, connective tissue also plays an important part in the formation of antibodies after invasion of the body by bacteria and other foreign substances. Reticulin, in particular, has special antigenic powers and the antibodies of a tissue can sometimes be shown to be located in it.

Connective tissue should be thought of not as a mere set of fibres, nor even of membranes, but as a material with varied and complex properties that are of great importance to the organism. The condition of the proteins of the connective tissues, together with those of the blood, probably goes far to determine the *constitution* of the individual, especially as regards resistance to disease.

8. The forms of connective tissue

The connective tissue assumes different forms in various parts of the body, according to the forces acting on it and the chemical conditions to which it is subjected. It makes protective layers around most of the organs. For example the capsules of glands, the meninges of the brain, the periosteum of the bones, perimysium of muscles, and perineurium of nerves can all be regarded as sheets of connective tissue, each with its special properties. There is often a distinct sheet of connective tissue around every cell of a tissue, for example each fibre of a peripheral nerve runs in an endoneurial tube (p. 333). The connective tissue is often in such close relation to the cell surface that nutrient and other substances can only reach the cell after passing through layers of connective tissue. The question of the permeability properties of this substance and the nature of the fluid spaces in connective tissue are therefore obviously of first importance, though unfortunately they are little understood. Connective tissue may perhaps contain minute spaces filled with *tissue fluid*, which thus intervenes between the walls of the capillaries and the cells (p. 261). The amount of this fluid varies from moment to moment in any organ; it is often absent and in general it only becomes abundant when irritation or some other abnormality produces the condition of *oedema*. It is not safe to make any assumptions about the composition of this intercellular fluid or about the extent to which the connective tissue forms a barrier to

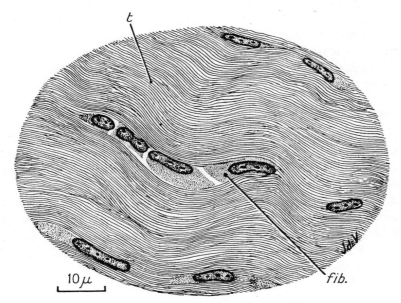

FIG. 17. Section of a portion of a tendon of *Macacus*.

fib. fibroblast (tendon cell); *t.* tendon fibres (collagen).
(From a preparation and photograph by Mr. K. C. Richardson.)

diffusion between the blood-stream and the cells. These questions of the extent, nature, and properties of the intercellular spaces are greatly in need of further investigation.

The fascia forms *loose connective tissue* or *areolar tissue* throughout the organs, allowing movement between them. It makes fine sheets, the *deep fascia*, between muscles and bones, dividing the limbs into 'compartments'. In situations where tension falls on the connective tissue the collagen fibres are laid down along the line of pull, producing a *tendon* (Fig. 17) or *ligament*. The characteristic cells in a tendon are fibroblasts of a special form, known as tendon cells. In certain situations elastic ligaments develop, although the stimulus for their production is not clear.

9. Serous membranes

In situations where the sliding of surfaces over each other is of special importance the connective tissue develops into *serous membranes*, the surface layers being covered with flattened cells known as *mesothelium*, which is not strictly an epithelium but a modified form of connective tissue. Such coverings are found over the abdominal viscera (*peritoneum*), lungs and thoracic cavity (*pleura*), and heart (*pericardium*). It is convenient to call these flattened cells mesothelium to distinguish them by their position and function from such flattened surface cells as the endothelium and epithelium that are found in other parts of the body.

10. Synovial membranes

The surfaces of the joint-cavities are lined by *synovial membranes*. These resemble the mesothelia of the viscera in some ways and may be considered as a modified form of connective tissue. They are not, however, covered by a complete layer of cells. These membranes produce the synovial fluid that occupies the joint-cavity (p. 74). A similar tissue lines the *synovial bursae* or sacks that occur where there is a play between one tissue and another, for instance between the skin and the knee-cap (*patella*). Again, there are synovial *tendon-sheaths* that allow smooth movement of the tendons where they are bound down by sheets of fascia.

11. Fatty tissue

Enzymatic systems capable of synthesizing or breaking down fat are present throughout the body, and in certain cells of the connective tissue they become specially developed for the storage of fat. Adipose tissue is found at many sites in the body, especially in the dermis and mesentery and around the kidneys. It serves mainly as a reserve but also has mechanical functions, forming soft and elastic pads in some places.

Fat cells are formed from fibroblasts by the appearance of small droplets of fat in the cytoplasm. These grow and fuse until the cell becomes a thin-walled bag, enclosing a single large droplet of neutral fat, with a flattened nucleus at one side. The deposition and withdrawal of fat is controlled partly by hormonal signals and partly by variation in the demand by other tissues. The anterior pituitary occupies a central place in the control of fat metabolism, being itself influenced by the nearby nervous centres of the hypothalamus

(p. 419). The provision of reserves of fuel is an obvious example of predictive action by the body. The reserve is maintained at a level that is adequate but not excessive, by the influence of a control system, mainly laid down by heredity. Environmental factors such as food-supply and demands for the output of work obviously influence the balance. No calculus is available by which the operation of these various factors influencing the fat depots can be described exactly.

12. Control of the connective tissues

The connective tissues provide a part of the relatively stable frame-work for the body and control of their organization is therefore little influenced by the quick-acting signals of the nervous system. The differentiation of the various types of cell and fibre is produced by hereditary factors, interacting with the local chemical and physical factors at each point (Fitton Jackson, 1954). The working of this system is of first-rate importance for the maintenance of the body but we understand little of the factors that control the production of the various cell types.

Some investigators claim that certain cells seen around the blood-vessels constitute a reserve of *undifferentiated cells*, capable of developing into most or all of the types seen in connective tissue. Unfortunately the whole question of the nature of the transformations of cell types and the stimuli that produce them is very obscure. There are certainly some similarities between, for instance, fibroblasts and histiocytes, and possible transitional forms between types as distinct as fat cells and fibroblasts can be found. Evidently the genus 'connective tissue', like the genus 'epidermis' contains many different species. The condition of any piece of tissue is the product of the powers of differentiation conferred on it during development and the forces that fall on it by the action of other tissues and the outside world.

An example of such interaction is the control of the deposition of collagen in fibrous tissue or tendon. The material is found to occur along the lines where the tissue is under tension. Weiss has shown how this state of affairs is reached, by study of tissue cultures and of such situations as a healing wound, in which new collagen is being laid down. The fibrin fibres of a blood clot are at first randomly orientated, but as the clot is dissolved the parts not subjected to tension disappear first, leaving a web of orientated fibrin fibres. Fibroblasts grow into this web and collagen is then laid down along the tension lines. Readjustment of the earliest network of the collagen proceeds by the same method, fibres being removed when they are not in the line of tension. In this way a piece of connective tissue, tendon, or ligament is produced, composed of fibres orientated along the lines of tension and hence well adapted to its position.

This is a good example of the way in which the organism makes the forecasts that ensure its survival (p. 22). The hereditary instruction of the genes ensures that collagen is laid down along lines of tension. The stresses of the environment may be regarded as providing information that selects those sites in which the collagen is produced. The two together provide the organism with a memory in the form of a set of collagen fibres so orientated that the organism can meet the stresses that are likely to fall upon it, assuming that the future stresses are like those of the past. The direction of orientation of the fibres thus provides a forecast based on past experience of the likely direction of tension stress in the future.

Thus the connective tissue, although not under the control of the nervous system, nevertheless carries memories of the situations that have been experienced. Such memories are provided by the arrangement of the fibres, the condition of the histiocytes and other defence mechanisms, the number of fat cells, and many other features. Moreover, the condition of these tissues is continually changing under the influence of the chemical and physical forces acting upon them and of chemical signals received from the endocrine organs. The connective tissues change with every change in the organism through use, accident, disease, or ageing. They play a major part in the operations of wound-healing. Pathological conditions in the connective tissue, such as arteriosclerosis and arthritis, may be of mortal importance to the organism. The demonstration of the effects of adrenal cortical and pituitary hormones on the connecting-tissue in such diseases (p. 549) shows that even this framework of the body is regulated by the endocrine signalling system. By these relatively slow methods of control the connective tissue is continually adjusted to suit the environment.

IV

SKELETAL TISSUE. CARTILAGE AND BONE

1. Resistance to tension and compression

COLLAGEN and the other scleroproteins of connective tissue provide resistance to tensile forces, but where parts of the organism are liable to be distorted by compression there develops either the protein *cartilage* or the combination of organic and inorganic particles that makes *bone* (see Dallemagne, 1950). This power of the tissues to produce materials that are appropriate to resist the forces that fall upon them obviously provides forecasts that are of central importance for ensuring the survival of the organization of the animal or man.

Knowledge about the control of bone formation is likely to help greatly with the study of various problems about living organization and its evolution. The investigation of skeletal structures plays an important part in the study of the evolution of mammals, because as fossils the bones constitute the main means of following the course of phylogenesis. The solution of certain clinical problems would also be easier if we knew more about how skeletal material forms normally and why it tends to appear in tendons, arteries, and other tissues that are subjected to powerful forces.

2. Cartilage

Cartilage is a form of connective tissue in which the general amorphous ground substance has been added to and thickened. The characteristic cells are the rounded *cartilage corpuscles*, which lie each in a little space, surrounded on all sides by matrix (Fig. 18). These cells are formed in development by the conversion of cells resembling fibroblasts, while the remaining cells in the neighbourhood are compressed and disappear. At the margin of the cartilage new cells are continually added from a special superficial layer of connective tissue, the *perichondrium*. The cartilage therefore grows mainly by addition from outside by appositional growth, but there may also be some interstitial growth by division of the cells within the formed or partly formed cartilage.

The characteristic interstitial substance of the cartilage is a basophil mucopolysaccharide material known as *chondrin*. In ordinary *hyaline* or *glass-like cartilage* this substance shares the matrix with a varying amount of collagen, little if the cartilage is truly glass-like, more if it is *fibrous cartilage*. The collagen fibres are readily revealed by digesting away the chondrin with trypsin. In the *elastic cartilage* of the external ear, epiglottis, and a few other regions the matrix contains elastic fibres.

Cartilage is the material that forms the first outline of part of the

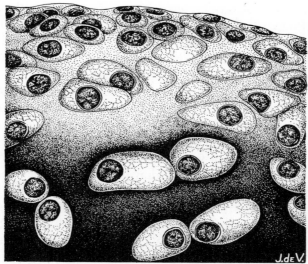

FIG. 18. Section of articular cartilage at the end of the femur of a frog. (From a preparation and photograph by Mr. K. C. Richardson.)

skull, the vertebrae, and the long bones, but in mammals it is mostly replaced in the adult by bone, cartilaginous remains being found only at the end of the bones, within the joints, at the ventral ends of the ribs, and in a few other situations. As a structural material cartilage stands between connective tissue and bone. It is much better able to resist compression than is connective tissue, though not so strong in this respect as is bone. It is also well able to resist tension, a property that is, of course, present also in bone, though bones may snap under strong muscular effort before rupture of the tendon that transmits the pull.

The structural unit of cartilage is a group of cells, together with the matrix and the fibres that surround them (Fig. 19). The fluid substance of the cells, enclosed within the fibre bundles, forms the compression-resistant component; the matrix itself is somewhat compressible and elastic, and ensures that the material is suitable for taking up mechanical shocks, such as occur between the bones. The third component of the material, the fibrous collagen, gives resistance to tension. Since the resistance to compression is a property of the fluid contents the effectiveness of cartilage in this respect depends on the integrity of the surrounding perichondrium. Cartilage is highly adapted to the

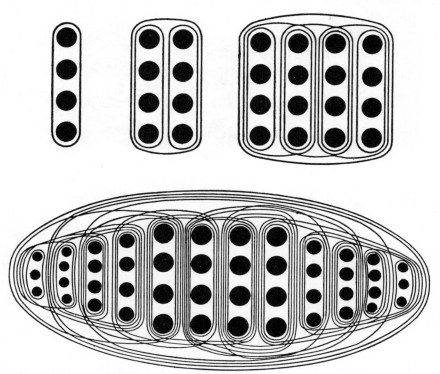

FIG. 19. The structure of hyaline cartilage. Each black circle is a single cartilage corpuscle with its sheath of fibres. The corpuscles are grouped into units, 'chondrones', with further fibrous sheaths, and the whole group is surrounded by a perichondrium. The fluid material resists compression, the fibres resist tension.
(From Murray after Benninghoff, *Bones*. Cambridge University Press.)

strains placed upon it, for instance in the ring-like cartilages of the trachea the outer region contains abundant fibres, as would be expected, since this side meets mostly tension stresses; the inner part of the cartilage, subjected mostly to compression, contains more matrix. The combination of materials in cartilage has been likened to that in reinforced concrete or a rubber tyre.

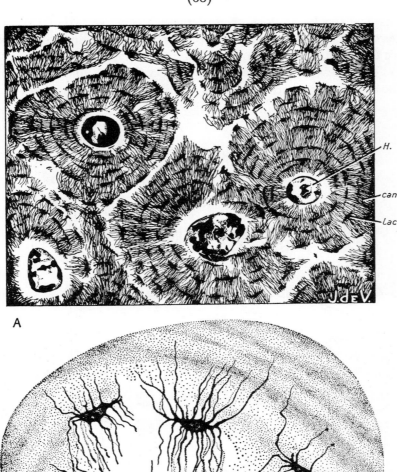

H.

can.

Lac.

A

B

FIG. 20. A. Portion of transverse section of a human femur after decalcification, showing Haversian systems.

can. canaliculi; *H.* Haversian canal; *lac.* lacuna.

B. Osteocytes from human adult compact bone after decalcification and staining. (From preparations and photographs by Mr. K. C. Richardson.)

3. Bone

Bone is a tissue especially adapted to meet the compression forces falling upon it but also able to resist tension. Unlike cartilage, which is nearly avascular, the bones are closely related to the blood system; indeed the central marrow of some bones is occupied by the chief blood-forming tissues. Bone is a plastic substance in the sense that it is readily modified, perhaps because the bone-cells are branched structures, whose fine processes penetrate the matrix, every part of which thus remains close to the protoplasm of the cells. Even the hard part of the bone is continually changed. If the radioactive isotope of phosphorus (P^{32}) is ingested with the food or injected it is taken up by the bones within a few hours. About one-third of the material taken up after a single test injection was found to be retained in the bones after three weeks in the rat. This plasticity of bone allows it to change its structure quite rapidly if the forces falling upon it change; each bone thus carries a memory of the stressing that has occurred in the recent past, providing a forecast to meet the forces likely to be applied in the future.

Sections of bone reveal a series of spaces, the *lacunae*, occupied in life by the cell bodies of the *osteocytes*, each surrounded by a system of *canaliculi*, which contain the long fibrous processes of the cells (Fig. 20). In young bone the processes of the cells unite and the canaliculi thus make a continuous communicating system throughout the bone.

The matrix of the bone consists of 70 per cent. of hard inorganic salts and 30 per cent. of a fibrous protein that is similar to collagen but is sometimes called *ossein*. This large protein content gives the bone a certain flexibility, avoiding the brittleness of a purely inorganic structure. The bone salt itself is a complex crystalline mixture of calcium phosphates and carbonates known to crystallographers as *apatite*. The arrangement of the spicules of this material gives the bone its characteristic hardness and the detailed organization differs with the function of the bone. It is usual to distinguish between *spongy* (or *cancellous*) *bone*, made of a network of spicules visible to the naked eye, and *compact bone*, where the spicules are closely packed and produce a hard white material; there are no essential differences, however, and all bone first passes through a spongy stage.

The shafts of long bones consist of a tube of compact bone and a central cavity, the marrow. In adults this marrow is mostly fat and is known as *yellow marrow*. The ends of the shaft are composed of spongy bone, among the trabeculae of which there is *red marrow*, which is a bone- and blood-forming tissue, found also in the flat bones of the skull, sternum, and ribs (p. 274).

In compact bones the bone-cells are arranged in a regular manner around arteries and veins running along the bone. Each group of vessels constitutes a *Haversian canal* and around it the bone-cells are arranged in concentric layers to form a Haversian system (Fig. 20). Within the lamellae the fibrils and the particles of inorganic material are placed in various directions, so that the whole constitutes a tube of great strength. Both in compact and in spongy bone the direction of the main spicules and lamellae is related in a definite manner to the forces acting upon the material, producing a structure suited to the load that must be carried. The details of the architecture of the bones will be considered later (p. 93).

The Haversian canals communicate at intervals with the vessels at the surface and centre of the bone by means of the *canals of Volkmann*. The outer and inner surfaces of the bones are known as *periosteum* and *endosteum* respectively; they consist of a special variety of connective tissue, able to produce bone. The periosteum is tightly attached to the bone over most of the surface by strands of collagen, which continue into the substance of the bone as the *fibres of Sharpey*. Muscles, tendons and ligaments are attached to the periosteum, which is here tightly fastened to the underlying bone. Where there is a joint at the end of a bone the periosteum becomes continuous with the joint-capsule. The periosteum thus serves three functions. (1) Its inner osteogenic layers produce bone. (2) Its outer fibrous layers prevent the spread of the bone-forming tissues. (3) It provides attachment for muscles, tendons, and ligaments.

4. Development of bone

The formation of bone occurs either in pre-existing cartilage (*endochondral ossification*, producing *cartilage bones*) or in a connective tissue membrane to produce a *dermal* or *intramembranous bone*. The dermal bones originate in phylogeny from scales lying near the surface. The skull bones still occupy this position, other dermal bones are more deeply sunken (clavicle). The conversion of cartilage into bone is preceded by changes in the cartilage itself (Fig. 21). The cells become arranged in rows and their nuclei degenerate. The matrix meanwhile becomes calcified by the deposition of lime salts, a process that occurs in other degenerating tissues, for instance the walls of diseased blood-vessels. This deposit is not bone, however, and it is soon removed by an ingrowth of blood-vessels and connective tissue, which appear to dissolve away the calcified matrix. Certain cells of the connective tissue that are similar to fibroblasts then differentiate into *osteoblasts*. These form layers of cells that produce new bone by the provision of the

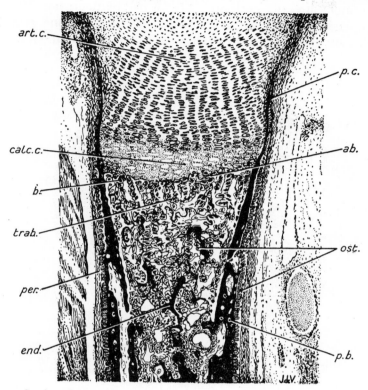

FIG. 21. Section of a developing metatarsal bone from a foetal cat, showing the formation of endochondral bone within the extending cylinder of periosteal bone.

ab. zone of absorption; *art.c.* articular cartilage; *b.* bone marrow invading cartilage; *calc.c.* calcified cartilage; *end.* endochondral bone; *ost.* osteoblasts; *p.b.* periosteal bone; *p.c.* perichondrium; *per.* periosteum; *trab.* trabeculae of calcified cartilage in which endochondral bone is deposited by the osteoblasts.

(Figs. 21–23 from preparations and photographs lent by Mr. K. C. Richardson.)

necessary enzymes. The first bone is a fibrous matrix; this becomes calcified and gradually surrounds the osteoblasts, which become converted into the adult bone-cells. It is not known what stimulus initiates the differentiation of the osteoblasts, nor how these cause the production of bone. The calcium is provided by liberation from calcium hexose monophosphate and other esters in the blood. The enzyme *phosphatase* that breaks down these esters is found abundantly in regions of active bone formation.

An elaborate reconstruction is undertaken before the bone reaches its final form, and this is made possible by the presence of *osteoclasts* (Fig. 22), which dissolve away unwanted bone and are abundant throughout the process of bone differentiation (Hancox, 1949). They are multinucleate cells, each probably formed by the fusion of several osteoblasts. One of the most surprising features of bone growth is that the cells can alternately produce and then destroy the bone, but

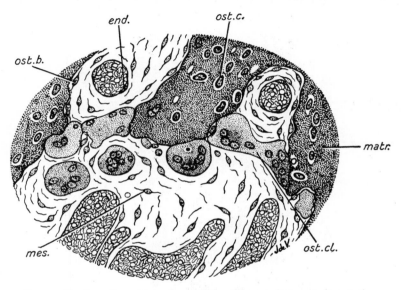

FIG. 22. Portion of a section of mandible of human foetus at six months.

end. endothelial cell of capillary; *matr.* matrix of bone; *mes.* cell of mesenchyme (in Fig. 23 in process of conversion to osteoblast), *ost.b.* osteoblast; *ost.c.* osteocyte; *ost.cl.* osteoclast; *ost.f.* osteogenic fibres.

little is known of the conditions that determine the differentiation of fibroblasts into osteoblasts or the conversion of the latter to osteoclasts and back again.

The ossification of a long bone proceeds in a characteristic manner. The cartilaginous precursor provides the general shape of the bone. Osteogenesis begins around the middle of the shaft; here the perichondrium produces osteoblasts and is henceforward known as periosteum. A layer of bone, the *periosteal bone collar*, forms around the middle of the shaft. Soon afterward blood-vessels and connective tissue penetrate into the shaft and replace its cartilage with bone. In this way the whole length becomes ossified, forming the *diaphysis* of the bone, with a bone-marrow cavity at its middle. The ends of the bone ossify by separate centres that develop somewhat later and are known as *epiphyses* (Fig. 21). There may be one or several such centres at the end of the bone; they remain separate from the diaphysis throughout the growth period. Growth occurs by the addition of new cartilage between the diaphysis and the ends and its conversion to bone, producing increase in length; growth in thickness comes largely from the periosteum. The epiphyses fuse with the diaphyses only

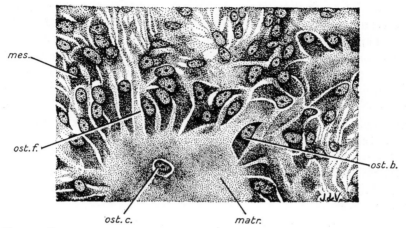

FIG. 23. Process of ossification in a membrane bone. Preparation and lettering as Fig. 22.

towards the end of development, when the bones are no longer elongating.

The formation of a membrane bone differs from the above account only in that the osteoblasts begin to appear in a connective tissue matrix instead of in cartilage (Fig. 23). They form rows of cells, which soon lay down trabeculae of bone. The membrane bones of the skull develop in this way from one or a few centres for each bone, bone formation spreading outwards until the bony area meets that of a neighbouring bone and the characteristic jagged suture line is formed. Subsequent enlargement of the skull is produced by addition of new bone externally and its removal from the inner side. Bone is also added at the sutures and the bones remain separate throughout the growth period.

5. Joints

The discontinuities between bones have a very different significance according to whether there is movement between them (see Gardner, 1950). Where little movement occurs, as between the bones of the skull, the bones are separated by *fibrous joints* and the thin connective tissue layers between them remain as a *suture* (Fig. 24). Some slightly moveable bones are united by *cartilaginous joints*, composed of a pad of fibrous tissue and cartilage, for example the intervertebral articulations. Where there is free movement there is a *synovial joint* between the bones. The articular surfaces are covered by smooth hard bone and this by a thin layer of smooth hyaline cartilage. The bones are held together by a *capsular ligament*, having fibrous thickenings arranged in directions that prevent disruption of the bones. The capsule consists of an outer dense fibrous layer and an inner more cellular *synovial membrane*. The latter has folds projecting between the bones and it secretes the very thin layer of *synovial fluid* that separates the bones. This fluid contains the large polysaccharide molecules of hyaluronic acid, combined with protein to give mucin, whose physical properties are suitable for lubrication. The articular cartilage has no nerves or blood-vessels but these are abundant in the capsule.

In some synovial joints there are pads of fibro-cartilage, the *articular discs*, which, being pliable, serve to maintain the congruity of the surfaces during movement. Pads of fatty tissue in the capsule also serve this function.

Synovial bursae are sacks, filled with synovia, which occur where one structure moves upon another. The *tendon sheaths*, which surround tendons where they change direction, are lined by synovial membranes and these continue over the surface of the fascial tunnels in which the tendons slide.

The control of the structure of joints is largely influenced by hereditary factors. Limb buds transplanted to atypical positions may produce bones united by synovial joints even though few muscles and no normal strains are present. Yet the details of the form of the joint develop in response to the conditions imposed. For example the fibres of the ligaments in the capsule that prevent disarticulation develop in the directions in which strain occurs.

6. Factors controlling bone deposition

The determination of part of the developing embryo to produce cartilage and bone occurs very early (Felts, 1954). Tiny fragments of material taken from a chick embryo at four days, or even earlier, when they consist only of apparently undifferentiated mesoderm, can be grown on the chorio-allantoic membrane (p. 587) of an older embryo. There they may develop into an almost perfect femur, with recognizable articular facets (Fig. 25). Many experiments of this sort could be cited to show that the existence of a 'cartilage' or 'bone' as a separate

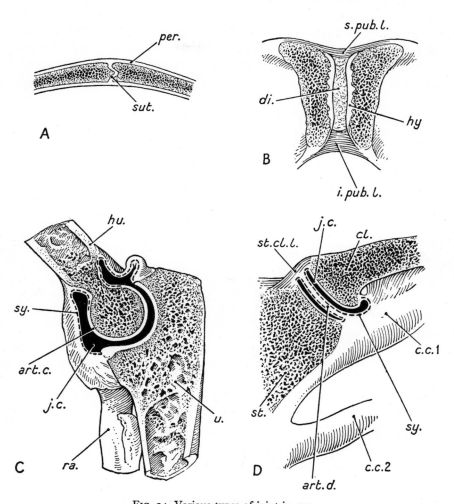

FIG. 24. Various types of joint in man.

A, Sutural joint between bones of the skull. B, cartilaginous joint at the pubic symphysis.
C, simple synovial joint at the elbow. D, sterno-clavicular joint, a synovial joint with articular
disk. The synovial membrane occupies the space between the dotted line and the joint
cavity, which is shown in black. *art.c.* articular cartilage; *art.d.* articular disk; *c.c.* 1 and 2
costal cartilages; *cl.* clavicle; *di.* interpubic disk (fibro-cartilage); *hu.* humerus; *hy.* hyaline
cartilage; *i.pub.l.* inferior pubic ligament; *j.c.* joint cavity; *per.* periosteum; *ra.* radius;
s.pub.l. superior pubic ligament; *st.* sternum; *st.cl.l.* sterno-clavicular ligament; *sut.* sutural
ligament; *sy.* synovial membrane; *u.* ulna.

entity is determined by inherited morphogenetic factors and is not the result of pressure, tension, or other mechanical influences. Nevertheless, the final detailed form of the bone depends on the forces that fall upon it (Glucksmann, 1942). Joint surfaces develop on bones that are not stressed but the surfaces only come to conform properly when

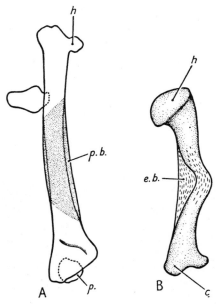

FIG. 25. Bones developed by growth of fragments of limb-buds in the chick. Pieces of the limb-buds of four-day embryos were grafted to the chorio-allantoic membrane.

A, Shows a femur developed from the basal part of the limb-bud. The bone is complete and has a rounded head (*h*), although there is no socket for it to fit into. B, is a humerus and also has a head (*h*), and condyles (*c*) for the radius and ulna. *e.b.* extra bone; *p.* patella; *p.b.* perichondral bone. (After Murray, P. D. F., *Bones*. Cambridge University Press.)

there is movement between them. Similarly the sizes and shapes of the various ridges and depressions to which muscles are attached depend upon the use of these muscles. In young rabbits compelled by means of splints to rotate the foot laterally the direction of twist of the femur was found to become markedly abnormal (Appleton, 1934). When there is a deficiency of certain vitamins or other nutritional requirements the outer shape of the bones may be nearly normal, but the walls are thin and there are other structural defects. The shape of a bone is therefore controlled by double dependence, partly by the hereditary forces acting from within, partly by the stresses imposed from without (see p. 22).

In view of the great importance of the shapes of bones for the study of evolutionary history it would be especially valuable to know something of the factors that determine the time and place of bone deposition and thus produce the characteristic patterns of 'bones'. In particular it is not clear how arrangement into a particular set of irregular bones has any advantage over ossification of the skull in some other pattern. The bones of the skull form in approximately their normal shapes in animals where for some reason the brain is very small, even though the reduced brain cannot give the normal pressure stimulus. When a whole bone, say the parietal, is removed from a young mammal the space is usually filled by growth of those that remain.

These observations do not tell us why bone does not form in uniform sheets in the skull, but they suggest that the division into separate 'bones' is not the result of simple mechanical factors. It is greatly to be hoped that the controlling factors will ultimately be found, and further experiments of the above sort might be interesting. It should be possible to discover experimentally how pressure, tension, or more general morphogenetic factors determine that bone is produced in restricted areas. We shall return to consideration of this subject in the next chapter, after examining the arrangement of the skeleton.

V

THE FRAMEWORK OF THE BODY

1. Forces acting upon the body

THE skeleto-muscular system provides a means by which the body can be supported in various positions against the force of gravity. It can also move the body as a whole or change the position of its parts so as to move other bodies, especially in the 'handling' actions of primates. The arrangement of the skeleton and muscles differs according to the environment in which each species of animal lives, in other words the hereditary organization provides an apparatus suitable to meet the conditions in which the animal will find itself. In this sense the skeleton and muscles provide a representation of certain features of the environment. Moreover, during the life of the individual, the stresses placed upon the tissues provide information by which this representation is made to conform more exactly to the particular conditions that the animal meets.

Study of the skeleton and muscles must take account of the physical principles that affect any system performing mechanical operations. The strength of the parts must be sufficient to meet the forces that fall upon them, with an adequate margin of safety. The frequency with which bones are broken and muscles and ligaments torn shows the severe limitations imposed upon the actions of the body by the need to carry its own weight under various circumstances. Anything that reduces this load will be of importance in ensuring the survival of the animal.

The loads that the tissues must bear are chiefly those imposed by their own weight (leaving aside the rather unusual load-carrying habits of man). It is therefore important that the body should be served by tissues that combine the maximum of strength with the minimum of weight. The forces that tissues must resist are the external forces, especially gravity, and the internal forces brought into play to counteract gravity or to move the body.

When two equal and opposite forces are applied to a body it is said to be under *stress* (force per unit area). Changes of shape of a body under stress are called *strains*. Stress is subdivided according to the direction in which the forces act (Fig. 26) into (1) compression, when parts tend to be pushed together, (2) tension, when parts of the body tend to be pulled apart, and (3) shear, when parts tend to be slid over each other. A pair of equal and opposite parallel forces that are not colinear form a couple tending to rotate the body. Two couples of the opposite sense of rotation are said to cause torsion. When a body is bent, tension, compression, and shear operate together but in different places.

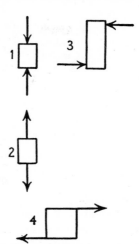

In considering the properties and arrangements of the tissues that resist external forces we can ask three questions: (1) Are the materials themselves well suited to retain their shape under the forces that they are likely to meet? (2) Are the materials arranged in such a way as to use the minimum amount of material necessary to meet the forces acting upon them? (3) Are these forces themselves kept to a minimum by efficient arrangement of the parts of the whole system? Such a discussion of efficiency of materials is, of course, subject to the limitations that restrict the organization of all living systems. The building materials available are the metabolizable carbon compounds. The engineer could make 'better'

FIG. 26. Diagrams of the action of external forces on a body. (1) Compression, (2) tension, (3) shearing or bending, (4) torsion. (After Steindler, A., *Mechanics of Normal and Pathological Locomotion in Man*, 1935, London: Baillière, Tindall & Cox.)

bones out of, say, alloys of aluminium. Further, the organism must grow in size, function properly at all sizes, and be constantly replaced, even in the adult. Hence bones cannot be used to apply constant tensions and muscles have to be used instead, although they have a lower strength/weight ratio than bone and use more metabolic energy. Finally, certain types of structure that are very efficient cannot be built by the body at all—notably wheels and axles.

2. The strength of living materials

The limiting conditions imposed by the nature of living systems and their dependence upon past history place discussions about the 'efficiency' of materials in a framework different from that used by the engineer. However, we may attempt to answer the first of the above questions by measurement of the strength of the materials under various conditions. Table A shows the figures given by Koch (1917) for various substances and tissues.

TABLE A

Substance	Ultimate strength lb./sq. in.		
	Tension	Compression	Shear
Hard steel . .	130,000	120,000	50,000
Cast iron . .	25,000	90,000	18,000
Granite . .	1,500	15,000	2,000
Concrete . .	300	3,000	. .
Bone . . .	18,000	24,000	7,000
Cartilage . .	2,000	4,000	. .
Tendon . .	10,000	. .	. .
Nerve . . .	13,000	. .	. .
Artery . . .	200	. .	. .
Muscle . .	80	. .	. .

These figures show the load at which the substance breaks under the three conditions, and it will be seen that bone and tendon compare favourably with all but the strongest non-living materials. Tendon is an efficient material in resisting tensile forces and bone resists both compression and tension, especially the former, but it is rather easily broken under shearing forces.

TABLE B

Substance	Ultimate strength in tension (lb./sq. in.)	Density (lb./cu. in.)	$\dfrac{Strength}{Density}$ (in.)
Hard steel .	130,000	0·28	460,000
Duralumin wire .	70,000	0·10	700,000
Granite . .	1,500	0·10	15,000
Bone . .	18,000	0·068	265,000

Table B shows the relationship between strength and density of various substances. The last column expresses the length of a piece of material that can be hung and support its own weight. Bone evidently combines strength and lightness as well as all but the best non-living materials.

3. Arrangement of materials along trajectories

The question of the arrangement of the material within the bones has attracted much attention since the anatomist Meyer and the engineer Culmann showed in 1880 that the trabeculae of bone in the human femur are arranged in an economical manner similar to that adopted by an engineer who disposes his material in order to make the best use of it in girders (p. 94). To understand this and also the principles on which the third of the above questions may be answered, we must consider how an engineer analyses the effects of forces acting upon a body. In a block of material supporting a load any small spherical region will tend to be deformed by the strains into an ellipsoid (Fig. 27). In any plane there will be a line of maximum com-

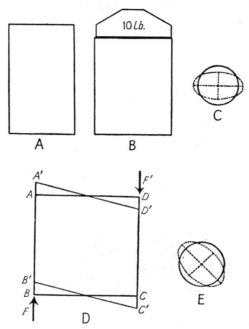

Fig. 27. The effects produced by the application of a load to a body.

A and B show how a block when loaded is shortened vertically but not decreased in volume, and is therefore expanded horizontally. This is to say that any small circle imagined on a vertical plane becomes an ellipse; there is maximum compression in the vertical and tension in the horizontal plane and these are called the principal axes of the strains (C). D and E show how shearing forces (FF¹) also produce two principal axes of strain set at right angles. (After Murray, P. D. F., *Bones*, Cambridge University Press.)

pression strain and at right angles to this a line of maximum tension strain. We can therefore easily state in a piece of material how the axes of strain will run when force is applied in any given direction. The stressing must be arranged to meet these strains. As Murray (1936) puts it, 'In the directions of principal stress there are no shearing stresses, but in any other direction there will be shearing stresses'. Lines indicating the axes of strain are called '*trajectories*' and they can be drawn so that the closeness of the lines corresponds to the degree of stress. Whether the lines are straight or curved they must fall into two sets, *compression lines* and *tension lines*, crossing each other at right angles. The engineer builds his structures so that the main girders lie in these lines of greatest stress.

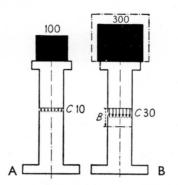

FIG. 28. Effect of increased load on stressing of a column. The lengths of the arrows are proportional to the stress. Increase of the load from 100 to 300 kg. increases the stressing (C) from 10 to 30 kg./cm.^{2} The breaking stress (shown dotted, B) is 60 kg./cm.^{2}, and the column therefore has a factor of safety of six times in the first case but only twice in the second.
(After F. Pauwels, *Z. f. Anat. u. Entwges.* **114**, 129, 1948.)

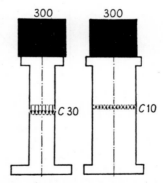

FIG. 29. Increase in the dimensions of the column carrying a load decreases the stress, giving a greater margin of safety. (After Pauwels.)

4. Symmetry of loading

Whether any material will be strong enough to meet a given load depends on the way the load is distributed. Fig. 28 shows how a load symmetrically placed on a girder produces compression strains uniformly distributed through it (see Pauwels, 1948). Increasing the load increases the stress until some breaking stress is reached. If we imagine that the breaking stress is 60 kg./cm.^{2}, then in Fig. 28A, where the stress is 10 kg./cm.^{2}, there is a margin of safety of six times; in

Fig. 28B of twice. The only way that a girder of given shape and material can be strengthened is by increasing its diameter. If the diameter of the girder is greater the margin of safety is increased (Fig. 29).

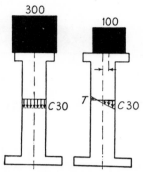

FIG. 30. In a column loaded asymmetrically compression strains (C) develop along one part of the axis and tension strains (T) along another. The breaking strain is reached with a smaller load. (After Pauwels.)

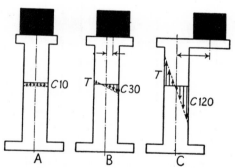

FIG. 31. As asymmetry of loading increases, the strain on the supporting column becomes very much greater. (After Pauwels.)

If the load is not symmetrically applied the compression and tension stresses will be as in Fig. 30. Moreover, the stresses are then no longer uniformly distributed and a given load may set up much higher stresses in some parts than were present with a symmetrical arrangement (Fig. 31). The breaking-point of the whole structure is limited by that of any one point, and it is therefore clear how important it is for a living body to shorten the length of any lever arms such as that of Fig. 31C, in order to avoid having to develop massive structures to meet the stresses that would result.

5. Counterweighting

There are various means by which the stresses set up can be reduced and the structure made lighter without loss of strength. A counterweight has the effect not only of distributing the stress uniformly through the girder (Fig. 32) but of greatly reducing the total stress and

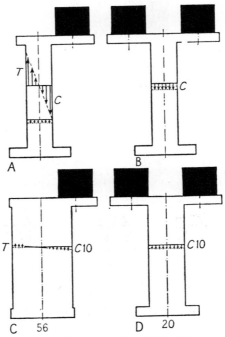

FIG. 32. Effect of a counterweight in reducing the strains set up by asymmetrical loading. The large compression and tension strains shown in A are reduced to smaller compression strains in B, in spite of the greater load carried. This allows a considerable reduction in the size of the column that is needed for a given margin of safety, C and D. Thus for a breaking limit of 10 kg./cm.² the column of a particular material needed can be reduced in weight from 56 to 20 kg. by counterweighting. (After Pauwels.)

hence the amount of material necessary to carry the load. Animals sometimes employ this principle of counterweighting even where it adds to the total weight to be moved; thus it has been suggested that the large weight of the tusks of elephants may serve as a counterweight to the body (Young, 1950, p. 670). In most mammals there is a careful balancing of weight about the main weight-bearing limbs, for instance by the tail in the kangaroo and the head and neck in the giraffe; no doubt it is only by such balance that the great weight can be supported by limbs of reasonable proportions.

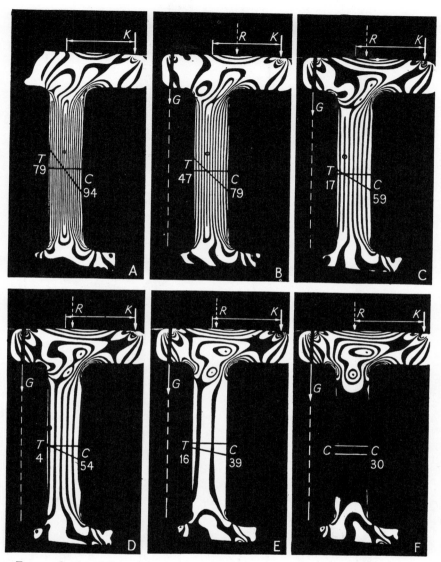

FIG. 33. Copies of photographs of a column of polymerized resin loaded and photo-graphed in polarized light. The closer the dark lines, the greater is the stress. In A the load (K) is applied asymmetrically and sets up large compression and tension stresses; in B a brace, G, is added, and the resultant force operates at R, reducing the stress. As the tension of the brace is increased in C–F, the resultant approaches the centre of the column and finally reduces the effect to a small compression stress. (After Pauwels.)

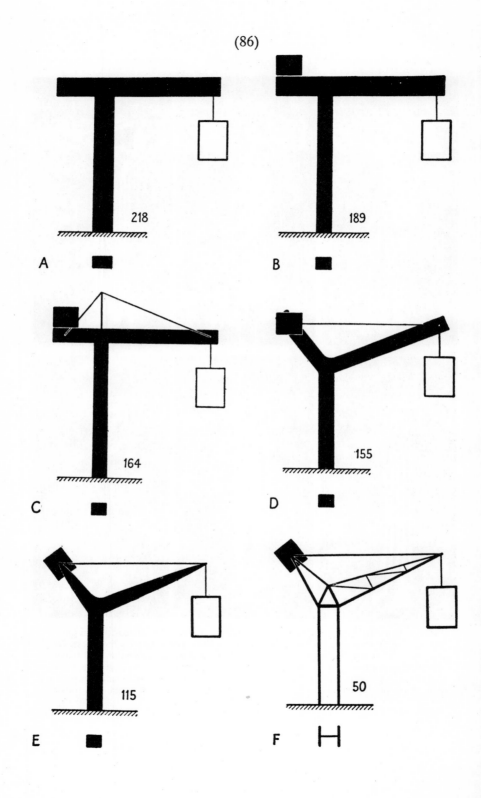

A   218

B   189

C   164

D   155

E   115

F   50

Even more important in animal organization is the reduction of size of compression members by appropriate *bracing*, whose effect is analogous to that of counterweighting. This effect can be shown by use of the photoelectric method illustrated in Fig. 33. In this technique a model of the girder or other object to be studied is cut out of a polymerized resin that becomes birefringent where it- is stressed and can therefore be made to show the trajectories of strain in the material by placing it in polarized light (Evans, 1953). The closeness of the dark lines then indicates the degree of stressing, each line representing a multiple of the stress represented by the first line from the nul region. Thus in Fig. 33A, the first line represents a stress of 10 kg./cm.² and with the asymmetrical load the maximum compression stress is about 90, tension stress 80 kg./cm.² Addition of a

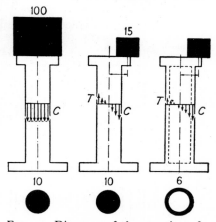

FIG. 35. Diagrams of the stressing of a column under asymmetrical loading, showing how the stressing lies at the periphery, allowing a reduction of the weight of the supporting column by use of a hollow construction. (After Pauwels.)

brace *G* of increasing tension reduces the total stress and converts it to a pure compression stress. There are many examples of such bracing action throughout the skeleto-muscular system (Figs. 36, 38, and 39).

6. Economy in use of materials

As an introduction to the application of these principles to the body we may look at the way the amount of material in a crane may be reduced. With the primitive form of Fig. 34A, the weight of a certain metal needed to make a crane able to carry a given load is 218 kg. By counterweighting this can be reduced to 189 kg. (Fig. 34B), by counterweighting and bracing to 164 kg., and with an appropriate bending of the girder to 155 kg. Further reductions are possible because not all parts of the cross-section of the material are equally stressed. A symmetrical load is distributed uniformly over the material (Fig. 35) but

FIG. 34. Diagrams to show the effect of proper counterweighting, bracing, and arrangement of girders in allowing reduction of weight of a crane of a given material carrying a given load. In the series A–F the weight of the girder necessary to carry the weight is progressively reduced from 218 to 50 kg. (see text). (After Pauwels.)

the bending stresses set up by an asymmetrical load fall mostly at the periphery. The centre part of the girders can therefore be omitted, the girder being left either circular (as in many bones), or of H shape, as is more usual in engineering practice (Fig. 34). Furthermore the stressing is least at the tip of the girder and increases downwards. This factor alone allows the members to be reduced by shaping, as in

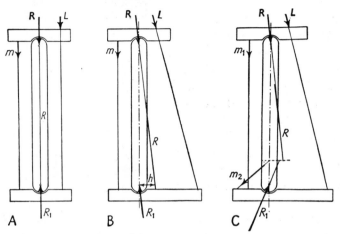

FIG. 36. The body-weight (*L*) and tension (*m*) set up by a two-joint muscle seldom have a resultant (*R*) as shown in (*A*) that acts directly along the bone. The resultant (*R*) usually acts at an angle to the bone as in (*B*) and tends to produce rotation about the lower joint. R_1 is the reaction offered by the resistance of the ground to the downward force (*R*) and *h* the length of the lever arm.

In (*C*) the bone is stabilized by the force (m_2) of a single-joint muscle, although it is now subject to a bending force. *R* is the resultant of m_1 and *L*, and R_1 the reaction at the lower joint. (After Pauwels.)

Fig. 34F. A reduction of weight of the crane from 218 to 50 kg. is thus possible by the use of appropriate design. Proper construction allows a reduction of over four times in the weight of material employed to support a given load. Comparable saving in animals would be of outstanding selective and evolutionary importance and architecture of the bodies of mammals and man shows abundant signs of the operation of such factors.

In the body the bones are subject to bending forces, such as those we have been considering in a crane. This is not immediately obvious, for in theory there are situations such as that of Fig. 36A in which the bone is under pure compression, since the resultant *R* of the action of the body-weight *L* and action of the muscle *m* acts along the line of the bone. However, in practice the situation is nearly always as in Fig. 36B, the resultant making an angle with the axis of the bone. This must mean that the bone has to be stressed against bending. Accompanying a muscle, m_1, that acts across two joints there is frequently a second one, m_2, acting across one joint only, and this tends to produce bending forces acting on the bones.

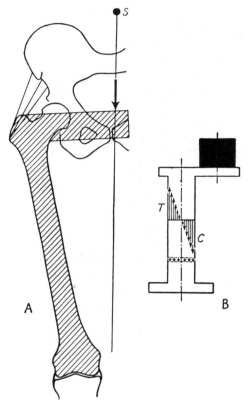

FIG. 37. A, the action of the body-weight through the sacrum (S) as an eccentric load on the femur. The model B shows the way that the femur is stressed.

7. Bracing of the long bones

If the long bones are subject to bending stresses we can immediately understand that their circular form with hollow centre leads to an effective and economical use of material, for example in the human femur shown in Fig. 43. When the weight is all on one leg the femur is loaded eccentrically (Fig. 37) and the hatched area shows the part that may be compared with the girder shown on the right. The situation is made less simple by the tilting of the pelvis at this stage of walking, which tends to bring the centre of gravity of the body over

the femoral head, but the femur still remains eccentrically loaded.
Such an arrangement would put severe compression and tension

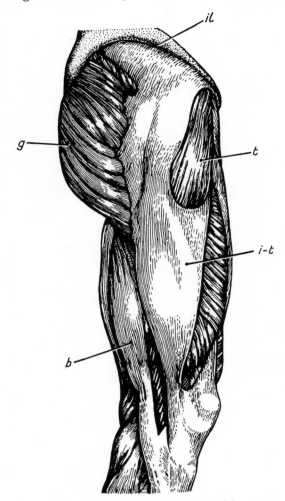

Fig. 38. Lateral view of human thigh.

b. biceps femoris; *g.* gluteus maximus; *il.* crest of ilium; *i–t.* ilio-tibial tract; *t.* tensor fasciae
latae. (After Pauwels.)

stresses on the edges of the femur, which would have to be very
massive to meet them were it not that the forces are reduced by the
action, as braces, of the abductor muscles, running from the ilium to
the femur (Fig. 38).

A further bracing action is performed by the ilio-tibial tract.
Fig. 39 shows by investigation of the photoelastic properties of a

model of the femur how the presence of the tract reduces the compression stress from 83 to 48 kg./cm.^{2} and the tension stress from 69 to 8 kg./cm.^{2} Such great reduction of tension stress is characteristic

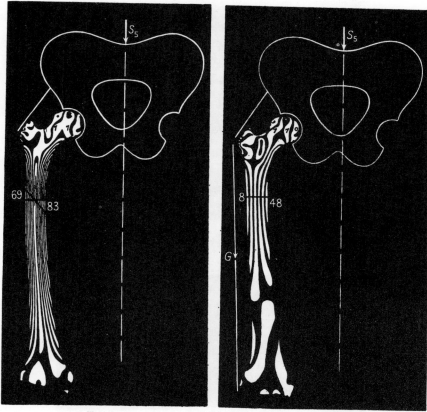

FIG. 39   FIG. 40

FIG. 39. The distribution of stressing in the femur shown by transmission of polarized light by a flat model.

FIG. 40. The effect of the ilio-tibial tract (G) is to reduce the tension stress greatly and the compression stress considerably. (After Pauwels.)

of this type of bracing and is especially valuable since bone is less resistant to tension forces than to compression forces. The effect of the ilio-tibial tract is to reduce the stressing of the femur by as much as one-half. The enormous advantage of this in allowing saving of material in the bones is obvious. Interference with the action of such braces as the ilio-tibial tract by severance or loss of tension through damage to muscles or their nerves may lead to the placing on the bones of stresses greater than they can bear.

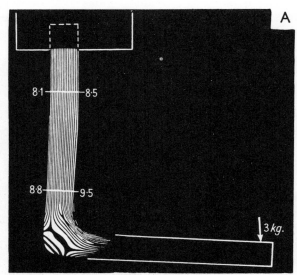

Fig. 41 A

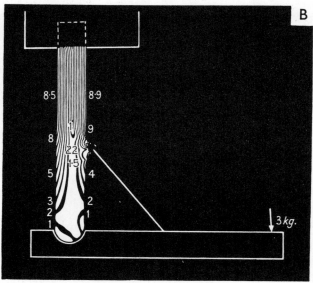

Fig. 41 B
(For underline see page opposite)

Confirmation of this action of the ilio-tibial tract is found in the fact that the femur is built in such a way that the strongest part of its circumference corresponds at each level to the part that would need to be most strongly stressed to meet the strains that remain after the combined action of the body-weight and the tension of the tract.

Many similar examples of the effect of muscles and ligaments in

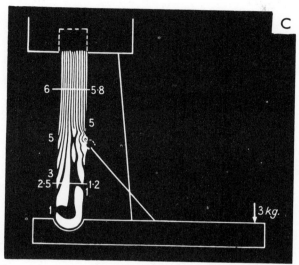

FIG. 41. Effect of the muscles on the stressing of the humerus, shown by a photo-elastic model. In a bent girder such as that shown in A the weight of 3 kg. applied to the 'hand' produces large stresses in the 'humerus'. Addition of a single-joint muscle as in B (corresponding to the brachialis) reduces the stresses in the lower end of the humerus. Addition of a two-joint muscle (e.g. biceps) as in C reduces the stresses also in the upper end of the humerus. (After Pauwels.)

reducing the strain by counterbracing can be found throughout the body. Fig. 41 shows that the brachialis muscle acts in this way on the lower end of the humerus (the deltoid acts similarly at the upper end). The long head of the biceps muscle, like other two-joint muscles, has a similar action along the whole length of the bone.

8. Arrangement of trabeculae within the bones

Within the bones themselves the trabeculae are so arranged as to lie in the directions in which the material is stressed. This was first noticed by Meyer and Culmann, who showed that in the human femur the trabeculae follow lines similar to the trajectories or lines of internal stress in a crane (Fig. 42). The trabecular lines cross approximately at right angles, suggesting that they are following lines of tension- and compression-stressing, as would the trajectories set up by the action of bending forces.

The main compression lines (cc^1) start from the surface of the head and run down to join the compacta of the shaft on its medial side. The tension lines (tt^1) run across the underside of the head and neck to the lateral side of the shaft. The situation is complicated by the fact that other forces fall on the bone, for instance the pull of the muscles

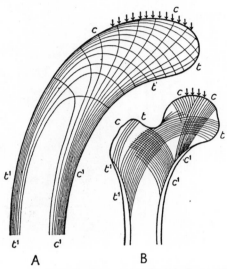

FIG. 42. A. Trajectories in the head of a crane of the type known as a Fairbairn crane loaded as shown by the arrows. cc^1 compression lines; tt^1 tension lines. B. Diagram of the trabeculae of the head of the femur; the arrows show the approximate method of loading. (Modified after Murray, following Culmann and Meyer.)

that are attached to the great trochanter (p. 178). Such attachments will themselves produce tension stresses in the bone, especially if the muscles are in frequent use, as in walking.

Similar arrangements of the bone trabeculae occur throughout the body but are often somewhat obscured, so that doubt has been thrown on the whole trajectorial theory. The trabeculae often do not cross at right angles and therefore cannot be simple stress lines. Yet the general agreement with the theory is striking (Figs. 43 and 44); divergences are only to be expected in a system such as a living body, which besides its great complexity is continually varying its activity. The action of muscles must produce varying forces acting on the bones. The fact that animals can jump so well shows that the muscle forces may greatly exceed those due to the weight.

There can be no doubt that the internal arrangement of the bony

FIG. 43. Frontal section of dried left human femur.
(After Koch, *Amer. J. Anat.* **21**, 1917.)

(96)

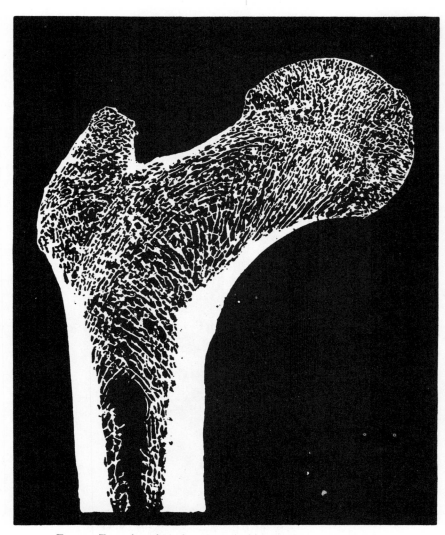

FIG. 44. Frontal section of upper end of human femur. (After Koch.)

trabeculae provides a stressing for the bone appropriate to the forces that act upon it. But how does it come about that the stress lines become 'materialized' in the bone? 'Functional' factors play a considerable part in determining bone structure. The trabeculae of the femur, for instance, do not have their characteristic arrangement at birth; this appears as the limb is used for walking (Fig. 45). Similarly,

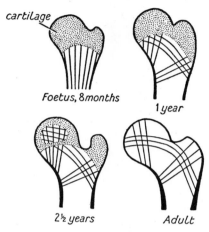

FIG. 45. Drawings of frontal sections of the heads of human femora at different ages to show the changes in the arrangement of the trabeculae with use. (Redrawn after Townsley, *Am. J. Phys. Anthrop.* **6**, 25, 1948.)

study of bones that have been badly set or have become fused together at unusual angles shows the development of a completely new architecture under the influence of the new forces.

Some explanation is to be found in the study of the incidence of stresses following the application to any material of forces that tend to distort it. The resulting strains can be considered as occurring along axes at right angles to each other but inclined to the main axes of the material. In the body bone is laid down along the lines of maximum stressing by compression and tension. As the loads increase further lines of bone are added. Any bone that is not stressed is removed. The bony material that remains therefore 'materializes' the stress trajectories, exactly as an engineer would do in his diagrams. It may be that as spicules of bone grow out into the cartilage at the epiphyses their tips become orientated by the stresses present in that region. Whatever the mechanism the effect is to produce a structure that combines strength with lightness by placing material only where it is stressed.

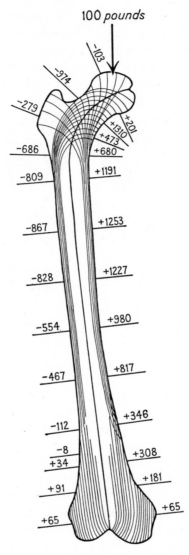

100 *pounds*

FIG. 46. Diagram of the lines of stress and their quantity (lb./sq. in.) in a normal femur for a load of 100 lb. on the head. The plus signs show compression- and the minus signs tension-stresses. Note that the greatest stressing is in the neck and upper third of the shaft. The stresses in the standing position are about 0·6 of those shown, when walking 1·6x and running 3·2x.

(Modified from Koch, *Amer. J. Anat.* **21**, 1917.)

9. Loading and safety margin of the human femur

The effectiveness with which bone fulfils its functions may be assessed by considering the factor of safety that it provides. Fig. 46 shows the calculations made by Koch of the distribution of lines of maximum stress in the femur under a load of 100 lb. applied to the head. For the purpose of the analysis he divided the bone into 75 sections and found that the greatest stresses are set up in the neck. Here they may reach 1,340 lb./sq. inch for compression and 974 for tension. This is a region in which fractures commonly occur in old people, whose bones have become brittle. Fractures are also common in the shaft, where the stress is nearly as great as it is in the head.

To determine the factor of safety we must estimate the stresses that the bone will bear not under a static load of 100 lb. but when the person is walking, running, jumping, or falling. Koch estimated that whereas in standing a man of body-weight 200 lb. carries 60 lb. on each femur, in walking the load may be 160 lb., in running 320 lb., and when falling or jumping considerably more. When running, the stresses in the neck of the femur will be 3·2 times those for 100 lb. load, namely, 4,192 and 3,117 lb./sq. inch for compression and tension respectively. With the strengths for bone given in Table A (p. 80) we thus have a safety factor of about 5·7 times for both forms of stress during running. These compare with the factors of safety of about five times usually allowed in a steel structure. The body evidently builds economically. The above calculations make rather simple assumptions about the way the load falls on the bone, and in practice the action of the muscles would complicate the situation considerably.

10. Control of bone organization

The moulding of bones during later development and throughout life is certainly influenced by mechanical factors, although, as we have seen, the trajectories follow stress lines rather more complicated than those found in simple girders. Three general rules may be stated about the control of bone growth. (1) Continuous pressure on bone leads to its absorption. This has been proved experimentally by pressing the neural spines of rabbits with bags of mercury and is shown in some brain tumours, whose local pressure may cause a hole to develop right through the skull. (2) On the other hand, intermittent pressure stimulates bone deposition, as can be proved by rhythmical application of weight on the neural spines. There is probably a similar effect of intermittent tension; thus the tendons of muscles that are frequently used may become ossified, for example a 'rider's bone' develops in the tendon of the adductor longus muscle of active horsemen. The formation of ridges and tuberosities at points of muscle attachment can be similarly explained. (3) Finally, the third rule is that bone that is unstressed undergoes atrophy. This can be seen in the texture of the bones of limbs that have not been used. The hollow form of long bones is probably determined, like their general shape, by hereditary factors, but the fact that no bony tissue is laid down later in life at the centre of the hollow shaft is presumably related to the fact that this central region is not stressed.

With this knowledge we can give some 'explanation' of the arrangement of the trabeculae in spongy bone, assuming that new bone, like other tissues, is being continually replaced and is laid down along lines of intermittent compression or tension and removed where there is none (Wolff's law). To proceed further we should need to understand the underlying physical and chemical factors that control bone formation. Deposition of bone is preceded by a concentration of calcium salts on the site by the action of the enzyme phosphatase, and further study of the factors causing the release of this enzyme or its activation should be helpful.

Bone formation is a modification of the metabolism of calcium that occurs in all cells. It may be that we shall come to understand the process better when we find out how it is related to the factors that maintain the ionic balance in other tissues. Some modification of the life processes that occur in other cells has produced this extraordinary substance, which is so hard and tenacious.

VI

MUSCLES

1. The significance of movement for homeostasis

MAMMALIAN life is largely based on the system of expending energy to achieve positions in which appropriate raw materials can be obtained. The elaborate system for receiving information from the environment is allied with correspondingly elaborate effectors, the muscles, triggered and ready to respond according to the signals they receive from the nervous system. In studying muscles we may therefore examine first how they produce their actions, converting supplies of food and oxygen into movement. Investigations of the visible structure and chemical and energy interchanges of muscle tell us much about the nature of the contractile process. Secondly, we can study how the process of contraction is controlled by the signals received from the nervous system. Thirdly, we can investigate the arrangement of the muscle-fibres in relation to the bones and other tissues and so reach an understanding of the various movements that are made.

2. Muscles for movement and for holding

Animals are able to keep themselves intact in spite of unfavourable circumstances either by moving to more suitable conditions or by so manipulating the surroundings as to make them favourable. In mammals this is achieved by a framework, composed of the skeletal parts, joined by ties that can be varied in length, the muscles. The mobility ensured in this way enables the body to perform varied feats that can as yet be only roughly paralleled by human tools and constructs. A horse can move rapidly over rough ground and jump over obstacles that no machine can pass. No instrument yet built approaches the human fingers in the number of delicate operations that can be performed.

The parts being freely mobile, the muscles serve to fix as well as to move them; they act as braces, holding the organs of the body in place. This postural action, important in all animals, is especially so in those that live unsupported by water and must therefore maintain themselves erect against gravitational forces. The recognition of these two distinct functions, of movement and of holding, enables us to reach a proper understanding of the various sorts of muscle. It explains the fact that the tension is developed at different speeds in different muscles, and especially that there is variation in the speed with which muscles contract and relax. We can thus recognize two main classes of muscles, the *holding muscles* and the *movement muscles*; the former contract slowly and relax slowly and can therefore maintain the parts in position for long periods. The latter contract and relax fast and are able to produce quick and quickly changing movements. The cross striation of the main body muscles is related to this speedy contraction and relaxation (p. 110).

3. Prime movers and antagonists

Muscle is a tissue specialized for the conversion of chemical energy into mechanical energy. When the muscle is serving for holding the energy appears as tension. When the muscle produces a movement the energy appears as external work.

It is characteristic of all muscles that they can pull but not push. Before they can do work again they must be elongated. The termination of the action of any muscle is followed by a more or less sudden diminution of tension, thus allowing whatever forces are acting against the muscle to elongate it. This general picture of muscle as acting in one direction is the clue to an understanding of the arrangement of the whole muscular system. It explains the fact that every muscle when it acts as a *prime mover* or *agonist* has an *antagonist*, able to restore it to its 'resting' length. A single muscle acting by itself can accomplish one single movement only and must then wait until it is elongated. Often this elongation will be accomplished by the opposing antagonistic muscle, but it may be brought about by gravity or other forces.

4. The neuro-muscular-skeletal system as a whole

Muscles are thus adjustable ties, able to vary their tension upon receipt of impulses from the nervous system. Therefore we cannot deal with the muscles without considering the nerves, sensory and central as well as motor. All these together form a single system, triggered to respond in such ways as will produce the adjustments necessary to maintain and reproduce the organism under whatever circumstances it may encounter. On the other hand, we cannot properly consider muscle without also dealing with the skeleton, since these two make the system of adjustable girders, the muscles being the chief tension members, the braces or ties, while the bones are the compression members or struts. The stability of the whole body must thus be considered as dependent jointly on the nervous, muscular, and skeletal systems. The body collapses when any part fails. Lack of control due to shortage of oxygen in the nervous system (as in a faint) disturbs the posture as effectively as does fracture of the femur.

Although the system is capable of so much movement it can at other times remain steady and still. Moreover, all the movements are smooth and precise. This is made possible by an abundant supply of receptor organs in the muscles, the proprioceptors, which provide information to the nervous system about the movement of every part. The nerve centres themselves are so arranged that this feed-back of information ensures that stability is maintained and that smooth, precise movements are produced.

5. Isometric and isotonic contraction

The function of muscular tissue is therefore to exert tension, which may or may not result in movement. If the ends of the muscle are fixed the effect of the initiation of its activity is to exert a force along its length without any actual movement and this is said to be *isometric contraction*. If a muscle is allowed to shorten without increase of tension, for instance in lifting a weight, the contraction is said to be *isotonic*. Muscles contract isometrically when they support loads or fix bones relative to each other. For instance, when a man carries a heavy suitcase in his hand the weight is sustained by approximately isometric contraction of the muscles that hold up the shoulder, such as the trapezius (see p. 148) at the back of the neck. During movements, for example in bending the elbow or raising the heel off the ground in walking, conditions are neither fully isometric nor isotonic. It is obvious that the two types of contraction are not likely to be fully separated, there is seldom shortening without some increase of tension, or vice versa.

6. Structure of smooth muscle

The muscles in which the powers of holding are most fully developed are the smooth (unstriped) muscles of the viscera. These have the functions of holding the organs in place and producing slow movements such as are needed to propel the food along the gut or to squeeze the secretion from a gland. Such movements are effective even if they are not quick or precise and they are usually produced by coats of muscle that are wrapped around the organs but not attached to any skeletal elements. Receptors are present in these abdominal viscera to record the amount of tension and thus provide the information with which the nervous system ensures regulation of the organs, but smooth muscle has no elaborate system of proprioceptors such as is used for the rapid and precise control of the muscles that produce actions of the limbs (p. 366).

The smooth muscle-fibres consist of elongated cells, of the order of 200 μ long and 6 μ wide, each with a single nucleus midway along

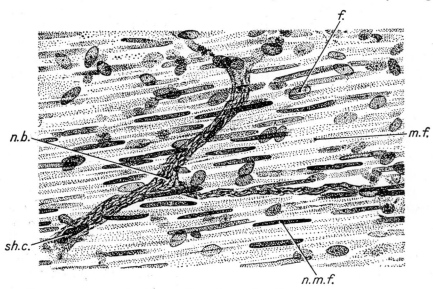

FIG. 47. Smooth muscle-cells.
f. fibroblast; *m.f.* muscle-fibre; *n.b.* nerve-bundle; *n.m.f.* nucleus of muscle-fibre; *sh.c.* sheath-cell.

its length (Fig. 47). Part of the protoplasm of these cells shows under suitable conditions a longitudinal striation ('myofibrils') and is birefringent in polarized light. There is, however, no sign of any repetition of structure along the axis of the fibre, which is therefore said to be *smooth*, in distinction from the *striped* or striated appearance of other muscles. Smooth muscles are also said to be *involuntary* because in man it is seldom possible to initiate their contraction at will. Nevertheless, by the technique of the conditioned reflex (p. 455) it is possible to arrive at a condition first in which ringing a bell causes contraction of the pupil of the eye and then one in which thinking about the bell produces the same result. Moreover, accommodation of the focus of the eye is produced 'at will' by unstriped muscles. The concept of volition is evidently a complicated one and it is better not to introduce it into discussions of muscular structure.

The exact nature of the contractile material of the smooth muscle-cell is still uncertain but it probably consists of longitudinally arranged protein chains, able to shorten by folding, or in some other manner, and hence to produce the tension in the muscle (p. 110). Not all the material of the fibres shows longitudinal striations, these are most marked near the outer edge; in the centre of the fibre it is possible to see small amounts of unstriated material known as *sarcoplasm*. Around each smooth muscle-cell there is a fine network of the supporting protein reticulin (p. 57) and this probably forms an inelastic container for the fibre, similar in a general way to the sarcolemma (p. 108) of striped fibres.

Smooth muscle is controlled by nerve-fibres, usually post-ganglionic fibres of the autonomic nervous system (p. 385), but the mode of connexion is still uncertain. No formed structures such as the motor end plates in striped muscle have been seen; probably the nerve-fibres wind in and out among the smooth muscle-cells and stimulate those they approach, perhaps by the liberation of active chemical substances (p. 398).

In mammals smooth muscle occurs in the wall of the gut and urino-genital ducts and blood-vessels, in the skin, in the iris of the eye, and, mixed with striped fibres, in the levator palpebrae superioris that raises the upper eye-lid. The structure of heart muscle is discussed on p. 285. Smooth muscle-fibres often occur in association with connective tissue and especially with elastic fibres. The individual smooth muscle-cells often run in various directions, crossing each other, especially in the investments of hollow organs; in some situations they run in parallel bundles and may make definite 'muscles' composed of parallel fibres, with an insertion, for instance in the arrectores pilorum muscles of the hairs (p. 34).

7. Structure of striated muscle

The greater part of movement in mammals is performed by *striated or voluntary muscles* and these also play a large part in the holding in position of organs and limbs without movement. The fibres of striated muscle (Figs. 48 and 49) are much larger than those of smooth muscle and commonly reach 5 cm. in length and 100 μ in diameter. Such masses of protoplasm are too large to be regulated by a single nucleus and the striped muscle-fibres are syncytia; each possesses hundreds of nuclei. These nuclei are probably all formed by division of the original nucleus of a single *myoblast*, from which the cell is formed. (It has been claimed that many myoblasts fuse together to make each fibre

`0·5 cm.`

FIG. 48. Striated muscle-fibres teased from a single bundle in an adductor muscle of the thigh in a rabbit. The fibres are shown approximately in their positions in the bundle. Note the differences in length: some fibres run for the whole length of the bundle (3·5 cm.). The ends attached to the tendon are rounded, those in the muscle substance are tapered. (After Huber, *Anat. Rec.* **11**, 1917.)

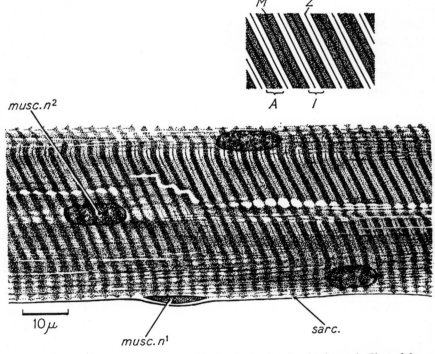

FIG. 49. Drawing made from a photograph of a fixed and stained muscle-fibre of the rabbit. The appearance of the cross striations varies according to the conditions under which fibres are fixed; forms that suggest a spiral arrangement may appear. The nuclei of the muscle-fibre all lie at the periphery in a very thin layer of sarcoplasm; *musc.n*[1] shows one of them in side view, *musc.n*[2] in surface view; *sarc.* sarcolemma. The inset shows the striations diagrammatically.

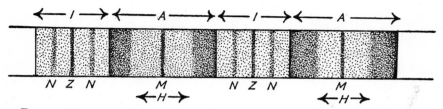

FIG. 50. Diagram of the main striations seen by electron microscopy in a single myofibril of the rabbit.

A and *I*, anisotropic and isotropic bands; *H*, Hensen's disc; *M*, mesophragma; *N* and *Z* lines in the isotropic band.

(After Barer, *Biol. Rev.* **23**, 159, 1948, based on data of Hall, Jakus, and Schmitt.)

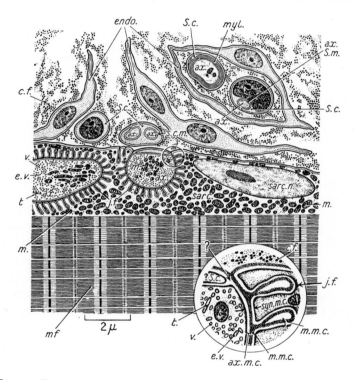

FIG. 51. Drawing of electron micrograph of section of a motor end-plate.

ax. axon; *ax.m.c.* membrane complex at axonal surface; *ax. S.m.* axon-Schwann cell surface; *c.f.* collagen fibrils; *e.v.* elongated vesicles in nerve terminals (?derived from threads); *endo.* endoneurial cell; *j.f.* junctional folds; *m.* mitochondria; *m.f.* myo-fibrils; *m.m.c.* surface membrane of muscle fibre; *myl.* myelin; *sarc.* sarcoplasm; *sarc.n.* sarcoplasmic nucleus; *S.c.* Schwann cell cytoplasm; *s.c.m.* mesaxon; *syn.m.c.* combined axon and muscle membranes; *t.* threads in axon; *v.* spherical vesicles in nerve terminal.

From a preparation and photograph by Dr. J. D. Robertson.

but this probably does not occur.) In the fully formed condition each fibre is a unit mass of protoplasm, surrounded by a single surface membrane and containing many nuclei.

Each fibre is composed of numerous distinct *myofibrils*, $1\,\mu$ across, and divided by conspicuous cross-striations, which appear as light and dark bands when viewed with transmitted light. The full details of the molecular organization that is responsible for this appearance are not understood. The following regions are generally recognized. The main division is into anisotropic *A*-bands and isotropic *I*-bands, the former being strongly, the latter only weakly, birefringent as seen in polarized light. Each *I*-band is crossed by a *Z*-disk (also called Dobie's line or Krause's membrane), and the length between successive *Z*-disks is called a *sarcomere* (Fig. 50). As seen with the light microscope the *A*-band has darker ends and a lighter central or *H*-zone (Hensen's disc), itself bisected by a dark *M*-line or mesophragma. Electron microscopy has shown the important fact that single more or less straight threads run from the light (*I*) to dark (*A*) bands.

8. Red and white muscles

Besides the myofibrils the muscle-fibres contain *sarcoplasm*, in which the fibrils are embedded. It is conspicuous at the region of the motor end plate (p. 112). Muscle-fibres vary in the relative amount of striated and unstriated material they contain and it is usual to recognize two distinct types; in *white muscle fibres* almost the whole cell is filled with striated substance, so that the nuclei are all closely pressed against the edge of the fibre. In *red muscle fibres* there is more sarcoplasm and the nuclei are more numerous and are rounded and lie away from the edge of the fibres. These red fibres, as the name implies, contain considerable amounts of the substance myoglobin, related to haemoglobin, and there are also other cell inclusions.

9. Sarcolemma and endomysium

Every striated muscle-fibre is enclosed in a complete membrane, the *sarcolemma*. There is still some doubt about the composition of this and as to whether it is of the nature of a distinct supporting membrane or of a cell membrane, such as that surrounding a red blood corpuscle or any other animal cell. To put it another way, Is the sarcolemma analogous to the cellulose wall of plant-cells or to the plasma membrane? Presumably the surface of the sarcoplasm constitutes a boundary layer capable of maintaining the difference between concentration of ions that is responsible for the action potential that propagates along muscle-fibres, as along nerve-fibres (p. 115). This layer may be called the *sarcoplasmic membrane*, but there is no reason to suppose that it forms a layer visible with the light microscope. The sarcolemma, however, is a distinct membrane, about 0.1μ in thickness, and with elastic properties (see Jones and Barer, 1948). The sarcoplasm may herniate through it or retract away, leaving the membrane as a transparent sheet, whose only feature as seen in the electron microscope is a series of spots spaced about 0.5μ apart. These do not correspond to any known periodicity of the substance of the muscle-fibre. The contractile substance is probably attached to the sarcolemma by the Z-bands. Probably the sarcolemma constitutes an elastic bag. The muscle substance being of a visco-elastic nature, perhaps force is transmitted from the contractile protein to the sarcolemma merely by friction. There may, however, be special means of attachment at the ends of the muscle-fibres.

The sarcolemma stains differently from collagen and elastin but may contain a scleroprotein allied to these. It is not clear whether the chief cellular agent for its formation is the muscle-cell itself or the surrounding fibroblasts that occur abundantly between the muscle-cells.

Outside the sarcolemma there is supporting connective tissue, the *endomysium*. This makes a packing between the fibres and holds together the various tissues in the muscle, including the blood- and lymph-vessels, which are very abundant, and the nerve-fibres. Bundles of muscle-fibres are held together by larger strands of connective tissue, known as the *perimysium*, and the whole muscle is often surrounded by a more definite sheet, the *epimysium*.

Individual muscle-fibres usually taper slightly at their ends and are attached either to the periosteum of bone or to a tendon, or, if they end within the substance of the muscle, to the connective tissue of the perimysium. The mode of attachment at the ends has been much discussed; it is probable that the sarcolemma provides the main attachment to the tendinous or other tissue and it is not likely that myofibrils continue directly into collagen fibrils as has been claimed. The means by which force is exerted from the contractile substance of the fibres through the sarcolemma to the ends of the muscle has never been satisfactorily determined.

10. The contractile mechanism

The relation of all these facts about the structure of muscle to its chemical composition and its contraction is only partly clear. A characteristic protein, *actomyosin*, can be extracted from muscle. This is composed of two associated proteins, *actin* and *myosin*. These are revealed by electron microscopy as distinct types of thread about 100 Å in diameter. Actomyosin when studied in vitro shows remarkable properties. It can be spun into threads and these contract on

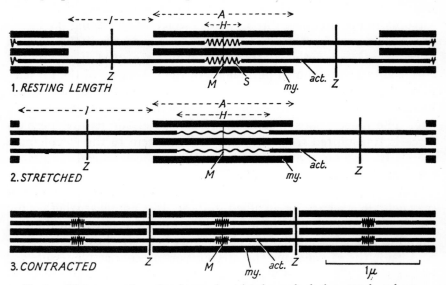

FIG. 52. Diagram to show the changes in striated muscle during stretch and contraction. 1 shows the elements at resting length in the body, 2 after passive stretch, and 3 after isotonic contraction to about 40 per cent. of maximum.

A. anisotropic band; *act.* actin; *H.* H-zone; *I.* isotropic band; *M.* region of attachment of *S* filaments to myosin filaments; *my.* myosin; *S.* elastic component; *Z.* Z-line.

During plastic stretch the actin filaments are partly withdrawn from the *A*-band. In contraction the actin filaments are drawn into the *A*-band. With further shortening the myosin filaments crumple. (Diagram prepared with the assistance of Dr. A. F. Huxley.)

addition of the substance *adenosine triphosphate* (ATP), which occurs in muscle (p. 116).

It is suggested that the myosin is all contained in the *A*-bands, in the form of rods, stretching the whole length of the band and giving the characteristic high refractive index and birefringence. The actin threads, on this view, extend from the *Z*-line of one *I*-band to the edge of the *H*-zone of the neighbouring *A*-band. When a muscle is allowed to shorten during contraction it is found that the *A*-band does not alter in length, whereas the *I*-band shortens (Huxley, A.F., and Niedergerke, 1954). It is therefore suggested that the actin filaments are drawn into the *A*-band, between the rodlets of myosin (Fig. 52).

At rest the ATP may be attached to the myosin and the initiation of contraction might thus depend upon a splitting of the ATP, leaving the myosin able to combine with actin to form actomyosin. It may be that the actin presents greater numbers of active groups if it becomes coiled, which would further increase the shortening. When the process that produces splitting of ATP stops there will be recombination of ATP with myosin, displacing actin and allowing the muscle to relax (Huxley, H., and Hanson, 1954).

This theory holds that during isometric contraction, also, the actin threads are drawn into the A-bands and there is stretch of a series elastic component. There is also an elastic component S within the H-zones, which elongates during plastic stretch and becomes crumpled during active shortening. Actomyosin belongs to the keratin-myosin-fibrinogen group of proteins, which are able to exist in two states, an elongated α and contracted β form (Astbury, 1933). The change from the one to the other is accompanied by a change in X-ray diffraction pattern, which may be interpreted as showing that there is a folding-up of the long chains of which the protein is composed. It has therefore long been suggested that the contraction of muscle is accompanied by a folding-up of protein chains, but there is no evidence that such folding actually occurs during contraction. If the interpretation of contraction as involving a sliding of the I-band material into the A-band is correct, there is no need to postulate any change in degree of folding of either actin or myosin.

11. Innervation of muscle

Striated muscle-fibres normally only produce their contraction when they receive impulses from nerve-fibres through the *motor end-plates* (Fig. 53). These are essentially regions in which the surface membranes of the nerve- and muscle-cells come into close apposition. The nerve-fibre passes through the sarcolemma, which is continuous at this point with the neurilemma, loses its myelin and spreads out into a number of processes in contact with the muscle-fibre surface. These processes vary in number and arrangement but the essential is that they allow an area of contact between axoplasm and sarcoplasm. They may be inflated into terminal bulbs, but it should be emphasized that the region of contact and not the terminal bulb is the essential agent of transmission. There has been much dispute as to the relations of nerve and muscle substances at the end-plates. The membranes of both fibres remain complete at the region of contact (Fig. 51). Nerve and muscle-cells contain much potassium but little sodium (p. 339), and we may express the condition by saying that the potassium spaces of the two tissues are not continuous (Fig. 54).

The region of the muscle where the contact occurs consists of specially differentiated sarcoplasm forming the *sole-plate*, in which are embedded a number of muscle nuclei, the *sole-plate nuclei*. The material of the sole-plate shows certain optical differentiations, which Boeke considered to form a *periterminal* network, a continuation of the neurofibrils of the nerve-fibre. An alternative and more probable interpretation is that of Couteaux and Taxi (1952), who have observed a series of rodlets in the sarcoplasm, lying at right angles to the surface of the fibre and somewhat recalling the brush border found at the surface of cells of the intestine and kidney. It may be significant that this type of structure occurs where substances pass into or out of a cell, as they must do at the motor end-plate. Electron microscopy shows that the 'rodlets' seen in the end-plate are formed by inturnings of the surface membrane of the muscle-fibre (Fig. 51).

It has long been considered that in mammals each striated muscle-fibre receives only a single nerve-fibre and no convincing evidence has been produced for sympathetic or other nerve-fibres running to the muscle-fibres, such as might produce either tonic or inhibitory effects. However, in some muscles, perhaps many, there is more than one motor end-plate on each muscle-fibre, which might therefore be caused to contract by excitation arising from more than one nerve-cell of the spinal cord. However, it is still usually considered that each nerve-cell controls a certain number of muscle-fibres, the whole constituting a *neuromyal unit* (Hunt and Kuffler, 1954). Sherrington and his colleagues have determined for a few different muscles the number of muscle-fibres in the unit and the tension that can be produced. For instance in the lateral head of the gastrocnemius muscle of the cat each nerve-cell controls a unit producing an isometric tension of 30 gm. There are 430 such units, so that the whole muscle can produce about 13 kg. These calculations need revision, however, because they were made before it was appreciated that many ventral root fibres innervate muscle-spindles and produce no tension (p. 366) or that one muscle-fibre may be controlled by several nerve-fibres. In muscles that perform delicate movements the units are smaller, so that the action of the muscle can be more finely graded; thus the ratio of muscle-cells to nerve-cells varies from upwards of 150 in the biceps muscle of the leg to 2 in human eye muscles.

In mammals, therefore, all action by striped muscles depends on the arrival of impulses in the motor nerve-fibres to set off the contractile process. The tension ceases to be developed when the impulses stop arriving. There are no separate inhibitory nerve-fibres able to switch the action off, although these may exist in other animals, certainly in

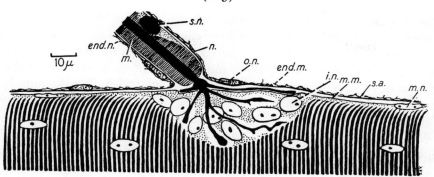

FIG. 53. Diagram of the relationship between a nerve-fibre and a muscle-fibre at the motor end-plate.

end.m. connective tissue of endomysium; *end.n.* connective tissue of endoneurium; *i.n.* inner nuclei of end plate; *m.* myelin; *n.* neurilemma; *m.m.* outer surface of muscle protoplasm (sarcoplasmic membrane); *m.n.* muscle nuclei; *o.n.* outer nuclei of end plate (? fibrocytes); *s.a.* sarcolemma; *s.n.* Schwann cell nucleus. (From Gutmann and Young.)

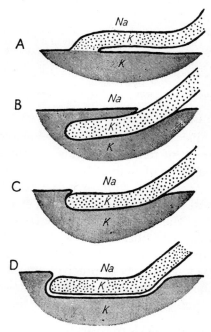

FIG. 54. Diagrams showing the various ways in which it has been suggested that the nerve- and muscle-fibre might be related at the motor end-plate.

K shows the spaces occupied by solutions rich in potassium, *Na* those rich in sodium. The arrangement shown at A, with continuity between the potassium spaces of nerve and muscle, is almost certainly never found. If the situation is as in B or C then one membrane separates the potassium spaces, whereas in D there is a sodium space all round the nerve ending. Histological studies have not yet decided whether the arrangement is as B, C, or D. (From Gutmann and Young.)

Crustacea. In mammals the balance between excitation and inhibition is struck centrally and the striped muscle itself receives from its nerve only excitor impulses. These impulses are all alike, there are not some that produce 'tonus' and others movement, the only variable is the frequency with which they arrive at the end-plate, sending the muscle into more or less frequent contraction.

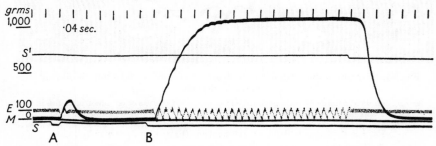

FIG. 55. Isometric responses of gastrocnemius muscle of frog to electrical stimulation of its nerve.

At A a single break induction shock produces a single twitch response. At B a series of shocks at 50/sec. produces a tetanus. Line E shows the shadow of the string of a galvanometer connected with electrodes to record the electrical activity of the muscle. Line M shows the movement of a stretched wire recording the tension of the muscle. Line S shows the onset and S^1 the cessation of tetanization. Time above = 0·04 seconds. Note the steps by which the plateau is reached and that the muscle continues to give discrete electrical responses during tetanization.

(From Fulton, J. F., *Muscular Contraction and the Reflex Control of Movement*, 1926, Fig. 57.)

12. Twitch and tetanus

The unit of muscular action is the *twitch*, which consists of a single process of development of tension spreading throughout the muscle-fibre following propagation of an impulse over its whole surface. When single impulses are fired along a motor nerve at sufficiently long intervals apart each will produce a single twitch, followed by complete relaxation (Fig. 55). If the impulses are more frequent the successive contractions of the muscle-fibre occur without time for relaxation. The result is more or less complete fusion of the contractions to produce a *tetanus*, whose tension may be much greater than that developed by the single twitches. In most of the ordinary actions of muscles the impulses arrive in such a way that the contraction is tetanic.

13. Transmission from nerve to muscle

The essential feature of the transmission from nerve to muscle is the production of minute amounts of a substance able to depolarize the muscle membrane, probably the ester *acetylcholine* (p. 342). The resulting local change in permeability causes a large ionic flow across the end-plate membrane and this current stimulates the adjacent regions of the muscle-fibre (Fatt and Katz, 1953). The end-plate thus acts as an amplifier of the minute electric signal in the nerve-fibre so that it excites the muscle-fibre. Transmission along a nerve-fibre takes place by the spread of electric currents in advance of the active region (p. 340), and presumably finally along the fine terminal branches that are in contact with the surface membrane of the muscle-fibre. Muscle-fibres themselves produce electrical action potentials ('muscle-spikes') that travel along their surfaces and are essentially like the action potentials that traverse nerve-fibres, though they move at a slower rate. The membranes interposed between the nerve- and muscle-fibres (Fig. 51) are highly specialized and the situation resembles that of a synapse (p. 347) rather than a stretch of peripheral nerve. The electric currents set up by the action potential of the nerve-fibre can only excite the muscle-fibre by the intermediate process of liberation of acetylcholine at the end-plate. Certain drugs such as the alkaloid curare and its synthetic analogue d-tubocurarine specifically block transmission at this point. When the region of a muscle that contains end-plates is stimulated with electric currents under conditions of fatigue in which no propagated muscle-spikes are produced, an *end-plate potential* can be recorded, a partial depolarization, corresponding to the local response of nerve seen under certain conditions with sub-threshold stimulation (p. 343). In normal transmission the chain of events is probably that the arrival of a nerve impulse liberates a small amount of acetylcholine and this alters the properties of the muscle membrane in such a way as to make it permeable to all free ions. The resulting electrical change is the end-plate potential and the currents set up excite the neighbouring muscle membrane, producing a propagated impulse, which in turn releases the contractile mechanism of the fibre (see Fatt and Katz, 1951).

Close intra-arterial injection of acetylcholine leads to contraction of muscle-fibres and there is evidence that this substance is produced during normal neuromuscular transmission and is then rapidly removed by the action of the enzyme *cholinesterase*, which can be shown to be abundant in the end-plates. The action of the enzyme can be prevented by specific poisons (*eserine*) and following the action of these the effect of nerve stimulation is prolonged.

14. The energy for contraction

Whatever mechanism is involved in contraction it must somehow be connected with the reactions by which energy is made available in the muscle-cell, essentially by the oxidation of foodstuffs. Much work has been devoted to study of the enzymatic reactions involving carbo-hydrates and other substances that take place in cell-free extracts of muscles and it is now becoming clear how such reactions are con-nected with the events in the living muscle-fibre. If the contraction involves the release of stored chemical energy then much of the chemical work can be done after contraction is over. It may be that the work for each twitch is done before the contraction takes place, though this assumes that no energy expenditure is needed to keep the 'spring' at stretch. A muscle is able to contract in the absence of oxygen and any individual twitch should be considered as an anaerobic change. Indeed the muscle is capable of a series of twitches, or a tetanus, even in the absence of oxygen, but it then becomes fatigued much more quickly than if oxygen is available. During anaerobic contraction lactic acid accumulates and the carbohydrates of the muscle (such as glycogen) decrease. If oxygen is then admitted the lactic acid dis-appears, some of it being burnt to carbon dioxide and water and another part remaining in the muscle and becoming resynthesized to its precursors, including glycogen, which increases during this period.

15. The carbohydrate cycle

There must therefore be materials available from which energy can be derived anaerobically in order to reset the muscle spring and indeed it is clear that such a mechanism is necessary in normal life to produce effective tension before combustion with oxygen can take place to provide the energy.

A key substance in these changes is *adenosine triphosphate*, which is a nucleotide containing the heterocyclic adenine radicle combined with a sugar (d-ribose) and three molecules of phosphoric acid. This substance readily serves as a donor of phosphate radicles, and the resulting *adenosine diphosphate* (ADP) acts as an acceptor of them. Interchanges of phosphate thus appear to play a large part in the energy changes of muscle, at least under anaerobic conditions. The enzyme *phosphorylase* breaks down glycogen to glucose if ATP is present as a coenzyme to donate phosphate and allow removal of the glucose as glucose phosphate. This latter can then proceed through a series of changes to pyruvic acid and finally lactic acid, the whole process yielding energy.

This *carbohydrate cycle* is related to the events occuring during con-traction, which involve a disappearance of glycogen and appearance of lactic acid. The breakdown of glycogen ultimately provides the energy for the recharging of the muscle spring. How this is done is now beginning to be clear from the discovery by Engelhardt that myosin itself acts as the enzyme adenosine triphosphatase catalysing the dephosphorylation of ATP, from which it accepts phosphate. Here our knowledge remains incomplete, but the suggestion is that actomyosin that has accepted phosphate splits into its components and the actin assumes the elongated α form. Contraction is then preceded by some breakdown of ATP, withdrawing the phosphate and making the myosin able to combine with actin. This change is initiated by the liberation of calcium ions, which are necessary for the breakdown of ATP. One difficulty is that no change in the amount of ATP extractable from a muscle occurs during contraction, at least until fatigue is far advanced.

The active work of recharging the muscle would on this view consist of resynthesis of ATP from phosphoric acid and adenylic acid, and there is some evidence that this takes place by the action of *creatine phosphate* (CP),

$$NH=C\big\langle{}^{NH-PO(OH)_2}_{N(CH_3).(CH_3).COOH}$$

In acid solution this substance readily hydrolyses to creatine and phosphoric acid. This change is found to have occurred in muscles that have been caused to contract anaerobically and it is an exothermic reaction, yielding energy and phosphoric acid, which are thus available for the ATP resynthesis. The amount of energy (heat and work) that can be obtained from a muscle in the absence of oxygen is proportional to the quantity of CP that disappears (if glycolysis is prevented), as would be expected if the CP provides the energy for the contraction. There is no doubt that in a normally contracting muscle the aerobic breakdown of glycogen ultimately provides the energy and it is possible to imagine how this may be done by using the energy to re-form the ATP and CP that have been used up in the immediate breakdown. As the ATP splits during contraction its products become engaged in the phosphorylation of glycogen and thus energy is made available for creatine phosphate resynthesis. The lactic acid resulting from the glycogen breakdown is partly burned to carbon dioxide and water to provide energy by which the remainder is resynthesized to glycogen, completing the carbohydrate cycle.

Some linking of the ATP and CP changes with the glycogen breakdown almost certainly provides the mechanism by which the sources of energy available for quick anaerobic recharging of the muscle are themselves later aerobically reconstituted. Certainly the breakdown of glycogen and formation of lactic acid does not provide the immediate source of the energy, because contraction can occur in muscles poisoned with iodoacetates, in which no lactic acid is produced; moreover, in aerobic functioning most of the lactic acid is produced after the contraction is over. It is probable that the phosphorylation cycles found in muscle extracts and under anaerobic conditions are not always strictly followed in the normal muscle, which may be able to make short cuts if well supplied with oxygen. It is certain, however, that the adenosine triphosphate and creatine phosphate are normally engaged somehow in the recharging, and it is easy to see that an anaerobic process is necessary to allow the muscle to work properly. As A. V. Hill puts it: 'With muscles, work precedes oxidation; with the internal combustion engine oxidation precedes work' (1927).

Not only the muscle but the body as a whole can work for a short time at much higher rates than respiration would seem to allow. An *oxygen debt* amounting to over 20 litres may be accumulated during a short sprint and paid back by increased respiration during the subsequent hour or longer. The debt is largely in the form of lactic acid, which escapes from the muscles to the circulation (it may appear in the urine) and is later oxidized throughout the body. It must not be forgotten, however, that muscles contain considerable quantities of haemoglobin and the red muscles, which are called upon for sustained contractions, are less quickly fatigued than the white (p. 121).

16. Energy output and efficiency of muscle

Study of the heat produced by muscle also shows that most of the metabolic work is performed when the contraction is already over. We can distinguish an *initial heat* occurring during the contraction whether the muscle shortens or not, and a *shortening heat*, proportional to the amount of shortening, and independent of the tension exerted. Later there is a *recovery heat*, more than half the total and present only under aerobic conditions.

The amount of work that can be done by a man or animal is limited by the rate of oxygen intake and the size of the oxygen debt that can be tolerated. In man the resting oxygen consumption is about 250 ml./minute and this can be increased to $4\frac{1}{2}$ litres or more during exercise, the maximum depending on the state of 'training' of the individual. The oxygen debt can reach about 16 litres and it is obvious that the maximum output of the individual can last only for the time during which this debt is incurred. Greater speeds of running can be maintained over shorter distances.

The work done in producing movement of a man over a flat surface is mostly consumed in overcoming the internal friction or viscosity of the muscles and the force necessary for this purpose is found to vary with the speed of movement; other factors, such as the air resistance, are relatively unimportant. 'An athlete . . . like a raindrop falling through air, rapidly attains a certain speed depending on the ratio of propelling force to resistance, and this speed remains constant until other factors, for example fatigue, cause it to fall off' (Hill). The propelling force demands the expenditure of about 2 horse-power when a man is running at maximum speed. From the oxygen consumption it is possible to estimate the energy used during such an effort and it is found that the mechanical work done is about 20–25 per cent. of the total energy used. This efficiency can rarely be achieved in the performance of external work, for which there is an optimum rate for any given set of conditions, up to a maximum of about 25 per cent. The work done is approximately inversely proportional to the speed of contraction but in practice there is an optimum speed for any given task.

The organism is so arranged that the force it can exert is generally less than that which would bring about its own downfall by breakage of bones or rupture of ligaments, though such accidents are not infrequent among athletes. The inherent strength of a contracting voluntary muscle-fibre is roughly constant (4–5 kilograms per square centimetre of cross-section) but large animals do not disrupt themselves because the speed varies a thousandfold or more, being greater in smaller muscles and the muscles of smaller animals (Hill, 1950). The net result is an approximately equal velocity of movement in relation to the earth on the part of all animals, irrespective of their linear dimensions. Hill points out that a race-horse and a whippet both move at about 40 m.p.h. and can jump to about the same heights, and that the jump of a grasshopper (or indeed a flea) is of the same order. A blue whale is 5,000 times heavier than a dolphin but both swim at a maximum speed of about 20 knots. The factor that limits the speed of contraction of muscles may be their own internal viscosity or the rate at which they can generate energy. There must be a safety factor that determines that the organism shall not disrupt itself. Such features of muscle action make it possible for organisms of different sizes to exist. 'If a man's muscles could be altered without altering his general design so as to allow him to run 25% faster, athletics would become a highly dangerous pastime; pulled tendons, torn muscles, even damaged bones, would be so frequent as to make it almost prohibitive' (Hill, 1950). In practice, if one animal is 1,000 times as heavy as another the movements of its parts will be ten times slower while the speed over the ground remains the same. One advantage of the greater size is that the larger animal will take ten times as long to become exhausted with maximum effort.

Similar differences exist between different muscles of one animal. Thus the muscles of the eyelid are small and very fast. If the muscles of the limbs contracted at this speed they would break the bones and, moreover, maintenance of posture would require great expenditure of energy.

17. Muscles for movement and for holding

We cannot say in detail how the structures visible in muscle are related to the functions but it seems that the cross-striations in some way enable the muscle-fibres to contract fast and to relax fast. This is obviously necessary for muscles that produce movement. The smooth muscles are pre-eminently used for holding, that is to say, their function is not so much to shorten as to stay at a given length. In order to maintain a given tension it is obviously efficient to have a system that only relaxes slowly. The tension is thus maintained with a minimal number of acts of shortening and therefore a minimal expenditure of energy. In some bivalve molluscs, such as the scallop, *Pecten*, the shell is provided with two adductor muscles, a striped one that contracts fast and quickly closes the shell, and a smooth one that contracts only slowly but, also relaxing slowly, is able to hold the animal closed for long periods.

In mammals the distinction is not so clear. Smooth muscles are used mainly in the viscera; in the limbs holding as well as movement is a function of the striped muscles. These, however, show differences according to whether they are mainly used for movement or for holding. The 'white' muscles, fully striped, contract and relax rapidly and are the muscles of movement, whereas the 'red' fibres, having more sarcoplasm, contract and relax slowly and are therefore better suited to hold tension. The large amount of myoglobin in these 'red' fibres may also assist in the prolonged maintenance of tension. Any maintained 'tonus' of a muscle depends upon a series of contractions, which, if they are sufficiently close together, fuse to a tetanus. To maintain a tension by means of a quickly relaxing fibre would therefore involve great expenditure of energy. On the other hand, quick movements can only be effected if relaxation follows soon after contraction. Red muscles assume a tetanic contraction at a much lower frequency than white.

There is no consistent association of speed with fibre diameter and although there are many reports of histological variations, for instance in the proportions of myofibrils and sarcoplasm, these have not been successfully correlated with the speed of contraction of the muscle. In the rabbit the distinction of colours is particularly marked and the white muscles are in nearly every case the more superficial and larger ones, often working across more than one joint and therefore well suited to produce movement (see p. 129). The red muscles lie deeper, close to the bones, and they usually work only across one joint, which they serve to fix. A typical example is to be found in the calf muscles, where the gastrocnemius and plantaris muscles (p. 183), lying super-ficially and working across both knee and ankle, are white, whereas the deeper soleus, arising from the tibia, is red. The duration of twitch of the gastrocnemius muscle of a variety of mammals has been shown to be 40–140 m.sec., whereas that of the soleus varies from 120 to 440 m.sec. Further, the condition of tetanus is reached at a frequency of 10 a second for the 'red' muscles, 30 a second for the 'white'.

These physiological differences between soleus and gastrocnemius are also found in the cat although here both muscles are white in colour. It is evident that differences of speed of contraction are more important than those of colour. Presumably the fast ('white') muscles are found throughout the mammal in situations where movement is important, whereas the slow ('red') fibres serve to hold or fix the bones, as in the action of maintaining the extensor muscles, which serve to maintain the weight of the body against gravity.

There are undoubtedly similar differences between muscles in man, although the colour difference is not usually so sharp as in the rabbit. Muscles such as the trapezius or the gluteus maximus that are con-tinuously or often in action, have redder fibres than those such as biceps or the finger muscles that are used mainly for movement. The factors that make for redness in a muscle are still not well understood. Not all the red muscles of the rabbit are slow: the masseter contracts as fast as the white muscles. Moreover, in birds the muscles of the wings, which contract very fast, are red, especially so in the stronger fliers. It seems that myoglobin is produced in muscle-fibres that often build up a large oxygen debt, because of either slow tonic or fast phasic actions. The capacity to react in this way to oxygen deficiency is another example of the process of 'adaptation' by which the or-ganism records its past history and prepares for the future. It is not known whether the development of the distinctive colour of muscle-fibres depends upon developmental factors or on the conditions under

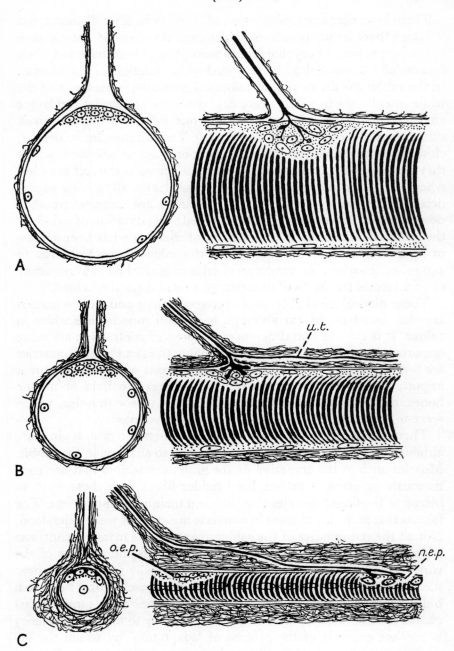

FIG. 56
(For underline see opposite page)

which the muscle contracts. In the crustacean *Daphnia* haemoglobin develops in the blood if the animal is kept in water deficient in oxygen (Munro Fox et al., 1951).

18. Effects of use and disuse upon muscles

It is interesting that when white muscle-fibres are put out of use, which can be done by cutting either their nerve or their tendon, they undergo a process of *atrophy* in which they shrink and lose some of their cross-striations (Fig. 56). The nuclei come to lie centrally and the sarcoplasm increases in amount, so that white fibres come to resemble red fibres. At the same time the contraction of the fibres, which, even if they are without nerves, can still be elicited by electrical, mechanical, or chemical stimulation (indeed they are hyperexcitable to such agents) becomes very slow and is followed by slow relaxation. After long periods the atrophy leads to complete disappearance of the muscle-fibres. Conversely use of muscles leads to their hypertrophy, probably by increase in size rather than number of muscle-fibres. Use and disuse, whose effects are profound throughout the body, affect muscles perhaps more rapidly than any other tissue. Muscles may become noticeably wasted after a few days in bed and are developed by a few long walks. The muscles like other tissues thus carry a memory of the demands made upon them in the recent past and are ready to meet similar situations in the future. The details of the chemical system that ensures this hypertrophy with use are not known; presumably it is related to the system that is responsible for ensuring that some muscles develop the fast and others the slow character.

19. The arrangement of muscle-fibres

The effect of the contraction of muscle-fibres depends on their direction and attachment, which vary greatly in different muscles. Smooth muscle-fibres often run in bundles around hollow organs, either in various directions, as in the wall of the bladder, or in regular layers of circular and longitudinal fibres, as in the gut. In a few situa-

FIG. 56. Stages in the atrophy and reinnervation of denervated muscle-fibres.

A, shows the normal condition near a motor end-plate, the neurilemmal tube being continuous with the sarcolemma. When the nerve-fibre degenerates it leaves a tube down which a new nerve-fibre can grow to the old end-plate as shown on the right. In B the muscle has been left for some months without innervation. The fibre has shrunk and its amount of sarcoplasm increased. A new nerve-fibre arriving can still reach the old end-plate but it also forms an 'ultraterminal' fibre (*u.t.*) in the thickened connective tissue. In C after a year of atrophy the muscle-fibre is very much shrunken, the nuclei lie centrally. The pathway to the old end-plate (*o.e.p.*) is closed and new nerve-fibres arriving must form a new end-plate (*n.e.p.*) (From Gutmann and Young, *J. Anat.* **78**, 1944.)

tions smooth muscle-fibres form a distinct muscle, for instance in the retractor of the penis of the dog. The little muscles of hairs are also of this sort. The pupil of the eye is closed by a sphincter in the iris composed of smooth muscle-fibres running round the edge of the pupil and is opened by radially arranged dilatator fibres.

Striped muscle-fibres are usually organized into rather definite

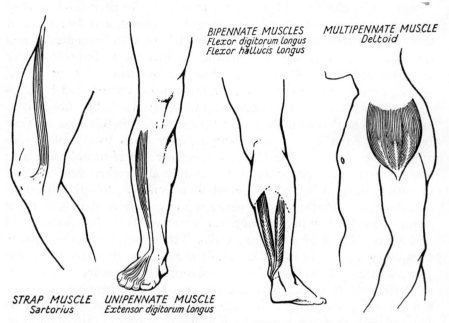

BIPENNATE MUSCLES
Flexor digitorum longus
Flexor hallucis longus

MULTIPENNATE MUSCLE
Deltoid

STRAP MUSCLE
Sartorius

UNIPENNATE MUSCLE
Extensor digitorum longus

FIG. 57. Diagrams of some human muscles to show the different arrangement of fibres within the muscle.

'muscles', often enclosed in an epimysium and further individualized by the presence of a single tendon at one or both ends. The arrangement of the muscle-fibres depends on the nature of the work to be done. Each muscle-fibre can contract to about one-half of its maximum length. Muscles that produce much movement but exert little force therefore consist of parallel bundles of long fibres, for example those of the sterno-hyoid muscles that pull down the hyoid apparatus during swallowing. On the other hand, muscles that produce much force consist of numerous short fibres, ending within the muscle belly with a more or less pennate arrangement (Fig. 57). This may mean that their direction of pull is slightly out of line with that of the whole muscle but greater force can be exerted by the presence of many short fibres. These *pennate muscles* may have the tendon along one side (unipennate), down the middle (bipennate), or many small tendons joining (multipennate) (Fig. 57). The last-named arrangement is found in muscles that are able to exert great force (e.g. the human deltoid). Muscles are attached to bones by union of the sarcolemma with the periosteum directly or through a tendon. The attachment is usually placed close to the joint, allowing the muscle to produce considerable movement quickly with little shortening, that is to say while contracting almost isometrically. However, in certain muscles the attachments are placed a long way from the joint, enabling them to exert a greater effect, even if slowly. Thus the deltoid of man is inserted far from the joint.

Muscles often serve to move a more distal movable part relative to the body and it is therefore common to distinguish the more fixed proximal 'origin' of the muscle from the more mobile (and usually more distal) 'insertion'. This use is harmless if it is realized that the distinction is arbitrary and that the action is equal at both ends of a muscle; which end is fixed depends solely on the conditions at the time. For instance the distal end of the biceps muscle is usually regarded as its insertion and often indeed it is the upper arm that is fixed and the lower which moves, but a man pulling himself up by flexing his arms has the lower arm fixed. Many such cases arise and it is wise to regard both ends of the muscle equally as points of attachment.

20. Levers in the body

The majority of the striped muscles of the body produce their effects by exerting a turning moment at a joint across which they act, that is to say they tend to move one member of the joint on the other with a force that is proportional to the distance of the line of direction of action of the muscle from the centre of the joint. The muscles are arranged in various ways to produce their actions. Many of them produce tension directly between their points of attachment, and the distribution of weight on the bones will then result in them being used as levers in various ways (Fig. 58). *First order levers*, in which the fulcrum lies between the load and the power, are not common in the body; an instance is the nodding of the head about the atlas as fulcrum. *Second order levers*, where the pull is applied at a greater distance from the fulcrum than is the load but on the same side, are more usual and the classic example is the foot, where the fulcrum is the balls of the toes (metatarsal heads), the weight bears on the ankle joint (talus) and the pull (gastrocnemius) is applied at the heel bone (calcaneum), the whole foot acting somewhat as a single lever. However, like so many other attempts to apply mechanical principles to

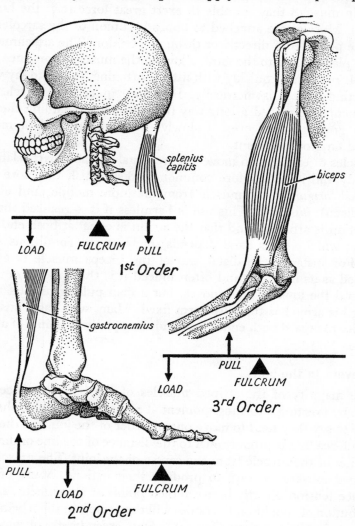

FIG. 58. Diagrams of some joints and muscles in man to show arrangements comparable to those of the different orders of lever.

the body this one must be used with caution: the foot is a complicated structure with many parts, not a simple lever. *Third order levers*, in which the pull is applied nearer to the fulcrum than the load, are also common, the action of the biceps in lifting a weight held in the hand is a good example.

The significance of many features of the skeleton can be understood by considering the mechanical advantages with which the muscles work. They are differently arranged according to whether speed of action or great force is the main consideration. Thus there is a striking contrast between the forelimb of animals that run at high speeds (such as the horse) and those that dig, for example the armadillo (Fig. 59).

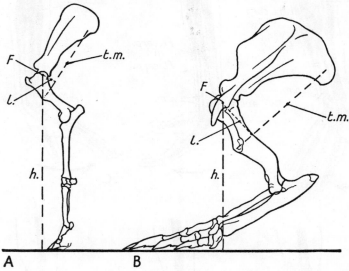

FIG. 59. Left forelimbs of A, horse, and B, armadillo, showing the line of action of the teres major muscle (*t.m.*).

l shows the moment arm of the muscle about the fulcrum *F*, and *h* the distance from the fulcrum to the ground. (Figure kindly supplied by Dr. J. Maynard Smith.)

We may consider the teres major, one of the main muscles flexing the arm at the shoulder, running from the scapula to the humerus (p. 165). The effectiveness of this muscle will depend upon the ratio between *l*, the moment arm of the muscle about the fulcrum, and *h* the distance from the fulcrum to the ground. In the armadillo *l/h* is large ($\frac{1}{4}$) and the movement is powerful though slow; it is therefore well adapted for digging. In the horse *l/h* is small ($\frac{1}{12}$) and the muscle is effective in the production of the rapid movement of running. The shapes of many bones are determined by such factors.

The muscles may be said to act in three ways (Elftman, 1941, p. 192). '1. When movement is not desirable, they must exert forces which will balance the forces present, so that the rotation of the levers does not take place. 2. When movement does take place, the muscles must be able not only to accelerate the movement but also to decelerate it. 3. The muscles must be able to regulate the energy of the system, by

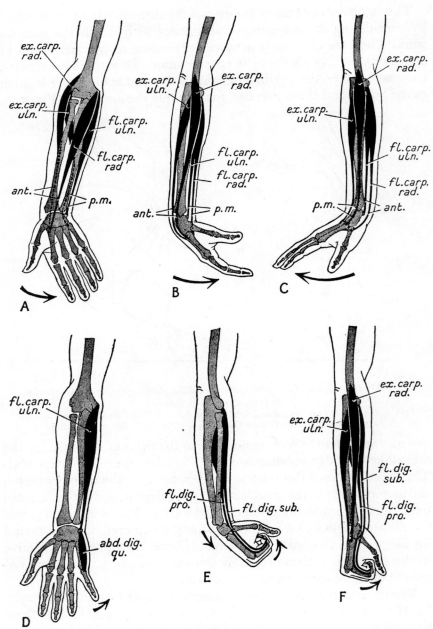

FIG. 60
(For underline see opposite page)

contributing energy from their chemical stores, or by removing energy by dissipation into heat, as occasion requires.'

In many situations where the muscles cross joints at which weight is carried it is convenient to consider them as elastic braces. Thus Gray has considered the legs of a mammal as if supporting the body balanced upon them (Fig. 69). Without braces the condition would obviously be unstable and the muscles about the joints compensate for the tendency of horizontal forces to upset the equilibrium. In a similar way the human body is balanced upon its two legs by a system of braces at front, back, and sides of the hip joint (p. 175). If the muscular action is cut off, for example by failure of the nervous system, the body falls down. By modification of their action as braces such muscles move the limbs and produce locomotion. Often they are assisted in this by special longer muscles, exerting greater leverage, and acting either across the same one joint or across several.

21. Actions of muscles in combination

A single muscle rarely acts alone to produce a movement. The actions that the brain demands are not the contractions of single muscles but the execution of specific movements, and for these the co-operation of various muscles is usually required. Nevertheless we can often recognize one or more muscles that specifically produce the movement of a joint, and such muscles are called the *prime movers* (agonists) of the action. For instance in bending the hand towards the little finger side (ulnar deviation) the flexor carpi ulnaris and extensor carpi ulnaris muscles are the prime movers (Fig. 60A). Every muscle after contraction has to be stretched again and in most situations, therefore, there are *antagonists* of the prime movers and these must relax during the action. They relax at a rate that ensures a steady movement. In adduction of the hand the antagonists of flexor and extensor carpi ulnaris are flexor and extensor carpi radialis, on the other side of the wrist. In other movements the muscles work in different combinations; for instance in flexion of the wrist, flexor carpi ulnaris and flexor carpi radialis act together as prime movers, the extensor muscles being now the antagonists (Fig. 60 B).

Contraction of the prime movers can only produce the required

FIG. 60. Actions of *fl. carpi ulnaris*, showing how muscles may act together in different combinations. In each case the prime movers are labelled *p.m.* and their antagonists *ant.*

abd.dig.qu. abductor of fifth digit; *ex.carp.rad.* extensor carpi radialis; *ex.carp.uln.* extensor carpi ulnaris; *fl.carp.rad.* flexor carpi radialis; *fl.carp.uln.* flexor carpi ulnaris; *fl.dig.pro.* flexor digitorum profundus; *fl.dig.sub.* flexor digitorum sublimis.

effect if the bone from which they act is fixed. On account of the mobility of the whole skeleto-muscular system this may involve the combined action of a surprisingly large number of muscles, working as *fixation muscles*. A good example of this can also be seen with flexor carpi ulnaris. The little finger is pulled aside ('abducted') by a short muscle (abductor digiti quinti) (Fig. 60 D). This runs from the pisiform bone, which can be felt at the wrist, to the side of the proximal phalanx of the little finger. Contraction along this line will pull the finger aside only if the pisiform bone is fixed by contraction of flexor carpi ulnaris, which is also attached to the pisiform. This muscle can easily be seen to be in action as a fixation muscle during the bending aside of the little finger (Fig. 60 D).

Movements are seldom as simple as they seem, and during many quite small movements a large part of the whole musculature may be brought into action. A special case of this is when a muscle passing over two joints is needed to produce action at only one of these, the other being then fixed by the action of *synergistic muscles*. For example, clenching of the fist is produced by the long flexors of the fingers, which would also bend the wrist forward were it not for the extensor carpi radialis and ulnaris, which can be seen to come into action as synergists (Fig. 60 E, F). It will be clear that this is really only a special case of muscles acting as fixators, and many writers do not limit the use of the word 'synergistic muscle' in this way, but make it synonymous with 'fixation muscle', in fact with any muscle whose action assists that of the prime movers. All of these terms signify only arbitrary divisions, useful in the attempt to present an account of the activities of this system of adjustable braces and ties by which the body is supported and moved to the various situations required for its survival.

VII

THE VERTEBRAL COLUMN

1. Posture of mammals and man

THE vertebral column and limbs, with their muscles and ligaments, are of particular importance in the life of terrestrial animals. In aquatic creatures the liquid medium supports the weight and the musculo-skeletal system enables the animal to move about and to find surroundings suitable to its needs. In land animals, in the absence of the support of a liquid medium, the skeleton and muscles must carry the entire weight of the body and we have therefore the conception of a *posture*, maintained by the combined action of these parts.

The members of the skeleton serve as struts, while the ligaments and muscles act as ties. It is clearly necessary to consider all these components together; it is senseless to consider compression members of a bridge, or any other structure for resisting deformation, without considering also the ties that go with them.

Discussion of the mechanics of a terrestial vertebrate is complicated by the fact that the animal is seldom in a situation where it can be considered as a static structure, such as a bridge. Its members are flexible and the ties connecting them include muscles that exert varying tension; therefore we have to think all the time of a system in a steady state rather than in static equilibrium. In nearly all positions work must be done to keep the body up and the energy for this work is obtained from outside the system. If the supplies of energy are not available the body collapses and the completeness of this collapse affords a measure of the importance of the muscles in maintaining the posture.

The system for the support of the body has become progressively improved throughout the period since the mammal-like reptiles first diverged from other amphibious fish-like stocks. At that early period the muscles of the back were arranged as a series of segmental blocks; the limbs were short and they rarely or never carried the body-weight. In the mammals the locomotor system has changed so much that few traces of the original metameric fish plan remain. The limbs and their muscles carry the whole weight of the body and are able to produce swift motion by acting as long levers. Some mammals can move over rough ground or through the trees in a way that excites the amazement of the engineer, whose machines can produce swift progression only over smooth surfaces. Moreover, many other forms of locomotion have been developed to a high degree in mammals, such as the leaping of some carnivores, the arboreal specializations of primates, the flying of bats, the burrowing of moles, and the swimming of whales, sea-cows, and seals. These developments of the locomotor system show perhaps more than any other part of the body how the exploration of new habitats by the animals has led to the appearance of special types of organization.

2. Some principles for analysis of the skeleton

It has been realized at least since the time of Galileo that there are similarities between the means for distribution of the weight of the body on to the legs and the stressing of bridges and other structures made by engineers. Certain principles are common to all bodies under such conditions. One of the simplest of them is given by Gray (1944): 'although a horse at rest can, by muscular effort, control the degree of support given by an individual leg towards the support of the body, yet the resultant of the thrusts of all four legs must always represent a force equal in magnitude but opposite in direction to the weight of the animal.' As the systems of statics and dynamics have developed, various attempts have been made to apply them to the animal body, and such analyses can be helpful in showing correlations between the positions and physical properties of bones, tendons, and muscles, and the life, posture, and activities of the whole animal. It is not yet possible to make the analysis complete enough to be the main basis for organizing communication of information about the animals: the living system is too complicated for us to be able to see it as a whole and also to name its parts according to any consistent scheme. We still continue to speak of 'the vertebral column' and not of 'the main mammalian compression strut'. Nevertheless, analysis with more exact methods takes us a considerable way towards an understanding of the parts played by the various bones and muscles and it brings us within sight of a general terminology and method of treatment that will make this part of biology both less laborious and more precise.

The basis for attempts made so far in this direction has been that bone is a tissue chiefly suited to resist compression; it also plays a part in resistance to tension, but consideration of the skeleton alone shows mainly the compression members or struts of the living girders. To understand properly how the weight is distributed we must also consider the ligaments and muscles, which resist tension. The principles of such an analysis can be shown by considering the distribution of strain during support of the weight of the body on the hind legs in a short-tailed quadruped such as the rabbit.

The whole back may be considered as a loaded beam and for simplicity we may compare it with a beam attached to a wall (Fig. 61). In

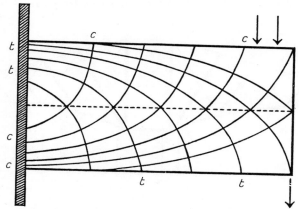

Fig. 61. Diagram of stressing in a loaded beam attached to a wall. The closer the lines the greater the stress in that region.
cc. compression lines; *tt.* tension lines.

such a structure, as already explained (p. 80), we can recognize (1) compression lines running downwards under the load but then horizontally to the position of attachment of the beam, and (2) symmetrically disposed tension lines which, as it were, support the load from above and cross the compression lines at right angles. Dissection of the back of the rabbit shows at once a muscle, the *sacrospinalis* (Fig. 68), the largest muscle in the body, attached to the sacrum behind and tapering forwards to be inserted all along the vertebrae of the back. The vertebrae thus form the compression members and the back muscles the tension members of a bracket or cantilever for supporting the weight of the body on the hind legs. The analogy can be pursued further, for the muscle mass is greatest and the bones are largest close to the point of attachment, where, as the stress diagram shows us, the tendency to strain is greatest.

This analogy serves as a simple introduction to the type of method used, but by more careful analysis more fruitful results can be obtained. Some simplification must always be introduced and no analysis yet devised gives full insight into the mechanics of the animal at rest and in motion. D'Arcy Thompson (1942) has made a suggestive comparison between the backbone of a quadrupedal mammal and two cantilever girders, which rest on the legs rather as the girders of the Forth Bridge rest upon their pillars (Fig. 62). A great part of the body-weight in a standing quadruped falls on the front legs and the similarity to a girder is clearly marked in this part of the backbone (Fig. 63). The compression member of the girder is represented by the bodies of the vertebrae, arranged in a row to form arches curving

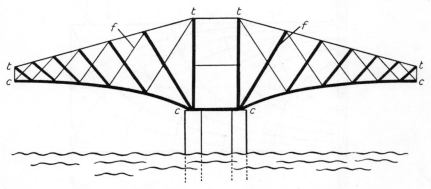

FIG. 62. Diagram of cantilever girder, such as is used in the Forth Bridge. *cc.* main compression member; *ff.* struts and ties of the filling of the girder; *tt.* main tension member. (After D'Arcy Thompson.)

upwards from a low point opposite the limb. The tension members are the *ligamentum nuchae*, which runs along the back of the neck, and other ligaments and muscles that run between the vertebral spines, some for long, others for short distances (p. 143). Between the main compression and tension members a cantilever girder is given a 'filling' of struts and ties. These are arranged on the principle that the triangle is the only geometrical figure that cannot be distorted if the lengths of the side remain constant. In the body the vertebral spines are the struts, and the short muscles and ligaments of the back are the ties. The slope of the vertebral spines is approximately forwards in front of the forelegs and backwards behind, as in a cantilever girder, but other forces operate to cause them to point slightly backwards even at the shoulders. As Fig. 63 shows the principle of triangles is used widely, combining strength with lightness.

A significant feature of the construction of girders by an engineer is that the depth and hence strength of the structure should be at every point proportional to the bending moments. These will be greatest over the point of attachment of the girder and the vertebral spines are

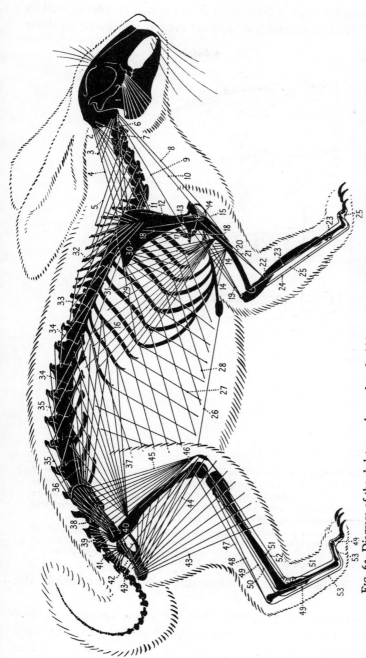

FIG. 63. Diagram of the skeleton and muscles of rabbit, to show the general arrangement of struts and ties.

1. masseter; 2. obliquus capitis; 3. splenius capitis; 4. semispinalis capitis; 5. longissimus capitis; 6. longissimus cervicis; 7. obliquus capitis inferior; 8. basioclavicularis; 9. levator scapulae; 10. sternomastoid; 11. scalenus; 12. supraspinatus; 13. infraspinatus; 14. pectoralis; 15. cleido humeralis; 16. latissimus dorsi; 17. subscapularis (displaced caudally); 18. deltoid; 19. triceps; 20. biceps brachii; 21. brachialis; 22. extensor carpi ulnaris; 23. extensor digitorum communis; 24. flexor digitorum sublimis; 25. flexor digitorum profundus; 26. rectus abdominis; 27. transversus abdominis; 28. external oblique; 29. serratus anterior; 30. trapezius; 31. ilio-costalis; 32. longissimus; 33. semispinalis dorsi; 34. longissimus dorsi; 35. multifidus; 36. sacro-spinalis; 37. psoas major; 38. gluteus medius; 39. piriformis; 40. gluteus maximus; 41. abductor caudae; 42. gemellus inferior; 43. biceps; 44. adductors; 45. rectus femoris; 46. vastus intermedius; 47. gastrocnemius and plantaris; 48. soleus; 49. flexor digitorum longus; 50. peroneal muscles; 51. extensor digitorum; 52. tibialis anterior; 53. plantaris.

longest above the forelegs. Many such features can be recognized in
the skeleton of the rabbit, and they appear even more clearly in those

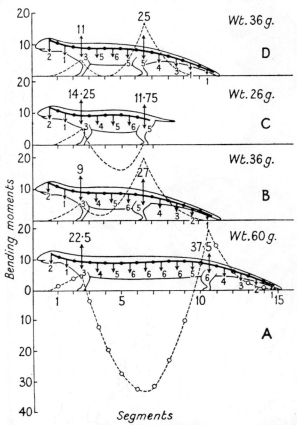

FIG. 64. Analysis of the bending moments along the vertebral column of a series of
tetrapod forms. The figures near the arrows show the load on each vertebra in grams,
the dotted line shows the bending moment curve, strain on the dorsal muscles above
and ventral muscles below the axis. The limbs are shown acting as vertical struts and
the proportion of the weight carried on fore- and hind-legs is given.

A, Long-bodied reptile; the greatest strain falls on the ventral musculature at the middle of
the body. B, effect of shortening the body. C, same without tail, showing strain on ventral
musculature. D, central part of back and belly relieved of strain by loading the weight on two
balanced cantilevers. (From Gray, *J. exp. Biol.* **20**, 1944.)

hoofed mammals that are large and rapidly moving, for example, the
horse.

Such comparisons are stimulating but there is a danger that they
may be accepted uncritically, without recognition of the fact that they
give only suggestions and not exact solutions of the statics, still less
of the dynamics of the vertebrate body. We can, however, pursue the

analysis further, as Gray has done, by determining the bending moments along the vertebral column. Fig. 64A shows a reptile with fourteen vertebrae, the loading of each vertebra being given near the vertical arrows and the bending moment curve shown by the dotted line, with strain on the dorsal musculature above and on the ventral musculature below the base line. Fig. 64 shows the effect of shortening of the body in relieving the strain on the ventral musculature. One of the most marked features of later reptilian and early mammalian stocks was this decrease in body length. The effect of the absence of a tail is shown by 64C, where the ventral musculature is again under strain. 64D is an animal so constructed that the loading of the central part of the body is asymptotic to the base line and such a type consists of two exactly balanced cantilevers.

3. The vertebrae

The vertebral column of mammals forms the main compression member of a complicated girder by means of which the weight of the body is carried and can be propelled forwards or stopped. The arrangement of the girder differs considerably in different mammals but five regions can always be recognized, the cervical, thoracic, lumbar, sacral, and coccygeal. They are developed to varying extents according to the way the weight is distributed. In the rabbit the back is used by the animal in two distinct ways. When springing forwards it forms a single girder, braced on to the hind legs. When standing still it is a double cantilever girder and much of the weight is carried on the forelegs. In the larger quadrupedal mammals this last is the usual arrangement, the weight being balanced on the forelegs, while the hind legs are used for pushing (Fig. 65). The head often acts as a counterweight (elephant, rhinoceros, giraffe). In man the situation is completely changed by the use of the vertebral girder as a vertical pillar.

In all mammals the vertebral column contains a number of *centra* and acts as a compression strut. These centra develop from a larger middle part, corresponding to the diaphysis of long bones, with smaller *vertebral epiphyses* in front and behind. The surfaces of the centra are usually flat and between them are plates of fibro-cartilage, the *intervertebral discs*. The central portion of each of these discs, the *nucleus pulposus*, represents the remains of the notochord (p. 720). The intervertebral discs act as elastic cushions between the centra. Movement between the bodies of the vertebrae is usually rather limited and the surfaces between them are not synovial joints. The

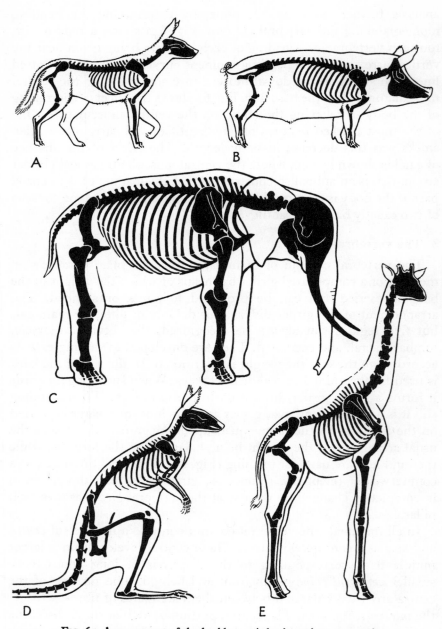

FIG. 65. Arrangement of the backbone girder in various mammals.

A, Balanced cantilevers (dog); B, single girder balanced on both legs (pig); C, single girder with balance largely about forelegs (elephant); D, single girder balanced on hind legs (wallaby); E, single girder balanced on forelegs (giraffe).

arrangement allows some bending and rotation to occur but this is checked by the interlocking articular facets of the vertebrae and by dorsal and ventral longitudinal ligaments, which run the length of the column.

The regular segmentation found in a fish-like vertebrate has been modified in mammals so that different types of vertebrae are produced along the length of the back (Figs. 66 and 67). The boundaries between the sets are sometimes fairly sharp, but throughout the vertebral column we can see well illustrated the operation of gradation of morphogenetic processes (p. 714). The neural spines and the various other projections and facets gradually change in direction and in length along the body; evidently the original continuous series of vertebrae has become modified by the interposition in a graded manner of special developmental processes. Whereas one process repeated many times produces the similar members of the backbone of a fish or newt, several diverse processes have been introduced to make the varied vertebrae of a mammal.

The vertebral girder of the rabbit may be considered to consist of two parts, a lumbo-sacral behind and a cervico-thoracic in front. Each of these has a central main compression member, with struts above and below. In the lumbo-sacral girder the upper struts are the neural spines and mamillary processes, and the lower struts are the transverse processes. In the thoracic region the upper struts are the neural spines, the lower struts are the transverse processes and ribs. The ribs have to be considered as part of the girder in spite of the fact that they are jointed with the vertebrae and move during respiration. The symmetry of this girder can be seen in the skeleton of a large ungulate such as an elephant (Fig. 65), which carries much of the weight on the forelegs.

The neck and the tail are integrated with the main girders of the back to differing extents in various animals. Many mammals have become short-bodied and the tail does not then have a balancing or cantilever function, as it does in lower animals. The neck retains this condition to a considerable extent in some mammals, as witnessed by the presence of long cervical neural spines and transverse processes. There is a tendency for the head to be supported in such a manner that the neck vertebrae act as a simple compression strut: that is to say, as a separate single-arm girder held in front of the thorax by long braces. In such necks the cervical vertebral processes are short, for example in the giraffe, rabbit, monkey, and man.

There are pronounced differences in the arrangement of the skeleton

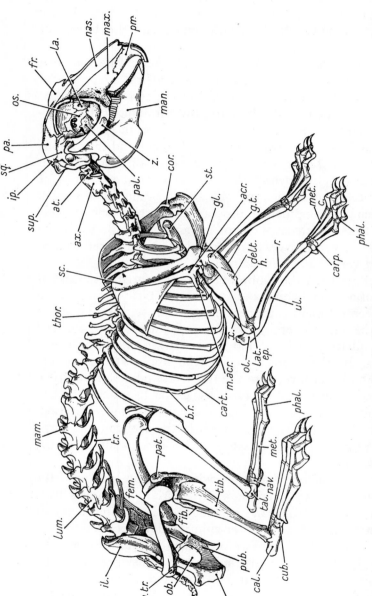

Fig. 66. Skeleton of a rabbit.

ac. acetabulum; *acc.p.* accessory process of lumbar vertebra; *acr.* acromional process; *at.* atlas; *at.-occ.* atlanto-occipital joint; *ax.* axis; *az.* rostral zygopophysis; *b.r.* bony rib; *cal.* calcaneum; *cart.* cartilaginous rib; *cl.* clavicle; *cor.* coracoid process; *cub.* cuboid; *cun.* cuneiform; *delt.* deltoid tuberosity; *dist.c.* distal carpals; *carp.* carpals; *fem.* femur; *fib.* fibula; *fr.* frontal; *g.t.* greater tuberosity; *g.tr.* greater trochanter; *gl.* glenoid; *h.* humerus; *ip.* interparietal; *is.* ischium; *la.* lachryma; *lat.c.* lateral candyle; *med.c.* medial candyle; *lat.ep.* lateral epicondyle; *lat.m.* lateral malleolus; *l.-sac.* lumbo-sacral joint; *l.t.* lesser tuberosity; *l.tr.* lesser trochanter; *lum.* lumbar vertebrae; *m.acr.* metacromion; *mam.* mamillary process; *man.* mandible; *mast.* mastoid process; *max.* maxilla; *med.ep.* medial epicondyle; *med.m.* medial malleolus; *met.* metatarsals; *met.c.* metacarpals; *nas.* nasal; *nav.* navicular; *ob.* obturator foramen; *occ.* occipital; *od.* odontoid peg; *ol.* olecranon; *os.* orbitosphenoid; *pa.* parietal; *pal.* palatine; *pat.* patella; *phal.* phalanges; *pm.* premaxilla; *prox.c.* proximal carpals; *pub.* pubis; *p.z.* caudal zygopophysis; *r.* radius; *sac.* sacrum; *sac.-il.* sacro-iliac joint; *sc.* scapula; *sp.* vertebral spine; *sph.* sphenoid; *sq.* squamosal; *st.* sternum; *sup.* supraoccipital; *tal.* talus; *thor.* thoracic vertebra; *tib.* tibia; *tr.* transverse process; *3rd tr.* third trochanter; *troch.* trochlea humeri; *ul.* ulna; *v.art.* vertebrarterial canal; *w.* wing of atlas;

and muscles in different mammals (Fig. 65) and it is difficult to make generalizations about the girders. Yet the same principles apply throughout and once understood they can be applied to the particular conditions in each species.

We shall deal in detail with the rabbit, where all the points mentioned can be verified by dissection.

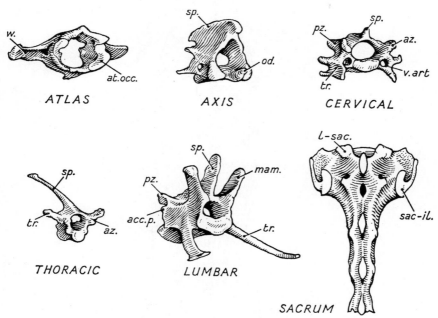

Fig. 67. Vertebrae of a rabbit. Lettering as Fig. 66.

4. The lumbo-sacral girder of the rabbit

In describing the vertebral column it is convenient to begin with the more posterior region, where the structure of the girder is simple. The *pelvic girdle* is firmly attached to the vertebral column in all mammals (except certain aquatic forms). In the rabbit four vertebrae are modified and fused to form the *sacrum*, but of these only the first articulates with the ilium (Fig. 67). The surfaces of articulation at this *sacro-iliac joint* will be found to be rather difficult to separate, but the two parts are not actually fused and they permit a small amount of movement. Such small movements are often allowed in the body even at points where great weight is carried. They serve to prevent fracture under sudden forces. The articular surfaces of the sacrum and ilium are partly covered with cartilage and partly roughened for the attach-

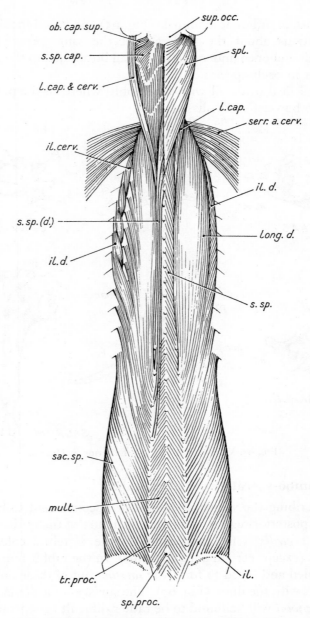

FIG. 68. Dissection of the back muscles of the rabbit.

il. ilium; *il.cerv.* iliocostalis cervicis; *il.d.* Iliocostalis dorsi; *l.cap.* longissimus capitis; *l.cap. & cerv.* longissimus capitis and cervicis; *long.d.* longissimus dorsi; *mult.* multifidus; *ob.cap.sup.* obliquus capitis superior; *sac.sp.* sacrospinalis; *serr.a.cerv.* serratus anterior cervicis (to scapula); *spl.* splenius; *sp.proc.* spinous process; *s.sp.* semispinalis (superficial); *s.sp.cap.* semispinalis capitis; *s.sp.(d.)* semispinalis (deep); *sup.occ.* supraoccipital bone; *tr.proc.* transverse process.

ment of the strong *interosseus sacro-iliac ligament*, which, together with bands of fibres above and below the joint, holds the parts together. The amount of movement possible at the sacro-iliac joints becomes greater shortly before parturition, the ligaments being loosened by the action of the hormones circulating at that time (p. 562).

The sacral vertebrae have low spines and expanded upper surfaces for muscle attachment. The pelvic girdle and sacrum thus form a platform, balanced on the hind leg, to the front of which the vertebral column is attached as a projecting bracket. The structure of the bones and muscles of this part of the back can easily be understood by considering the distribution of stress in such a bracket (Fig. 61). The compression lines occupy the lower portion of the girder and the tension lines the upper. In the backbone the bodies of the vertebrae are the compression members and the *lumbar vertebrae* have large bodies for this purpose. The movements allowed between them are mainly in the sagittal plane, giving arching or straightening of the back and some rotation. The vertebrae in this region have large surfaces for the attachment of muscles. Besides the broad neural spines and transverse processes there are also large *mamillary processes*, not found elsewhere in the vertebral column. To these vertebrae are attached the tension members of the girder, in the form of the sacrospinalis muscle (Fig. 63).

5. The muscles of the back in the rabbit

The essential pattern of the arrangement of the muscle of the back is that close to the midline most of the fibres run cranially and medially, so that caudal lateral parts of the vertebral girder are joined to cranial medial parts. More laterally the muscle-fibres run cranially and laterally, so that here caudal medial parts of the vertebral girder are joined to cranial lateral parts (Fig. 68).

The medial muscle mass lies over the vertebral column between the spinous processes in the midline and the mamillary and transverse processes laterally. Its fibres originate on the mamillary and transverse processes and insert on to more cranial spinous processes. In the lumbar region, from the sacrum to the more caudal thoracic vertebrae, this muscle is called *multifidus* and more cranially it is called *semispinalis dorsi*. Superficially the fibres originate directly on the mamillary and transverse processes of the vertebrae and are inserted on more cranial spinous processes. The deeper fibres originate from long tendons that join more caudal mamillary and transverse processes with spinous processes further cranially.

In the neck the medial part of the muscle mass includes the *semispinalis capitis*, arising from the transverse processes of the caudal cervical vertebrae and the cranial thoracic vertebrae. It is inserted on to the lateral surface of the external occipital protuberance but is also attached between the external occipital protuberance and the transverse process of the atlas. Ventral to the semispinalis capitis is the *semispinalis cervicis*, which originates on the articular processes of the more caudal cervical vertebrae and the first thoracic vertebra. It is inserted on to the spinous processes of the cervical vertebrae, especially on to that of the axis.

The more lateral muscles make up the *sacrospinalis* muscle, which is the dominant feature of the dorsal and lumbar regions after the lumbo-dorsal fascia has been removed. It forms a large mass, lateral to the multifidus, between the crest of the ilium and the thorax. Its fibres originate on the crest of the ilium, the dorsal surface of the sacrum, the mamillary processes of the more caudal lumbar vertebrae, and the lumbo-dorsal fascia. They run cranially and laterally and are inserted on to the transverse processes of the lumbar vertebrae. Fibres belonging to this muscle are originating and inserting all along its length; as some leave it others join it.

In the thoracic region it divides into a more medial *longissimus dorsi* and a more lateral *costalis dorsi*. Both muscles are inserted on to the ribs. The longissimus dorsi receives fibres from the semispinalis muscle in the thoracic region and these are inserted with it on to the ribs. The costalis receives fibres, originating on the ribs, which run cranially to the seventh cervical vertebra as the *costalis cervicis*. In the neck longissimus dorsi is inserted on to the transverse processes of the more caudal cervical vertebrae and carries on cranially to the transverse process of the atlas as the *longissimus cervicis*.

From the transverse processes of the second, third, and fourth thoracic vertebrae, a bundle called *longissimus capitis* runs forward along the lateral border of the *splenius* muscle. The latter is a triangular sheet arising from the ligamentum nuchae; its fibres run cranially and laterally to the mastoid part of the skull and the transverse process of the atlas. Cranially the fibres of longissimus turn and run parallel with the fibres of splenius and are inserted with them on the mastoid part of the skull.

6. The tail

The tail varies from the four minute structures making the *coccyx* of man to the fifty or so vertebrae of the scaly anteater *Manis* and the powerful swimming organ of the whales. The muscles (*abductor caudae*) are well developed only in the cranial portion of the tail, the terminal segments being moved by tendons. By these muscles the tail can be moved in all directions, since there are usually no articular facets on the caudal vertebrae. The muscles are developed to different extents in various mammals. In man they are still present in spite of the absence of the tail, being incorporated in the *levator ani* muscle, which forms a floor to the whole pelvis, an important function in the upright position.

The tail is put to various uses, illustrating the adaptability of mammalian organization. It acts as a balancing organ in many species (p. 37), especially in animals that walk or leap mainly on the hind legs, such as kangaroos and squirrels. In the ungulates, which are sufficiently well balanced on their legs without it, we find the tail converted into a fly-whisk. In the extinct *Glyptodon* it formed a defensive mace. In some monkeys it is a prehensile organ, strong enough to carry the whole animal and provided with a sensitive under surface, which has a considerable representation in the cerebral cortex (p. 439). In whales it is a swimming organ of immense strength. In rabbits and many artiodactyls its white underside is shown as a warning of danger to others, marking a degree of social organization and power of communication. Even the pig is said to raise the tail when he is enraged. Man is one of the few mammals who, finding no use for his tail, has lost it.

7. The thoraco-cervical girder of the rabbit

There are usually seven lumbar vertebrae in the rabbit and in front of them there is a sharp change of structure, marking the point where the two portions of the vertebral girder join. The more caudal thoracic vertebrae resemble the lumbars in some respects, but whereas the lumbar transverse processes point headwards the ribs point caudally and the neural spines also change direction just in front of this point. Evidently the whole direction of the ties and struts reverses at this central point in the girder.

The arrangement in the thoracic region is conditioned by the fact that the forelimb does not articulate directly with the vertebral column.

The foreleg and scapula make a pillar on which the weight of the body hangs by means of a sling of muscle, the *serratus anterior* (Fig. 63), whose fibres run from the ribs to the border of the scapula, where the bending moment is greatest. Thus in spite of the difference in arrangement at the two ends of the vertebral girder we can recognize a general similarity. The lumbar transverse processes correspond as lower struts to the ribs and the fibres of sacrospinalis 'hang' the weight on to the ilium, as the fibres of serratus anterior do on the scapula.

8. Ribs and sternum

The ribs, characteristic of the thoracic region, are attached to the vertebrae at two places. A *capitulum* at the end of each articulates with the body of its own vertebra and in the ribs at the head end of the series also with the body of the vertebra in front, while a *tuberculum*, on the side of the rib, articulates with the transverse process. The dorsal part of each rib is, of course, under compression stress from the weight of the body and the pull of the serratus, and this region is ossified as the *bony rib*. The ventral parts of the ribs turn cephalad and medially; these parts are under tension rather than compression and are *cartilaginous* instead of bony. This is a beautiful example of the way in which the consistency of the tissue varies with its function.

The ventral ends of the ribs are attached to the *sternum*, the more cephalic ones directly by the cartilaginous ventral pieces, the more caudal indirectly (Fig. 66). One or two free or floating ribs at the hind end of the series are not attached at all. The sternum is formed by endochondral ossification in a number of paired segmental *sternebrae*, which unite to form the main 'body' or *mesosternum*, to which is attached a posterior *xiphisternum*. In mammals with a well-developed clavicle there is often a large separate plate, the *presternum* ('manubrium' of man). The point of articulation between the manubrium and the body is known in man as the *sternal angle*, and it lies opposite the articulation of the second costal cartilage. Being easily felt through the skin it makes a convenient landmark for counting the ribs.

9. Abdominal muscles

The ribs also serve for the transfer of much of the weight of the abdominal viscera to the vertebral column through the action of the abdominal muscles. These muscles are derived from the hypaxial portion of the myotomes (p. 715) and are innervated from ventral roots. They serve to hold the viscera in place, acting as slings attached to the ribs, lumbar vertebrae, and pelvic girdle. In a well-balanced animal little strain falls on this region (p. 137) and the abdominal muscles are usually thin. The *obliquus externus abdominis* (Fig. 63) runs from the ribs and wall of the thorax caudally, ventrally, and medially to form a broad aponeurosis meeting its fellow in the middle line at the *linea alba*. Some of its fibres run to the crest of the ilium and the portion of the lower border of the aponeurosis between the ilium and the pubis forms the *inguinal ligament*, marking the caudal border of the abdomen. The *obliquus internus* consists of fibres running nearly at right angles to those of the externus, from the lumbo-dorsal fascia, ilium, and inguinal ligaments to the linea alba and the caudal ribs. The fibres of *transversus abdominis* lie still deeper and run in the same general direction but more transversely. The *rectus abdominis* consists of fibres close to the midline, running directly from the lower end of the thoracic cage to the pubis. This muscle is crossed by tendinous insertions, which at least approximately mark the segmental divisions. These are also sometimes present in the other abdominal muscles in some animals. In species where this musculature is well developed seven or eight such segments can be recognized; usually, however, only three or four are present. The abdominal muscles serve to assist in flexing the body in the sagittal plane and the obliqui are also responsible for lateral bending and rotation. All the muscles aid in respiration by fixing the lower ribs and by supporting the viscera.

10. Thoracic vertebrae and muscles

A characteristic feature of the thoracic region is the great length of the neural spines, which in the rabbit point backwards. These upper struts of the girder are united by a ligament, the *supraspinous ligament*, making the upper tension member of the girder. The spines are highest over the withers, where the bending moments are greatest; their length and slope varies greatly in different mammals. In quadrupeds the more cephalic thoracic spines usually point caudally and the lumbar spines headward, with one *anticlinal vertebra* almost vertical between. This represents the point between the two cantilever girders with which the column has been compared (p. 141).

In man, where the column is not constructed as a cantilever girder system, all the spines point caudally, but the thoracic spines more sharply than the lumbar, so that the eleventh thoracic may be considered anticlinal.

The muscles of the thoracic and cervical region are arranged as already explained to form a system of ties bracing the cranial part of the vertebral girder on to the more caudal part. Thus in the rabbit the large *semispinalis dorsi* muscles form a series of powerful ties, running from a more lateral lumbar to a medial thoracic attachment (p. 143). Their more caudal attachments are by long tendons to the lumbar mamillary processes and each divides into conspicuous serial slips inserting on to the more cephalic thoracic spines. Each portion of the muscle has thus an elongated fan shape, with a tendinous caudal base and several muscular cephalic endings. These ties extend from the cephalad to the lower cervical spines. Just as the sacrospinalis serves to carry the front part of the body braced on to the hind legs, so the semispinalis is able to transfer the weight of the hinder part of the body on to the front legs. The girder is thus designed to carry weight either mainly on its front or mainly on its hinder portions or on both.

The *serratus posterior* muscles consist of slips running ventrally and caudally from the thoracic spines to the ribs. These fibres correspond functionally to the multifidus in the posterior girder, running across the semispinalis.

Further muscles attached to the thoracic spines assist in supporting the body on the scapula. The *trapezius* in the rabbit is a broad superficial sheet running from the midline in the neck and thoracic region to the spine of the scapula. Ventral to the trapezius the *rhomboid* muscles are further slips with the same general direction, from the thoracic spines to the vertebral scapular border.

11. The neck muscles

The arrangement for the support of the head consists essentially of long muscles running from the cephalic end of the thoracic region to the back of the skull. The function of the seven cervical vertebrae thus tends to become that of a simple single flexible compression member, without any long projecting struts. The neural spines may be quite small, as in the rabbit, but in animals such as the gorilla, where a heavy head is carried on the neck as a projecting girder, they are long. In man the head is balanced on the vertebral column acting as a vertical girder and the cervical spines are short. The cervical transverse processes, though not long, receive the insertions of many muscles, especially in the posterior neck region, and are divided into dorsal and ventral portions, between which runs the vertebral artery in a foramen characteristic of neck vertebrae.

In the rabbit the more caudal cervical vertebrae serve as a base for the whole neck and receive attachments of *semispinalis* on to their spines and of *longissimus* (p. 145) on to their transverse processes, thus bracing the whole neck and head on to the two main parts of the vertebral girder. The head is held up on the neck mainly by two sets of muscles that run from the back of the skull to the lower cervical and upper thoracic regions. *Semispinalis capitis* is the more dorsal of these, passing between the occipital protuberance and the transverse processes all the way from C_3 to T_4. The second brace, *longissimus capitis*, is attached to the mastoid process and acts below the atlanto-occipital joint, bending the head downwards; it is attached caudally to the transverse processes T_{2-4}. Below these muscles lies a still deeper layer, the *semispinalis cervicis*, which, from the spines of the axis and cervical vertebrae, runs to the articular processes of C_4-T_1 and thus also holds the head back. There are also other small, short muscles between the neck vertebrae.

On the ventral side the musculature of the neck is weaker; *longus cervicis* runs from the ventral side of the atlas and other cervical vertebrae to the vertebral bodies farther back. The *scalene muscles* pass from the lower sides of the transverse processes of C_{4-7} to the outer side of the first five ribs. These muscles work with the sternomastoid and longissimus capitis and semispinalis capitis in balancing the head on the neck, a function particularly important in types with long or vertically held necks such as the giraffe or man.

12. Cervical vertebrae

The neck is characteristically developed in mammals to allow movement in all directions of the head, with its sense organs and mouth. Whereas the head of a fish or an amphibian can only be turned by movement of the whole body, that of a mammal is like a separate organ and can be directed to almost any point in space by the muscles of the thin neck. The cervical vertebrae allow a considerable degree of movement and provide attachments for the muscles that hold up the head. They have small bodies, with a large neural canal (since the spinal cord is large in the neck, see p. 360), and are broad in proportion to their length. The cervical articular facets are of simple form: the cephalic zygopophyses point dorsally and the caudal ones ventrally on each vertebra. They have flat surfaces allowing a considerable degree of movement in the sagittal plane and some lateral movement (bending the head sideways), though this is always combined with rotation.

13. Atlas and axis

Although there is considerable mobility along the whole neck the extensive movements of the head are mostly due to the special arrangement of the first two cervical vertebrae, the *atlas* and *axis*, which are larger than the others and form joints that allow much movement. The two occipital condyles rest in large concave facets on the front of the atlas and this *atlanto-occipital joint* allows movement in the sagittal plane, as in nodding the head. The first or *atlas* vertebra is very wide and has a thin neural arch but no centrum; its transverse processes are broad and long, giving good leverage for the muscles that hold and rotate the head and neck.

The *axis* vertebra, on the other hand, is narrow in the transverse plane. It bears on the cranial surface of the centrum a knob, the *odontoid process*, which can be shown by its development to represent the centrum of the atlas segment. This knob and the articular facets of the axis are so arranged that the atlanto-axial joint allows rotation of the head and atlas on the neck, thus, with the atlanto-occipital joint, allowing movement in all directions. The odontoid articulates with the atlas, and is separated from the neural canal proper by a transverse ligament. The neural spine of the axis presents a large flat surface for the muscles running forwards to the skull and backwards to the other vertebrae; these muscles hold up the head and extend the neck backwards in the sagittal plane.

14. Proprioceptors of the neck

The head and neck are thus supported by an elaborate set of muscles; these have departed a long way from the simple segmental myotomes present in fishes and amphibia and they allow delicate and controlled movement. The position of the head in space is evidently of great importance to a mammal and especially to a man. It is perhaps not an accident that when our 'personality' is in some way reduced we 'hang our heads' and on recovery again 'hold our heads high'. The extensor muscles of the neck of man are at work continually throughout waking life to maintain the position of the head, but if we fall asleep when sitting they allow it to flop forwards on to the chest. This 'tonic' action of the muscles is produced by stretch receptor organs (p. 365), which are numerous in these as in other 'anti-gravity' muscles. The proprioceptor organs of the neck muscles have also a wider function to perform in producing adjustments of posture in other parts of the body. Together with the receptors of the eyes and the static organs of the ear

(p. 514) they provide the information that determines the position of the eyes and of the muscles controlling the limbs (p. 364). For every position of the head there is an appropriate position of the eyes and limbs, and the whole constitutes a delicate system by which the animal or man directs itself to whatever feature of the environment is claiming attention for the moment. The neck is thus of great importance in controlling the life of a mammal.

VIII

THE FORELIMB

1. The position of the limbs in a mammal

AFTER the fishes first came on land the limbs changed from flaps projecting laterally to struts with a skeleton on an axial plan. A fin with dorsal and ventral muscles, serving to raise and depress it for purposes of steering, thus became changed into a limb, turned under the body, and able to move in various directions and to carry and move the weight of the body. Distinct traces of the original fin plan still remain and they can be made the basis of a simple account of the various muscles of the limbs.

The human arm and hand possess an exceptional mobility and can be placed in positions that serve to illustrate the changes that have taken place during evolution. The relation of a limb to the original position of the fin is shown by stretching the arm out sideways with the thumb pointing towards the head. We can then recognize that the limb has a *pre-axial border*, occupied by the radius bone and the thumb (pollex, digit 1), corresponding to the front of the fin, and a *post-axial border*, with the ulna and little finger.

The muscles of a fish fin serve mainly to raise and lower it and are divided into upper abductor and lower adductor sets. These muscles have become modified to form the muscles of the limbs, which are moved forwards and backwards in locomotion. The more cephalic of the original adductors and abductors now work together as protractors, the more caudal ones act as retractors. Around the shoulder and hip joints there are therefore muscles that move the limb in each of the four chief directions and also produce actions of rotation by which the whole limb is revolved on its axis. At the more distal joints (elbow and knee) movement is mainly in two directions, distinguished by the arbitrary terms flexion and extension. It is not possible to say exactly how the flexor and extensor muscles are related to the original adductors and abductors of the more distal segments of a fin.

The mammalian limbs have therefore changed from a condition in which they projected laterally from the body until they are brought under the body for support and elongated to act as levers. The first change was the bending of the limb at the elbow and wrist, allowing the ventral surface of the 'hand' to be placed on the ground while the radius and ulna were held vertically. This stage was already reached in mesozoic amphibians and reptiles. To produce a less broad base and more efficient support the humerus then came to be held directed backwards, so that the elbow pointed back and the limb was brought directly under the body. This, however, would have the effect of leaving the hand pointing outwards and backwards. To avoid this the radius early became partly twisted round the ulna, so that in the *prone* position typical of most quadrupedal mammals the radius is lateral at the elbow but passes across the front of the ulna to become medial at the wrist. The hand is thus directed forwards and the first digit is medial. The bones are fixed in this position in many mammals (e.g. the rabbit) but in primates the hand can be returned to the more primitive *supine* position, with the radius and ulna parallel and the thumb pointing laterally. In man much use is made of the possibility of changing from one position to the other and thus turning the hand in various directions.

Somewhat simpler changes have been necessary to bring the hind limb into a position underneath the body. The first change from a simple lateral fin was, as in the forelimbs, a bending at knee and ankle, bringing the sole on to the ground and the tibia and fibula to a vertical position, with the tibia pre-axial. The limb was then brought under the body by rotation medially at the hip joint, so that the knee points towards the head. The foot is thus placed under the body, pointing headward, with its sole on the ground and the tibia medially: there is no need for a 'pronation' to direct the foot headward.

This analysis gives us a means of understanding the changes that have taken place during the evolution of the limbs and is a help in understanding the present arrangement of the muscles. There are not sufficient paleontological data to allow a fully satisfactory history to be given of the detailed sequence of events as they actually occurred.

2. Functioning of the limbs

The limbs provide the chief means by which the body moves about in the world and moves other objects towards or away from itself. In most mammals the limbs support the weight in a standing posture, and it is convenient to consider how the muscles and bones co-operate to maintain this posture and to provide the horizontal forces by which the animal is propelled or stopped. For this purpose Gray (1944) suggests that we may treat the muscles as elastic springs. For an analogy he takes a table whose four legs are attached to the top by universal joints (Fig. 69). Each leg contains within it a spring to represent the muscles that extend the legs. Compensation against horizontal forces is produced by four elastic braces running between each leg and the table top. In the animal these are provided by the muscles attaching the limbs to the body, which serve to brace the leg when it acts as a strut and also to move it as a lever. Many of the muscles lie in positions that can be closely compared with such braces, and we shall find

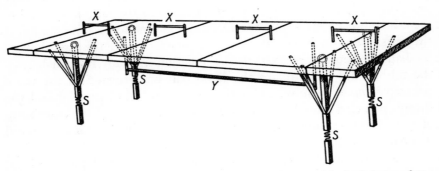

Fɪɢ. 69. Diagram of a balanced table top for comparison with the balance of a quadruped. The top consists of sections jointed together and supported by elastic braces X above and Y below. The legs articulate with the top by means of universal joints, each protected by four elastic braces (see text). Each leg is itself extensible by a spring, S. (From Gray, *J. exp. Biol.* **20**, 1944.)

in this conception a further insight into the significance of the arrangement of the musculo-skeletal system.

The table top of Gray's analogy is made further comparable with the segmented animal by imagining it divided into sections, united by hinges and stabilized by braces attached either above or below. These braces can also be recognized in the body, and this part of the analogy could obviously be developed to give some idea of the form and distribution of the ties of the vertebral column. The effect of the analysis is to compare the body to a segmented overhung beam supported on four legs, which can act either as struts or as levers. When they act as struts alone they exert forces only along their mechanical axis, the effect of the muscles acting at the shoulder and hip being zero. When the limbs are acting as levers, on the other hand, the extrinsic muscles are used, so that forces are applied at right angles to the mechanical axes of the limb both to the ground and to the body. This causes the body to be pushed along in a manner that Gray suggests to be analogous to the propulsion of a canoe by a two-handed paddle.

Another method of locomotion is provided by the fact that the struts themselves are extensible by means of their intrinsic muscles, the body then being pushed forward, as in punting a boat with a pole. Analysis of the effects of the limbs in pushing in various ways can be developed in some detail to give a picture of the diagonal co-ordination of the limb movements and the effects produced by the thrust of each limb in tending to produce forward movement (or braking action), together with unwanted pitching or rolling couples, which must be compensated by contraction of muscles of other limbs or of the vertebral column.

As the use of analogies such as these becomes more familiar we shall doubtless be able to state propositions about the whole musculo-skeletal system that are both shorter and more satisfactory than those currently used. Each type of animal presents a complete co-ordinated action system, suitable to maintain life in the way appropriate to the species. The long legs of swiftly running animals and the long bodies of climbing types can only work in conjunction with suitable body and legs respectively, and the whole organization has to be considered together. By looking at the anatomy of animals in this way we can see the meaning of the shapes of the various parts.

3. Functions of the forelimb

Whereas the hind limb of mammals is attached to the vertebral column by the ilio-sacral joint, the forelimb remains relatively free; the scapula is attached to the vertebral column only by muscles. There has been much discussion about the significance of this difference, since it is not immediately obvious that in a four-footed animal, such as a horse, there is less need for firm attachment of the forelimb than the hind. The matter is especially puzzling because in the fishes that came on land to become the earliest tetrapods the pectoral girdle was jointed to the skull. Presumably this connexion was lost to allow greater mobility of the head. As the forelimbs were increasingly used to take weight they became connected with the main axis by a muscular sling rather than by bony or joint attachments.

The hind limbs usually play the main part in pushing the body forwards, but the front limbs carry more than half the weight in a quadruped in the standing position. Nevertheless, the forelimb retains greater freedom than the hind and has tended to acquire other functions such as digging, collecting food, or otherwise handling the surrounding world. Moreover, the region to which the forelimb is attached (the thorax) must participate in respiration, necessitating independent movements. For all these reasons, therefore, power to move the limb

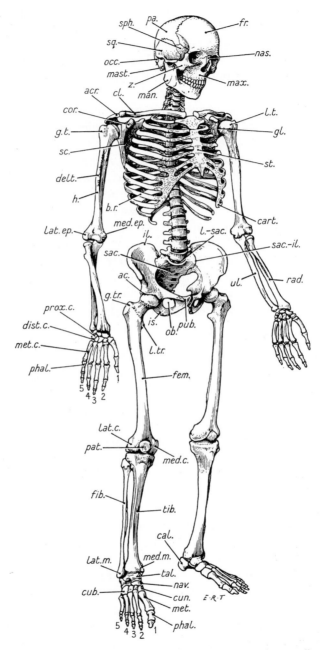

FIG. 70. Skeleton of man, approximately as it would be in the standing position. Lettering as for Fig. 66, p. 140.

in various directions is more important than firm attachment, and is conspicuously developed in man.

4. The shoulder girdle

The *shoulder girdle* in fishes was a point of attachment for the segmented body musculature, as well as a support for the limbs. In the amphibia and reptiles it has retained both functions and hence has a complex structure. With the raising of the body off the ground, however, it takes on the new function of transmitting the weight of the body to the limb, and for this purpose it becomes modified and simplified until it consists in mammals of two elements, the scapula and clavicle, or often of the former alone.

The *scapula* (Figs. 66 and 70) is a flattened bony plate, carrying the attachment of many of the muscles that transfer the weight of the body to the limb and anchor the latter to the vertebral column. In four-footed mammals the direction of movement of the limb is mostly antero-posterior and all the parts of the shoulder girdle except the scapula are reduced. The clavicle disappears, or remains only as a very thin vestige, as, for example, in the rabbit. However, in those mammals where the limb has acquired increased mobility and can be abducted away from the body, for example man (Fig. 70), the scapula itself is able to rotate, allowing the glenoid facet to be turned in various directions. This rotation takes place about the axis provided by a well-developed *clavicle*, articulating with the sternum and with the scapula. Although this human condition involves retention of the primitive clavicle it must be regarded as a specialization; no such mobility of the shoulder girdle is possible in the primitive condition, seen still in the monotremes, where there is a plate-like pectoral girdle, with a well-developed ventral region, the dorsal region of the scapula being relatively small.

The girdle of placental mammals is relatively constant in structure (Figs. 66 and 70) with a large plate-like scapula, carrying a ventrally directed *coracoid process* and bound to a clavicle if the latter is present. The coracoid ossifies in two parts but the significance of this is uncertain. The scapula bears on its outer side an *acromial spine*, characteristic of mammals, ending ventrally in an expanded knob, the *acromial process*, which is the point of articulation of the clavicle. A backward *metacromiun* is developed at this point in four-footed animals that have reduced clavicles.

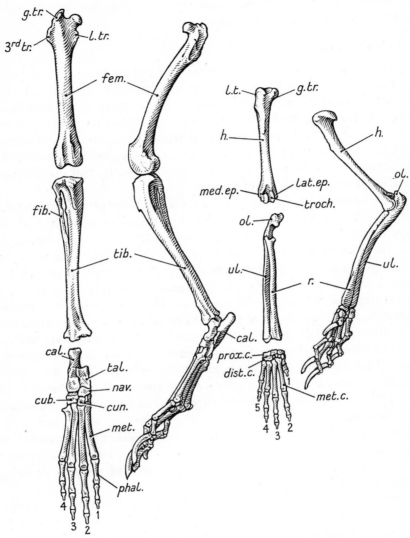

Fig. 71. Skeleton of the limbs of a rabbit. Lettering as for Fig. 66, p. 140.

5. The components of the forelimb

   The glenoid cavity for articulation with the humerus is a relatively shallow cup compared with the deep acetabulum of the hip joint and this is so even in the four-footed mammals. In man, where mobility is the characteristic of the shoulder joint, the glenoid cavity is saucer-like and the head of the humerus is a large spherical structure, able to rotate in the saucer. The *humerus* itself is a typical long bone, carrying roughenings and protuberances where the muscles are attached (Fig. 71). At the upper end the *greater tuberosity* lies on the lateral side and is the point of attachment of muscles fixing the limb to the shoulder and abducting and externally rotating it. The *lesser tuberosity*, on the medial face, carries muscles that serve for adduction and internal rotation. The main muscles for moving the limb are attached farther down the shaft, where they obtain a greater leverage.

At the lower end the humerus is expanded into *lateral* and *medial epicondyles*, from which arise respectively extensor and flexor muscle masses for the wrist and hand. In man, where flexion is more powerful than extension, the medial (flexor) mass is the larger and the medial epicondyle is larger than the lateral one (Fig. 70). The humerus of the rabbit ends in a pulley-like *trochlea* for the ulna and the only movement possible is flexion and extension. In man there is also a second facet, the rounded *capitulum* for articulation with the radius.

The bones of the forearm, wrist, and hand vary greatly with the use to which the forelimb is put but in all mammals we can recognize a *radius* and *ulna*, though the latter may be reduced. These bones articulate with a proximal row of *carpals* at the wrist joint which allows a considerable range of movement. The proximal carpals articulate with a distal row and these with *metacarpals*, but at the intercarpal and carpo-metacarpal joints there is usually little movement, except in animals where the thumb is free. The next important joint is therefore that between the metacarpals and *phalanges*; here and at each of the two interphalangeal joints movement is possible, usually in one plane only.

The forelimb is thus a jointed strut consisting of four main segments, the scapula, humerus, radio-ulna, and hand, the last having three subsidiary terminal segments on each of the digits except the thumb. The most mobile joints are at the shoulder, elbow, wrist, and fingers.

6. Transmission of weight from forelimb to vertebral column

We shall consider the use and structure of the limb where it is an organ for weight-bearing, as in the rabbit; in the running digitigrade mammals it is, of course, still further developed for that purpose. The characteristics of the forelimb musculature in man, where they are suited mainly for manipulation of outside objects, will be referred to where necessary.

The forelimb is not jointed to the main vertebral axis and the whole

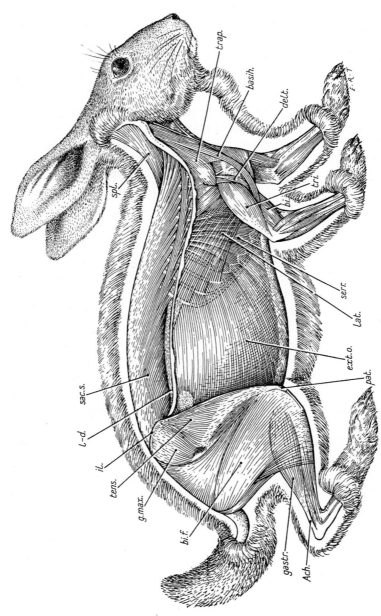

FIG. 72. Muscles of the limbs and back of the rabbit.

Ach. tendo Achillis; *basih.* basihumeral; *bi.* biceps brachii; *bi.f.* biceps femoris; *delt.* deltoid; *ext.o.* obliquus externus abdominis; *gastr.* gastrocnemius; *g.max.* gluteus maximus; *il.* crest of ilium; *lat.* latissimus dorsi; *l-d.* lumbodorsal fascia (cut); *pat.* patella; *sac.s* sacrospinalis; *serr.* serratus
anterior; *spl.* splenius capitis; *tens.* tensor fasciae latae; *trap.* trapezius; *tri.* triceps.

transmission of weight is accomplished by muscles. The muscle mainly concerned is the *serratus anterior* (Figs. 72 and 73) which in the rabbit forms a set of large bundles. The thoracic portion consists of slips running from the ventral part of the ribs to the upper border of the scapula and thus makes a sling by which the weight of the body, transferred through the vertebral column to the ribs, is hung on to the limb which acts as a pillar (p. 139). An anterior, cervical portion of the muscle helps to take the weight of the head and neck in the same way, running from the transverse processes of C_{3-7} and the first two ribs to the scapula (Fig. 73). In man the weight-bearing function of the muscle is lost and the serratus anterior helps the trapezius to rotate the scapula upwards, thus suspending the weight of the arm; it also pulls the whole scapula forward round the chest and its serial slips can be seen contracting in actions involving pushing or punching.

The scapula is also attached to the body by muscles on its dorsal side. The most superficial and conspicuous of these is *trapezius*, a muscle mainly of lateral plate origin (p. 717), innervated by the spinal accessory nerve. This arrangement is presumably a relic of the time when the pectoral girdle was attached to the hind end of the gills. The trapezius muscle in all mammals is a broad band of fibres arising from the occiput and spines of the vertebrae all along the neck, thorax, and cephalic part of the lumbar region and converging to insertion on to the clavicle, if present, and along the spine of the scapula (Fig. 72). The effect of the muscle is thus to hold the scapula against the body in quadrupeds and in man also to hold up and rotate the bone, so as to turn the glenoid upwards. The trapezius does not play a great part in weight-bearing in quadrupeds and is a less important muscle in such animals than in man, where it carries a large part of the weight of the arm and is active in the lifting of weights. This rotation of the scapula is characteristic of the freely moving scapula of man. It allows the glenoid cavity to be turned so as to face either upwards or downwards, thus greatly increasing the range of movement of the arm. The clavicle moves to some extent at the sterno-clavicular joint but the main movement is of the scapula on the clavicle at the acromio-clavicular joint. The rotation can be seen and felt every time that the arm is abducted.

Deep to the trapezius the *rhomboid* muscles (Fig. 73) pass from the ligamentum nuchae and spines of the anterior thoracic vertebrae to the dorsal border of the scapula. These are members of the set of muscles by which in quadrupeds the scapula is held against the chest wall. In man they work with the trapezius in holding up the

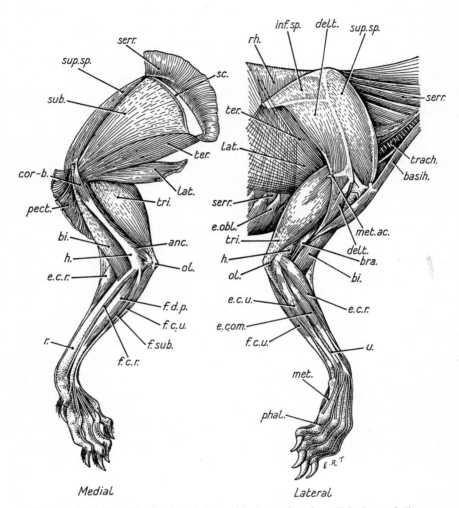

Medial

Lateral

FIG. 73. Muscles of the foreleg of the rabbit. Lateral and medial views of dissection of right forelimb of the rabbit.

anc. anconeus; *basih.* basihumeral; *bi.* biceps brachii; *bra.* brachialis; *cor.-b.* coracobrachialis; *delt.* deltoid; *e.com.* extensor communis; *e.c.r.* extensor carpi radialis; *e.c.u.* extensor carpi ulnaris; *e.obl.* externus obliquus abdominis; *f.c.r.* flexor carpi radialis; *f.c.u.* flexor carpi ulnaris; *f.d.p.* flexor digitorum profundus; *f.sub.* flexor digitorum sublimis; *h.* humerus; *inf.sp.* infraspinatus; *lat.* latissimus dorsi; *met.* metacarpal; *met.ac.* metacromion; *ol.* olecranon; *pect.* pectoralis; *phal.* phalanges; *r.* radius; *rh.* rhomboid; *sc.* scapula; *serr.* serratus anterior; *sub.* subscapularis; *sup.sp.* supraspinatus; *ter.* teres major; *trach.* trachea *tri.* triceps; *u.* ulna.

scapula but since the fibres take a downward course their effect is to rotate the scapula downwards.

The cranial border of the scapula is held in to the body by the muscles known in the rabbit as *levator scapulae major* and *minor*, running from the skull to the metacromion and inferior angle of the scapula respectively (Fig. 63). The arrangement of these muscles is one of the chief differences between the forelimb of quadrupeds and man. In the latter the levator scapulae runs from the transverse processes of the upper cervical vertebrae to the medial border of the scapula; it thus holds the scapula up and also assists the rhomboids in rotating the glenoid downwards.

7. Ties around the shoulder joint

The scapula of the rabbit is firmly attached to the body, and we may consider it as the upper segment of the jointed strut on which the body is balanced and by whose lever action it is moved. Although mobility of the scapula is no doubt an important part of the locomotion of quadrupeds the balancing of the body on the foreleg occurs mainly at the shoulder joint, and there are here a number of muscles that act as contractile braces to produce this balance (see p. 154). These braces occur all round the joint, preventing unbalance in any direction, but movement is much freer in the sagittal than in the transverse plane and the braces are therefore strongest in front and behind, especially behind, since it is by drawing the whole limb backwards that the body is propelled forwards. Indeed we can here, as throughout the limb, divide these muscles into two sets, (1) more cranial protractor, flexor-adductors, which are often more ventral, and (2) caudal retractor, extensor-abductors, lying more dorsally and innervated from more caudal segments. This division is not always sharp but it reminds us of the originally segmental arrangement of these muscles and that the movement of the limb, first forward and then backward, is related to the metachronal contractions of the segmented swimming muscles of a fish. (Young, 1950, p. 127.)

Description of the braces around the shoulder joint is made difficult by the fact that whereas some of them run direct from the axial skeleton to the humerus others are shorter and arise from the scapula. We may consider first the longer and then the shorter ones. A conspicuously long anterior brace is the *basi-humeral* muscle of the rabbit (Figs. 72 and 73), running from the base of the skull to the humerus and clavicle. The clavicular portion represents the cleido-mastoid part of the *sterno-cleido-mastoid*, the muscle that appears in the neck of man during the action of turning the head.

The chief long brace of the limb on its medial side is the *pectoralis*, which is ventral and cranial; it may also draw the limb forwards. The muscle is divided into several portions in the rabbit, some fibres running to the scapula and clavicle. The *latissimus dorsi* is a long brace behind the shoulder joint, running from the lumbo-dorsal fascia and ribs to the humerus. It plays an important part in locomotion by drawing the limb backwards.

The shorter braces around the shoulder joint are important not only for the movement they produce but also because they hold the head of the humerus into the shallow glenoid cup and make the joint stable and yet capable of a wide range of movement.

These muscles, whose tendons are inserted close to the upper end of the humerus, thus act as ties of adjustable length. In quadrupeds, where movement of the whole forelimb is an important part of locomotion, these shorter muscles become very large, particularly in the digitigrade and unguligrade types such as the horse, where they act as protractors and retractors and move the limb as a lever.

These muscles arise from the surfaces of the scapula. On the lateral side *supraspinatus* and *infraspinatus* are inserted on to the greater tuberosity and therefore act in quadrupeds as lateral and cranial braces of the humerus on the scapula (Fig. 73). In man they protect the upper part and back of the shoulder joint from dislocation. A further muscle that acts as a 'ligament muscle' at the shoulder is *subscapularis* (Fig. 73), running from the costal surface of the scapula to the lesser tuberosity. It acts as a medial brace in quadrupeds and in man protects the front of the joint. These muscles also act as rotators, the first two turning the humerus laterally, the subscapularis turning it medially. The action of infraspinatus during lateral rotation can easily be felt in man by a hand placed over the muscle.

Besides these muscles attached close to the head of the humerus there are also others attached lower down. *Coracobrachialis* passes from the coracoid process to the humeral shaft. The *deltoid* is one of the chief muscles that move the whole arm at the shoulder. In the rabbit (Figs. 63 and 73) it arises from the spine of the scapula and the fascia covering the infraspinatus muscle and is attached to the conspicuous tuberosity on the humerus. The deltoid of man is the muscle that gives the rounded appearance to the shoulder. It arises from the clavicle, acromion, and spine of the scapula and is inserted on to the lateral side of the shaft of the humerus. The deltoid is important in all animals but is especially well developed in man since it lifts the arm sideways from its hanging position. In this action of abduction it is helped by supraspinatus, which holds the head of the humerus into the glenoid, making a fulcrum, as a man standing on the foot of a ladder helps another to push it up. Besides acting as an abductor the various parts of the deltoid of man can also act separately, the anterior fibres drawing the arm forwards and also producing medial rotation, the more posterior fibres having the opposite actions. Another muscle running from the scapula to the humerus is *teres major*, which draws the limb caudally and is an important retractor in quadrupeds (Fig. 73).

8. Muscles of the upper arm

The limbs consist of articulated rods which, as Gray puts it, 'have little or no natural rigidity and whose ability to resist bending forces depends almost entirely on the activity of their associated muscles'. The internal musculature of the limbs is so arranged as to allow them to function as struts or levers, which in a quadruped are in equilibrium with three groups of external forces: (1) those exerted on the limb by the body, (2) the force exerted by the ground against the foot, (3) the weights of the individual limb segments. In a plantigrade quadruped, such as the rabbit, it is not difficult to see how the strains resulting from these forces are met by muscles at the front and back of the joints. We shall consider this more in detail in connexion with the hind limbs (p. 175). In the forelimb the joints, besides that at the shoulder, are those (1) at the elbow, (2) at the wrist, (3) between the metacarpal bones and the phalanges, and (4) between the phalanges themselves (Fig. 73). There is also some movement between the carpal bones, allowing adjustment of the foot when moving over uneven surfaces. In plantigrade animals the whole sole may provisionally be considered as a single lever arm and the main joints to be considered are therefore those at elbow and wrist. The muscles of the foreleg may be divided into sets for stabilizing and moving these two joints. In the mobile hand of man movements at other joints will also have to be considered.

Movement at the elbow, between the humerus and ulna and/or radius is in many mammals restricted to simple flexion and extension about a single axis, but in man the movements of supination and pronation are also possible. The anterior, flexor muscle is the *biceps brachii*, so-called because in man (Fig. 74) it arises at the upper end by two heads, the short head from the coracoid process and the long head by a narrow tendon that runs through the shoulder joint to be attached to the scapula above the glenoid. This tendon serves as a strap helping to hold the head of the humerus into the glenoid. The two heads of biceps unite in the forearm of man to make a single muscle inserted below the elbow into the tuberosity that lies on the medial side of the radius and also by an aponeurosis to the deep fascia. By virtue of this insertion the biceps, besides acting as a powerful flexor of the elbow, also turns the palm forwards in the movement of supination (see below). In the rabbit and most quadrupeds only the short head of biceps is present (Fig. 73).

Biceps is a muscle crossing both shoulder and elbow joints and serving to flex both. The second flexor of the elbow, *brachialis*, crosses the elbow joint only and is attached to the lower part of the humerus and to the ulna.

Extension at the elbow is a powerful movement, especially in digitigrade quadrupeds, where the raising up on the toes decreases the strain on the wrists and ankles but increases that at the elbows and knees. The extensors take this strain and serve to increase the length of the whole leg, which can thus act as a propellant lever. The action is performed by the *triceps* muscle, whose three upper origins include a long head from the scapula and lateral and medial heads from the humerus. At the lower end the tendon of the muscle is inserted into the *olecranon process*, which projects from the ulna. The olecranon is especially well developed in digitigrade animals, which have large extensor muscles. The *anconeus* is a shorter muscle extending the elbow, running from the humerus to the olecranon process (Fig. 73).

9. Forearm : pronation and supination

The structure of the lower part of the forelimb varies greatly according to whether the limb is used for walking, climbing, flying, swimming, or, as in man, as a sensory and manipulating organ. The two bones of this region, radius and ulna, originally lay one in front of the other and were unable to rotate. However, as we have seen, early in the history of the quadrupeds there was a rotation in order to allow the forefoot to point cranially when the whole foreleg was brought in beneath the body and the elbow was directed backwards. Thus the radius, primitively lying cranial and parallel to the ulna, comes to lie across in front of the latter, so that while its upper end remains lateral the lower lies medially. This prone position is, therefore, characteristic of the mammals, and the bones are fixed thus in monotremes and in many marsupials, insectivores, rodents, and other primitive mammals, including the rabbit (Fig. 71). In this condition both the forearm bones articulate with the humerus and the only movement at the elbow joint is one of flexion-extension.

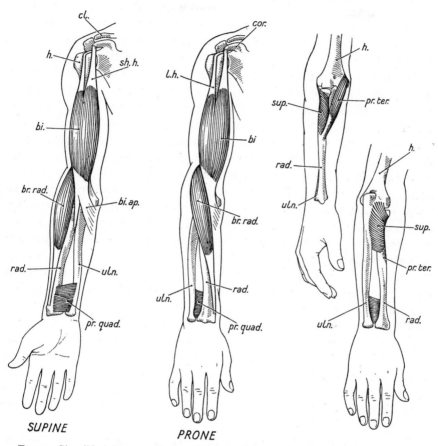

SUPINE   PRONE

FIG. 74. Simplified diagram of some of the muscles producing pronation and supination of the hand.

bi. biceps; *bi.ap.* bicipital aponeurosis; *br.rad.* brachioradialis; *cor.* coracoid process of scapula; *cl.* clavicle; *h.* humerus; *l.h.* long head; *pr.quad.* pronator quadratus; *pr.ter.* pronator teres; *rad.* radius; *sh.h.* short head; *sup.* supinator; *uln.* ulna.

We can recognize two lines of development from this beginning. In the mammals that became highly specialized as quadrupeds, such as horses, ruminants, &c., the bones of the lower end of the limbs are simplified, making stable pillars. The ulna becomes fused with the radius and reduced to little more than an olecranon process to serve as an attachment for the triceps muscle. All the weight is carried by the radius, which acquires large surfaces of articulation with the humerus and with the carpus. A somewhat similar reduction of the ulna has occurred also in bats.

The other development increases the mobility of the hand by allowing a rotating movement of the radius on the ulna, and is especially characteristic of the arboreal primates and of the working hand of man. The mobility results from a change in the articular facets such that the main articulation at the elbow is that of the ulna with the trochlear facet of the humerus. The radius, however, carries the hand and is able to rotate with it around the ulna from the prone position by the act of supination, until the two forearm bones lie side by side and the palm of the hand faces forwards (Fig. 74). To allow this movement the radius of these animals has acquired a special circular facet at its upper end, by which it rotates on the rounded capitulum of the humerus; there are also joints between the radius and ulna at their upper and lower ends. The essence of the arrangement is that pressure from the hand is transmitted to the forearm mainly through the radius and then to the humerus by the ulna. The two bones are bound together firmly for this purpose by the *interosseus membrane*, running between the sharp ridges that mark their adjacent borders. It is easy to confirm the essentials of this arrangement on one's own arm. In the prone position, with the hand held facing backwards, the radius can be felt crossing in front of the ulna. As the hand is turned over to face forwards (supination) the radius moves but the ulna does not, until the two bones lie parallel. Further, it can be verified that the head of the radius, which can be felt at the back of the elbow, lateral to the olecranon, rotates during this movement. The ulna does not articulate with the carpus but ends at a higher level than the radius above the wrist. This can be confirmed by feeling the styloid processes that mark the lower ends of the ulna and radius.

This movement of supination not only enables the individual to bring the hand into a variety of positions but is also in itself a powerful twisting action, which can be used to exert considerable force (Darcus, 1951). It is effected mainly by the biceps muscle, whose attachment to the radius in man is such as to pull the latter around the ulna, an action easily verified on oneself during a screw-driving or cork-screwing action (Fig. 74). There is also a *supinator* muscle, running across the back of the elbow between the ulna and the upper part of the radius. The opposite movement, pronation, is performed by two bands of fibres running across the front of the forearm, the upper *pronator teres* and lower *pronator quadratus*. Where the position of the radius and ulna is fixed, as in the rabbit, these muscles are small.

10. The hand and digits

The terminal part of the forelimb of mammals varies profoundly with the use to which it is put. The fundamental plan is based on a row of 3 proximal carpals, 1 central, 5 distal carpals and 5 digits, with 2 phalanges in the first, and 3 in each of the others (2·3·3·3·3). Unfortunately the nomenclature of the carpus has become involved by the use of various systems, especially in man. However, since the human carpus is of primitive type, retaining nearly all the bones, we may list first the bones of an ideal form and then give the names as commonly used in British human anatomy.

	Ideal carpus	*Human carpus*
Proximal Row	Radiale	Scaphoid
	Intermedium	Lunate
	Ulnare	Triquetrum
	Centrale	(Fused with scaphoid)
Distal Row	Carpal 1	Trapezium
	„ 2	Trapezoid
	„ 3	Capitate (Os magnum)
	„ 4 and 5	Hamate (Uncinate)

In the human hand (Fig. 70), which may serve as an introduction, there is movement only between some of the bones. The radio-carpal joint allows flexion and extension and some degree of the lateral movements of abduction and adduction, which are important for bringing the hand to a particular spot. Movements also occur between the carpal bones during flexion and extension, but there is little movement where the carpals articulate with the metacarpals. The next level of active movement is, therefore, the metacarpo-phalangeal junction, where there is flexion and extension, and also the power of drawing the fingers apart (abduction and adduction). Finally, the proximal and distal interphalangeal joints allow only flexion and extension. The thumb is peculiar in that a considerable range of rotation and flexion is possible at the carpo-metacarpal joint, allowing the digit to be brought across to meet the fingers in the movement of *opposition*.

The movements of the hand and digits are accomplished by a series of muscles lying partly outside and partly within the hand. They will be described mainly in man. The extrinsic flexors arise from the medial epicondyle of the humerus and from the front of the ulna, radius, and the interosseus membrane. Conversely the extrinsic extensors arise from the lateral epicondyle and from the back of the two bones and interosseus membrane. Movement at the wrist or radio-carpal joint is controlled by two flexors and three extensors, some of whose tendons can be identified above the wrist. *Flexor carpi radialis* is attached mainly to the base of the second metacarpal. *Flexor carpi ulnaris* inserts on to a sesamoid bone, the *pisiform*, which is easily felt at the wrist, and from this the pull is transferred to the palm by liga-ments running to the hamate and fifth metacarpal. Similarly, on the back of the hand, *extensors carpi radialis longus* and *brevis* pull mainly on the base of the second metacarpal and *extensor carpi ulnaris* on the fifth metacarpal. By various combinations these muscles can bring the hand into any position (p. 128). For example the two flexor muscles work together as prime movers in flexion, the two muscles of the ulnar side in adduction. Flexor and extensor muscles of the wrist can also be found in the rabbit on both radial and ulnar sides, running from the lower end of the humerus to the carpus (Fig. 73).

The system for moving the fingers includes large extrinsic extensors and flexors for each finger and also small intrinsic muscles (Figs. 63 and 73). The more superficial flexor mass, *flexor digitorum sublimis*, sends four tendons through the hand and each splits before it inserts on to the second phalanx of each digit, so that this muscle flexes the second phalanx on the first. Each tendon of *flexor digitorum profundus* runs between the two parts into which each sublimis tendon divides and is attached to the distal phalanx. *Extensor digitorum* similarly divides into one tendon for each of the four medial digits and pulls on the back of the phalanges.

Movements of the fingers are further controlled by muscles within the hand (intrinsic), which are well developed in the mobile hand of man but are minute in the rabbit. They are known as the *interossei* and *lumbricals* and are partly responsible for movements of abduction and adduction and also co-operate with the extrinsic muscles in the finer movements of flexion and extension.

The movements of the thumb are brought about by special muscles, both extrinsic and intrinsic, which correspond in the general plan to those of the other digits and have been derived by specialization of the latter. These muscles are, of course, well developed in man to enable the thumb to meet the other digits in its movements of opposition.

11. Various types of locomotion in mammals

The full plan of the bones and muscles of the wrist and hand is found in those mammals that walk on the whole sole of the fore and hind feet and are hence said to be *plantigrade* (Fig. 75); this is the primitive condition. In so far as locomotion is produced by the fore-limb in plantigrade quadrupeds it is partly by movement of the whole limb by the upper extrinsic muscles and partly by lengthening of the lever by straightening at the elbow and wrist, brought about by the triceps and forearm extensors. With further development of quadru-

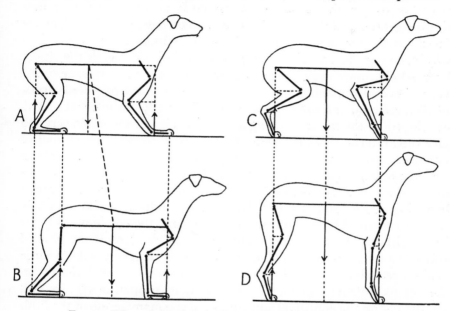

FIG. 75. Effect of change from plantigrade to digitigrade posture.
A, Plantigrade habit, limbs advanced so that centres of pressure are at their posterior ends. B, by retraction of the limbs the centres of pressure are moved to the toes, reducing the strain on the extensors of elbows and knees, but increasing it at the wrists and heels. C, by raising the knees and elbows the wrists and heels are brought nearer to the line of the re-actions of the feet, reducing the strain on extensors of wrists and heels, but increasing it at elbows and knees. D, by extending the knees, elbows, hip, and shoulder joints the strain on all extensor muscles is reduced. (After Gray, *J. exp. Biol.* **20**, 1944.)

pedal locomotion the animal tends to rise up more and more on the limbs, which are straightened and converted into levers. In *digitigrade* locomotion, such as that of the dog, the metacarpals are raised off the ground and the weight rests on the underside of one or more phalanges of each digit (Fig. 75). With this raising on the toes the movement of locomotion becomes increasingly a movement of the whole limb, used as a lever and operated by the more proximal muscles. As already explained (p. 166) extra strain is thus put upon the extensors of the elbow but strain and movement at the wrist and the joints of the digits are reduced.

Finally, in the most rapidly moving quadrupeds the weight is carried on the tip of the distal phalanx. This is the *unguligrade* condition, associated with reduction in the number of digits either to two in artiodactyls, such as the cow and sheep, or one in the perissodactyls, such as the horse. In these animals there is further progress towards converting the limb into a single lever. Besides reduction of the ulnar bone (see p. 167) the carpals are arranged in an interlocking manner to give greater stability and the two metacarpals of artiodactyla are fused together to give a 'cannon bone'. It is interesting to speculate why fusion of the carpals has not gone farther. Although the whole limb is held much straighter in unguligrade than in plantigrade forms yet joints still remain at radio-carpal, carpo-metacarpal, metacarpo-phalangeal, and interphalangeal levels. Probably no great thrust is developed by the muscles acting at these levels but the joints serve to give the limb the slight flexibility that allows it to carry the animal so fast over uneven ground. The radio-carpal joint of the horse allows considerable movement and is provided with elastic ligaments allowing it to act as a shock-absorber and to conserve energy, the animal bouncing off the ground at each step. It must indeed be a wonderfully sprung system of levers and ties that will carry the whole weight of a horse without breakages, even allowing it to lift high off the ground and to land again securely. The possibility of carrying such a large load on relatively long and thin struts presumably depends partly on the flexible character given to the bone by its protein matrix (p. 69), but mainly on the continual adjustment of the many joints of the limb by variation in the tension of the muscles in such a way as to minimize strains.

IX

THE PELVIC GIRDLE AND HIND LIMB

1. Functioning of the hind limb

THE hind limb of mammals is usually involved mainly in propulsion and support and shows less tendency than does the forelimb to modification for special functions. The pelvic girdle has become articulated with one or more sacral vertebrae and forms functionally one piece with the vertebral column. The pelvic girdle and vertebral column, with their muscles, thus form a 'girder' for the support of the whole body (p. 139). The hind limb may therefore be thought of as an extensible, moveable pillar, on which the main girder is balanced and propelled at the hip joint.

When a quadrupedal animal is standing, the weight of the hinder part of the body is carried by the hind limb, the system approaching that of a balanced cantilever, especially in animals with a long tail. Gray's analogy of the table top (p. 154) may be applied; braces running from the vertebral column and pelvic girdle stabilize the limb at the hip joint. Movement is produced by retraction of the limb by shortening of the more posterior braces (Fig. 63). With the foot fixed this has the effect of producing a horizontal force acting forward at the head of the femur. In this action the whole limb is used as a lever. Propulsion is also effected by lengthening of the limb by its intrinsic muscles, acting especially at the knee and heel in plantigrade and at the knee in digitigrade types when the hip has passed in front of the foot.

In considering the skeleton and muscles of the hind legs, therefore, we have to look at (1) the pelvic girdle as a means of balancing the weight of the body on the limb or vice versa transmitting the thrust of the latter to the body, (2) the muscle ties that balance the body on the limb and move the whole limb as a lever, (3) the bones and muscles that make the limb a jointed extensible strut.

2. Sacrum and pelvic girdle

The modified sacral transverse processes and ribs articulate with the iliac bones by a joint that usually allows only little movement (p. 143). The attachment of the girdle to the vertebral axis is therefore performed by ligaments rather than, as at the pectoral girdle, by muscles. In man the weight of the body is transferred by the fifth lumbar vertebra to the sacrum and the latter partly rests on the ilia and is partly suspended from them (Fig. 70). The sacral and iliac articulating surfaces are such that the sacrum acts partly as the key-stone of an arch formed by the ilia but the greater part of the weight is transferred by the ligaments, especially those at the back, by which the sacrum is slung between the iliac bones.

The mammalian *pelvic girdle* shows a characteristic development of its more dorsal portions and especially of the *ilium* and *ischium*. In quadrupeds the muscles acting from the surfaces of these bones are the braces that stabilize the balance of the body on the leg and propel it forwards or backwards (Howell, 1938). The anterior ilia and posterior ischia are large dorsal expansions for the attachment of these muscles. The acetabulum lies between the ilium and the ischium, and the *pubis* forms a narrow tie member across the mid-ventral line.

In man the adoption of the bipedal posture has led to great modifications of the pelvis. Locomotion is no longer effected mainly by the upper muscles moving the whole leg as a lever but by a complicated set of actions including those of the calf muscles, which raise the body on the toes. The ilium of man is large and broad and lies above the acetabulum. Attached to it are the gluteal and other muscles that are the posterior braces, extending the thigh, that is to say, keeping the body braced backwards and the vertebral column in line with the legs (Joseph and Nightingale, 1954). The pubis and ischium are relatively small in man and form, with the ilium, a system of arches by which weight is transferred to the femora. From the sacro-iliac joint, which as we have seen carries the weight of the sacrum, a thickened strip of bone extends down to the acetabulum and constitutes the main portion of the arch. The pubis acts as a tie-beam, preventing spreading of the arch under the weight. The three bones that make up the pelvic girdle enclose an aperture, the *obturator foramen*, which in life is closed by the obturator membrane with muscles attached both to its internal and external surfaces.

3. The femur

The articulation of the head of the femur with the pelvis allows less freedom of movement than is found at the shoulder. The acetabulum is a deep cup and the head fits far into it. This, together with the arrangement of the ligaments, limits the movements, which occur mainly in an antero-posterior plane both in the rabbit and in man.

The pillar supports of the ilio-sacral arch are continued downwards in the femur, the lines of the trabeculae in the head and neck being arranged to distribute the weight downwards on to the tubular shaft of the bone (see p. 93). The head of the femur is carried on a long neck that holds the bone out at a distance from the body and allows a swinging motion of the leg both in the rabbit and in man. At the upper end the femur bears large knobs (trochanters) for the attachment of muscles. The *great trochanter* is on the lateral surface and is divided in the rabbit into an upper *first* and lower *third trochanter* (Figs. 66 and 71). On the medial side of the femur, below the head, is the lesser or *second trochanter*. The shaft of the femur is made of a tube of compact bone, thickest near the middle. The lower end is expanded into lateral and medial condyles, each bearing a facet for articulation with the tibia.

4. Braces around the hip joint

The pelvic girdle moves only slightly on the vertebral column and the hip joint is the point about which movements of the body on the hind legs take place. The muscles that act at this joint have been evolved, like those of the forelimb, within the dorsal (abductor) and ventral (adductor) sheets. The details of the stages of this transformation are obscure but, as in the forelimb, we may distinguish a cranio-ventral group that draws the limb forward and a caudo-dorsal group drawing the limb back. They have become arranged around the joint, however, to form the braces at front, sides, and back, which we have already seen serve to balance the body on the limb and move it as a lever (Joseph and Nightingale, 1954).

In quadrupeds the more caudal braces are especially large and serve to draw the limb caudally, giving the main locomotor thrust. More cranial braces are also prominent, and lateral ones prevent the body falling medially. Medial braces prevent lateral falling, but this is less likely to happen. In man the braces all round the joint are important since the balance is likely to be upset in any direction; however, the anterior (cranial) and posterior (caudal) braces are especially large, for obvious reasons.

The more cranial braces include the *ilio-psoas* muscles, which act to bend the body ventrally or to flex the leg on the body. They arise from the ventral surfaces of the ilium and of the lumbar vertebrae and are inserted on to the lesser trochanter of the femur (Fig. 63). This muscle mass forms part of the posterior (dorsal) wall of the abdominal cavity and is therefore conspicuous during dissection, though it is

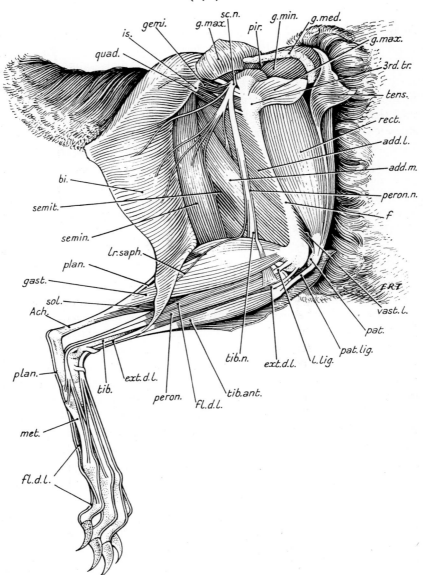

FIG. 76. Drawing of a dissection of a hind limb of a rabbit.

Ach. Achilles' tendon; *add.l.* adductor longus; *add.m.* adductor magnus; *bi.* biceps; *ext.d.l.* extensor digitorum longus; *f.* femur; *fl.d.l.* flexor digitorum longus; *gast.* gastrocnemius; *gem.i.* gemellus inferior; *g.max.* gluteus maximus; *g.med.* gluteus medius; *g.min.* gluteus minimus; *is.* ischium; *l.lig.* lateral ligament; *lr.saph.* lesser saphenous (sural) nerve; *met.* metatarsus; *pat.* patella; *pat.lig.* patellar ligament; *peron.* peroneal muscles; *peron.n.* peroneal nerve; *pir.* piriformis; *plan.* plantaris; *quad.* quadratus femoris; *rect.* rectus femoris; *sc.n.* sciatic nerve; *semim.* semimembranosus; *semit.* semitendinosus; *sol.* soleus; *tens.* tensor fasciae latae; *tib.* tibia; *tib.ant.* tibialis anterior; *tib.n.* tibial nerve; *3rd tr.* third trochanter; *vast.l.* vastus lateralis.

difficult to feel it in the living human body. It makes an anterior brace for the hip joint. Other muscles that stabilize the front of the joint and draw the leg forwards originate from the front of the ilium and from the pubis. Some of them cross the hip joint only and are inserted on to the femur; others run a long course to the tibia and therefore act as extensors of the knee as well as flexors of the hip. The most superficial of these muscles, *tensor fasciae latae* and *sartorius*, run this long course from ilium to tibia, the former attaching laterally, the other medially (Fig. 76). The fascia lata is thickened laterally to form a broad band of connective tissue on the side of the thigh, the ilio-tibial band, which is pulled upon by the gluteus maximus as well as by its own tensor (Fig. 76). At its lower end it makes a strong fibrous band, which can be easily felt in man at the lateral side of the knee. This band of fascia, kept tight by the muscles at its upper end, acts as a brace (see p. 90) that distributes the weight of the body sym-metrically on the femur.

Deep to this band lie the four parts of the *quadriceps femoris*, the great muscle of the front of the thigh. This muscle assists the psoas by acting as an anterior brace at the hip. It also plays the main part in extending the knee joint. This action is obviously of great impor-tance in the locomotion of quadrupeds, since it straightens the limb, lengthening it as a strut, and thrusting the body forwards. In man the main thrust is delivered with the leg straight (see p. 184) and the quadriceps plays little part in it. It remains, however, an important muscle because of its action in balancing the body at the hip and in producing extension and balance at the knee. The great amount of use that we give to this muscle is shown by the rapidity with which it wastes if we do not stand for a week or two. During an illness the muscle may become so reduced that the femur can readily be felt along the front of the thigh.

Of the four parts of the quadriceps muscle one arises from the ilium, three from the femur. The *rectus femoris*, or straight portion of the muscle, runs from the ilium and is inserted with the others into the patellar tendon, a broad band reaching across the front of the knee and containing the characteristic *patella*, or knee cap, perhaps the best known example of a *sesamoid* or tendon bone (Figs. 76 and 77). Such bones are often found where the direction of action of a muscle changes as it crosses a joint and thus tends to exert a pressure on the joint and bones. The effect of the sesamoid is to 'increase the working distance of the muscle from the centre of rotation of the joint and provide a bearing surface for the main bones forming a joint' (J. Gray,

1944). In this case the patellar ligament proceeds downwards to be inserted on to the front of the tibia.

The other three parts of the quadriceps are the *vastus medialis, lateralis,* and *intermedius,* all arising from the femur and inserted on to the patellar ligament, so that the whole muscle mass acts together for extension of the knee, such as is produced reflexly when the patellar tendon is struck. This tendon and the whole muscle are richly supplied with sensory nerve endings (proprioceptive), which are brought into action when the knee bends and pulls on the tendon. The resulting nerve impulses produce others that volley back from the spinal cord into the muscle and thus check the tendency for collapse of the knee. By this characteristic action the anti-gravity muscles maintain the body in a standing posture (p. 364). It is to be noted, however, that the quadriceps is only one of the muscles stabilizing the joints that it crosses. A balance is maintained by the proper co-operation of all the muscle braces, which must be tense when necessary. All act as anti-gravity muscles at some time and in some degree.

The remaining muscles of the flexor-adductor group of the thigh are the *adductor* muscles, *longus, brevis* and *magnus,* and *pectineus.* They all arise from the pubis and ischium and are inserted on the femur. They are the braces that in man stabilize the hip joint medially, preventing the body from falling laterally. In quadrupeds the true adductors also have this action and other adductors also assist in drawing the leg caudalwards. The muscle known as *adductor magnus* of the rabbit is very large, running from the ischium to the femur and tibia (Figs. 63 and 76); down its middle runs a red muscle, *semitendinosus.*

The posterior (extensor abductor) group of muscles includes those that stabilize the lateral side and back of the hip joint and also includes many that cross both hip and knee joints and thus serve at once for extension of the former and flexion of the latter. The uppermost members of the series are the *gluteal muscles,* which lie immediately above the hip joint and are well developed in man. These muscles arise from the sacrum and ilium; *gluteus maximus,* the most superficial, from the iliac crest, *gluteus medius* and *minimus* from the outer surface of the ilium (Figs. 63 and 76). All are inserted on to the femur. Their action in quadrupeds is therefore to abduct the limb or, acting from the femur as a fixed point, to prevent the body falling medially, that is to say, to stabilize the lateral side of the joint.

In man gluteus medius and minimus retain this action as abductors or lateral braces, but gluteus maximus comes to act as the great posterior brace, preventing the body falling forwards. It also acts to raise up the whole body from a stooping (quadrupedal) position and this action has led to the great development of gluteus maximus in the buttocks of man. This is the muscle by which we rise and stand upright, and in this sense it is responsible for the achievement of our characteristic posture, though, of course, many muscles act together to maintain the balance. In man gluteus maximus does not come into action strongly as a propellant during the movements of walking but it is at work almost constantly in balancing the body on the legs. Gluteus medius and minimus have a more strictly abducting action and are the braces of the lateral side of the hip joint and therefore also very important for human posture. When one leg is off the ground there is obviously a tendency for the body to fall over to the unsupported side, that is to say medially. This is prevented by the action of these glutei on the supporting side, bracing the whole body on the leg that is on the ground.

Deep to these gluteal muscles lie various other short muscles running from the sacrum, walls of pelvis, and obturator membrane to the greater trochanter. These are the *piriformis*, an abductor, *gemelli, quadratus femoris* (Fig. 76), *obturator internus* and *externus*, which all act as lateral rotators and adductors. Besides these actions these muscles help to hold in the head of the femur, rather as supraspinatus, infraspinatus, and subscapularis stabilize the shoulder joint. The movement of lateral rotation of the femur is important to keep the toes turned sufficiently outwards during locomotion.

The muscles of the more caudal group that cross both hip and knee joints are the *biceps, gracilis, semitendinosus*, and *semimembranosus*. These are at the back of the joint and their action is of the greatest importance in quadrupeds, since they change the angle at which the whole leg is held relative to the body and thus produce a main part of the forward thrust. To give some of these muscles good leverage the ischium of the rabbit and other quadrupeds is prolonged backwards. The tendons of these muscles are variously arranged in different animals as the *hamstrings* at the back of the knee.

In quadrupeds (rabbit) the muscles form long tendinous insertions extending from the knee all along the back of the leg, thus increasing the effectiveness of their action (Figs. 63, 72, and 76). In man these muscles are inserted by three compact tendons easily felt at the back of the knee and ending on the head of the fibula or the upper end of the tibia.

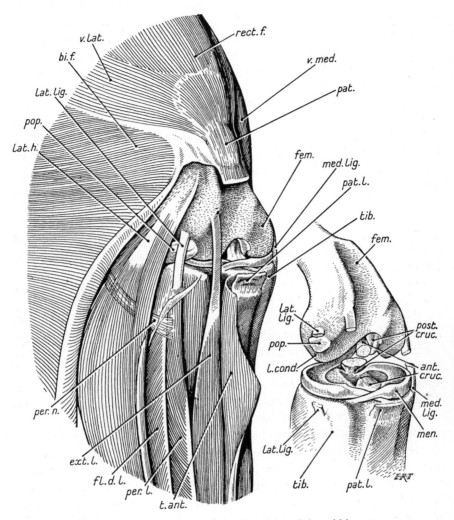

FIG. 77. Dissections of the knee joint of the rabbit.

ant.cruc. anterior cruciate ligament; *bi.f.* biceps femoris; *ext.l.* extensor digitorum longus; *fem.* femur; *fl.d.l.* flexor digitorum longus; *l.cond.* lateral condyle; *lat.h.* lateral head of gastrocnemius; *lat.lig.* lateral ligament; *med.cond.* medial condyle; *med.lig.* medial ligament; *men.* meniscus; *pat.* patella; *pat.l.* patellar ligament; *per.l.* peroneus longus; *per.n.* peroneal nerve; *pop.* popliteus; *post.cruc.* posterior cruciate ligament; *rect.f.* rectus femoris; *tib.* tibia; *t.ant.* tibialis anterior; *v.lat.* vastus lateralis; *v.med.* vastus medialis.

To summarize the muscles acting at the hip joint we have:

Protractor muscles (anterior braces, flexors of the hip)	Ilio-psoas	L2 and 3
	Rectus femoris	L3 and 4
	Sartorius	L3 and 4
	Tensor fasciae latae	L5
Retractor muscles (posterior braces, extensors of the hip)	Biceps femoris	L5–S3
	Semitendinosus	L5–S2
	Semimembranosus	L5–S2
	Gluteus maximus	L5–S2
Adductor muscles (medial braces)	Adductors	L2 and 3
	Gracilis	
	Pectineus	
Abductor muscles (lateral braces)	Glutei medius and minimus	
Rotators	Piriformis.	
	Obturators	
	Gemelli	
	Quadratus femoris	

In the last column are shown the segmental nerves from which some of these muscles are supplied in man and it is clear that there is a distinct progression, the flexors (protractors) are innervated more cranially than the extensors (retractors). It is reasonable to see in this arrangement a survival of the action of the limbs in conjunction with the myotomal musculature in early land animals, swinging forwards and then back. Indeed action of these muscles, which is so important for the locomotion of quadrupeds, might still be said to be activated by passage of a wave of activity caudally through the lumbosacral segments, as in fishes.

For stabilization of the hip joint a variety of braces is provided. Besides strong ligaments there are muscles, some short and acting close to the joint, presumably mainly as balancers, others, much longer, exert greater turning moment at the joint (p. 129) and are used for locomotion. Some act only across the hip joint, others cross both hip and knee and serve as economical stabilizers and movers of them both. Although we still have not organized our knowledge of these muscles well enough to be able to consider them in a wholly simple and logical manner, an analysis, such as that given by Gray, has taken us a long way from the position where it was necessary to consider each of these muscles only as a separate morphological entity. There is room for the exercise of much ingenuity in further extending this treatment.

5. The knee

The bones and muscles of the lower leg and foot are arranged on a plan essentially similar to that of the forelimb but modified for the purpose of providing a locomotor thrust. In arboreal species, the limb has a grasping action. Of the two bones in the lower leg the pre-axial *tibia*, corresponding to the radius, is always the better developed and lies on the medial side of the leg (Figs. 70 and 71). Usually it alone articulates with the femur at the knee. The *fibula* articulates with the tibia (Haines, 1953) but little movement is possible between the two (Barnett and Napier, 1953); the fibula is reduced in many mammals and fused with the tibia at its lower end. In man the fibula is a separate bone along its whole length and there are distinct upper and lower tibio-fibular joints. In the rabbit the fibula is separate only at its upper end.

At the knee there is little rotation and movement is limited mainly to the transverse plane. The joint surfaces are not, however, closely congruous as are those of the elbow joint. The lower end of the femur bears conspicuous lateral and medial condyles, easily felt in man, articulating with two slightly concave condyles on the upper end of the tibia. The large size and the shape of these facets allow full flexion at the knee, but would seem to leave the joint unstable and easily dislocated. To minimize this the depth of the tibial facets is somewhat increased by the two *menisci*, partial rings of cartilage, present in all mammals (Fig. 77). In man they are the 'cartilages' that may become torn and displaced if gripped between the members of the joint during sudden movements. There are also two strong *cruciate ligaments* within the joint, holding the femur and tibia together (Fig. 77). Lateral and medial ligaments, such as are found at all hinge joints, also increase the stability, which is further assured by the muscles acting across it.

The tendons of the quadriceps, the patella and its ligament, support the joint in front and are the main extensors. The flexors are the biceps laterally and the semitendinosus, semimembranosus, and sartorius medially, assisted by the two heads of gastrocnemius and by plantaris (see below), which complete the stability by support at the back (Figs. 63 and 76). The action of these muscles, especially the extensors, is an important item in maintaining posture, particularly in man, where the body is balanced so that the centre of gravity in the fully erect position often falls in front of the knee, the quadriceps being then relaxed and the patella movable.

The *popliteus* muscle, which runs from the lateral surface of the lateral femoral condyle through the capsule of the knee joint to the medial side of the tibia, flexes and medially rotates the latter on the femur (Fig. 77).

6. The foot and walking

The *foot* in both man and the rabbit is based on the plantigrade plan, the whole sole being applied to the ground (see Hicks, 1953). The tarsals are fundamentally arranged on the same plan as the carpals (p. 169), but only two members of the proximal row remain; the *talus*, also known as the *astragalus*, is the medial proximal carpal (tibiale), fused with the intermedium, and it provides the main articulation with the tibia by a characteristic pulley-like facet. In man the talus is gripped between the lower ends of the tibia and fibula, the *medial and lateral malleoli*, which are the familiar ankle bones (Fig. 70). The ankle joint thus allows movement only in one plane, the upward movement of the foot being known as dorsi-flexion, the downward as plantar-flexion (by comparison with the condition in more primitive verte-brates the upward movement, dorsiflexion, would be considered one of extension, the plantar movement being one of flexion). The sides of the ankle joint are supported by strong lateral and medial ligaments, which may, however, become strained if the foot is turned over acci-dentally as in walking over rough ground (an ankle 'sprain').

The more lateral proximal tarsal (fibulare) forms the *calcaneum*, modified to support the talus and having a conspicuous and charac-teristic backward prolongation to receive the attachment of the great calf muscles *gastrocnemius*, *soleus* and *plantaris* (Fig. 76). These are the muscles that produce a large part of the forward thrust, raising the body up on the toes. The action is essentially similar in man and the rabbit, both being plantigrade animals, which distribute the weight along the tarsals, metatarsals, and digits.

The essence of the action of *walking* may therefore be said to be a rhythmical change in the balance of tension in the braces about the hip, knee, and ankle. In both rabbit and man this produces a raising of the weight of the body on the foot acting as a second order lever, the fulcrum being located at the front end of the foot. The details of the way in which the rhythm of movement is produced of course vary greatly with the build and balance of the animal (Elftman, 1944). In the rabbit the resting posture is squatting, with the knee and ankle joints flexed. This is presumably correlated with the burrowing habit and necessitates the hopping method of progression by lengthening and retracting the limb and extending the back.

In man, where the weight is balanced on the legs in standing, move-ment is produced by complicated rhythmical adjustments of the balance at all the joints so that the weight is first allowed to fall forwards. The fall is then stopped and the centre of gravity raised again and so on. A considerable part of the thrust comes from the calf muscles, serving to raise the heel, with the heads of the metatarsals as a fulcrum. The bones of the foot are especially modified to make an arched structure for supporting and propelling the weight (p. 186).

The gastrocnemius muscle arises by lateral and medial heads from the back of the lower end of the femur and is attached by the *tendo Achillis* to the calcaneum (Fig. 76). It thus acts across both knee and ankle, whereas the deeper-lying muscle *soleus* runs from the back of the fibula and tibia to the heel. In the rabbit the more superficial muscle, acting across two joints, consists of white fibres, presumably quick-acting and used for movement, whereas the deeper muscle (soleus) is composed of red fibres and probably acts to fix the single joint in the flexed position of squatting.

The *plantaris* muscle, large in the rabbit (Fig. 76) but small in man, runs from the lateral femoral condyle to be inserted on to the second phalanges and is thus able to act upon the knee, heel, and metatarso-phalangeal and proximal inter-phalangeal joints. A muscle having a similar action is *flexor digitorum longus*, running from the back of the tibia and fibula to the distal phalanges. It will be seen that this muscle corresponds to flexor digitorum profundus in the arm, the plantaris being similar to flexor sublimis. In man a separate *flexor hallucis longus* acts on the great toe, serving to keep the under surface pressed against the ground. The *tibialis posterior* runs from the back of the tibia round the medial side of the ankle to be inserted on to the navicular and other tarsal bones. The muscle is highly developed in man as a support for the arch of the foot (p. 186).

The antagonists of these flexor muscles of the calf are weaker in action but have important functions to play, especially when acting from below to balance the leg on the foot. The more lateral members are the *peronei*, four muscles in the rabbit, three in man, arising from the fibula (*Lat. peroneus*: a skewer); their tendons run round the lateral border to be inserted on to the metatarsals. Peroneus longus runs round under the cuboid and across the foot to the first metatarsal; therefore, besides plantar-flexing the foot it raises the lateral border and supports the arch (p. 186). The more medial extensors of the ankle include *tibialis anterior* from the tibia to the first cuneiform and meta-tarsal and *extensor digitorum longus*, running in the rabbit from the femur through the knee joint to the phalanges; there is also a separate *extensor hallucis longus*.

The foot contains only two members of the proximal row of tarsals but retains the centrale, absent in the hand, as the *navicular* bone (Figs. 70 and 71). This articulates proximally with the talus and distally with the more medial members of the distal row of tarsals, the *cuneiform bones*, three in man, reduced to two in the rabbit, where the first digit (hallux) is missing. The two lateral distal tarsals are fused, as are the medial in the hand, to a single bone, known here as the *cuboid*. The *metatarsals* provide long levers for the locomotor functions. The phalangeal formula is as in the hand 2·3·3·3·3, but the phalanges are short and provided in the rabbit with pads and claws by which they grip the ground and prevent the limb sliding forward as the heel is raised. The claws have also, of course, other functions—for example digging and cleaning the fur. The metatarsals and digits are all held parallel, but in man this is probably a secondary condition. The ape-like form from which man has descended may have possessed opposable great toes and a more freely movable first metatarsal.

The relative lengths of the toes, like that of the fingers, varies greatly in different mammals. Among primates the members usually regarded as more primitive (for example lemurs) have the lateral toes relatively longer. In other primates the central digits are the longest, as in the hand, but in man the great toe is the strongest and at least in modern man often the longest. This is a modification connected with the assumption of the bipedal habit, the weight being carried on the medial border of the foot and all the metatarsals held together to make a compact structure.

7. Movements within the foot. Inversion and eversion

The joint at which most of the movement in the distal part of the foot takes place is that between metatarsals and phalanges, the point at which the foot bends in order that the metatarsal heads shall act as a fulcrum. The interphalangeal joints also permit considerable flexion and extension but this mobility of the toes is reduced in man.

In order to serve as a lever and a support the foot acts as a moderately rigid whole but some important movements take place in man between the tarsal bones, especially at the calcaneocuboid and talocalcaneonavicular joints, turning the sole of the foot inwards or outwards. To allow this the calcaneum and navicular are able to slide sideways on the talus, so that the whole foot turns either medially, *inversion*, or laterally, *eversion*. The former movement, which is of greater extent, corresponds to adduction, with a twist comparable to that of supination. Inversion is performed mainly by tibialis anterior and tibialis posterior acting together, eversion by the peroneal muscles.

Slight movements also occur between the proximal and distal tarsals and between the latter and the metatarsals, both during inversion and eversion and especially when weight falls on the foot. The movements are probably important in giving the suppleness that enables the foot to take large loads suddenly without breaking and especially in walking over rough ground.

8. The arches of the foot

A characteristic feature of the human foot is that the bones do not lie flat on the ground but are arranged to form a structure that may be described as consisting of longitudinal and transverse arches. The medial part of the longitudinal arch is the most marked and consists of the talus as apex, resting on the calcaneum posteriorly and the navicular, cuneiforms, and medial metatarsals anteriorly. The arch serves as a means to distribute the weight of the body, which falls on the talus. The lateral part of the longitudinal arch is flatter and consists of the calcaneum, cuboid, and the two lateral metatarsals. The transverse arch is at the bases of the metatarsals and, with the other tarsal bones, has the effect of making the whole foot into half a dome, by which the weight is distributed all round from the talus to the ground.

The arched form of the foot results partly from the shape of the bones but is to a considerable extent maintained by the action of the ligaments that hold the bones together and by muscle action, so that when the muscles are weak the arches tend to collapse. The extra strain thus thrown on the ligaments may cause them to stretch and the condition of *flat foot* results.

The chief ligaments on the plantar surface are the calcaneo-navicular—the 'spring' ligament—which lies directly below the head of the talus, and the plantar ligaments running from the calcaneum to the cuboid and to the bases of the metatarsals. These ligaments support the longitudinal arches; intermetatarsal ligaments support the transverse arch and prevent the toes from spreading outwards.

The most important muscles supporting the arches are the tibialis posterior and the long flexors for the medial side of the arch, and the peroneus longus for the lateral side. In addition there are short muscles within the foot, especially *flexor digitorum brevis*, which supports the longitudinal arches, and *adductor hallucis*, which supports the transverse arch and helps to hold the great toe parallel to the others. *Interossei* and *lumbricals* act upon the digits, as in the hand, but are of small importance either in man or the rabbit, since mobility of the toes is slight.

X

THE HEAD OF MAMMALS

1. Functions of the head

THE head has six main activities: (1) It contains the brain. (2) It carries the organs of special sense, nose, eyes, ears. (3) It carries the mouth and jaws and is the entrance of the alimentary canal. (4) The jaws may be used for offense or defence. (5) Through the nasal apertures it provides passage for the oxygen needed for respiration. (6) In many mammals the head is used to produce characteristic expressions that perform an important part in communication and the social life of the species.

These functions are important in all animals, and the mammals show special developments of them, leading to great complexity of the organization of the head. The many small parts make this region difficult to understand; there are so many little bones with odd shapes, such a maze of passages and so many nerves, blood-vessels, and irregularly arranged muscles that at first it is difficult to grasp the anatomy of the whole head. The significance of its parts will appear if we look at the head as a system for the performance of activities of the six types mentioned, that is to say, by consideration of the nervous, sensory, feeding, fighting, respiratory, and expressive activities that the mammals have developed from the organization they inherited from reptilian ancestors.

The mammalian head is sharply marked off from the body and carried on a long and mobile neck. It is therefore a single 'organ', whose structure has been moulded by its activities even more than has the head in fishes, amphibia, and reptiles, which could often be said to be merely the anterior part of the body. Moreover, the shape of the head in mammals is usually less affected by considerations of frictional resistance during motion than is the case in aquatic or aerial animals. Movement over the land surface is not often fast enough for the air resistance to be serious and the head is therefore free to take on the different forms that we see in the horse, elephant, or man. In those mammals that have returned to aquatic life there is usually a reintroduction of the 'streamlined' form of the head and body.

Our thesis is, then, that the shape of the head of any particular type of mammal is determined by the way its parts are used for the purposes mentioned above and we shall hope to be able to organize our knowledge about the various structures in the head in terms of these functions. We shall not recount lists of names or describe the shapes of numerous, unrelated structures but shall hope to find simple ways of describing the parts by considering how the special conditions in the mammals have been derived from the ancestral segmental type of organization.

First we shall deal with the container provided for the brain, showing how it develops a shape and size suitable for the sort of nervous structures that mammals use. This will be a way of describing the shape of much of the skull. Secondly, we shall consider the provision made for eyes, ears, and nose, the last-named being closely associated with the respiratory passages. Finally, the structure of the lower part of the head is determined by the activities of the apparatus for seizing the food, the jaws and teeth; while considering this we shall also deal with the muscles for moving the jaws and other muscles of the face, including those of expression. In this way, when we have described the activities that go on in the head, we shall have given a complete description of the whole organ and the various details will appear in their proper places.

2. The skull

The main outlines of the skull are determined by genetic factors. Bone tends to form in parts of the body that are liable to be stressed (p. 74). In the case of the skull this stressing is mostly that produced by the outward pressure during growth of the brain, sense organs, and nasal passages but the form is also affected by the pull of muscles. The hereditary factors and these stresses produce bony capsules of shape corresponding to the organs they contain, perforated only where nerves or blood-vessels pass through them. The irregular shape of the whole skull is due partly to the multiplicity of the various capsules and passages and partly to the presence of special protuberances for muscle attachments (de Beer, 1937).

The shape and appearance of the head as a whole are determined to a large extent by the structure of the box provided for the protection of the brain. The shape of the skull conforms with that of the brain; there is no wide space between the cranial wall and the contents. The factors determining brain shape are discussed on p. 435; they produce in lower mammals such as the rabbit an organ approximating to a tube of circular cross-section. The cranial cavity of these forms is therefore of approximately cylindrical form, with suitable enlargements where there are special dilations of the brain (Fig. 78).

The whole head has not a simple tubular form even in the lowest

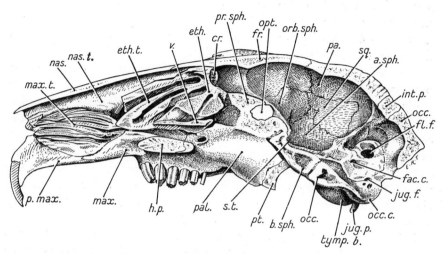

FIG. 78. Sagittal section through the skull of a rabbit.

a.sph. alisphenoid; *aud.m.* external auditory meatus; *b.sph.* basisphenoid; *c.* canine; *car.* carotid canal; *cereb.f.* cerebellar fossa; *cond.* condylar foramen (XII); *cor.* coronal suture; *cr.* cribriform plate; *cr.g.* crista galli; *eth.* ethmoid; *eth.t.* ethmo-turbinal; *ex.car.f.* external carotid foramen; *fac.c.* facial canal in periotic bone (VII and VIII); *f.lac.* foramen lacerum; *fl.f.* floccular fossa (for cerebellum); *f.m.* mandibular fossa; *f.occ.* fossa for occipital lobe; *f.ov.* foramen ovale; *for.m.* foramen magnum; *fr.* frontal; *fr.f.* fossa for frontal lobe; *f.rot.* foramen rotundum; *f.sp.* foramen spinosum; *h.p.* hard palate; *hyp.* hypophyseal fossa; *i.* incisors; *i.a.m.* internal auditory meatus (VII and VIII); *int.p.* interparietal; *jug.f.* jugular foramen (IX, X, XI); *jug.p.* jugular process of occipital; *la.* lachrymal; *lamb.* lambdoid suture; *m.* molars and premolars ; *mas.* mastoid process of temporal; *max.* maxillary; *max.t.* maxillary turbinal; *nas.* nasal; *nas.t.* nasoturbinal; *occ.* occipital; *occ.c.* occipital condyle; *occ.pr.* occipital protuberance; *opt.* optic foramen (II); *orb.sph.* orbitosphenoid; *p.max.* premaxillary; *pa.* parietal; *pal.* palatine; *pet.t.* petrous part of temporal (periotic); *ph.t.* pharyngeal tubercle, *p.m.* premolars; *pr.sph.* presphenoid; *pt.* pterygoid; *pt.l.* lateral pterygoid lamina; *pter.* pterion; *s.m.* stylomastoid foramen (VII); *s.o.f.* superior orbital fissure (III, IV, VI, V1 and 2); *sph.* sphenoid; *sq.* squamosal; *sq.t.* squamous temporal; *s.t.* sella turcica; *st.p.* styloid process; *sup.nuch.* superior nuchal line; *temp.f.* fossa for temporal lobe; *tr.s.* groove for transverse venous sinus; *tymp.* tympanic; *tymp.b.* tympanic bulla; *v.* vomer; *z.* zygomatic.

mammals because of the influence on the shape of the other systems (nose, jaws, &c.) that are associated with the cranium. In the rabbit the nasal apparatus is a large tubular structure placed in front of the brain case and internally divided to form a complicated set of passages (Figs. 78 and 82). The teeth are carried on the premaxillary and maxillary bones above, mandible below, and are divided into the long incisors in front and a battery of grinding molars behind. The jaw muscles for moving the lower on the upper teeth are attached to the surface of the brain case and to the zygomatic arches that project on either side (Fig. 83).

In man (Fig. 79) the cerebral hemispheres have become greatly enlarged relative to the rest of the brain and their nearly spherical form has imposed itself on the skull. The nasal apparatus is relatively much smaller than in the rabbit and causes only a slight deviation from the spherical in front. The jaws attached below also cause some deviation from the spherical form of the whole head.

We can thus consider the skull as a tube in a rabbit or a sphere in man, but as soon as we begin to look at the parts that make up its walls we see in the bones the marks of the past history of mammalian life. Bones that are separate in reptiles are often united in mammals. Sometimes they appear as separate bones during development but are fused in the adult. This obviously makes it difficult to provide suitable names for the bones in different animals and thus it is that the names used by anatomists for the skull of man, where the bones show much fusion, are not always consistent with those used by zoologists.

In lower vertebrates there is a large number of small skull bones but in mammals a relatively small number of large bones. This further justifies us in considering the shape of the skull as a whole as being more important than that of the constituent bones.

A large part of the skull is first developed in cartilage as the *chondrocranium*. This includes most of the skull base, parts of the side walls and capsules surrounding the nasal and auditory sacs. A series of rods forms the visceral (branchial) arches. In mammals nearly all the chondrocranium ossifies to make cartilage bones. Early in embryonic life dermal bones are laid down more superficially and they may become fused with the cartilage bones.

3. Bones surrounding the cranial cavity

The bones that are present in a rabbit may be dealt with in three series, those of the roof, sides, and floor (Fig. 78), arbitrary divisions of the surface of a cylinder. In the roof (speaking all the time only of the brain box proper) are the paired *frontals*, *parietals*, and *occipitals* and a small median *interparietal*. The roof bones continue down over the sides and without abrupt changes of shape the surfaces pass into other bones. The *orbito-sphenoid* forms the wall of the back of the orbit and behind this the *squamosal* and *alisphenoid* continue the tube back to the ear region, where the *periotic bone*, the ossification of the wall of the auditory capsule, makes part of the side wall of the brain

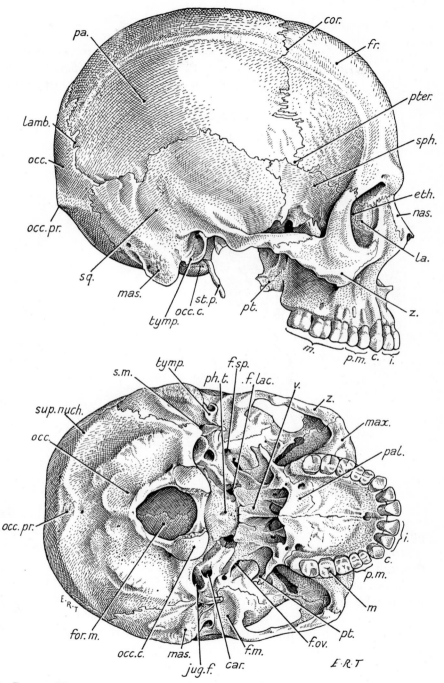

FIG. 79. Human skull seen from the side and from below. Lettering as Fig. 78.

box. The extreme posterior end of the lateral portion of the box is made by the *occipital* bones and these carry the occipital condyles.

Proceeding forwards again from the foramen magnum the floor of the cranium is made by the occipital. In front of this the *basisphenoid* forms a considerable part of the skull floor and is hollowed out in the

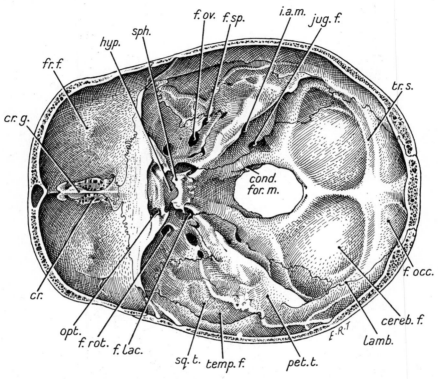

FIG. 80. Inside of human skull seen from above. Lettering as Fig. 78.

shape of a saddle, hence known as the *sella turcica*, in which lies the pituitary body. The remainder of the floor is made up by the *pre-sphenoid* and *ethmoid*, and the cavity ends in front at the *cribriform plate*, through which pass the fibres of the olfactory nerve.

Parts of the surfaces of twelve bones, therefore, make up a continuous wall for the brain box. The inside of the box is approximately moulded to the form of the brain and externally there are departures from the smoothly cylindrical form where muscles are attached. Thus the back of the skull is flattened to form a nuchal surface, with a conspicuous *external occipital protuberance* above it. Over this area are attached the splenius, part of the trapezius, semispinalis capitis, obliquus capitis,

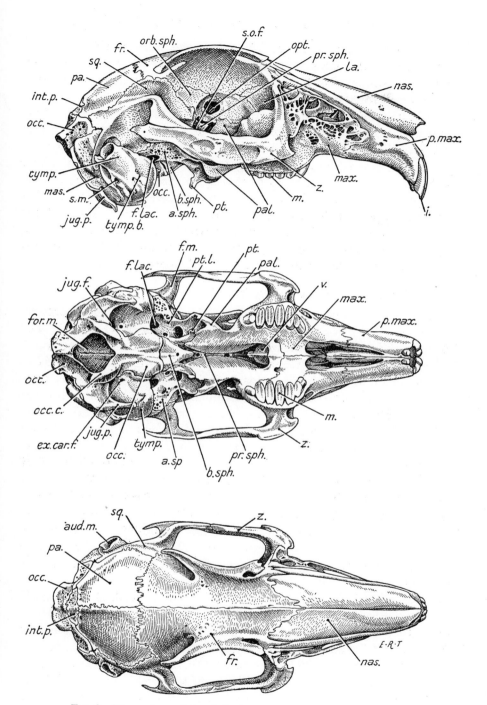

FIG. 81. Three views of the skull of a rabbit. Lettering as Fig. 78.

and rectus capitis muscles. These are the muscles that hold the head up on the neck and tilt it backwards at the atlanto-occipital joint. In animals that have a heavy head conspicuous *occipital crests* are formed for the attachment of these muscles.

The *mastoid process* of the periotic bone marks the attachment of the sternomastoid muscle and of longissimus capitis, muscles that brace the head back on the neck but rock it forward on the atlas. A further irregular point is made by the *jugular process* of the occipital, where the muscles of the tongue and hyoid (p. 204) are attached. After removal of the temporal muscle of newborn rats it has been found that there is imperfect development of the crest on the skull and of the coronoid process of the mandible, to which the muscle is attached, showing that these ridges and processes on the skull are formed partly as a response to the stresses placed upon the bones.

4. Foramina of the cranial cavity

The cranium makes a complete box for the brain, pierced only by holes for the passage of nerves and blood-vessels (Fig. 81). The numerous foramina for the olfactory nerves pass through the ethmoid. The optic nerves pass through a large *optic foramen* in the orbito-sphenoid bone, and behind this is the *superior orbital fissure*, lying between the orbito-sphenoid and alisphenoid bones and providing the aperture for the exit of the eye-muscle nerves (III, IV, and VI) and the ophthalmic branch of the trigeminal (V). The remaining branches of the trigeminal leave by separate openings in most mammals, the maxillary by a *foramen rotundum*, passing into a canal in the alisphenoid bone, the mandibular through the *foramen ovale*, close to the lower jaw articulation. In the rabbit the skull is little ossified in this region and the maxillary branch of the trigeminal leaves with the ophthalmic, there being no foramen rotundum. The mandibular nerve of the rabbit leaves through an aperture that also transmits the internal carotid artery, which in other mammals passes in a separate *foramen lacerum*, just in front of the periotic bone.

The seventh and eighth nerves pass through the skull in the *auditory foramen* (facial canal), the eighth (auditory) passing directly to the inner ear, while the facial nerve leaves above the ear by the *stylomastoid foramen*. Between the periotic and exoccipital bones the *jugular foramen* gives exit to the ninth, tenth, and eleventh cranial nerves, and the internal jugular vein. The twelfth nerve, hypoglossal, leaves by the *condylar foramen*, through the occipital bone. Finally, there is the *foramen magnum*, by which the spinal cord leaves the cranium.

5. The nasal apparatus

The shape of the head and skull is much influenced in the rabbit, which is a macrosmatic animal (p. 430), by the very large nasal passages, set in the form of cylinders on the front of the brain box (Fig. 78). In some *microsmatic* animals, such as man, the head has a more nearly spherical form. The nasal tube is roofed above by the *nasal bones*, laterally by the *pre-maxillaries* and *maxillaries*, tooth-bearing dermal bones. Medial palatine processes of these bones make the front part of the floor of the nasal tube (hard palate) and this bony palate is continued backwards by *palatine bones*. Behind these are conspicuous bony plates, the *pterygoid processes* of the basisphenoid, serving for the attachment of the pterygoid muscles (p. 201). The nasal tube opens in front by the large external nostrils and behind to the pharynx by the internal nostrils (Fig. 82). These lie much farther back than the hind end of the bony palate, the floor of the tube being continued behind the palatine bones as a *soft palate*. The walls here contain muscles that allow the tube to be closed to prevent the passage of food from the mouth to the nasal cavities. A pair of fine *nasopalatine ducts* connects the nasal cavity with the mouth by an opening behind the incisors. Jacobson's organ is a part of the olfactory organ opening into these ducts.

The nasal passages have two functions, first that of smell and secondly of moistening and warming the air that passes to the lungs and of filtering dust and other particles from it. This function of cleaning the air is especially well developed in rabbits, probably because they live much of their life underground and line their nests with fur. Anyone who has dissected a nursing rabbit will soon feel that the fine hairs are very irritating to the nose and will appreciate the value of the continual 'snuffling' movements, which the rabbit makes with the wings of skin covering the nostrils (Fig. 83). The *levator alae nasae* muscle and tendon responsible for these movements are well developed in the rabbit. Evidence of the dangers of nasal infection is shown by the fact that the nasal epithelium of nearly all wild rabbits shows signs of past disease.

The moistening and warming of the air is performed in all mammals by an extensive epithelium with rich blood-supply, supported by thin bony plates, the *turbinals* or scroll-bones, attached to the maxillae, nasals, and ethmoid bones. The lower part of the ethmo-turbinals forms a long median bone, the *vomer* (Fig. 78). The surfaces of these turbinals are covered with a ciliated, mucus-secreting epithelium,

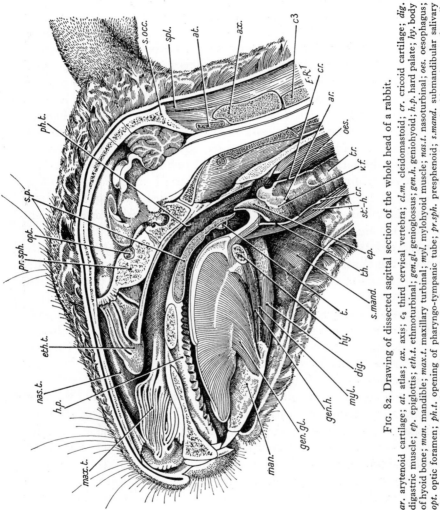

FIG. 82. Drawing of dissected sagittal section of the whole head of a rabbit.

ar. arytenoid cartilage; *at.* atlas; *ax.* axis; *c₃* third cervical vertebra; *cl.m.* cleidomastoid; *cr.* cricoid cartilage; *dig.* digastric muscle; *ep.* epiglottis; *eth.t.* ethmoturbinal; *gen.gl.* genioglossus; *gen.h.* geniohyoid; *h.p.* hard palate; *hy.* body of hyoid bone; *man.* mandible; *max.t.* maxillary turbinal; *myl.* mylohyoid muscle; *nas.t.* nasoturbinal; *oes.* oesophagus; *opt.* optic foramen; *ph.t.* opening of pharyngo-tympanic tube; *pr.sph.* presphenoid; *s.mand.* submandibular salivary gland; *s.occ.* supraoccipital; *s.p.* soft palate; *spl.* splenius and other neck muscles; *st.-h.* sternohyoid; *t.* pharyngeal tonsil; *th.* thyroid cartilage; *tr.* trachea; *v.f.* vocal fold.

which maintains a current of mucus towards the mouth. The olfactory epithelium itself (p. 522) occupies an area at the back of the nasal cavity.

The nasal cavity is therefore a complicated chamber, roughly cylindrical but with a form not easily referable to any simple mechanical principles. It serves the purpose of making the air pass over extensive moist, vascular surfaces, parts of which are olfactory. Communicating with the nasal cavity is a further system of spaces, the *maxillary* and *frontal sinuses*, lying within those bones. These spaces serve to lighten the bone; on account of their communication with the nasal passages they may become infected from the latter and if their openings into the nasal cavity are blocked, they may become painful in man.

6. The auditory capsule

The cartilaginous wall of the auditory capsule ossifies in mammals to form a single *periotic bone*, leaving three apertures, a foramen for the auditory and facial nerves medially and *fenestrae rotunda* and *ovalis* laterally, at which the membranous inner ear comes into contact with the wall of the middle ear. The *stapes* fits into the fenestra ovalis and carries sound-waves to the perilymph (p. 516), whose vibrations are made possible by the presence of the other aperture, the fenestra rotunda. The periotic bone is a complicated sac enclosing the various parts of the membranous labyrinth (p. 517). Externally its *mastoid* region appears on the surface of the skull and is drawn out into the mastoid process for attachment of the sternomastoid muscle. The bone is not compact but contains many spaces (mastoid air cells). The tympanic membrane, which serves to receive air-borne vibrations, is stretched across a tube communicating internally with the pharynx and externally with the outside air by the external auditory meatus. The tympanum develops approximately at the junction of the first pharyngeal (branchial) pouch and the first of the series of external grooves, which separates the mandibular and hyoid arches (p. 726). The whole passage thus retains the general character of the gill slits present in fishes.

The inner part of the passage, the *pharyngo-tympanic (Eustachian) tube*, leads from the pharynx (Fig. 82) to the cavity of the middle ear, medial to the tympanum. The outer canal, the external auditory meatus (Fig. 81), is surrounded by a bony tube, the *tympanic bone*, derived from the angular, a bone of the lower jaw of reptiles.

The whole arrangement thus serves to support the tympanic

membrane as a receptor for sound-waves, providing it with air on both sides so that it may vibrate freely. Blockage of the passage at either end in man, from within by the mucous secretions of a cold, or from without by water during bathing, produces a characteristic impairment of hearing.

The sound vibrations are carried from the tympanic membrane to the inner ear by the chain of auditory ossicles, *malleus*, *incus*, and *stapes* (Fig. 510). These ossicles provide considerable amplification for the vibrations and their peculiar shape makes them vibrate aperiodically and therefore they transmit complex sound-waves faithfully (p. 516). Small muscles, the *tensor tympani* and *stapedius*, are attached to the malleus and stapes respectively and serve to hold the ossicles and tympanum in a condition suitable for vibration (p. 518). The whole constitutes an elaborate arrangement for receiving sound-waves, and is especially developed in mammals, for the detection of both the direction and form of the sound.

Study of mammal-like reptiles shows that the malleus and incus have been formed by modification of the bones that provided for the articulation of upper and lower jaws in early reptiles. Probably at first, sound-waves reached the ear from the ground, through the jaw. When the first vertebrates came on land they possessed no tympanum and therefore little sensitivity to air-borne vibrations. When the tympanum first developed it probably served to increase the sensitivity of the lower jaw to vibrations. The apparatus then became still more sensitive by freeing the bones at the hind end of the jaw, so that they could carry vibrations directly from the tympanum to the inner ear.

The large *external ears* of the rabbit serve to increase the time difference of arrival of a sound-wave at the two tympana and thus provide means for detecting sound direction, which is important to a defenceless herbivore. The *pinna* of the ear is strengthened by cartilage and is moved by a series of muscles attached to the back of the skull (Fig. 83). The large supply of sensory nerves to the pinna suggests that the 'ears' of rabbits also serve as tactile organs, perhaps responding to small air movements, a function that is still more highly developed in bats. The variation in size of rabbits' ears in different climates (p. 37) shows that they also influence the temperature of the animal. In the elephant, where the surface-volume ratio of the body is small, ear movements constitute an important part of the cooling mechanism (p. 38).

7. The orbit

The nearly circular eye-ball is enclosed in a cavity lying in front of and below the brain case. The medial wall of the orbit is formed in man by the frontal, orbito-sphenoid, ethmoid, and alisphenoid bones. The frontal forms a characteristic protecting supraorbital ridge above the eye, continued at its front end by a small bone, the *lacrimal* (Fig. 81). The side of the eye is protected by the *zygomatic arch*, made by the early fusion of a *zygomatic (jugal) bone* in front and the zygomatic process of the *squamosal* behind; this bar also serves for the attachment of the masseter muscle (p. 200). The lower side of the orbit is unossified in the rabbit, but is closed in some other mammals (and in man) by bony processes of the jugal and maxilla. In the rabbit, as in most mammals, the orbit is continuous behind with the *temporal fossa*, though a process of the zygoma further separates these spaces laterally.

The structures accessory to the eye are highly developed in mammals and provide protection from desiccation and irritation by dust and other particles (Fig. 83). The upper and lower lids are hairy folds, with long eyelashes and a row of modified sweat glands, the *Meibomian glands*. The lids are closed by a slight ring of muscle the *orbicularis oculi*, most conspicuous behind the eye and innervated from the facial nerve. The function of raising the upper lid is performed by the *levator palpebrae superioris* muscle, which is a derivative of the first myotome (p. 717) and therefore innervated from the third cranial nerve. The third eyelid (*nictitating membrane*) is well developed in the rabbit as a curved plate of cartilage covered with glandular epithelium and moulded to the shape of the front of the eye, across which it can be drawn by a sheet of smooth muscle, cleaning and moistening the cornea.

There are six extrinsic eye-muscles in mammals, as in all other vertebrates, and they develop from the three myotomes at the front of the head, though the relations are less obviously segmental than in lower forms such as the dog-fish. The oblique muscles are attached to the more anterior portion of the wall of the back of the orbit but in mammals the *superior oblique* takes a sharp turn through a pulley or *trochlea*, which gives its name to the fourth nerve. This change of direction is especially marked in the forwardly directed eyes of man, where the muscle originates with the recti at the back of the orbit. The *inferior oblique* arises from the lacrimal bone and is inserted on the postero-ventral portion of the eyeball. It is a large muscle in the rabbit, whose eyes are directed laterally and show much movement in an antero-posterior direction. The four *rectus muscles* arise from the orbito-sphenoid bone around the optic foramen and are inserted on the four quadrants of the eyeball. The six muscles together thus serve to turn the eye in any direction. The eye of the rabbit is also provided with a retractor muscle, which arises with the recti and is inserted around the entrance of the optic nerve to the eyeball.

The glands of the orbit are highly developed in the rabbit, perhaps in order to keep the eye moist underground. *The Harderian gland* in front, between the oblique muscles, is composed of two parts, which have very different structures but open together inside the third lid. The *lacrimal gland* itself is smaller and lies in the temporal region of the orbit. The tears are carried away from the orbit by a *naso-lacrimal duct*, opening into the nasal cavity. The cornea is thus well protected, both by mechanical means, through movement of the lids, and by abundant secretions. Stimulation of the sensory nerve-fibres of the cornea brings both of these means of protection into action.

8. The jaws and muscles of mastication

The remaining features of the skull are largely concerned with the apparatus for taking the food by use of the teeth, which are highly differentiated in the rabbit. The anterior incisors serve for collecting materials by nibbling and gnawing, the premolars and molars for grinding the material obtained. The jaws and their muscles are highly specialized to make these movements possible. The teeth are carried in the pre-maxillary and maxillary bones of the upper jaw and in the single lower jaw bone, the *mandible* (*dentary*), a membrane bone covering the embryonic Meckel's cartilage. The articulation of the dentary with the skull is a facet on the lower side of the squamosal bone (Fig. 81), and the articulation is such that it allows mainly opening and closing of the mouth but also some movement forwards and backwards and sideways. Muscles are present for closing the jaw and for drawing it forward and back, while combinations of these produce the rotation.

The main muscle raising the jaw is the *masseter* (Fig. 84), which is a prominent feature of the lateral side of the head, running from the zygomatic arch to the lateral surface and lower edge of the mandible. This muscle is large in the rabbit and its insertion gives the characteristic deep jaw. The *temporal* muscle arises from the surface of the cranium in the temporal fossa and passes downwards medial to the zygomatic arch to be inserted behind the last tooth on the lateral surface of the *coronoid process*, a projection on the mandible in front of the articulation. The muscle thus not only closes the jaw but pulls the bone backwards. The temporal muscle and coronoid process are small in the rabbit. The *medial pterygoid* muscle runs from the pterygoid process of the basisphenoid bone to the medial surface of the mandible and therefore also closes the jaw. The *lateral pterygoid* has a similar origin but is attached to the front of the neck of the mandible close to the joint and thus pulls the jaw forward. The movement of chewing in the rabbit and man is produced by alternate action of the elevators of the jaw of one side and the lateral pterygoid of the other, giving a slightly rotatory action between the surfaces of the teeth.

9. Comparison of the skull of man and the rabbit

The activities of the head are different in the rabbit from those in man and the shapes of the heads may be correlated with these differences in activity. Classification of the differences and interpretation of their significance serves to emphasize the characteristics of the two types. On account of the development of the cerebral cortex, the brain of man approaches a sphere in shape. The reduction of the olfactory organs leads to a reduction of the snout and the eyes have come to face forwards. The rounded head is carried balanced on top of the vertebral column, rather than on the front end of a vertebral girder (p. 141). The nasal passages are not essentially different in the two types but they are simpler in man, because of the reduction in the olfactory functions and perhaps also because of a lesser necessity for cleaning the air. The human dentition is suited for an omnivorous diet and lacks the specializations for gnawing and grinding that are found in the rabbit. Finally, in man the superficial musculature of the face, instead of controlling the vibrissae and snuffling movements, produces the complicated movements of expression, which form such an important feature of the communication system upon which man's social life is based.

These differences in function are accompanied by considerable differences in the bony structure of the skull, especially in shape and the development of prominences for attachment of muscles. The shortening of the snout has led to great reduction of the nasal bones in man and to the disappearance of the premaxillaries as distinct bones. The rounded shape and characteristic posture of the head lead to many differences. The foramen magnum lies underneath rather than at the back of the skull. The ridges for attachment of the muscles of the occiput are less prominent in man than in most mammals. The

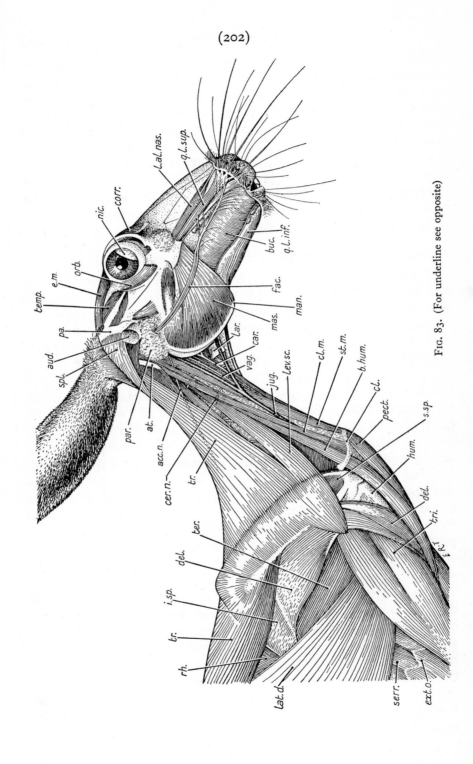

FIG. 83. (For underline see opposite)

differences in method of mastication have led to a relative reduction in the size of the masseter and to some development of the temporal muscle in man, with corresponding differences in the shape of the mandible and skull. In carnivorous mammals the temporalis is typically the dominant muscle, in herbivorous mammals the masseter. Man is omnivorous and both are well developed.

Finally, certain fusions of bones take place in adult man. The two frontals come to form a single bone. The various sphenoids make a single *sphenoid bone*, which, however, has a complicated shape, with processes for the attachment of the pterygoid muscles. The squamosal fuses with the periotic and with the tympanic to give a single *temporal bone* of complicated form.

10. The lips and muscles of the face

The appearance of the head of a rabbit or other mammal is largely determined by the arrangement of the lips and their movements (Fig. 83). Around the nostrils the skin is highly specialized by the presence of the tactile *vibrissae*, long hairs with a special sensory innervation (p. 476). The skin is characteristically divided in the midline in the rabbit to give a cleft upper lip and the fold between this margin and the nostril, together with the skin above the nostril, in life perform continual rhythmical twitching movements, serving to keep the air passage clear (p. 195). These and other movements of the skin of the head are produced by special portions of the *platysma* muscle, a muscle of the skin (not myotomal, see p. 45), innervated by branches of the facial nerve. The *facial muscles* are differently developed in various mammals according to the movements required of the face. They are large and highly differentiated in man as the *muscles of expression*, which have acquired great significance as a means of communication between individuals in a social species. Beginning perhaps from simple actions such as baring the teeth, which occurs preliminary to biting and hence is an indication of rage, the whole pantomime of emotional expression has developed into a means of communication second only to that afforded by speech.

Fig. 83. Drawing of dissection of the head and shoulders of a rabbit.

acc.n. accessory nerve; *at.* wing of atlas; *aud.* external auditory meatus; *b.hum.* basihumeral; *buc.* buccinator; *car.* carotid; *cer.n.* cervical nerves; *cl.* clavicle; *cl.m.* cleido-mastoid; *corr.* corrugator supracilii; *del.* deltoid; *e.m.* ear muscle; *ext.o.* external oblique; *fac.* facial nerve; *hum.* humerus; *i.sp.* infraspinatus; *jug.* jugular vein; *lar.* larynx; *l.al.nas.* levator alae nasae; *lat.d.* latissimus dorsi; *lev.sc.* levator scapulae; *man.* mandible; *mas.* masseter; *nic.* nictitating membrane; *orb.* orbicularis oculi; *pa.* parietal; *par.* parotid gland; *pect.* pectoralis major; *q.l.inf.* quadratus labii inferioris; *q.l.sup.* quadratus labii superioris; *rh.* rhomboid; *serr.* serratus anterior; *spl.* splenius capitis; *s.sp.* supraspinatus; *st.m.* sternomastoid; *temp.* temporalis; *ter.* teres major; *tr.* trapezius; *tri.* triceps brachii; *vag.* vagus.

In the rabbit the parts of this musculature that are well developed are concerned with moving the lips (Fig. 83). The *quadratus labii superioris* is the main muscle that produces retraction of the upper lip. It arises from the surface of the skull in front of the eyes and consists of several separate parts inserted forward on the lip. The skin around the mouth is also moved by a circular ring of muscle, the *orbicularis oris*; though large in man this is small in the rabbit. The *quadratus labii inferioris* is a large muscle occupying the side of the mandible and retracting the lower lip (Fig. 84).

The sides of the mouth are occupied by a large sheet of muscle, the *buccinator*, running from the upper jaw to the mandible and especially well developed in a chewing animal such as the rabbit, in which the food is passed backwards and forwards into cheek pouches through a gap in the tooth row, the *diastema*. The platysma includes several portions and its main sheet consists of longitudinal fibres running beneath the skin from the angle of the jaw down under the neck.

11. The mouth, tongue, pharynx, and larynx

The *tongue* projects as a conical lobe from the floor upwards into the mouth. It is covered with papillae containing the taste-buds (p. 521) and is attached by a system of muscles whose action helps in the act of swallowing. The mouth continues backwards into a cavity under the back of the head, the *pharynx*, into which the nasal tube (naso-pharynx) opens from above and from which the oesophagus dorsally and larynx ventrally open backwards (Fig. 82). The Eustachian tube (pharyngotympanic tube) opens into the back of the nasal tube. The pharyngeal cavity is thus an important meeting-point for several passages. Being a likely seat of infection it is guarded by collections of lymph glands (p. 265), especially around the *tonsils*, which are depressions in the side walls of the front of the pharynx (Fig. 82). In development the tonsil arises from the second pharyngeal pouch.

The ventral and side walls of the pharynx contain a series of bones and cartilages. These are derived from the branchial arches and serve to support the tongue and to give attachment to the muscles that control swallowing and the passage of air; similar functions have been performed by this apparatus from the fish stage of evolution onwards. The *hyoid bone* lies between the angles of the mandible and from it two cartilaginous processes, the *greater and lesser cornua*, pass upwards to be attached to the jugular process of the occipital bone by the *stylohyoid* muscles (Fig. 84). The anterior (lesser) cornu represents the lower portion of the hyoid arch, the more posterior (greater) cornu the first branchial arch; the body of the hyoid is the basibranchial cartilage.

The *larynx* (Fig. 82) is a cavity forming the first portion of the respiratory tract and with its front and sides strengthened by the *thyroid cartilage* (Adam's apple) above and *cricoid* cartilage below. These represent the lower portions of the second and third branchial arches. The *arytenoid cartilages* are a pair attached to the cricoids in the larynx, and the *vocal folds* are ridges projecting into the larynx between the arytenoids and the thyroids, in a position to be vibrated by the air stream. They are small in the rabbit. Muscles tighten the folds and regulate the note. The entrance to the larynx is protected by the *epiglottis*, a fold projecting upward from the floor of the pharynx and stiffened by elastic cartilage.

The tongue is moved by muscles attaching it to the inner surface of the mandible (the *genioglossus*), to the hyoid (*hyoglossus*) and to the skull (*styloglossus*) (Fig. 82), while its own internal fibres (*lingualis*) run in various directions and allow changes of shape and projection.

The act of swallowing consists first of a compression of the cavity of the mouth and raising of the hyoid. This is achieved by the action of the buccinator muscle and of the *mylohyoid*, a set of fibres running on each side between the mandible and the hyoid bone (Fig. 84). These are assisted by the hyoglossus, stylohyoids, and the *digastric*, a muscle running from the jugular process of the skull to the mid-point of the lower jaw, through a ligamentous loop attached to the hyoid. The resultant upward movement of the larynx raises the epiglottis to close the entrance, assisted by the action of sphincter muscles of the larynx itself. At the same time the opening to the nasal tube is closed by the contraction of the small muscles that raise the soft palate. The bolus of food is thus passed over the epiglottis into the oesophagus, which, provided with its own muscular wall, passes the food onwards by contraction behind the bolus and relaxation in front (peristalsis, p. 240). Long muscles, the *sterno-hyoid* and *sterno-thyroid*, then draw the whole apparatus downwards (Figs. 82 and 84).

The larynx is provided with an internal musculature by which the air flow is regulated and the position of the vocal folds altered to modify the note of the voice. These muscles are, of course, much larger in man than in the rabbit, which makes only limited use of its voice.

12. The cranial nerves

The central nervous system of any vertebrate is connected with the periphery by one dorsal and one ventral root on each side in each segment (p. 359). In the spinal region these roots join but in the head they remain separate; hence in the cranial region the segmental plan is not at first sight obvious. Nevertheless we can recognize dorsal and ventral roots in the cranial as in the spinal segments. The ventral (anterior) roots innervate the myotomes and in the front part of the head these persist as the eye-muscles. The first ventral root is thus the *oculomotor* (third cranial), innervating the superior, inferior, and anterior rectus and the inferior oblique, all of which are derivatives of the first myotomal segment. The second ventral root is the *trochlear nerve*, innervating the superior oblique, and the third is the *abducent nerve*, supplying the posterior rectus. All these nerves carry motor fibres to their muscles and also afferent fibres of proprioceptive function.

The dorsal (posterior) roots of the cranial region differ from those of the rest of the body in that they carry efferent (motor) as well as afferent fibres. This is explained by the fact that in the head much of the musculature is derived not from the myotomes but from the muscles of the branchial arches, the lateral plate musculature (p. 717). In the trunk all the striped muscles are derived from myotomes and are therefore innervated by ventral roots.

Thus the *trigeminal nerve*, which embryology shows to be derived from the dorsal roots of the first two head segments, contains besides many afferent fibres, efferent fibres supplying the muscles of mastication associated with the first (mandibular) pharyngeal arch, namely, the temporalis, masseter, and pterygoids. The *facial nerve*, which is the nerve of the third head segment, whose ventral root is the abducent, carries motor fibres to the muscles derived from the hyoid arch, as well as many sensory fibres.

The segments behind these first three are obscured by the development of the auditory sac, which is formed as an inpushing from the surface of the head. The myotomes in this region are thus obliterated, but the series of dorsal roots continues as the ninth (*glossopharyngeal*), tenth (*vagus*), and eleventh (*spinal accessory*) cranial nerves. Each of these contains both sensory and motor fibres, and the last two are composed of the combined dorsal roots of several segments. The series of ventral roots begins again with the *hypoglossal* (twelfth cranial) nerve, which represents the ventral roots of the more posterior segments of the vagus-spinal accessory series and innervates muscles of the tongue, derived from myotomes.

Thus the third, fourth, sixth, and twelfth cranial nerves represent ventral (anterior) roots. They consist mainly of motor fibres (together with some proprioceptive ones) and they carry no ganglia. They arise from the ventral surface of the brain (Fig. 166), except the trochlear, whose cells of origin lie ventrally but the axons run round within the substance of the brain on their way to the superior oblique muscle. The fifth, seventh, ninth, tenth, and eleventh cranial nerves are dorsal roots with ganglia corresponding to those of the spinal dorsal roots; they carry many afferent and some efferent fibres. The arrangement of the cranial nerves thus shows that the head, in spite of its specialized structures, is produced by a modification of the fundamental segmental plan that can be traced throughout the vertebrates.

13. The trigeminal nerve

The trigeminal nerve retains the three main branches found in lower vertebrates. The *ophthalmic division* is purely sensory and runs from its exit at the superior orbital fissure forwards along the median wall of the orbit. It divides into branches supplying the skin of the upper eyelid and passing through a supraorbital foramen reaches the skin of the front of the head and of the inside as well as the outside of the nose. The afferent fibres for the cornea also arise from the ophthalmic division within the orbit and run in the ciliary nerves. Some part of this division represents the dorsal root of the first somite (corresponding to the n. ophthalmicus profundus of fishes. See Young, 1950, p. 149).

The second or *maxillary division* of the trigeminal is also purely afferent. As it leaves the skull it passes in most mammals into an *alisphenoid canal* in that bone, so that the foramen rotundum, through which the nerve leaves, does not appear on the surface; in the rabbit this canal is not ossified. The nerve then runs across the floor of the orbit, giving branches to the upper jaw, and finally passes through an infra-orbital foramen to reach the face. The *mandibular* or third division of the trigeminal leaves the skull by the foramen ovale and contains motor fibres for the muscles of the mandibular arch, namely those of mastication, as well as sensory fibres for the lower jaw. It therefore gives off on its course branches to the temporal muscle, the pterygoids and masseter. A *buccal branch* passes through the buccinator muscle to the skin of the mouth and the *lingual nerve* continues down to supply receptors for touch and pain on the front of the tongue.

The inferior dental nerve supplies the mylohyoid muscle and anterior belly of the digastric and then enters the mandible to supply the teeth. A large *auriculo-temporal* nerve turns backwards and upwards to supply the skin of the back of the head.

14. The facial nerve

The dorsal root of the third (hyoid) pro-otic somite includes the *auditory* (p. 518) and *facial* nerves (Fig. 83). In mammals the facial is largely a motor nerve supplying the lateral plate muscles of the head, face, and neck but also containing fibres for the sense of taste from the front part of the tongue. The nerve leaves by the stylomastoid foramen, near the ear, and passes through the parotid gland, branching where it emerges on the face to supply the platysma and its derivatives the muscles round the eye, nose, and mouth. In man the facial nerve therefore controls the muscles that express the emotions.

The gustatory fibres of the facial run in the *chorda tympani* nerve, which crosses the tympanic cavity and is distributed with the lingual branch of the trigeminal nerve to the tongue. The facial nerve also carries pre-ganglionic parasympathetic fibres for the control of the secretion of the salivary glands. These run to the sphenopalatine, otic, and submaxillary ganglia (p. 390).

15. Glossopharyngeus, vagus, and spinal accessory

In the region of the otic capsule and immediately behind it no myo-tomal muscle remains and no ventral roots develop. The dorsal roots form a series, the first separate as the *glossopharyngeus* and the sub-sequent ones fused to form a complex set of trunks, which are ascribed by anatomists, rather arbitrarily, to two 'nerves', the *vagus* and *spinal accessory* (Figs. 83 and 84). The *hypoglossus* represents the combined ventral roots of some of these hinder cranial segments.

The first of the post-otic dorsal cranial roots, the ninth nerve (*glossopharyngeus*), supplies gustatory fibres for the back of the tongue and motor fibres for some of the muscles of the pharynx wall. It has two branches, a lingual and a pharyngeal. The dorsal roots of several segments behind the glossopharyngeal unite to make the vagus and spinal accessory trunks. These two nerves are only conventionally separable; they leave the skull as independent trunks but then inter-change fibres, so that some of the fibres in the 'branches' of the vagus actually leave the skull in the spinal accessory root. The series makes a system of fibres for innervating the striped muscles derived from the lateral plate in this region (laryngeal muscles, trapezius, sternomastoid) and also provides pre-ganglionic parasympathetic as well as sensory fibres for many of the viscera. It is not clear how it has come about that the nerves of a few segments should fuse in this way and then spread so far outside their territory but the arrangement is as old as the vertebrates.

The *vagus* or tenth cranial nerve (Fig. 84) is a large mixed nerve, providing sensory and motor fibres to a great part of the gut, respiratory system, and heart. The nerve emerges through the jugular foramen and the ganglionic swelling containing the cell bodies of its afferent fibres is divided into an upper *jugular ganglion* within the skull and a *ganglion nodosum* lower down. The cell bodies of the parasympathetic pathways of the vagus do not lie in these ganglia but more peripherally among the tissues (p. 385). Shortly below the ganglion nodosum the nerve gives off the *superior laryngeal nerve*, supplying muscles in the larynx, and the *cardiac depressor nerve*, which carries sensory fibres from the heart and aortic arches (p. 286). Other small cardiac branches leave the vagus in the neck and make a plexus of fibres in the sinu-auricular node of the heart (p. 285). These plexuses contain the fibres and cells of the vagal parasympathetic system, which slows the heart-beat (p. 395).

At the lower end of the neck the vagi give off *recurrent laryngeal nerves*, which loop round the subclavian artery on the right and ligamentum arteriosum on the left before running cranially again on either side of the trachea to reach the intrinsic muscles of the larynx. This peculiar course is a result of the elongation of the neck during development.

Below this point the vagi break up into a series of plexuses. The pulmonary plexuses carry sensory and motor fibres to the tissues of the lungs and below them the nerves continue as an oesophageal plexus so dense and tangled that separate right and left vagal trunks can hardly be recognized in man. From these plexuses fibres proceed on to the stomach and others join the sympathetic fibres of the solar plexus (p. 387) and reach back as far as the lower end of the small intestine. The motor (preganglionic) fibres of these vagal gastric and intestinal plexuses act upon a variety of functions, often in a direction 'antagonistic' to that of the sympathetic nerves to the same parts (p. 396). In addition to these motor functions the vagi also provide pathways for afferent impulses such as those of 'hunger', produced by contraction of the stomach (p. 240).

The *spinal accessory nerve* (Fig. 84) arises by rootlets not only in the skull but from the cervical cord as low as the fifth or sixth segment.

These rootlets lie between the dorsal and ventral rootlets of the cervical nerves and their cell bodies lie in the grey matter dorsal to those of the ventral roots. More cranially this column of cells continues as the *nucleus ambiguus*, which in turn is continuous with the motor nuclei of the vagus and glossopharyngeus (p. 381). The morphology of the spinal accessory is therefore quite clear; it is a motor dorsal root, supplying muscle that is formed from the lateral plate and therefore innervated in a manner different from the muscles of the trunk, which are all myotomal. After emerging through the jugular foramen the accessory nerve makes anastomosis with the vagus, supplying it with the fibres that operate the striped musculature of the larynx (superior and recurrent laryngeal nerves); it then divides into branches to the sterno-mastoid and trapezius muscles.

16. The hypoglossal nerve

The twelfth cranial nerve, *hypoglossus*, is also a pure muscle nerve, but in this case representing the ventral roots of the more posterior of the vagal-accessory segments and supplying the derivatives of the ventral portion of the myotomes of this region, which are limited to the tongue. The so-called descending branch of the hypoglossal consists of fibres that have joined the trunk within the skull from the more cranial cervical nerves and this branch rejoins these nerves in the neck to form the *ansa hypoglossi*, from which fibres run to the sterno-hyoid and other muscles that draw the larynx caudally.

17. The cervical spinal nerves

The eight *cervical spinal nerves* emerge through foramina in front of the cervical vertebra and the first thoracic vertebra. They have the typical dorsal and ventral roots but they have no white rami communicantes, since no preganglionic autonomic fibres leave the spinal cord in the neck (p. 386). The first cervical nerve, leaving in front of the atlas, is small and lies at the back of the neck. The second nerve is also small but the third and subsequent nerves are conspicuous bundles. They innervate the muscles and skin of the neck and also provide the fibres of the *phrenic nerves* (Fig. 84). These arise mostly from the fourth cervical in the rabbit, with contributions from neighbouring nerves. The phrenic trunks run back over the pericardium and along the mediastinum to end in the striped musculature of the diaphragm. This course of the phrenic nerves is a result of the backward movement of the diaphragm, which begins its development in the septum

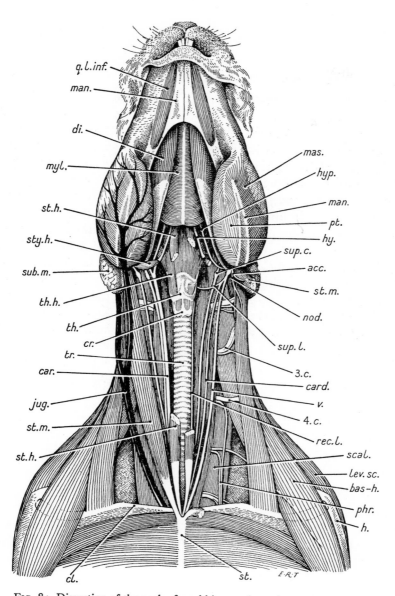

FIG. 84. Dissection of the neck of a rabbit seen from the ventral surface.

acc. spinal accessory nerve (XI); *bas.h.* basio-humeral; *car.* carotid artery; *card.* cardiac depressor branch of vagus; *3c, 4c.* cervical nerves; *cl.* clavicle; *cr.* cricoid cartilage; *di.* digastric; *h.* humerus; *hy.* cornu of hyoid; *hyp.* hypoglossal nerve (XII); *jug.* jugular vein; *lev.sc.* levator scapulae; *man.* mandible; *mas.* masseter; *myl.* mylohyoid; *nod.* nodose ganglion of vagus; *phr.* phrenic; *pt.* medial pterygoid; *q.l.inf.* quadratus labii inferioris; *rec.l.* recurrent laryngeal; *scal.* scalenus anterior; *st.* sternum; *st.h.* sternohyoid; *st.m.* sternomastoid; *sty.h.* stylohyoid; *sub.m.* submandibular gland; *sup.c.* superior cervical ganglion; *sup.l.* superior laryngeal branch of vagus; *th.* thyroid cartilage; *th.h.* thyrohyoid; *tr.* trachea; *v.* vagus.

transversum at the level of the heart and pushes backwards as the lungs develop (p. 736).

18. The cervical sympathetic trunks

The *cervical sympathetic trunks* (Fig. 84) are conspicuous nerves running along the neck. They consist of preganglionic fibres that leave the spinal cord in the white rami of the thoracic region and run forward to end in either the *inferior cervical ganglia*, at the level of the subclavian arteries, or the *superior cervical ganglia*, lying dorsal to the point of division of the carotid arteries. From the inferior ganglia, also known as *stellate ganglia*, postganglionic fibres run to a variety of organs, accelerator fibres to the heart, bronchomotor fibres to the lungs, and vasomotors and sudomotors to the forelimb. The superior cervical ganglion is the cell station for the sympathetic fibres to all the organs of the head, including vasomotors, pupillo-dilators, fibres for the nictitating membrane and others that assist in control of salivation and sweating. The post-ganglionic fibres leave the superior cervical ganglion and pass with the branches of the carotid artery as the internal carotid plexus. They are distributed to the peripheral organs with the branches of the cranial nerves (p. 387).

XI

THE INTAKE OF FOOD. MOUTH AND TEETH

1. The supply of raw materials

THE matter within the system of any animal needs continual renewal; the body is in a steady state, not an equilibrium, and life depends upon the availability of fresh supplies. Moreover the homeostatic actions of the body depend upon the expenditure of energy for moving substances against concentration gradients and for many similar purposes. In a mammal energy-giving foods are required to maintain the high temperature and to make possible all the many special actions that ensure homeostasis. The whole system of life of a mammal is thus based upon the expenditure of large amounts of energy, the information available through the nervous system ensuring that such expenditure brings the body into conditions in which life can be maintained.

A large part of the activity of every mammal is therefore devoted to obtaining supplies of material for building and rebuilding the body and for the provision of energy. Mammals have acquired the power to gain the necessary nourishment from all sorts of odd corners of the varied world of land, sea, and air. Yet the basic pattern of their digestive system shows few special features and is essentially that common to all vertebrates. It is surprising that such a wide variety of diets can be digested by means of the familiar apparatus of a stomach with its acid and pepsin and an intestine with enzymes acting in alkaline solution.

The differences between alimentary systems are mainly in the apparatus for obtaining the food from the environment, the mouth and teeth, and in the presence of special chambers of the gut for the cultivation of symbiotic bacteria to assist in breaking down cellulose. The placental mammals of the Cretaceous period, more than 70 million years ago, were insectivorous; from these all the specialized carnivores and herbivores have been evolved and many types, like men, have become omnivorous. Indeed most mammals show considerable flexibility in the way they obtain the materials necessary for their maintenance, as would be expected from animals with such an adaptable nervous organization.

Whatever their specializations all mammals take some proteins, carbohydrates, and fats, together with water and certain special molecules, inorganic salts, and vitamins. Proteins, besides providing the necessary nitrogenous materials, can be used as fuel for the provision of energy and warmth, which are otherwise supplied by carbohydrates and fats.

2. Selection of food

The activities by which the animal seeks, selects, and eats its food are an important part of its behaviour and the types of food chosen depend largely on the nervous organization (p. 520). In this as in other matters the mammals show exceptional powers. They are provided even more fully than other animals with a system that provides a 'drive' to seek food and they use great ingenuity until they find it. We know little of the source of this drive, or how it is related to the needs of the organism. The initiation of food-collecting activity is not the result of the receipt of signals from tissues that lack some component. It depends primarily on the hunger contractions, movements of the empty stomach, which are supposed to be associated with the feeling of hunger in man. This leaves unsolved the question of what starts the hunger contractions. Evidently either the stomach or the brain, or both, contain systems that drive the organism to action unless proper nourishment is taken.

In a young child the hunger contractions initiate the behaviour of crying, which ensures a supply of food from the mother. Probably as development proceeds a pattern of food intake at various times throughout the day is set up, triggered partly by hunger contractions, partly by complicated memories within the central nervous system. The cerebral cortex controls the activities of digestion as it does nearly everything else in the body (Chapter XXIII). One proof of this control is the fact that after removal of part of the frontal lobe of the cortex the food intake may be greatly increased (p. 440).

It is a common belief that animals and men seek and find food that is 'good for them', for instance game will move many miles to a 'salt lick' to obtain the small amounts of inorganic salts that they need. Little is known about the receptor and central nervous mechanisms related to these appetites. It is certain that they do not provide unfailing guidance for the creature and yet it remains an astonishing thing that organisms with such complicated chemical constitutions continually renew themselves, seeking and eating the raw materials that they need. The chemo-receptors probably play a large part in finding the right food, those of the nose acting as distance receptors and those of the mouth serving to test the food at the point of intake (p. 521). Whether any given chemical stimulus leads to acceptance or rejection of the object as food no doubt depends largely on past experience as recorded in the cortex. In mammals food choice is probably mainly determined by acquired rather than by hereditary information, but little evidence is available about this.

An interesting example of the influences affecting food choice is the difference in behaviour between wild and laboratory rats when presented with food consisting of an assortment of purified substances in separate containers. Offered a protein, a fat, a carbohydrate and twelve other dishes of pure minerals and vitamins a laboratory rat makes a selection that allows normal growth. A wild rat only eats the fat and dies in a short time. These wild animals are so 'suspicious' that they will not taste new foods, and this, incidentally, makes it difficult to poison them. Richter, who conducted these experiments, found many other signs of the 'suspiciousness' of wild rats (p. 550).

The rabbit is a herbivore, able to eat not only relatively soft vegetable foods such as dandelion or lettuce leaves but also much harder roots and grasses. For this activity it possesses sharp, continually growing incisors to crop the grass, large grinding molars, and an enormous intestinal sac, the caecum, in which bacteria make the cellulose of the grass available to the rabbit. Such unpromising food is not easily digested and rabbits have the habit of passing it through the gut several times by eating their faecal pellets and thus ensuring maximum use of the material available.

The dentition and gut of man, like his tastes, are those of an omnivore, able to obtain his nourishment from either plant or animal food, or from a mixture of both. Neither the teeth nor gut of man are able to deal with the hardest plant foods.

3. Development and structure of the teeth

The features of the digestive system that are peculiar to mammals are found mainly at the point of intake, where the moist internal meets the dry external world, that is to say in the mouth and teeth (Orban, 1953; Kutuzov and Sicher, 1952). Here the food is seized and the salivary glands are developed to moisten it for swallowing. The teeth have become differentiated from the original series of cone-like reptilian teeth, known as a *homodont dentition*. In mammals the more anterior ones retain the single cusp pattern, but farther back along the jaws, new developmental processes have led to the appearance of broad molariform teeth with uneven biting surfaces (Romer, 1947). In this way the *heterodont dentition* has arisen, the incisors in front serving to seize the food, canines to pierce and tear it, and molars to cut and

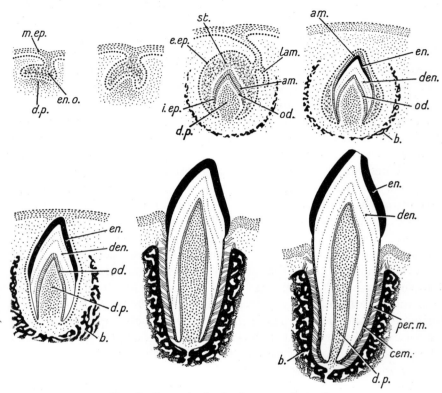

FIG. 85. Stages in the development of a tooth.

am. ameloblasts; *b.* bone; *cem.* cement; *d.p.* dentinal pulp; *den.* dentine; *en.* enamel; *en.o.* enamel organ; *e.ep.* external enamel epithelium; *i.ep.* internal enamel epithelium; *lam.* lamina for permanent tooth; *m.ep.* oral epithelium; *od.* odontoblasts; *per.m.* periodontal membrane; *st.* stellate reticulum. (After Orban.)

grind it. Moreover the mammals have proved able to vary this dentition greatly according to their diet. In a few there has been a reversion to the homodont condition, with a large number of single-cusped teeth, like those of fishes or reptiles (e.g. some toothed whales).

Mammalian teeth are formed in two series, first a 'milk' or deciduous, then a permanent dentition. This condition is said to be diphyodont, in contrast to the polyphyodont dentition of lower vertebrates, in which several series of teeth appear. Each tooth is the product of the collaboration of a thickening of the ectoderm, the *enamel-organ*, whose *ameloblasts* secrete the enamel, and a mesodermal *dental-papilla,* whose *odontoblasts* secrete the dentine (ivory) (Figs. 85 and 86). The first sign of the appearance of the tooth rudiments is a line of thickenings of the epithelium of the mouth, the dental lamina. Along this line there form groups of cells, the tooth buds (Fig. 85). The cells of these buds proliferate faster than their neighbours, so

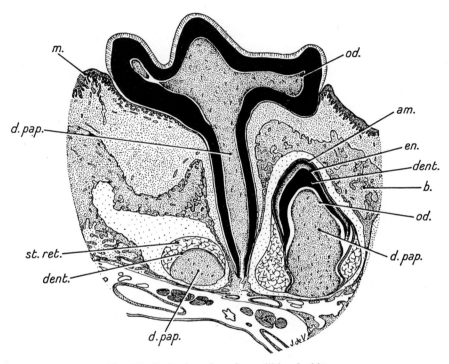

FIG. 86. Sagittal section of mandible of a kitten.

am. ameloblasts; *b.* bone; *d.pap.* dental papilla; *dent.* dentine; *en.* enamel; *m.* mucous membrane of gum; *od.* odontoblasts; *st.ret.* stellate reticulum.
(From a preparation kindly lent by K. C. Richardson.)

that each bud extends into the mesoderm. Here its tissues differentiate to form two layers, the inner and outer enamel epithelia, separated by a central mass of cells, the stellate reticulum. The inner enamel epithelium differentiates into the ameloblasts. It soon invaginates to make a cup-like structure enclosing a mesodermal core, the dentinal papilla, within which the odontoblasts and pulp of the tooth develop.

The cells of the inner enamel epithelium differentiate to form a row of ameloblasts (Figs. 86 and 87), whose first function is to induce the differentiation of the underlying mesodermal cells to form odontoblasts. As soon as the latter begin to produce dentine the ameloblasts begin to produce enamel. They are then cut off from their original source of blood and are nourished from the outside by the stellate reticulum. Each ameloblast produces a rod of enamel by calcification

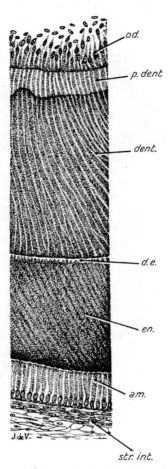

FIG. 87. Part of section of tooth of a kitten.

am. ameloblasts; *dent.* dentine; *d.e.* dentino-enamel junction; *en.* enamel; *od.* odontoblasts; *p.dent.* pre-dentine; *str.int.* stratum intermedium.
(From a preparation kindly lent by K. C. Richardson.)

of its inner end (Tomes' process) (Fig. 89). The enamel produced before and after birth is different (presumably for nutritional reasons) (Fig. 88). Similar neonatal lines can be seen in the dentine.

The tooth is thus an elevation with a mesodermal core, covered by two sorts of hard material and set in a bony socket of the jaw known as the *alveolus*. A third material, the *cement*, may be added to the surface of the tooth by the extension of the bone around the base into the depressions of the crown (Fig. 85). The differing hardness of the three materials ensures the maintenance of a rough grinding surface, which

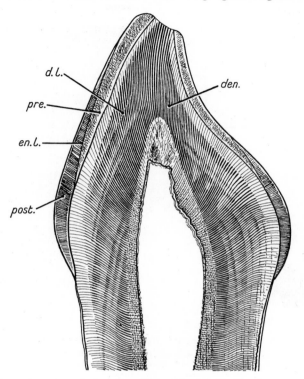

FIG. 88. Ground section of a human milk molar, showing the lines separating the enamel and dentine formed before and after birth.

den. dentine; *d.l.* neonatal line in dentine; *en.l.* neonatal line in enamel; *pre.* prenatal enamel; *post.* postnatal enamel. (After Orban.)

is especially important in the grazing herbivores for chewing the hard siliceous stems of grasses.

4. Enamel

Enamel is the hardest tissue in the body on account of its high content of mineral salts (96 per cent.) and their crystalline arrangement. It forms a layer up to 2·5 mm. thick over the cusps of the teeth. The tissue is composed of a number of enamel rods (prisms), separated by sheaths and by a cementing substance related to keratin. The rods run in a general direction at right angles to the surface of the dentine but they pass along oblique or wavy courses, forming patterns that minimize the likelihood of cleavage during mastication (Fig. 90). Each rod is composed of a number of hexagonal submicroscopic units of the mineral apatite, with axes arranged in the direction of the long axis of the rod but not exactly along it (Fig. 93). The material of the enamel

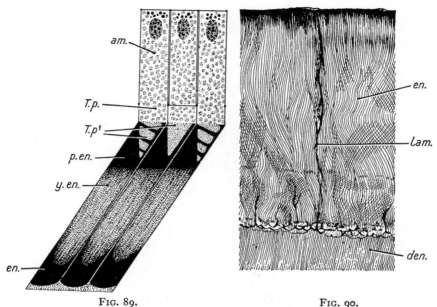

FIG. 89. FIG. 90.

FIG. 89. Diagram to show formation of enamel by ameloblasts.

am. ameloblast; *en.* fully formed enamel; *p.en.* pre-enamel; *y.en.* young enamel; *T.p.* Tomes' process; *T.p.*[1] the same where it is becoming 'homogenized' and converted to pre-enamel. (After Orban.)

FIG. 90. Section of enamel of a human tooth to show the direction of the enamel rods.

den. dentine; *en.* enamel rods; *lam.* lamella of organic material running through the enamel. (After Orban.)

is thus highly organized into a crystal pattern, and this is shown by the fact that it is strongly birefringent in polarized light.

5. Dentine

The bulk of the tooth is made up of *dentine*, which is a material resembling bone but harder on account of the regular arrangement of its constituents. It is composed of 70 per cent. of inorganic material and 30 per cent. water and organic material, the latter being chiefly collagen. The tissue consists of a fibrillar calcified ground substance through which run the protoplasmic processes of the odontoblasts (Tomes' fibres). These latter thus lie in canals, known as dentinal tubules, which may branch and anastomose (Fig. 91). The odonto-

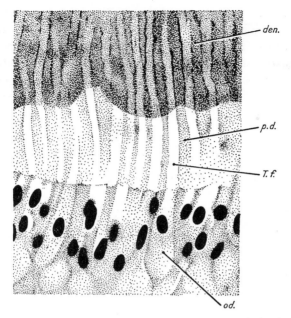

FIG. 91. Section of human tooth showing Tomes' fibres (dentinal tubules) extending into the dentine.

den. dentine; *od.* cell body of odontoblast; *p.d.* predentine (uncalcified); *T.f.* Tomes' fibre. (After Orban.)

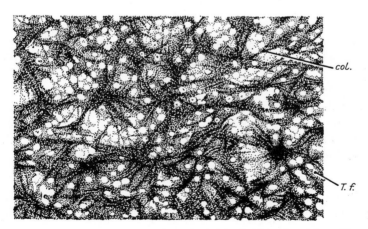

FIG. 92. Decalcified transverse section of tooth stained to show the collagenous ground substance.

col. collagen fibres; *T.f.* Tomes' fibre. (After Orban.)

blasts penetrate the substance of the dentine and it continues to grow throughout life. The collagenous fibrils run in a plane at right angles to these tubules (Fig. 92) and the inorganic matrix is laid down in the form of crystals parallel to the fibres, that is to say radiating around the dentinal canals. The general arrangement of the crystal structure

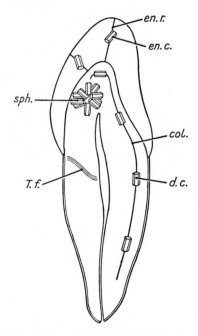

FIG. 93. Diagram to show the arrangement of the apatite crystals in a tooth. *col.* direction of collagen fibres in dentine; *d.c.* dentinal crystals; *en.c.* enamel crystals; *en.r.* direction of enamel rods; *sph.* 'spheroid' of dentinal crystals; *T.f.* direction of dentinal tubules. (After Orban.)

of the dentine is thus opposite to that of the enamel but there are also areas in which the crystals form 'spheroids' and radiate from a centre (Fig. 93). There are abundant nerve-fibres around the odontoblasts and probably some of them extend into the dentinal tubules.

6. Cement

Cement is a modified type of bone which surrounds the roots of the teeth and serves to bind them to neighbouring structures. In herbivores such as the rabbit it extends between folds of the tooth so as to form part of the grinding surface. It is less hard than dentine. Between the cement and the surrounding bone of the jaw is a system of collagenous fibres, the *periodontal membrane*, by which the tooth is attached (Fig. 85).

The tooth narrows at the base to make a *root*, but remains open, allowing blood-vessels and nerves to enter the pulp cavity. In teeth that grow continually, such as the incisors of the rabbit, the pulp is widely open below and these teeth are said to be 'without roots' and to have 'persistent pulps'. They are usually without a complete covering of enamel and are either worn away continually, as the molars of ungulates, or grow to a great size as in the tusks of elephants and spear of the narwhal.

7. The dentition

Rows of tooth germs arise along the lines of the developing upper and lower jaws and give rise to the *milk dentition*. Later in life each permanent tooth is formed by the development of a new rudiment from the stalk of the original ectodermal invagination (dental lamina) and this new bud acquires a dental papilla. The milk dentition contains fewer teeth than the permanent set. The incisors and canines are replaced, as are the anterior of the molariform teeth, the premolars. Behind these are the molars, which form only later in life and are not preceded by milk teeth. Thus in man there are 20 deciduous teeth, represented by the formula D i. $\frac{2}{2}$. c. $\frac{1}{1}$. pm. $\frac{2}{2}$ on each side. This set is complete by the second year. In the sixth year the first of the permanent teeth appears, a molar, behind the last of the milk premolars. Then between 6 and 12 years old all the milk teeth drop out and are replaced by permanent teeth. In the twelfth year a second molar is added and finally, sometime after the seventeenth year, a third molar (wisdom tooth) appears. The adult set therefore contains 32 teeth: 2x (i. $\frac{2}{2}$. c. $\frac{1}{1}$. pm. $\frac{2}{2}$. m. $\frac{3}{3}$) on each side. This is a more complete set than is found in specialized mammals, such as the rabbit, but the primitive placental dentition probably contained as many as 44 teeth: 2x (i. $\frac{3}{3}$. c. $\frac{1}{1}$. pm. $\frac{4}{4}$. m. $\frac{3}{3}$).

The shape of the teeth varies in a regular manner along the row, evidently by a gradation of the morphogenetic processes responsible for production of the hard matter. The shape of the surface of the tooth is determined by that of the enamel organ, which falls into folds whose lines control the differentiation of the odontoblasts. Grafts of complete embryonic tooth germs to different parts of the body grow well and form complete teeth, but the dentinal papilla grafted alone produces only irregular bands of dentine. The isolated enamel organ cannot produce enamel; evidently therefore the two parts are mutually dependent. Isolated tooth germs can also differentiate in tissue culture. There is at present no information about the nature of the process that determines the folding of the enamel organ and hence the form of the cusps.

In many species there is no sharp boundary between the anterior, single-cusped, incisors and canines and the series of molariform teeth. The more anterior premolars may be quite simple. There is usually

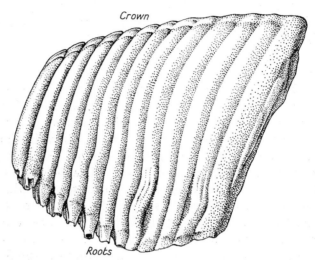

FIG. 94. Unerupted molar of an elephant to show formation by union of a number of separate units, each with its own pulp and root. These are held together by cement. The most recently formed units are to the left.

an increase in complexity of cusp passing backwards but there is no constant feature other than the history of the replacement that distinguishes premolars from molars. The incisors are the teeth that in the upper jaw occupy the premaxillae, the canines being the first teeth of the maxilla. In the lower jaw the canine is the tooth that bites in front of the upper canine. Such definitions are necessary because in some animals these anterior single-cusped teeth are all closely similar, although typically the incisors have sharp cutting edges, whereas the canines form pointed cones for piercing.

8. The evolution of mammalian teeth

The nature of the changes in morphogenesis that have produced the mammalian molar are still obscure in spite of long controversy. Two types of theory can be distinguished, according to whether the many-cusped molar is supposed to be produced by fusion of a number of reptilian teeth ('concrescence') or by formation of ridges and knobs on the sides of a reptilian cone-like tooth. Perhaps consideration of the processes of tooth development will show that there is less difference between these theories than their protagonists suggest.

In thinking about such questions it is important to bear in mind the elementary point that the teeth are produced by developmental processes! Evolutionary change consists in a change in these processes, so that some new form is produced. The morphogenetic processes that produce the reptilian tooth are extended both in space and in time. Change in the position in which the teeth rudiments form could produce 'concrescence'. Change in the time at which they appear might lead to the same result by forming one many-cusped instead of many single-cusped teeth. Thus the many single-cusped teeth could be replaced by fewer many-cusped teeth by reduction either of the distance between the tooth germs or between the times of their formation, or by reduction in both. In either sense the mammalian molar could be said to be formed by the 'fusion of reptilian teeth'. Some compound molars, those of the elephant for instance (Fig. 94), are formed by the union during development of many, at first separate, cones.

9. The dimer theory

According to the 'dimer' theory of Bolk, the ancestral reptilian teeth each carried a row of three cusps, one behind the other. Such teeth are termed 'triconodont' teeth. Bolk suggests that each mammalian molar is formed by the fusion of two such teeth that have come to lie side by side. He believes that there is evidence of this double or dimeric nature of the teeth in a septum sometimes seen in an early stage of the enamel organ. The fundamental pattern of the tooth would thus show six cusps, three on the labial and three on the buccal side.

Probably we shall never find out exactly how the embryological processes that made reptilian teeth became changed to give those of mammals. Our only evidence is the study of the embryology of modern forms and the teeth preserved as fossils. The remains of the molars of many of the earliest mammals show three cusps and therefore do not support Bolk's theory, which requires that the most primitive molars should have six cusps.

10. Trituberculy

An important generalization that makes possible an analysis of all cusp patterns was the recognition by the American palaeontologist Cope that the basic arrangement in all early mammals was a triangle of cusps in the upper molars (Young, 1950, p. 524). In 1883 Cope pointed out that of forty-one species known from the Puerco (Paleocene) period, 70 million years ago, all but four had three tubercles on the upper molars. From this observation the theory of *trituberculy* has been developed by Cope and his successors Osborn, Gregory, Scott, Simpson, and others (Gregory, 1934). The theory has had some critics, mainly because of failure to distinguish between the use of morphological, embryological, and palaeontological criteria for its terms, but it constitutes the best means at present available for expressing the historical facts and for naming the cusps.

Observation of the jaws of the simpler types of mammals shows that the upper teeth bite outside the lower and are triangular and three-cusped in shape, leaving wedge-shaped spaces between them (Figs. 95 to 98). This is true of the earliest fossil forms and of modern 'primitive' types such as the opossum and some Insectivora, and also of lower primates (*Tarsius*, fig. 95). The lower teeth also carry triangles of cusps and their surfaces form pyramids fitting into the wedge-like gaps between the upper molars. Each lower molar has in addition a posterior extension or heel (talonid), which occludes (bites) with the apex of the triangle of the upper molar.

Both upper and lower molars therefore carry triangles of cusps, with the apical member of the triangle on the inside in the upper and outside in the lower jaw. Osborn proceeded to give names to the cusps by starting from the assumption that every tooth is based on the original reptilian cone, to which other cusps have been added. He supposed that in the upper molar the inner (palatal) cone, lying at the apex of the triangle, represents the reptilian cone, and accordingly he called it the *protocone*. The outer two cones were supposed to be secondary and the anterior was called *paracone* and the posterior *metacone*.

In the lower teeth the cone at the apex of the triangle, namely, this time, the *outer* (buccal) cone, was supposed to be the original one and was called *protoconid*, the other cusps being named consequently *paraconid* and *metaconid* and the heel called *talonid*. This system of names proved remarkably convenient and it has persisted and been extended. The above cusps can be recognized in the molars of most mammals and others may be added. An internal (buccal) posterior cusp on the upper molar, called the *hypocone*, makes the tooth quadrilateral. *Protoconule* and *metaconule* added between the main upper cusps then produce a six-cusped molar, from which many modern types can be derived. Further ridges along the outer side of the tooth are known as styles. In the lower molar *entoconid* and *entoconulid* added to the heel also make a six-cusped tooth.

The tritubercular system of nomenclature lacks generality in that it assigns undue importance to the individuality of the 'cusps' and too little to the distribution of tissue-forming activities that produce them. Those who support this theory have recognized the triangular pattern in the teeth of the early members of many of the orders of mammals. The relation of these names used by comparative anatomists to those given to the cusps in human anatomy shown in Fig. 96 is as follows:

Upper molars

Anterior palatal	Protocone	
Anterior buccal	Paracone	original triangle (trigon)
Posterior buccal	Metacone	
Posterior palatal	Hypocone	heel (talon)

Lower molars

Anterior buccal	Protoconid	
Anterior lingual	Metaconid	remains of original triangle (trigonid)
Posterior buccal	Hypoconid	
Posterior lingual	Entoconid	heel (talonid)
Posterior mesial	Hypoconulid	

11. Origin of the cusp pattern

It is almost certain that the identification of the 'protocone' as the original reptilian cone cannot stand. It was early noticed that if one follows along the tooth row, the cusps of the incisors and canines, which may reasonably be supposed to be the 'primitive' cones, lie in line with the outer cusps, paracone and metacone, of the upper molar (Figs. 96 to 98). This 'premolar analogy' therefore suggests that these latter cusps represent the original centre of the tooth. This has been confirmed by the discovery in the Cretaceous deposits of Mongolia of the remains of very early placental shrew-like animals (*Deltatheridium*) in which the centre of the tooth is occupied by a ridge (*amphicone*) that is hardly divided into paracone and metacone, while the 'protocone' is a less conspicuous tubercle on the inner face of the main ridge. In the lower teeth the protoconid may more reasonably be supposed to represent the original cusp.

The evolutionary changes in the arrangement of the cusps were of course connected with changes in the way the teeth were used. The original single-cusped reptilian teeth probably interlocked when the jaw was closed, and were used for piercing the hard cases of insects (Fig. 95A). The development of the triangular form of the teeth allowed their surfaces to become more closely related and thus to serve to some extent for grinding as well as for piercing (Fig. 95B). Only when the teeth began to overlap and meet each other in a bite could they serve for grinding. The stages by which this came about are not known with certainty but may have been somewhat as follows. The lower molar developed a heel carrying a hypoconid biting in the centre of the triangle formed by the three cusps of the upper molar (Fig. 95C). Then the upper molar developed a backward heel, which produced a grinding surface with the paraconid of the lower molar behind it (Fig. 95D). Thus the effect of the whole change was to convert the teeth from piercing styles into an apparatus capable of cutting and grinding. In herbivorous mammals further modification has been in the direction of producing extensive grinding surfaces, whereas in carnivores the cusps form blades for cutting. In an omnivorous type such as man the low cusps are preserved.

12. Various types of molar teeth

Terms have been devised for certain general types of cusp pattern. When the cusps remain separate (as in man) the tooth is said to be *bunodont*. If they are 'fused', that is to say joined by intermediate masses of dentine to form loops or ridges, we speak of a *lophodont* dentition (as in the horse). When the cusps are crescentic the tooth is *selenodont* (sheep and cow). The molars of grazing animals often become very large and deep, allowing for grinding and continual replacement and are then said to be *hypsodont*, in distinction from the normal shorter or *brachydont* molars.

13. Teeth of the rabbit

In the rabbit the teeth are highly specialized, the incisors for gnawing and the molars for grinding the food. The characteristic 'rodent' incisors are arranged to give continually sharp edges. The enamel is much thicker on the anterior than on the lingual surface and since this material is harder than the dentine a sharp cutting face is always available as the tooth wears away. To replace the wear the tooth grows continually at its base and the curved roots of these incisor teeth occupy a considerable part of the skull. The small second upper

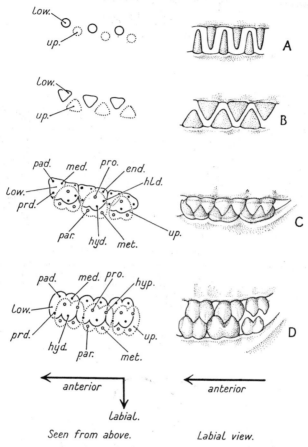

Seen from above.   *Labial view.*

Fig. 95. Diagrams to show stages of arrangement of teeth and cusps.

A, Reptilian pointed teeth with no occlusion. B, hypothetical stage in which the teeth have become triangular and rub against each other. C, *Tarsius*. Upper molars tritubercular, lower tritubercular with a heel. The protocone occludes with the heel. D, old world monkey. Upper and lower molars quadritubercular, the hypocone of the upper molar biting between two lower teeth. *end.* entoconid; *hld.* hypoconulid; *hyd.* hypoconid; *hyp.* hypocone; *low.* lower molar; *med.* metaconid; *met.* metacone; *pad.* paraconid; *par.* paracone; *prd.* protoconid; *pro.* protocone; *up.* upper molar.

incisor teeth are characteristic of the rabbits and hares (Order Lagomorpha). The true Rodentia (rats, mice, &c.) possess only a single pair of incisors and in other features show an extreme specialization for gnawing, including a joint between the two halves of the lower jaw,

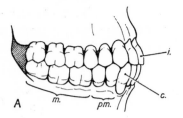

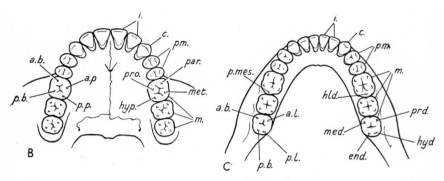

FIG. 96. Diagrams of the dentition of man.

A, in profile; B, upper jaw; C, lower jaw. *c.* canine; *i.* incisors; *m.* molars; *p.m.* premolars. In B and C the cusps are labelled with the nomenclature of human anatomists on the left, comparative anatomists on the right. *a.b.* anterior buccal; *a.l.* anterior lingual; *a.p.* anterior palatal; *p.b.* posterior buccal; *p.l.* posterior lingual; *p.p.* posterior palatal; *p.mes.* posterior mesial. Other letters as Fig. 95.

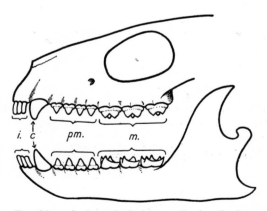

FIG. 97. Dentition of a hypothetical generalized eutherian mammal.
c. canine; *i.* incisors; *m.* molars; *pm.* premolars.
(After Le Gros Clark, *Early Forerunners of Man.*)

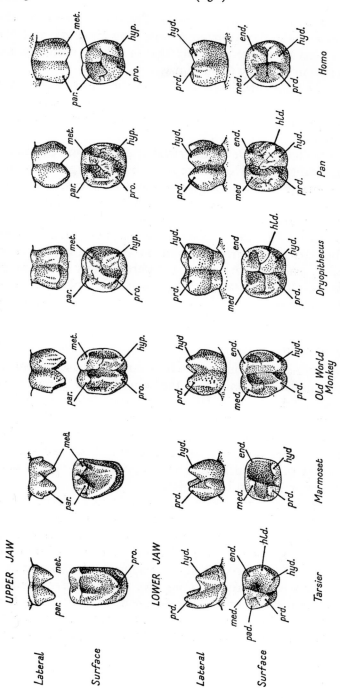

FIG. 98. 2nd molar teeth of various Primates.

end. entoconid; *hld.* hypoconulid; *hyd.* hypoconid; *hyp.* hypocone; *low.* lower molar; *med.* metaconid; *met.* metacone; *pad.* paraconid; *par.* paracone; *prd.* protoconid; *pro.* protocone; *up.* upper molar. (Drawn from skulls except upper molar of *Dryopithecus* from Gregory, *Origin and Evolution of Human Dentition*, lower molar from a cast in the British Museum.)

allowing of a grinding action of the molars. The division between the Lagomorpha and Rodentia occurred a very long time ago and the similarities between them are probably due mainly to convergence, rather than common ancestry (Young, 1950, p. 617).

The absence of canines and lower incisors in the rabbit makes a big gap or *diastema* in the tooth row, allowing the food to be passed into cheek pockets, which are chambers almost separated from the central cavity of the mouth.

The molariform teeth of the rabbit, six in the upper and five in the lower jaw, are arranged to give a large and continuous grinding surface. They no longer show a triangular pattern of cusps, but are crossed by a series of transverse ridges, developed by fusion and extension of the cusps and deepening of the valleys between them, which become filled with cement. Continual chewing of hard grasses wears away the teeth. The three different materials composing them (dentine, enamel, and cement) wear at different rates and a rough grinding surface is thus maintained. The material is replaced by persistent growth, made possible by the wide, open roots and good blood-supply.

14. The teeth of man

In the early primates the molar teeth resembled those of insectivores and this condition is retained by the living *Tarsius* (Figs. 97 and 98) and in lemurs. Triangular molars are still found in some monkeys (marmosets, Fig. 98), but in most of the higher primates the upper molars are quadrangular and carry four cusps. The lower ones lose the paraconid and often also the hypoconulid; they thus also come to have four cusps (Fig. 98). In herbivorous monkeys the molars often develop transverse ridges, as in ungulates.

In the anthropoid apes the lower molars still carry a hypoconulid and are five-cusped. The human molars are derived from a similar type, perhaps close to that of *Dryopithecus* found in the Miocene 25 million years ago (Fig. 98). In the course of human evolution the hypoconulid has usually become lost, producing the four-cusped lower molar, but traces of it remain (Fig. 96). A characteristic feature of primate dentition has been the development of spatulate cutting incisors and in man there has also been reduction of the canines towards a similar form. The whole tooth row thus acquires a smooth unbroken outline.

15. The mouth

In mammals the food is more thoroughly treated in the mouth than it is in other vertebrates. Besides the tearing action of the anterior teeth the molars break up food by grinding and this process is assisted by the action of the tongue, whose roughened upper surface rubs the food against the hard and ridged roof of the mouth.

16. The tongue

The *tongue* is a fleshy mass attached posteriorly to the pharyngeal floor. It contains bundles of striped muscle-fibres running in various directions and these give it the power to mix and manipulate the food. The front part of the tongue is covered by papillae carrying a stratified squamous epithelium, from which flakes are continually falling to form the *saliva cells*. Some of the papillae carry the taste-buds (p. 521) connected with the seventh and ninth cranial nerves, and the skin of the tongue also contains fibres for the senses of touch and pain. Like other parts of the wall of the mouth and pharynx the tongue bears numerous mucous and serous glands and also follicles of lymphoid tissue. The mouth is a region that cannot be kept sterile and it requires elaborate defence against infection. This is provided by the co-opera-tion of the rapidly desquamating skin, secretions of the glands, actions of the lymphoid tissue, and not least by the movements of the lips, cheeks, and tongue, which keep the fluids in circulation, allowing no time for decay. In spite of these defences pockets of bacteria con-tinually form in the mouth of man, especially at night, and may pro-duce unpleasant smelling products and substances with a deleterious action on the teeth (*dental caries* or decay).

17. Salivary glands

The rabbit shows a great development of the salivary glands that are characteristic of all mammals. These glands have evolved by increase in number of the gland cells found in the mouth epithelium of lower vertebrates and they include two types of cell, *serous cells* secreting a mobile liquid and *mucous cells* a more viscous one. These two are present in varying proportions in different glands and animals (Fig. 99). In man it is possible to recognize three pairs of salivary glands, *parotid*, *submaxillary*, and *sublingual*; in the rabbit there are other large masses of cells in addition to these. All are caused to secrete by the action of a reflex originating from the presence of food in the mouth. The motor path to the serous cells runs through the preganglionic parasympathetic fibres in the seventh and ninth cranial nerves and the postganglionic fibres pass to the glands from the otic and submandibular ganglia (p. 390).

Electrical stimulation of the chorda tympani nerve therefore pro-

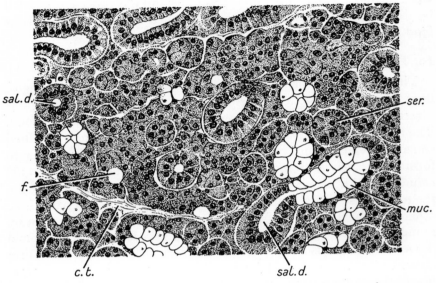

FIG. 99. Section of human submaxillary gland, showing mixed serous and mucous cells.

c.t. interlobular connective tissue; *f.* fat; *muc.* mucus-secreting alveolus; *sal.d.* salivary duct; *ser.* serous cells. (From a preparation and photograph by Mr. K. C. Richardson.)

duces a flow of watery saliva. Stimulation of the sympathetic pathways to the glands is followed by secretion of a concentrated solution of mucin and this is often held to show that the mucus-secreting cells receive motor nerves from the sympathetic system, but other interpretations are possible, since these sympathetic nerves control the blood-supply of the glands (p. 392).

Secretion of saliva is easily influenced by afferent stimuli from other sources besides the mouth and the famous experiments of Pavlov showed that impulses from almost any part of the body can be 'conditioned' to give salivary secretion if they are made to arrive shortly before, or together with, impulses in the 'unconditioned' afferents for the reflex (see p. 455).

The saliva serves to moisten the food and its mucus to lubricate it and make its passage easy. In addition it contains an amyloytic (starchsplitting) enzyme *ptyalin*, which, at the nearly neutral pH of the saliva, acts on starch, as can be followed by chewing potato and watching the changing action of the products on iodine. Instead of the blue colour produced by the starch itself there is first a red colour, due to the intermediate product erythro-dextrin, and then no colour when all the starch has been completely changed to maltose. The action of the ptyalin continues in the centre of the bolus of food after it reaches the stomach, until the acid there stops it. Evidently this mechanism for the break-down of starch soon after the food has been eaten forms an important part of the digestive system of mammals.

XII

DIGESTION

1. The dissolution of food materials

THE process of breaking up the food is begun in the mouth by the teeth, tongue, and enzymes of the saliva. The rest of the alimentary canal is concerned with completing the physical break-up of the tissues that have been eaten and the absorption from them of the molecules needed by the mammal.[1]

The dissolution of the food is accomplished chemically by the combined effects of enzymes secreted by the gut and its glands and the action of symbiotic bacteria living within the gut. The high temperature of the body assists the action of the ferments and the gut becomes a great vat in which the macerated food is quickly acted upon by the enzymes and bacteria. The most striking special developments of the mammalian plan of digestion are indeed not regions of special enzyme production but large chambers harbouring symbionts, such as the elaborate 'stomach' of sheep, cows, and other ruminants, or the caeca of the large intestine of rabbits and horses. The movement of food along the gut and the secretion of the glands are so regulated as to keep the mass in the right physical and chemical conditions for these processes. The movement of *peristalsis* by which the food is propelled operates rhythmically and continually, rather as does the heart-beat (p. 285). It is regulated by the operation of receptors in the wall of the gut, which signal if conditions are not favourable for digestion, setting up reflexes that speed or slow peristalsis. Chemical signalling by hormones is also employed (p. 527).

Thus the regulation of digestion is ensured mainly by a series of mechanisms laid down by heredity. Like the food intake it is also influenced by the operation of higher nervous centres in the medulla oblongata, hypothalamus, and cerebral cortex. Electrical stimulation of the hypothalamus, or of parts of the frontal lobes of the cerebral cortex, produces changes in gastric and intestinal motility. Following removal of parts of the frontal lobes from monkeys it was found that the stomach becomes more active and excessively large amounts of food

[1] For references on digestion see Gregory, 1954.

are consumed; similar symptoms may appear in man after injury or operations on the frontal lobes.

The processes of digestion thus also come under the influence of the higher cerebral centres, whose actions are influenced by memories set up during the lifetime of the individual. In man digestion may be profoundly influenced by learning processes. When habits of food consumption or digestion are interfered with, the balance of the organism may become severely disturbed.

2. Structure of the gut

The gut is a tube of varying width, extending from mouth to anus and including oesophagus, stomach, small intestine, caecum, large intestine, and rectum (Fig. 100). As the food mass passes along the gut it meets the characteristic secretions of each part and these, together with the fermenting action of the bacteria that live in some parts, change the food and make its constituents available for absorption. The *oesophagus* is a simple passage through which the food passes within a few seconds after eating. The *stomach* is a much wider sac where the food is received. Here it is sterilized by mixing with acid, a most important provision, especially for a warm-blooded animal. Here also the enzyme pepsin begins to act on the proteins. The *small intestine* is a long narrow tube where the food is mixed with enzymes and quickly broken down into simpler constituents, which are then absorbed into the blood-stream (Jacobson and Noer, 1952). The reaction of this region is only faintly acid and its bacteria are 'fermentative', that is to say they act upon carbohydrates and produce organic acids. The following *caecum* and *large intestine* have nearly neutral contents and are highly charged with bacteria, some of which are 'putrefactive' and act on proteins. In the rabbit there are other bacteria here that play an important part in breaking up refractory foodstuffs such as cellulose. An important function of the large intestine is the absorption of water from the gut contents. Residual matter is then extruded at the anus, in man some twenty-four hours after eating.

The various portions of the canal therefore have different roles in the mixing, movement, and absorption of the actively fermenting mass that continually passes through the body. Nevertheless all parts conform in structure to a common plan (Fig. 101). There is a central lining or *mucosa*, derived from the endoderm, and outside this is a thin layer of muscle, the *muscularis mucosae*. Below the mucous membrane the wall is composed of a layer of connective tissue, the *submucosa*,

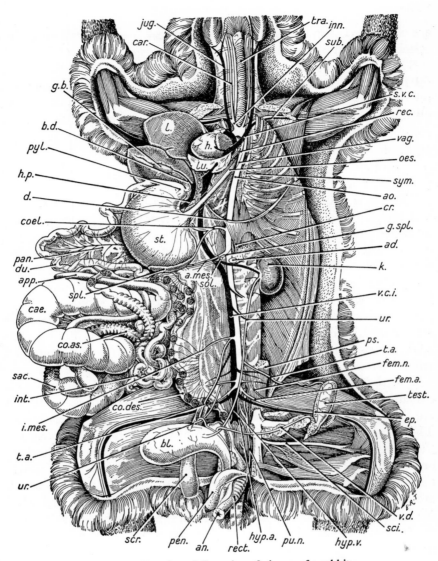

FIG. 100. Drawing of dissection of viscera of a rabbit.

ad. left adrenal; *a.mes.* anterior mesenteric artery and nerves; *an.* anus; *ao.* thoracic aorta; *app.* appendix; *b.d.* bile duct; *bl.* bladder; *cae.* caecum; *car.* common carotid artery; *co.as.* ascending colon; *co.des.* descending colon; *coel.* coeliac artery; *cr.* crus of diaphragm; *d.* diaphragm; *du.* duodenum; *ep.* epididymis; *fem.a.* femoral artery; *fem.n.* femoral nerve; *g.b.* gall bladder; *g.spl.* great splanchnic nerve; *h.* heart; *h.p.* hepatic portal vein; *hyp.a.* hypogastric artery; *hyp.v.* hypogastric vein; *i.mes.* inferior mesenteric artery; *inn.* innominate artery; *int.* small intestine; *jug.* jugular vein; *k.* left kidney; *l.* liver; *lu.* lung (collapsed); *oes.* oesophagus; *pan.* pancreas; *pen.* penis; *ps.* psoas muscle; *pu.n.* pudendal nerve; *pyl.* pylorus; *rec.* recurrent laryngeal nerve; *rect.* rectum; *sac.* sacculus rotundus; *sci.* sciatic nerve; *scr.* scrotum; *spl.* spleen; *sol.* solar plexus (coeliac and anterior mesenteric ganglia); *st.* stomach; *sub.* subclavian artery and vein; *s.v.c.* superior vena cava; *sym.* thoracic sympathetic chain; *t.a.* testicular artery; *test.* testis; *tra.* trachea; *ur.* ureter; *vag.* vagus nerve; *v.c.i.* inferior vena cava; *v.d.* vas deferens.

and outside this are layers of *circular* and *longitudinal muscles*. The outer surface of the oesophagus is attached by connective tissue to other structures, but most of the remaining portions of the gut are covered by a layer of flattened mesothelial cells, making a smooth serous membrane, the peritoneum which allows free movement within the peritoneal cavity. The gut is suspended from the dorsal wall of the

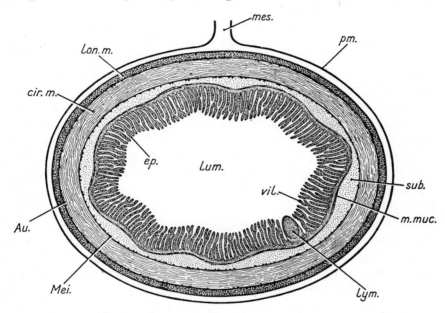

FIG. 101. Diagram of structure of intestine as seen in transverse section.

Au. Auerbach's (myenteric) plexus; *cir.m.* circular muscle layer; *ep.* epithelial lining of mucosa; *lon.m.* longitudinal muscle layer; *lum.* lumen; *lym.* lymph nodule; *mes.* mesentery; *Mei.* Meissner's (submucous) plexus; *m.muc.* muscularis mucosae; *pm.* peritoneum; *sub.* submucosa; *vil.* villus.

coelom by a fold, the mesentery, which consists of connective tissue covered with mesothelium and carries the blood and lymph vessels and nerves to and from the gut.

The inner surface of the mucosa is folded in the small intestine into *villi*. Some of the lining cells (Dalton, 1951) secrete mucus and there are other glands that have developed from the endodermal epithelium by sinking more or less deeply into the wall of the gut or even outside it like the pancreas. Secretion is controlled by the nerve-fibres of the submucous or *Meissner's plexus*, lying between the muscular and mucous layers and connected with the sympathetic and parasympathetic systems (p. 391). Between the two main muscle layers is the *myenteric plexus of Auerbach*, which controls the main movements of the gut and is of course also part of the autonomic nervous system.

3. Movements of the gut. Peristalsis

The movements of the gut show a certain similarity throughout, but characteristic features appear in each region. The food is moved along by the process of *peristalsis*, which consists essentially in a contraction of the circular muscles of the wall of the gut at and behind (oral to) any point distended by the presence of a bolus of food. The effect of this is to push the food onwards towards the anus. Bayliss and Starling described the movement by saying that the 'law of the intestine' is constriction on the oral side and relaxation on the anal side of any stimulated point. The contraction is usually more prominent than the relaxation. Peristalsis is well marked in the oesophagus and stomach. In the latter it occurs during digestion soon after a meal and begins again some hours later as the *hunger contractions*. These are accompanied by characteristic sensations, presumably due to stimulation by the contractions of receptor organs lying in the stomach wall. The afferent impulses from hunger contractions probably serve early in life simply to activate the higher centres much as do pain impulses. Thus they initiate the crying of an infant that has never yet been fed. The tendency to stomach peristalsis is therefore inborn and, far from being 'reflex', is itself a powerful initiator of action. It is of course possible that the actual contractions are initiated by the action of the gastric secretions, but either these or some previous stage in the chain of events must be inherent in the system rather than reflexly induced (see Gregory, 1954).

Peristaltic waves occur in the small intestine but here we find in addition the *segmenting movements*, which are simple non-travelling constrictions by which the food is churned and mixed. In the intestine there are also marked *pendular movements*, contractions primarily of the longitudinal muscle, shortening a loop of the intestine and throwing the chyme from one end to the other, mixing it as in a cocktail shaker. These movements occur rhythmically at a frequency as high as twenty per minute in the duodenum of the rabbit during certain phases of digestion.

The large intestine shows relatively infrequent movements, the contents being distributed and divided by a series of segmenting constrictions. Peristaltic waves occur and in man may take the form of mass peristalsis in which one large wave sweeps the contents forward into the rectum. The latter is normally empty and its filling by mass peristalsis provides the stimulus for defaecation.

The movements of the gut are under the influence of the central nervous system, acting through the autonomic nervous system, but many of them are able to continue after isolation. The segmenting and pendular movements of the small intestine continue in strips of muscle from which all nerves have been removed. Peristalsis depends on the presence of the nerve plexuses and is usually increased by action of the vagus, decreased by the sympathetic nerves (see p. 391), though it can continue in absence of connexion with both of these. Movements of the stomach have been shown to be influenced by stimulation of the hypothalamus and even of the frontal region of the cerebral cortex (p. 421).

4. The oesophagus

The bolus of food is passed from the mouth through the pharynx to the oesophagus by raising the tongue and contraction of the muscles of the palate, the soft palate being raised to close the nasopharynx and the hyoid bone to close the larynx as described on p. 204. The oesophagus is a straight tube with some striped and unstriped muscle in its wall and a lining of stratified squamous epithelium, with some mucous glands in man. Its muscles push the food along by an involuntary movement of peristalsis, by which the food is passed through the neck and thorax to the stomach.

5. The stomach

The stomach is a portion of the alimentary canal formed by special development of the lower end of the oesophagus; it is not found in the lowest vertebrates (lampreys). In mammals it shows its affinity with the oesophagus to various degrees in different species. In its most developed parts (Fig. 102) it has a lining of high columnar mucus-secreting cells, folded to form myriads of deep pits, into the bases of which open the ducts of long, tubular *chief glands*. These glands are lined by two types of cell, the *pepsin-secreting* or *chief cells* and the larger *parietal* or *oxyntic cells*, which produce hydrochloric acid. In fishes the pepsin and acid are both produced in a single type of cell and the mammalian condition may be said to show a more differentiated or 'advanced' state in this respect. In addition the openings of the glands are in mammals guarded by special mucus-producing '*neck cells*' not present in fishes. On account of the presence of the gastric glands the mucosa of the stomach is very thick. Outside of it lie the other layers, arranged in the way explained on p. 239.

The stomach is a bag whose shape varies in different mammals. It

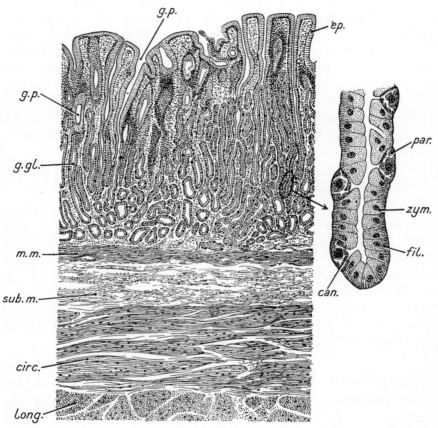

FIG. 102. Part of transverse section of gastric mucosa, from the fundus of the stomach of a cat.

can. canaliculus of parietal cell; *circ.* circular muscle; *ep.* columnar, mucus-secretory epithelium; *fil.* filaments in chief cells; *g.gl.* gastric gland; *g.p.* gastric pit; *long.* longitudinal muscle; *m.m.* muscularis mucosae; *par.* parietal (HCl) cell; *sub.m.* submucosa; *zym.* zymogen (chief or pepsin-secreting) cell. (From a preparation and photograph by Mr. K. C. Richardson.)

shows an upper *cardiac region*, close to the opening of the oesophagus, then a main portion, the *fundus*, and finally a *pyloric region*, close to the *pyloric sphincter*, which guards the opening to the duodenum. The cardiac region usually contains only mucous glands. The fundus has the typical stomach structure with 'chief glands'. In the pyloric region the glands have no parietal cells; the juice they produce contains no acid and is mostly mucus. In some mammals a large part of the stomach has the structure of the cardiac part, that is to say resembles the oesophagus. For instance the *rumen* of sheep and cows is a large chamber of this type, in which the food ferments under the action of symbiotic bacteria (Young, 1950, p. 702).

In man the stomach varies in shape but is generally elongated, often turning up at its lower end as a J. Food enters it almost immediately after swallowing, being only briefly retained by a weak *cardiac sphincter* at the entrance. Waves of peristalsis pass along the human stomach at the rate of about three every minute. With the arrival of each wave at the pylorus the latter opens and some of the food is passed into the duodenum. Some material therefore passes through the stomach within a few minutes after the beginning of a meal, especially if the food is liquid; solid food remains in the stomach for as long as four hours. While it is there it is acted upon by the *pepsin* of the gastric juice which, in the acid solution of the stomach (about 0·4 per cent. HCl), breaks down proteins into polypeptide fractions known as *peptones* and *proteoses*. These molecules are not absorbed until they have been further broken up in the intestine. Little food is absorbed from the stomach but under some conditions small molecules, for example those of alcohol, may pass through its wall and quickly enter the blood-stream. Another action that goes on in the stomach is the clotting of milk, by means of an enzyme *rennin*, which is particularly active in new-born mammals.

The secretion of the gastric glands of the stomach is controlled partly by a reflex action, whose afferent pathway may be the sight or smell of food or the presence of food in the mouth or stomach itself, the efferent pathway being through the vagus nerve. In addition the presence of food in the stomach causes liberation into the blood of a hormone that excites secretion of gastric juice (*gastrin*).

6. The small intestine

In the stomach the food is churned up into a paste of mucus and enzyme known as *chyme*, ready to be passed in a liquid condition into the duodenum.

A sharp change takes place in the process of digestion as food passes the pyloric sphincter and enters the intestine. This corresponds to the point at which the mid-gut proper began in the lowest vertebrates and here the breaking up of all the various types of foodstuff proceeds actively. The stomach, for all its importance, can be considered as a bag to contain the food that has been taken in. Until the food passes the pylorus the only important enzymatic actions upon it are those of the ptyalin and pepsin, and little absorption has taken place. Beyond the pylorus the food is mixed with enzymes responsible for breaking down all the chief classes of foodstuff and absorption of the products into the blood-stream begins.

The gut distal to this point is essentially a tube with the basic plan already described, namely a mucous lining, connective tissue sub-mucosa, two layers of muscles, and an outer covering of peritoneum. The intestine may be divided into two main sections, the *small intestine*, in which the breakdown of foodstuffs is completed and absorption takes place, and the *large intestine*, which is a region concerned with the absorption of water from the food mass. Between these two great divisions of the intestine there lies a blind diverticulum the *caecum*. This is small in man but very large in the rabbit and some other herbivorous mammals, serving as a receptacle in which the food stagnates while cellulose and other constituents refractory to the action of the animal's own juices are broken down by the enzymes of symbiotic bacteria.

The first part of the small intestine is the *duodenum* (Figs. 100 and 103), which receives the juices of the liver and pancreas and has itself a very glandular wall. In the rabbit it makes a U-shaped loop within which lies the *pancreas*. The bile-duct enters at the upper end of the duodenum. The pancreatic duct in the rabbit enters at the distal loop, about 10 cm. lower down. The chyme coming from the stomach is therefore mixed with bile and the secretions of the special duodenal glands (Brunner's glands) before it receives the pancreatic enzymes. In man the bile-duct and pancreatic duct enter the duodenum together, shortly beyond the pylorus. Distally the duodenum passes without abrupt change into the second part of the small intestine the *ileum*.[1]

The mucosa of the whole small intestine is thrown into characteristic finger-like villi, which are continually contracting and re-expanding and serve to increase the absorptive surface and to move the liquid in contact with it. The surface of the extremities of the villi is covered by columnar cells, having on the face turned towards the intestinal contents a series of striations or 'brush border'. The striations consist of filaments running at right angles to the surface and presumably indicate the presence of a permeable membrane that allows the passage of the foodstuffs. The intake of food molecules is at least partly an active process. The outer region of the cell is rich in

---

[1] In some animals the small intestine below the duodenum can be divided into jejunum and ileum, the former having a thicker, more vascular wall.

the enzyme phosphatase, which is probably part of a system for making the necessary energy available. Mucus-secreting cells are also present on the villi and are known from their form as *goblet cells.*

The depressions between the villi are known as the *crypts of*

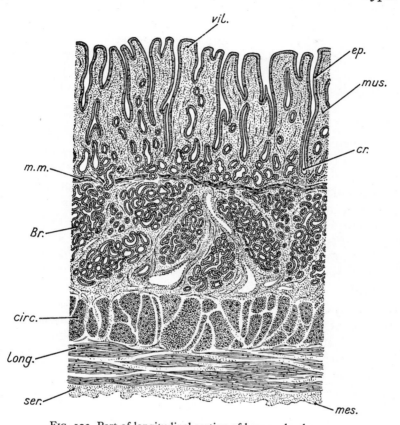

FIG. 103. Part of longitudinal section of human duodenum.

Br. Brunner's glands; *circ.* circular muscle; *cr.* crypt of Lieberkühn; *ep.* epithelium with columnar and goblet cells; *long.* longitudinal muscle; *m.m.* muscularis mucosae; *mes.* mesothelium; *mus.* smooth muscle of villi; *ser.* serosa; *vil.* villus.

Lieberkühn and they are lined by columnar and goblet cells, together with other cells also apparently secretory, the *argentaffin cells* and the *Paneth cells*, which are probably responsible for production of the intestinal enzymes. In the duodenum there are further numerous *pyloric* or *Brunner's glands*, lying deeper within the submucosa and having a structure and secretion similar to those of the glands at the pyloric end of the stomach. This secretion is alkaline and contains mucus but little enzyme.

As the chyme enters the duodenum it is mixed with bile and the *succus entericus* from the intestinal wall and Brunner's glands. These render the chyme less acid and provide powerful enzymes, so that the whole becomes a copious liquid mass of rapidly changing composition. In spite of the alkaline juices added to it the reaction of the duodenal contents is usually acid, about pH 5·5 in man. The pancreatic enzymes therefore do not work at their optimum, which is alkaline. The lower regions of the small intestine are also acid, as a result of the presence of organic acids produced by bacteria. The contents of the large intestine are usually slightly acid or neutral.

7. The pancreas

The *pancreas*, occupying the space between the limbs of the duodenum, is a branching set of tubes ending in blind secretory sacs or *acini* (Fig. 104). The secretory cells contain a number of zymogen granules, which are discharged during activity and replaced from prezymogen granules, associated with the Golgi apparatus of the cell, lying near the nucleus. Among the alveoli lie a number of masses of cells, the *islets of Langerhans*, constituting an endocrine organ that is responsible for secreting into the blood the hormone *insulin*, whose presence is necessary to allow the tissues to utilize glucose (p. 567).

Control of secretion of the pancreatic juice is both hormonal and nervous. Bayliss and Starling showed in 1902 that the presence of food in the duodenum excites the production of the hormone *secretin*, which circulates to the pancreas and excites its secretion. This was the first clearly demonstrated case of chemical action at a distance in the body and its discovery led to the introduction of the word 'hormone' and to the development of the concept of endocrine secretion (p. 527). Stimulation of the vagus also excites secretion of pancreatic juice, small in amount but especially viscous and rich in enzymes.

The pancreatic juice has a wide variety of actions, as its name implies. It is an alkaline liquid, containing the protease trypsin, also amylase, lipase, maltase, and the clotting enzyme rennin. The *trypsin* is secreted in an inactive form *trypsinogen*, which is readily activated in the intestine by an enzyme *enterokinase*. Acting in alkaline solution trypsin splits proteins or polypeptides into fractions that contain two or at most a few amino-acids (dipeptides). These are then acted upon by the enzyme *erepsin* that is produced by the intestinal mucosa, forming single amino-acids, which are absorbed into the cells of the gut. The *pancreatic amylase* is more powerful than the amylase in the saliva and rapidly breaks down either boiled or unboiled starch. The digestion of starch and other carbohydrates is completed by enzymes of the succus entericus, such as *maltase, sucrase,* and *lactase;* the end products that are absorbed are monosaccharides such as glucose.

For the digestion of fats the *pancreatic lipase* is the most important

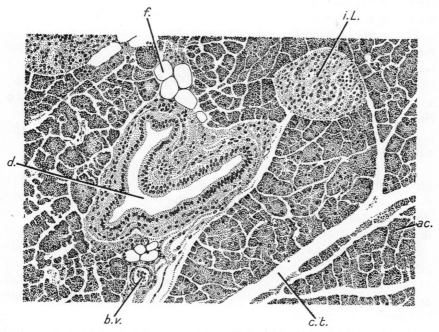

FIG. 104. Section of the pancreas of the guinea-pig.
ac. acini; *b.v.* blood vessel; *c.t.* interlobular connective tissue; *d.* interlobular duct; *f.* fat; *i.L.* islet of Langerhans.
(From a preparation and photograph by Mr. K. C. Richardson.)

agent; it splits them into glycerol and fatty acids, which are absorbed. Owing to the high surface tension fat suspended in water tends to form large globules, which would not be easily acted upon by the enzymes. The breaking up of these to make an emulsion of fine globules is largely the work of certain substances in the bile secreted by the liver, such as sodium glycocholate, whose parent acid is formed from the amino-acid glycine and cholic acid. These *bile salts* have great powers of reducing surface tension and thus of emulsifying the fats. In some forms of *jaundice* the bile-duct is blocked by in-fection, or the liver otherwise disturbed; fat is not emulsified and foods containing it therefore remain undigested. The bile-salts have a further specific action on the lipase of the pancreas, which is unable to exert its action if they are absent.

The secretions of the duodenal wall, pancreas, and liver therefore provide a number of enzymes able to split many types of ingested matter into products useful for the body. In addition to the enzymes mentioned there are also others in the succus entericus able to act on nucleotides and other materials, making them available for the body.

The food is passed from the stomach into the duodenum as fast as it can be acted upon in the latter. The pylorus is a thick ring of circular muscle, which relaxes each time that a peristaltic wave arrives from the stomach, provided that the contents of the duodenum are not too acid. Probably there are receptors in the duodenum that respond to the presence of the acid and their discharge reflexly inhibits the opening of the pylorus, thus ensuring sufficient neutralization of the stomach acid.

Food is passed along the intestine by waves of peristalsis and it is mixed, shaken, and churned by the segmenting and pendular movements. During passage along the duodenum the processes of breakdown are completed and most of the absorption takes place in the jejunum and ileum. The protein products are taken in either as single amino-acids or as simple peptides. Probably they are immediately acted upon by enzymes within the intestinal cells, so that they appear in the blood as di- or tri-peptides as well as amino-acids. The glucose and other products of carbohydrate digestion pass directly through the intestinal wall into the blood.

The fatty acids absorbed mostly do not reach the blood-stream, but pass either through or between the intestinal cells into the lymph spaces lying behind. Here fats are resynthesized and collected by special lymph-vessels, the *lacteals*, discharging ultimately into the thoracic duct (p. 264). If an animal is dissected soon after taking a fatty meal the mesentery will be seen crowded with rows of these beautifully white lacteal channels.

8. The liver

To provide for the absorption of the food products the intestine has a large blood-supply from the branches of the *superior mesenteric artery*, which leaves the aorta close behind the coeliac artery and sends many branches spreading out through the mesentery. From the intestine the blood does not pass directly back to the heart but to the liver, by the *hepatic portal vein* (Fig. 100). This enables the liver to perform those of its functions that are concerned with conversion and storage of the food taken in. Perhaps at an early stage of evolution the liver may have served directly as an organ for breaking down food. In *Amphioxus* the liver is represented by a hollow diverticulum, which secretes digestive enzymes (Young, 1950, p. 33). This strictly digestive function of the liver is still represented in mammals by the action of the bile in emulsifying fats (p. 247). But the main action of the liver is to convert the foodstuffs into whatever products are needed by the body. The liver develops as an outgrowth of the gut, but comes to form a compact mass of gland cells (Figs. 105 and 106), arranged in radiating lines, usually forming a pattern of lobules.

The branches of the hepatic portal vein break up around the outside of the lobules to form the *interlobular veins*, from which branches carry the blood to *liver sinusoids*, spaces in which the blood comes close to the columns of liver cells, thus allowing interchange of substances to take place. At the centre of each lobule is an *intra-lobular vein* and all of these join to form the *hepatic vein*, by which blood is carried back to the heart.

The liver is an organ with many functions, which may be grouped under five headings: (*a*) those concerned with metabolism of the food, (*b*) production of the bile, (*c*) activities concerned with the composition of the blood, (*d*) protective and detoxicating activities, (*e*) perhaps the production of heat. Under several of these headings we could recognize subdivisions and it is clear that the liver occupies a very important place in vertebrate life; its cells, primarily digestive in function, have come to constitute a chemical workshop for the body.

The actions of the cells of the liver on the food are varied and depend upon the condition of the animal at the time. Thus if amino-acids are needed for building the body they are passed on in the blood-stream, but in an adult more amino-acids are usually taken than are needed for building and the excess is *de-aminated* in the liver, the nitrogen being converted into urea, which is passed to the kidney for removal, while the remaining parts of the molecules are available for combustion to provide energy. Similarly carbohydrate may be either passed on or converted into *glycogen*, in which form it is stored in the liver. A third set of activities in the liver is concerned with fat metabolism and the liver-cells are commonly filled with fatty granules. Many other substances are also dealt with by the organ, for instance vitamin A is synthesized from its carotene precursor, hence the richness of fish liver oils in this vitamin. Iron and copper are metabolized and stored in the liver and many other processes go on there.

The production of bile by the liver reflects the origin of the gland as an outgrowth of the gut and we may indeed consider the columns of liver-cells as tubular glands with the blood running in the sinusoids

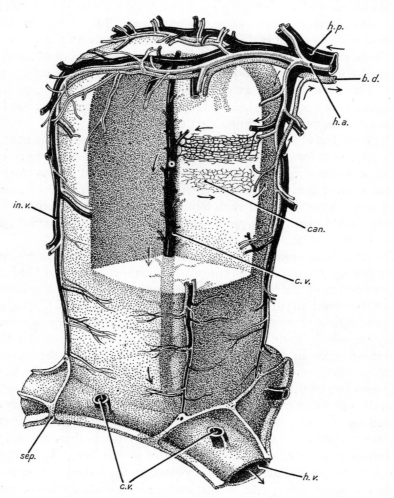

Fig. 105. Diagram of the arrangement of the parts of a lobule of the liver of a pig.
b.d. bile duct; *can.* bile canaliculi; *c.v.* central (intralobular) vein; *h.a.* hepatic artery; *h.p.* hepatic portal vein; *h.v.* hepatic vein; *in.v.* interlobular vein (hepatic); *l.* liver cells; *sep.* interlobular septum; *sin.* liver sinusoid. (From a wax model, after Braus.)

between them; at the 'centre' of each tube is a virtual space, the *bile canaliculus*, into which the cells pour the bile. As actually observed in sections this arrangement shows columns of cells, separated by spaces that are alternately sinusoids and bile canaliculi, but special methods are required to identify the latter. The bile canaliculi join around the outside of each lobule to form major bile-channels, which unite to lead to the *gall-bladder*, from which the bile-duct proceeds to the duodenum. The bile is alkaline in man but acid in the cat and dog. It contains, besides the bile-salts already mentioned, the *bile-pigments*,

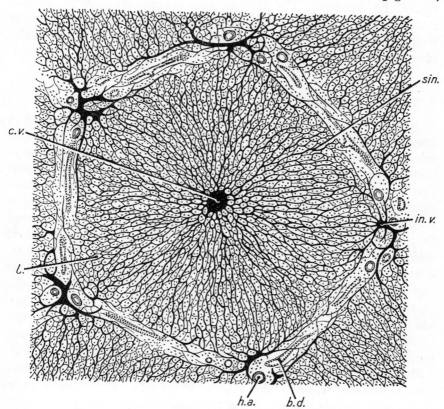

FIG. 106. Section of liver of rabbit after injection of the portal vein. Abbreviations as Fig. 105. (After Sobotta.)

which are derived by breakdown of the haemoglobin of the blood, and also the polyhydric alcohol *cholesterol* and the phosphatide *lecithin*; the former of these is the main constituent of gall-stones. Several functions have been suggested for the bile; only those concerned with the digestion of fats are certain but the bile probably also has an action on the movements of the gut.

The detoxicating functions of the liver are perhaps connected with those that are more strictly metabolic. Many substances that have a pronounced action when introduced into the body, such as alcohol or anaesthetics, are broken down in the liver and rendered ineffective.

The sinusoids of the liver contain in their walls many cells of the reticulo-endothelial system (histiocytes), here known as the *cells of Kupffer*. These are responsible for removing from the blood-stream particles of foreign matter, dead bacteria, &c. The liver is also concerned in regulating the amount and composition of the blood, destroying old red cells and, in the embryo, forming new ones, as well as producing some of the protein components of the blood, the fibrinogen and prothrombin (p. 271).

9. The large intestine

Nearly all the absorption from the gut takes place as the food is passing along the small intestine; the large intestine is a region in which the water secreted previously to make the fermenting mass is reabsorbed. This is evidently a very important function in mammals that live on land and are liable to be short of water. The large intestine may also have other functions. In the rabbit the small intestine is swollen at its lower end to form the *sacculus rotundus* and just beyond this is attached an enormous blind sac, the *caecum*, where cellulose and other resistant materials in the food are acted upon by symbiotic bacteria. The caecum is a thin-walled sacculated structure, whose surface is increased by a spiral valve. Presumably materials liberated by the bacteria are absorbed through the wall of the caecum, as they are from the rumen of the sheep (Young, 1950, p. 701). The caecum terminates in the *vermiform appendix*, which has thick walls and much lymphoid tissue, perhaps concerned here, as elsewhere in the gut, with the neutralization of bacterial toxins. In man and other mammals with a reduced caecum the appendix perhaps retains some antibacterial functions, though it can be removed without any evident ill effects.

The *large intestine* proper (*colon*) proceeds from the sacculus rotundus and is characteristically constricted at regular intervals, especially in its lower part. The wall of the large intestine differs from that of the small in having no villi but there are glands of Lieberkühn and many mucus-secreting goblet cells. The action of the bacterial population on the contents of the colon, and especially on proteins, produces a variety of putrefactive products, some of which are toxic when injected into the blood-stream (histamine, skatole, indole, &c.). It had often been suggested that absorption of these products produces ill effects in man, especially in constipation, but probably the wall of the colon normally prevents the absorption of these substances almost completely. Like other parts of the intestine it contains large amounts of lymphoid tissue.

10. Digestion and homeostasis

The importance of intake of materials and digestion for maintenance of living organization needs no emphasis. Yet it is interesting to recall how little we understand about the system that controls the rate at which food is taken and hence growth and replacement proceed, although these processes limit the size and many other aspects of the organism. No doubt hereditary influences control the setting up of the peristaltic and reflex processes of the gut that are the basic triggers for the actions that lead to intake of food. Nevertheless the actual food-gathering behaviour of an adult mammal is largely controlled by the higher nervous centres (p. 479). Food is sought at certain times and in certain ways, according to a pattern that has been acquired during the lifetime of the individual.

We can say therefore that the basic pattern of feeding and digestion is controlled by the hereditary instructions, determining especially the structure of the teeth and of the alimentary canal. The regulation of the sequence of events during digestion involves many reflexes passing through the autonomic nervous system and these are also laid down by heredity. Chemical signalling also plays a part. Information acquired during the lifetime greatly influences the whole process, through the higher cerebral centres. There are also changes in the alimentary canal and its glands according to the type of food consumed. The gut of rats becomes longer on a vegetable than on a meat diet and the enzymes of the pancreas become adjusted to suit the type of food that is habitually consumed.

So far as is known there is no detailed system of feed-back by which shortage of raw material in any single organ sets up processes that lead to intake of supplies of it. Shortages lead to hunger contractions and hence to the search for food and consumption of it. The adequacy of these processes is ensured in the long run by the operations of natural selection. Those organisms whose methods of food selection and digestion are inadequate fail to grow or to survive.

XIII

THE INTERNAL ENVIRONMENT AND COMPOSITION OF THE BODY FLUIDS

1. The internal environment

MANY of the characteristic properties of cells depend on the difference between the composition of the cytoplasm and that of the surrounding fluids. One marked difference is that the substance of the cells is rich in potassium and poor in sodium, whereas in the blood and perhaps intercellular fluids the reverse is the case. The significance of this difference in the activities of the nervous system is discussed on p. 339; no doubt similar differences maintained across the surface membranes are important in many other tissues. It was suggested by Macallum that the low sodium concentration within the cells represents the condition of the sea at the time when protoplasm first became separated from it, little salt having as yet been washed down from the land. Similarly the concentration of the sodium chloride in the blood plasma (0·75 per cent. in mammals), which is much lower than that in the sea today (up to 3·5 per cent.) has been held to represent the condition in the sea of the Cambrian period 500 million years ago, when the vertebrate blood system became established.

Whatever truth there may be in these historical speculations (see Pantin, 1931) the difference between cells and their surroundings is certainly fundamental to the life of mammals today. The system of spaces around and between the cells has become developed into an elaborate set of channels, sometimes called the *internal environment*. In some of these spaces the fluids circulate actively, notably in the vascular and lymphatic systems, but there is much in common between the cells that line the blood-vessels and the cells of the connective tissues that make up the packing between the special cells of each organ.

Various systems are adopted to classify the fluids of the internal environment for purposes of description and analysis. These distinctions between blood, lymph, and connective tissues are important and valuable, but it must be remembered that even when a fluid is enclosed in a relatively complete set of vessels, as is the blood, it is still not by any means isolated from the rest of the body. Considerable amounts of fluid may leave and re-enter the blood-vessels through the walls of the capillaries and we cannot regard 'the blood' as a distinct substance, constant in amount (Ravdin *et al.*, 1953). Moreover rapid interchanges take place between the cells and the 'spaces' in the body that contain fluid, including the cell contents.

We may list the intercellular spaces as:

1. The blood system.
2. The lymphatic system.
3. The cerebro-spinal spaces.
4. The coelomic spaces of the pleural, pericardial, and peritoneal cavities.
5. Other tissue spaces.

The liquids contained in these spaces, together with a few special liquids, such as the humours of the eye, provide the media within which the cells lie. Not all of the 'spaces' have equally definite boundaries. The coelomic cavities are limited by well-marked covering mesothelia. The blood and cerebro-spinal fluids are enclosed in channels that are mostly circumscribed but are 'open' in some places, for example the sinusoids of the liver. The lymphatic system includes some definite lymphatic vessels, which may communicate also with a system of tissue spaces between the cells; the latter is not definitely demarcated nor lined by endothelial cells.

In view of this complexity and vagueness of the spaces within the body it is not easy to specify exactly the limits of the internal environment that is often supposed to be provided for the cells. Claude Bernard planted the conception of an internal environment in the brains of biologists with his dictum that 'la fixité du milieu intérieur est la condition de la vie libre'. He was thinking mainly of the blood and in particular of the blood in the larger vessels of mammals, which is kept remarkably constant in its content of inorganic salts, oxygen, hydrogen-ion, and materials necessary for the cells, such as glucose, protein, and fat. Even this fixity is only a steady state based on a continual change in the composition of the blood; as it passes through the capillaries, as we shall see, it loses water, salts, and other small molecules and becomes temporarily a more concentrated protein solution.

To regard the blood as a fluid of fixed composition is to ignore the first lesson that biology learned from the study of the circulation, namely that the apparent stability of living things is a steady state, achieved by intense underlying activity and change. The constancy of the composition of the arterial blood of mammals is a sign that these animals, like others, are systems that preserve a constant organization.

As Barcroft has pointed out, mammals maintain a greater constancy in the blood than do lower animals and by this means they achieve the possibility of especially delicate adjustment of processes, particularly in the brain.

Investigation of the composition of the various body fluids has made it even more difficult to recognize any one 'internal medium', since these fluids differ among themselves in composition and also vary with the metabolic states of the tissues. It is therefore necessary to describe the various spaces, their linings and the fluids they contain, considering each of them as part of the whole system of the body, neither more nor less 'living' than the cells, for which they provide an 'environment' only in the literal sense that they partly surround them. The interchange of ions across cell membranes is now known to be rapid and continuous (see Bartley, Davies, and Krebs, 1954). It is doubtful, therefore, whether we are even justified in regarding the cells as units, each with an 'environment'. Some of the most important interchanges go on at the surface of the mitochondria and other intracellular constituents. In describing living organization we have to take account of all these various barriers and try to discover how they play a part in providing a system that maintains a steady state in spite of fluctuations in the environment.

2. The blood-vessels

These are commonly divided into *arteries, capillaries,* and *veins,* through which the blood flows in that order. But distinctions are not sharp within the blood system; there are arteries of different sorts, grading down to arterioles and arterial capillaries, and similarly on the venous side. Moreover there is no sharp difference between the cells of the blood itself, of the walls of the vessels, and of the connective and other tissues. This is not a set of fixed tubes through which blood flows as does water in metallic pipes. The finer branches of the network are formed of cells continually growing and adapting themselves from moment to moment to the activities of the tissues. Even the larger vessels rapidly change their structure if they are differently used. Occlusion of the main artery supplying a tissue is followed by the opening up of a new circulation through roundabout channels. This regulation of the pattern of the blood-vessels proceeds by processes that are little understood. It is slower than the regulations produced by nervous or hormonal action, but it resembles these in ensuring that the body stores a representation of the events that have occurred in the past and are thus likely to occur in the future (p. 15).

The walls of arteries and veins (Fig. 107) have three layers: (1) the *tunica interna* or *intima*, (2) the *tunica media*, and (3) the *tunica externa* or *adventitia*. The intima consists of a layer of *endothelium*, flat cells of polygonal outline, which are similar to the fibroblasts of connective tissue and can probably become converted into these. Such cells line all the vessels and are the sole constituent of the walls of the capillaries.

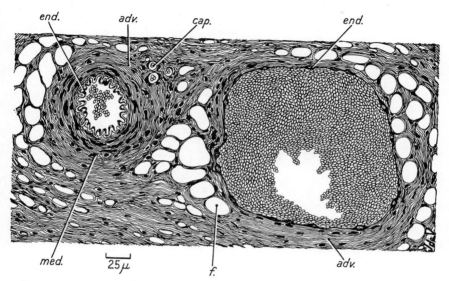

FIG. 107. Sections across a small artery and vein from the submucosa of the human intestine.

adv. adventitia; *cap.* capillary; *end.* endothelium; *f.* fat cell; *med.* media.
(Modified after Maximow and Bloom.)

The intima of arteries is bounded externally by a thin layer of elastic fibres (internal elastic membrane). Next to it lies the *tunica media*, which consists of smooth muscle-fibres, running mostly round the vessel. Outside this is the *tunica externa*, composed of collagen and elastic fibres, running mainly along the vessels.

The structure of the arteries varies continuously proceeding from the heart. The larger arteries contain little muscle and their tunica media is almost wholly composed of elastic tissue. These vessels are therefore dilated by the systolic pulse-wave and they contract during relaxation of the ventricles (diastole), thus smoothing the flow of blood. The medium arteries have a well-developed muscular tunica media and this, with its supply of nerves from the sympathetic system, enables regulation of their diameter so that the flow of the blood is directed to parts where it is needed (see p. 392).

The walls of the veins are essentially similar to those of arteries but they contain less muscle and elastic tissue and it is difficult to distinguish clearly between the various layers. Because of their thin, inelastic walls veins usually do not retain a rounded form when empty. In the medium-sized veins there are large valves to prevent the reflux

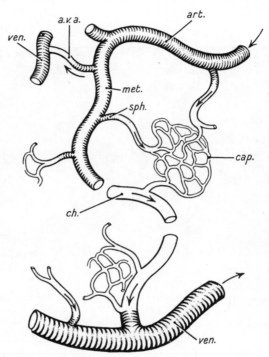

FIG. 108. Diagram of a portion of the capillary bed. The vessels with muscles in the wall are shown with cross shading.

art. arteriole; *a.v.a.* arterio-venous anastomosis; *cap.* capillary; *ch.* through channel; *met.* metarteriole; *sph.* precapillary sphincter; *ven.* venule.
(Modified after Davson, *General Physiology.*)

of blood. These valves are covered by folds of the endothelium and they contain a core of elastic fibres, continuous with those of the tunica interna.

Arterioles gradually become smaller and smaller until they become capillaries, the distinction being that the latter consist of an endothelial layer, without a muscular wall (Fig. 108). The final portion of the arteriole is sometimes called a metarteriole and its muscle-fibres constitute a precapillary sphincter, whose contraction can stop the circulation through the capillary bed. The true capillaries are simple tubes, composed of endothelial cells. They are about 8–10 μ in diameter (Figs. 109 and 110), and liquids readily diffuse through their walls. White cells can enter or leave between the cells. Various forms of supporting tissue have been described and probably some capillaries are surrounded by connective tissue sheaths composed of scleroprotein.

The true capillaries have no muscles in their walls (at least in

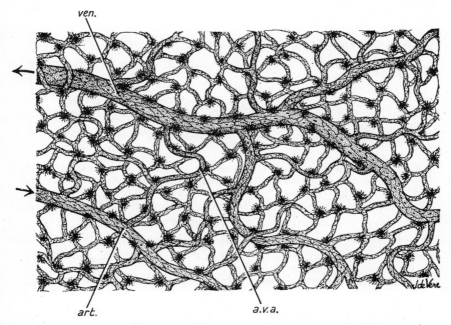

FIG. 109. Portion of capillary bed from web of frog's foot. (Abbreviations as in Fig. 108.) Many star-shaped chromatophores are seen.

mammals) but they may be able to change their diameter by changes of shape of the endothelial cells themselves. There are no nerves to the capillaries and any changes of diameter must be chemically controlled by metabolites and circulating hormones. These substances may also act upon the arterioles and pre-capillary sphincters, but these are provided with nerves.

Besides the channel from arterioles through capillaries to venules there are also direct *arterio-venous anastomoses* (Fig. 109). These are like capillaries in having no muscle in their walls, but they are larger. In tissues such as muscle, in which the amount of blood needed varies, there are many arterio-venous anastomoses acting as direct short circuits between large arterioles and venules.

The whole capillary system makes a fine network by means of which blood is brought to within a few microns of all parts of a tissue. The details of the arrangement of the finer vessels are able to change rapidly to provide for variations in demand. The vessels form a common anastomosing system covering a wide field and if any arterial channel becomes severed or obstructed the tissues it formerly served soon come to be supplied by the opening of channels from neighbouring arterial fields.

3. Composition of the blood-plasma

The blood consists of a fluid, the *plasma*, in which float *blood-cells*

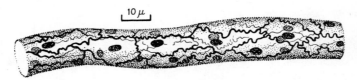

FIG. 110. Portion of a capillary in the mesentery of a frog seen after staining with silver nitrate to show the boundaries between the endothelial cells. (After Ranvier.)

referable to three types, red corpuscles (*erythrocytes*), white corpuscles (*leucocytes*), and blood platelets (*thrombocytes*) (see Dougherty and Dougherty, 1953). The plasma of venous or arterial blood of man contains about 8 per cent. of solid matter, distributed as follows:

1. Protein (serum albumin, serum globulin, and fibrinogen) .　.　.　.　.　.　.　.　.　7·0%
2. Other organic constituents (urea, amino-acids, glucose, fats, &c.) .　.　.　.　.　.　.　.　0·1%
3. Inorganic constituents (sodium, calcium, potassium, chloride, &c.) .　.　.　.　.　.　.　0·9%
4. Hormones, enzymes, antibodies, &c.. .　.　.　traces

4. The circulation from capillaries to tissues

The composition of the blood is similar in arteries and veins but liquid does not pass unchanged through the capillaries. Starling first showed that considerable amounts of liquid may leave through the walls of the arterial ends of the capillaries and enter the tissue spaces or the tissue-cells. Fluid is then reabsorbed into the venous portion of the capillary. This capillary circulation is an important part of the mechanism for supplying the cells. It depends upon the pressure provided by the heart-beat and on the difference in composition between the capillary contents and their surroundings, which is a result of the properties of the capillary wall.

In man the hydrostatic pressure of the blood, derived from the heart-beat, is about 44 cm. H_2O at the point where the capillary structure begins. This pressure tends to force water across the capillary wall, together with dissolved salts, oxygen, glucose, amino-acids, and other small molecules that can pass the barrier. The back hydrostatic

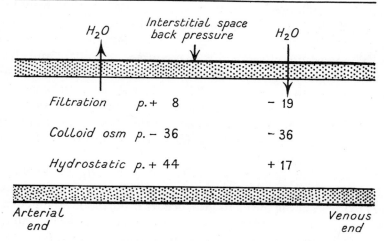

FIG. 111. Scheme of the fluid exchanges across the walls of a capillary. At the arterial end the hydrostatic pressure from the heart beat exceeds the colloid osmotic pressure and the varying back pressure from the tissues. Water therefore leaves, but returns at the venous end of the channel. Pressure in cm. H_2O.
(Modified after Davson, *General Physiology*.)

pressure in the tissue fluids or surrounding cells, due to the mechanical resistance of the tissues, varies from 2 cm. H_2O upwards; it leaves an outward pressure from the capillary of more than 40 cm. H_2O.

In addition to these hydrostatic forces we must consider the osmotic pressures across the capillary wall (Fig. 111). The proteins of the plasma are molecules too large to pass out of the vessels and the tissue fluid is poor in protein. There is therefore a colloid osmotic pressure, of about 36 cm. H_2O, tending to suck liquid from the tissue spaces into the capillaries. At the arteriolar end of the capillary there is thus a net outward pressure of the order of 4–8 cm. water, driving fluid from the arterial end of the capillaries into the tissues. As the blood passes through the capillary towards the venous end the hydrostatic pressure within it becomes less and less, while the osmotic pressure of the proteins becomes greater. Eventually the combined hydrostatic pressure in the fluid around the capillary and the osmotic pressure of the plasma proteins produces suction of fluid back into the venous part of the capillary.

It is not known to what extent this circulation of fluid from the vessels to the tissue-spaces takes place in normal life. Probably the proportion of the blood that passes through the capillary and extra-capillary circulations varies in different tissues and under different conditions. Solutes with small molecules probably pass through the walls of the capillaries by diffusion at least as fast as they would do if carried with the flow of fluid produced by the net filtration pressure.

The existence of this lesser circulation can be shown in a variety of ways. The most direct method is to compress a capillary and then to watch the movement of fluid along it proximal to the compression, owing to escape through the capillary wall (Fig. 112). In practice, the movement of blood-cells along the capillary provides a satisfactory index of the rate of flow. Landis showed that this rate varies directly with the pressure in the capillary, measured by insertion of a micro-pipette, used as a manometer.

The circulation between capillaries and tissue can also be shown to vary by altering the colloid osmotic pressure in the vessels. Oedema, that is to say swelling of the tissues, occurs if the blood colloid osmotic pressure is lowered so that fluid accumulates around the cells in tissue spaces. It is uncertain whether such 'spaces' normally exist in the tissues. Knowledge about this capillary circulation is obviously of first importance for understanding the condition of the tissues, their maintenance in good health, and the effects on them of trauma and disease.

5. The lymphatic system

The lymph channels (Fig. 113) constitute an additional mechanism by which material is returned from the tissues to the blood system. The lymph capillaries are vessels like the blood capillaries but they end blindly in contact with the cells or tissue spaces. These vessels therefore have normally no open ends, but their walls are permeable, not only to water and crystalloids but also to colloids. Moreover the finest branches of the lymph capillaries are modifiable structures, changing from moment to moment, so that gaps in their walls open and then close again. The lymph system is thus able to take up par-ticles and bacteria from the tissues; one of its main functions is to filter off and neutralize such intruders.

The lymph capillaries unite to form larger vessels, essentially like

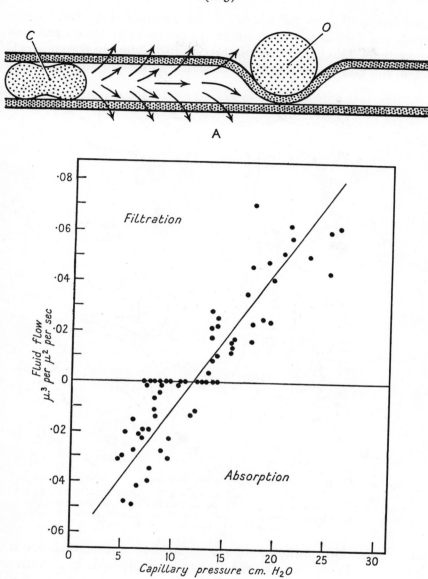

FIG. 112. Landis's experiment to determine the rate of flow across the wall of a capillary.

A, The capillary is obstructed at O and the rate of movement of the corpuscle C measures the rate of filtration or absorption of fluid. The results with various capillary pressures are shown in B. (After Landis from Davson, *General Physiology*.)

veins but with even thinner walls. At intervals along the lymph-
vessels are the lymph nodes, which are the main protective filters of
the body (p. 266). After passing through the nodes the lymph is collected into still larger lymphatic vessels. The majority of these ulti-

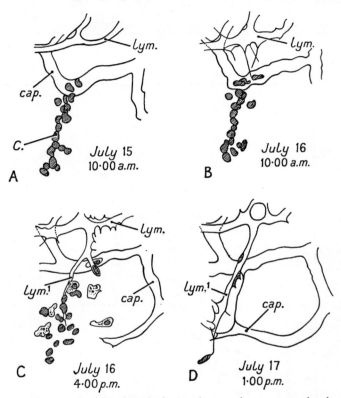

FIG. 113. Outgrowth of fine lymphatic vessels towards extravasated red cells.

A, The cells (c) have escaped from a capillary (*cap.*). B, The lymph vessel (*lym.*) puts out
lateral processes. C, Some of these approach the red cells and form a channel (*lym.¹*) with a
lumen. D, The cells are absorbed. Note that the capillaries have also grown meanwhile.
(From Clark and Clark, *Amer. J. Anat. 38*, 1926.)

mately join a large sack, the *cisterna chyli*, lying on the aorta below the
diaphragm. From this sack the *thoracic duct* proceeds headwards to
open into the left innominate vein. The lymph-vessels of the intestinal
villi are known as *lacteals* (p. 248) and serve to carry away the fat,
which is unable to enter the blood-stream.

There is a continual slow movement of fluid through the lymphatics
back to the venous system and by this means material such as protein
that cannot re-enter the capillaries returns to the blood. The lymph
is therefore a fluid of variable composition, containing less protein

than the plasma and having a salt composition similar to that of the blood. It contains few cells at the periphery but some lymphocytes in the main channels. The flow of the lymph depends only to a small extent on the pressure within the tissues produced by the heart. The propulsion comes mainly from the massaging actions produced by the muscles when they contract. This pushes the lymph in one direction because the lymph-vessels are provided at frequent intervals with valves similar to those of the veins. The lymph flow is increased in conditions that lead to extra permeability of the blood capillaries, such as increased muscle movement, presence of certain poisons and of oedemas of varied origin.

6. The lymph nodes and defence mechanisms

One of the most characteristic features of all living things is that they preserve their composition intact in spite not only of changes in the surroundings but also when foreign bodies are introduced within them. Such bodies may be either walled off from the other tissues, or extruded altogether, or, most commonly of all, dissolved, digested and made part of the organism itself. The defence mechanisms by which these results are achieved are therefore an integral part of the mechanism for self-reproduction and self-preservation. *Phagocytosis*, the ingestion of foreign particles by amoeboid cells of the body, involves both digestion and growth; by it the invader is made part of the host. Great numbers of cells are used for phagocytosis and their nuclei are active, as elsewhere, in maintaining the specific characteristics of the body.

A large part of this work of defence takes place in the lymphoid tissue, consisting of masses of cells, the lymph nodes (Fig. 114) and lymph nodules, scattered throughout the body in strategic situations at which infection is likely, such as the tonsils, the walls of the intestine and appendix, the lymph nodes of the groin and axilla, where lymph-vessels from the limbs converge, and in the spleen.

The lymph nodes are places at which the lymph vessels break up into fine channels so that the fluid is forced to pass through a fine system of reticular and collagenous connective tissue, where it comes into close contact with macrophages and lymphocytes (Fig. 115). The nodes vary in size from minute invisible collections to masses that are large and easily felt. They occur along all the lymphatic drainage pathways, especially in situations in which infection is liable to occur. The afferent lymphatic vessels enter the node round its outer surface and the lymph then filters through an ill-defined system of spaces. The liquid collects at a hilum and is carried away by large efferent lymph-vessels.

In between the trabeculae that carry the lymph sinuses are solid masses of cells, the lymph nodules, each consisting of an outer mass of lymphocytes and a centre composed of lymph-producing tissue.

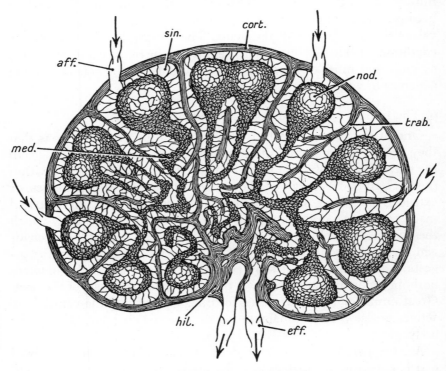

FIG. 114. Diagram of a lymph node.

aff. afferent lymphatic; *cort.* cortex; *eff.* efferent lymphatic; *hil.* hilum; *med.* medullary cord; *nod.* lymph nodule; *sin.* lymphatic sinus; *trab.* trabecula. (Partly after Maximow and Bloom.)

This consists of a fine reticulum of supporting substance containing *reticular cells*, which according to the *unitary theory* (p. 271) are able to develop into either macrophages, lymphocytes, or erythrocytes. The lymph nodules are therefore composed of these active reticular cells and masses of lymphocytes and macrophages, presumed to be their descendants. The lymphocytes are of various diameters between 8 μ and 12 μ. They have a very large nucleus, containing deeply baso-philic nucleoli, and relatively little cytoplasm (Fig. 117). They are present in vast numbers in the lymph nodes and some pass into the lymph- and blood-streams. In the adult they are mostly formed by mitotic division of existing lymphocytes, germinal centres within the nodes becoming active for a while and then subsiding. In the young and to some extent in the adult they are formed by rounding up and division of reticular cells.

The lymph nodes are characteristic of mammals and birds; in lower vertebrates blood-cell producing (haemopoietic) and leucopoietic tissues are usually found together. The presence of well-

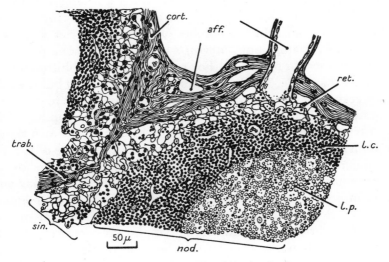

FIG. 115. Portion of a lymph node of a dog.

aff. afferent lymphatic; *cort.* cortex; *l.c.* small lymphocytes; *l.p.* lymphopoietic tissue at centre of nodule; *nod.* lymph nodule; *ret.* reticular cell in lymph sinus; *sin.* lymphatic sinus; *trab.* trabecula. (After Maximow and Bloom.)

developed discrete lymph nodes is probably a sign of the greater need for defence mechanisms by the warm-blooded animals, but there is still much uncertainty as to how the lymphoid tissue functions in this capacity. The nodes are certainly efficient filters; if fluids heavily infected with staphylococci are injected into the lymphatics of a dog's leg the lymph in the thoracic duct remains sterile. This filtering function is performed mainly by the macrophages of the nodes. Granules of dye injected into the lymph are taken up by the macrophages. But the lymph nodules as well as the macrophages of the trabeculae react to infection or the introduction of a foreign body. The function of the lymphocytes that are produced in great numbers during infections has not been accurately determined. Many of them pass continually by way of the lymphatic duct into the blood-stream and there is some evidence that they may be converted into red blood-cells in the bone marrow (p. 275). Lymphocytes are certainly not phagocytic, but it is possible that they are concerned with the production of antitoxins and other anti-bodies able to neutralize the harmful effects of foreign matter or actually to bring about its destruction.

7. Tissue grafts

An example of this action is seen when living tissue is transplanted from one species of animal to another. Such a *heterograft* becomes surrounded by a mass of lymphocytes and is then destroyed. *Homografts* from one individual to another of the same species also usually produce this reaction, but *autografts* of tissue from one part of the body to another do not do so. For example in the rabbit homografts of skin never survive. The host at first tolerates the graft but then after a few weeks comes to contain a substance (antibody) that reacts against the graft and causes it to fall off. Fig. 116 A shows the condition eight days after grafting a piece of a rabbit's thyroid under its own skin. In this autograft the outer follicles have survived, the centre of the piece becoming necrotic because of lack of blood-supply. C and D show that if the rabbit's own thyroid has been removed these grafts may go on to develop into large masses of tissue. B shows that in a homograft of a piece of thyroid from another rabbit there is survival of some follicles at eight days, but numerous lymphocytes are present and as Figs. E and F show these penetrate the cells of the graft and apparently produce enzymes that lead to the break-up of the grafted tissue. The details of the process are not known but the clear zone around each lymphocyte is characteristic. At the time when the graft is being most actively dissolved immature *plasma-cells* (p. 60) appear, apparently by conversion from lymphocytes. After the reaction has subsided many mature plasma-cells remain in the tissue.

Many cases of such antibody formation are known and it is reasonable to assume that the active substances are produced by the lymphocytes, which become converted to plasma-cells in the process. The fact that the lymphocytes consist to a great extent of nuclear matter is of great interest in this connexion. Presumably these large nuclei are concerned with elaborating the molecules of antibody, whose specificity in relation to the particular invader is one of the most remarkable features of living chemistry. Much of theoretical and practical interest may therefore be expected from study of the functions of the lymph nodules.

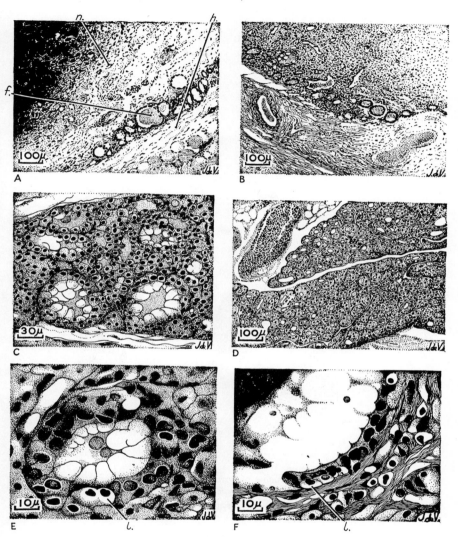

FIG. 116. Pieces of thyroid tissue of the rabbit grafted beneath the skin.

A, autograft 8 days. B, homograft 8 days. C, autograft one year, from partially thyroidectomized rabbit. D, autograft 6 months from completely thyroidectomized rabbit. E and F,
homograft 8 days, lymphocytes (surrounded by haloes) are invading the follicles and in F are
actually within the epithelial cells, which are caused to come away from the basement
membrane.

f. thyroid follicle; h. host tissue; l. lymphocyte; n. necrotic part of graft.

(Drawn from photographs in thesis by Dr. D. A. D'Arcy by permission of the author.)

8. The white blood-cells

The white blood-cells of mammals (Fig. 117) are of five types:

1. Lymphocytes
2. Monocytes
3. Polymorphonuclear cells (= neutrophil cells or microphages)
4. Eosinophil cells
5. Basophil cells.

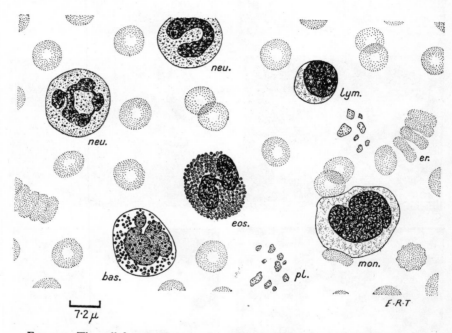

FIG. 117. The cellular constituents of normal human blood as seen after staining. (It would be very unusual to see all the types close together in one field in this way.)

bas. basophil granulocyte; *eos.* eosinophil granulocyte; *er.* erythrocyte; *lym.* lymphocyte; *mon.* monocyte; *neu.* neutrophil cells (= polymorphs = microphages); *pl.* platelets.

Altogether there are about 7,000 white corpuscles per ml. in normal human blood.

The first two types are often classed together as agranulocytes, the remainder as granulocytes, but it is not certain that the members of the two groups have much in common beyond the presence or absence of granules. The *lymphocytes* of the blood arise from lymph nodes and presumably have functions similar to the lymphocytes considered above. The *monocytes* are 10–15 μ in diameter and characterized by a kidney-shaped nucleus, showing a kink in one side. They may be phagocytic and are held by many to be derived from the histiocytes of the tissues, but the unitarian view of Maximow holds that they arise from lymphocytes. The *polymorphonuclear* or *neutrophil* cells are the most numerous of the leucocytes (70 per cent.) and are characterized by a many-lobed or band-like nucleus. They are active phagocytes and appear in immense numbers around any focus of infection or foreign body. Metchnikoff called them *microphages* to distinguish them from the larger *macrophages* of the tissues and blood. Many of them are destroyed by the toxins of bacteria and these dead cells constitute the main part of the *pus* that collects in an infected tissue. They probably also produce proteolytic enzymes that assist in the removal of damaged tissue.

The *basophil* and *eosinophil cells* constitute about ½ per cent. and 3 per cent. of the total of white cells respectively, under normal conditions. They are not phagocytic and their significance is unknown. The eosinophils increase greatly in number in animals carrying heavy infections of nematode worms.

9. Clotting of the blood

The power of the blood to become converted to a solid substance is one of the most familiar and important protective devices of the body (see Jaques, 1954). It depends on the presence in solution in the blood-plasma of a protein *fibrinogen*, which under suitable conditions precipitates to form threads of *fibrin*. The change is brought about by the action of an enzyme *thrombin*, which is present in the circulating blood in the form of a precursor *prothrombin*. Damage to the tissues liberates a substance *thrombokinase* and this, in the presence of calcium, converts the prothrombin to thrombin and sets off the clotting. Circulating in normal blood there are numerous non-nucleated bodies the *platelets* or *thrombocytes*, which also constitute a source of thrombokinase, breaking down when the blood is shed. The platelets are probably formed from the giant cells of the red bone marrow, *megakaryocytes* (Fig. 119) and they serve further protective functions by sealing small gaps in blood-vessels.

The mechanism of clotting can therefore be expressed as:

$$\text{Prothrombin} + \text{thrombokinase} + \text{calcium} \rightarrow \text{thrombin};$$
$$\text{thrombin} + \text{fibrinogen} \rightarrow \text{fibrin}.$$

The coagulation can be prevented by acting at various points in the chain. Perhaps the most familiar method is to remove all the free calcium. Blood treated by the addition of sodium oxalate will not clot, calcium oxalate being insoluble. *Heparin* is an anticoagulant substance, found in liver extracts, which prevents the action of thrombin on fibrinogen. The heparin probably arises from the *mast cells*, which are found in all connective tissues, and its presence normally serves to prevent clotting in the smaller vessels. The hereditary disease of *haemophilia*, transmitted as a sex-linked recessive gene, is a condition in which the activation of prothrombin is delayed, probably due to the inability of the platelets to break down when the blood is shed. Men carrying the gene therefore bleed vigorously and continuously from the smallest wound.

A blood clot does not remain in the same condition after it has been formed. The particles of fibrin contract, probably by an intra-molecular change somewhat similar to muscular contraction, fibrin being a protein related to myosin (p. 110). During this contraction the remains of the red cells become enmeshed in the clot and as a result a straw-coloured liquid, the *serum*, is pressed out. This liquid contains the salts and proteins present in the blood but being devoid of fibrinogen it remains liquid.

Blood clots play an important part in the *healing process* that follows an injury. Besides holding the damaged surfaces together the clot forms a matrix into which fibroblasts can move in order to lay down new collagen and make a firm union of divided surfaces. The ease with which this takes place depends on the direction of orientation of the fibrin fibrils, which is in turn influenced by the forces operating upon the clot. Within a day or so after injury the fibrin begins to be dissolved by enzymes. The first fibres to dissolve are those that do not lie in lines of stress and the clot is thus converted into a set of fibres orientated approximately along the stress lines. Fibroblasts and other cells grow along the surfaces thus provided and lay down collagen fibres in directions suited to prevent straining by the forces falling on the tissue.

10. The red blood corpuscles

The red corpuscles are among the most highly specialized structures of the body. In mammals they are bags of haemoglobin, without nuclei, devoted solely to the transport of oxygen and surviving in men only for 100–120 days; then they are destroyed by the liver and spleen and replaced by others formed in the red bone marrow. There are about 5 million red cells per mililitre of blood in a normal man (less in woman, more in children) and therefore some 35×10^{12} of them in the body, of which they constitute a major part.

The shape of the corpuscles is characteristic and is usually described as showing a biconcave or dumbell outline (Fig. 118). The effect of this shape is to give the corpuscle a much larger surface area for its volume than would be presented by a sphere. It also allows rapid and equal diffusion from the surface to all inner parts. These are obviously efficient features for the purpose of oxygen transport. The surface is not one of minimum area and it is difficult to see how the

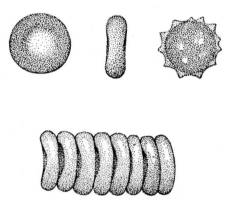

FIG. 118. Erythrocytes as seen under various conditions.

shape is produced: it must be maintained by some structure having considerable rigidity. This structure is presumably provided by the cell membrane. This is birefringent and contains phosphatide and protein components. The membrane can be pulled away as a distinct structure with micro-dissection needles. The consistency of the contents of the corpuscle is that of a rather soft gel; the water content (60 per cent.) is lower than that of many tissues. Yet the mechanical structure of the whole is such that the corpuscle can be deformed in shape, for instance during passage through a capillary, and immediately afterwards resume its biconcave appearance.

The red corpuscles vary little in size, the mean longest diameter being $7 \cdot 2 \ \mu$ and the thickness $2 \cdot 2 \ \mu$ as measured in fixed preparations. In the fresh state they are certainly over $8 \cdot 0 \ \mu$ in diameter and may show fluctuations with the composition of the fluid in which they are placed.

The surface membrane is permeable to water but certainly not to all solutes, so that the cell shape is markedly affected by the tonicity of the surroundings. The 'normal' shape is preserved in $0 \cdot 9$ per cent.

sodium chloride; various signs of plasmolysis ('crenation') occur in stronger solutions (Fig. 118) and with weaker ones the corpuscles become inflated. The contents approach those of other cells in inorganic composition, that is to say they contain more potassium and less sodium and chloride than does the blood-plasma.

The red corpuscle thus retains many characteristic features of cells, but has lost its nucleus, centrosome, Golgi bodies and mitochondria, leaving a homogeneous 'cytoplasmic' material composed almost wholly of haemoglobin, which indeed makes up 95 per cent. of the dry weight of the corpuscles.

11. Formation of red cells

The life of red cells, lacking a nucleus, is limited to about three months in man; they are continually formed anew by the process of *haemopoiesis*. Production of these as of the other components of the blood is basically a function of the connective tissues of the body, which are indeed allied both to the endothelial linings of the vessels and to the blood itself. In the earliest embryo the blood is formed from the connective tissue of various parts of the body, especially in the yolk sac, liver, spleen, lymph nodes, and bone marrow (p. 69). The power becomes gradually more restricted until in adult life all the haemopoiesis goes on in the *red marrow* of the ends of the long bones and especially in the flatter bones such as the bodies of the vertebrae, the ribs, and sternum. The shafts of the long bones are filled with a fatty, *yellow marrow*, which is not haemopoietic.

The red marrow or myeloid tissue (Fig. 119) is a soft material having, like lymphoid tissue, a basic stroma of reticular tissue. This consists of a fabric of fine sclero-protein fibrils among which lie 'primitive reticular cells', which are presumed to give rise to all others in the tissue. In addition myeloid tissue contains fat cells, many macrophages and blood-cells in all stages of formation. The blood-supply is peculiar in that instead of capillaries there are numerous large sinusoids, which have a very thin wall and allow free passage of cells.

Although much remains to be discovered about blood formation it is probable that, as the unitary theory holds, all types of blood-cell can be produced from a single undifferentiated cell type the *haemocytoblast* (Fig. 120). This resembles the large lymphocytes of lymphoid tissue, having a large and deeply staining nucleus and slightly basophil, non-granular cytoplasm. It is probable that some of these cells that give rise to red blood corpuscles are derived from lymphocytes entering the blood-stream from the thoracic duct. Lymphocytes obtained from an extract of lymph nodes can be 'labelled' by immersion in a dye (diaminoacridine) that is fluorescent in ultra-violet light. If such labelled lymphocytes are injected intravenously they soon dis-

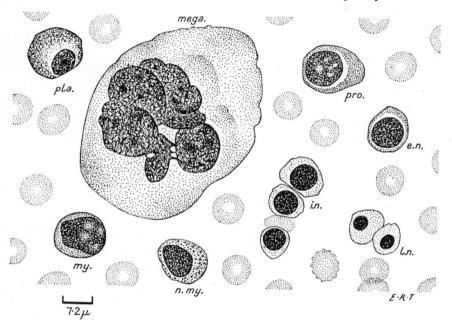

Fig. 119. Some of the types of cell seen in red bone marrow.

e.n. early normoblast; *i.n.* intermediate normoblasts; *l.n.* late normoblast; *mega.* mega-karyocyte (shown less than usual size); *my.* myeloblast; *n.my.* neutrophil myeloblast; *pla.* plasma cell; *pro.* proerythroblast.

appear from the circulation but fluorescent cells appear in the bone marrow and have apparently become haemocytoblasts (Farr, 1951).

The haemocytoblasts undergo division and some of them differentiate into *pro-erythroblasts*, the precursors of red cells. During the process of further differentiation these cells are known as *normoblasts*. The nucleus and especially the nucleolus becomes deeply basophilic; presumably this is a sign here as in other tissues of intense synthetic activity. The gradual appearance of the haemoglobin converts the cytoplasm from blue (as seen stained with a blue basic dye) to purple and finally pink. The nucleus then shrinks to a darkly staining mass and disappears, probably by extrusion from the cell. The young red corpuscle can be shown by special staining to contain at first a network of basophil threads and is therefore called a *reticulocyte*.

Others of the original haemocytoblasts become myeloblasts, able to differentiate into white cells, the three types of granulocytes being distinct early in their formation. The *megakaryocytes* are huge (40 μ) cells with complex nuclei, characteristic of mammalian red marrow. They are formed from haemocytoblasts and probably give rise to the blood-platelets. They may also have other functions and are often found close to foreign bodies, suggesting that they produce enzymes or antibodies.

The elements of the blood change continually and the red bone marrow is in constant activity and adjusts its behaviour to suit the special needs of the time. For instance sojourn at high altitudes leads to a rapid and lasting increase in the number of circulating red cells: apparently the deficiency in oxygen stimulates the bone marrow to extra haemopoiesis. On the other hand, if there is a general infection the number of 'microphages' (neutrophil granulocytes or 'polymorphs', p. 271) is greatly increased, again by appropriate activity in the marrow. Evidently the proper functioning of this tissue is of the first importance for the maintenance of health.

Red blood corpuscles are thus produced continually in the red bone marrow and after a life of a few months they are destroyed by the spleen. This continual replacement of the tissues of the body is another and clear example of the general rule that the living organism must be considered not as a particular set of stuff carried from the cradle to the grave but as a way of so transforming energy that a particular plan of organization is preserved. It is calculated that in man *10 million red corpuscles are formed and destroyed every second* and this gives a clear idea of the great changes that are going on in spite of the constant appearance of the whole body.

12. The spleen

The *spleen* (Fig. 121) is a portion of the circulatory system having some characteristics of lymphoid tissue and others of bone marrow. It lies in the mesentery, close to the stomach, supplied with its own artery and vein. It assists in various ways in the adjustment of the blood. In normal health its functions are chiefly (1) forming a reservoir of red corpuscles, (2) destroying outworn corpuscles, (3) acting as lymphoid tissue. Under some conditions it also takes part in the formation of red and white corpuscles. The spleen has a muscular contractile wall, surrounding a pulpy substance in which the blood comes into contact with a network of macrophages that acts as a filter system. Around the branching arteries of the organ are masses of

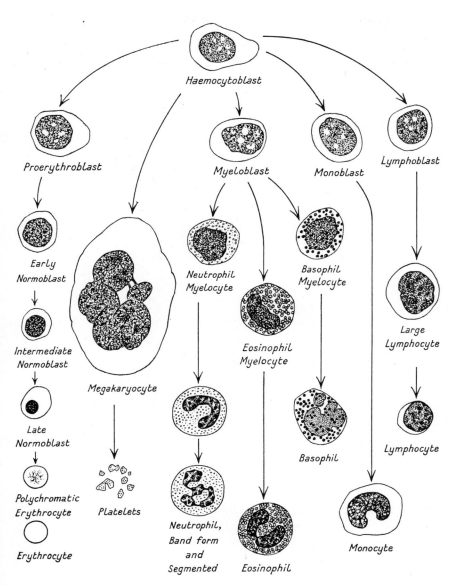

Haemocytoblast

Proerythroblast

Myeloblast

Monoblast

Lymphoblast

Early
Normoblast

Neutrophil
Myelocyte

Basophil
Myelocyte

Intermediate
Normoblast

Eosinophil
Myelocyte

Large
Lymphocyte

Megakaryocyte

Late
Normoblast

Basophil

Lymphocyte

Polychromatic
Erythrocyte

Platelets

Neutrophil,
Band form
and
Segmented

Eosinophil

Monocyte

Erythrocyte

FIG. 120. Diagram of the processes of formation of red and white cells.

lymphoid tissue ('white pulp') and between these there lies the 'red pulp', which is essentially of the same nature but contains many free erythrocytes, giving the red colour.

There has been much discussion as to the nature of the communication between arteries and veins in the spleen and it is uncertain whether

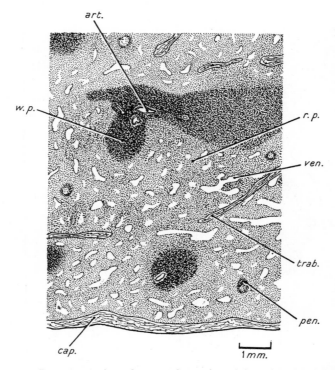

FIG. 121. Low power view of a part of a section of the spleen of a rabbit.

art. artery of Malphigian corpuscle; *cap.* capsule; *pen.* penicilli of white pulp; *r.p.* red pulp; *trab.* fibrous trabecula; *ven.* venous sinus; *w.p.* white pulp.
(From a photograph lent by Mr. K. C. Richardson.)

there is a system of open sinuses. Certainly its substance provides, like the lymphoid tissue, a means by which the blood is brought into close contact with the elements of the reticular tissue. Red cells in process of destruction can be seen at all times in the macrophages of the spleen, and bacteria or coloured matter injected into the blood-stream soon appear in the red pulp. The organ thus functions as a filter for the blood rather as the lymp nodes do for the lymphatic system.

Its special feature is that it stores a considerable proportion of the available red corpuscles and these can be expressed into the circulation when exercise or reduced oxygen supply make extra calls on the oxygen transport system. This action is performed by contraction of the smooth muscle in the walls of the spleen, under the control of the sympathetic nervous system. A considerable proportion ($\frac{1}{3}$ in the dog) of all the red corpuscles of the body are stored in the spleen when the body is at rest.

13. Regulation of the internal environment

Our analysis has shown that the conception of a single internal environment in which the tissues lie is only of limited value. Exchange between the cells and their surroundings is exceedingly rapid and the surfaces that are significant in regulating it may lie within the cells, for instance in the mitochondria (p. 22). Nevertheless, the composition of the fluids that circulate rapidly in the body has a special importance since it affects all cells alike and therefore provides a common factor producing a somewhat similar influence on all parts.

In order to be able to fulfil its functions it is not necessary that the blood should maintain an equally constant composition of all its components and they are in fact regulated to different extents. The regulation is quickest and the constancy greatest in the oxygen content, which affects the performance of the tissues from moment to moment. The glucose that provides the material for oxidation to provide energy is also maintained nearly constant (Ch. XXXII). Materials for growth and replacement, although ultimately essential, are not constantly required and they fluctuate in amount in the blood. Changes in the composition of the blood may be actually used as a method of signalling, not only by the specific hormones (Ch. XXIX) but also by such effects as are produced by the accumulation of carbonic acid produces upon the respiratory centre of the brain or of amino-acids on the liver. The presence of a common circulating fluid thus provides the possibility of an integration of activities in many parts of the body. Alterations in the amount of fluid in the body are regulated by intake and output rather than in the blood itself.

The oxygen-carrying power of the blood is one of its most important properties and is regulated both quickly by nervous action to anticipate rapid changes in demand and also by slower processes. The spleen provides a store of red corpuscles that can be discharged into the circulation during exercise. Moreover the speed of circulation of the blood can be increased (Ch. XIV) and the direction of flow regulated by contraction of some of the arteries, so that blood is available where it is most needed. Slower adjustment of oxygen-carrying power is seen in the increase in number of red corpuscles produced by sojourn at high altitudes. No doubt there are still slower changes in the blood produced by the operation of the evolutionary processes of variation and natural selection. These have provided the characteristic features that give to mammalian blood its great capacity for transport of oxygen.

In its protective functions the blood is also regulated at various rates, but here the nervous system plays little or no part, since the regulation is slow. The capacity to form a clot is an inherited anticipation of the probability that vessels will at some time become damaged. Moreover the clot becomes invaded by fibroblasts and its fibrinogen molecules dissolved in a manner that provides for the laying down of collagen so that future stresses will be met (p. 272).

The capacity to resist invasion by foreign substances and organisms is conferred ultimately by heredity but in each case the antibodies are produced in the blood as a response to the presence of a particular type of extraneous invader. The hereditary system confers on the blood the power to carry a specific memory of past 'experience'. This is only one example of a whole complex of changes that take place in the capacity of the organism to react to invasion and to stress (p. 548). The entire white-cell system is continually changing, for example in the number of microphages or lymphocytes that are being produced, according to the influences that have been falling upon the organism.

In many features therefore the internal environment provides a representation of the past and thus anticipates events that are likely to occur to the organism in the future. This anticipation is secured by selection among various possible reactions of those that conform to the conditions that have occurred in the environment. For example fibrin fibres are laid down in all directions in a clot and those that are not pulled upon are removed first. This has been ensured during evolution by the process of natural selection. Organisms are produced with a variety of different sorts of fibrin and those whose clots do not show this property are eliminated. We can see vaguely how by these selective mechanisms it is ensured that the internal environment can receive 'information' and thus adequately represent conditions outside. Far more study is needed to complete our understanding of the relationship and to make the formulation of it precise.

XIV

THE HEART AND CIRCULATION

1. The functions of the blood

THE circulation of the blood is one of the most striking signs of the continuous activity of life. The body appears outwardly a relatively fixed or stable thing but there is continual change going on in almost every part within. Much of this change is chemical and cannot be seen, but the circulation provides a direct sign of it. At a short distance from the skin surface millions of capillaries carry enormous volumes of fluid continually round the body. Here indeed is evidence of the active state of the living organism. The blood is the supply system, providing materials for the ceaseless changes by which the steady state of life is maintained.[1]

The modern period in biology might be said to begin with the discovery of the circulation of the blood by William Harvey in 1616. Once it had been demonstrated that a flow of blood goes continually round the body it became possible to realize the activity underlying all life; 300 years later we are still in the process of adjusting ourselves to this view. As perhaps the most obvious and important of the inner animal activities the circulation has been intensively studied since Harvey's time and we possess a better knowledge of it than of almost any other part of the body. Moreover we can speak exactly about some aspects of the circulation by using the language that physicists have developed for description of the flow of liquid in tubes. Harvey's original discovery was largely based upon comparison of the heart and its valves with a man-made pump. Since that time hydrodynamic analogies have been the basis of our knowledge of the circulation, though it is now clear that some of the liquid leaves through the walls of the finer branches of the vessels (p. 260).

The maintenance of a rapid circulation is especially important for mammals, whose life is more intense than that of any other animals, except the birds. To maintain a high and constant temperature they need to transport large quantities of fuel for combustion, and oxygen with which to burn it. With the high temperature all reactions can be accelerated and all movements made faster, with consequent further

[1] For references on the heart see Soulié, 1954.

increase in demands. Moreover the nervous organization of mammals rarely leaves them passive, but drives them on to activity, making them seek persistently for their requirements even if these can be obtained only by indirect means, involving prodigal expenditure of energy.

For all these purposes mammals require a circulation that is both abundant and adjustable; it would be inefficient for them to maintain a maximum circulation to all parts simultaneously. The whole life and activity of the animals therefore depend in an especially intimate manner on the performance and regulation of the circulation, and this has found recognition in the detailed observations of its functions by physiologists and physicians (see Burton, 1953; Barcroft, 1954).

It is perhaps ridiculous to ask what are the 'functions' of so important a part of the body as the blood; it is an indispensable part of the life of the animal. However, it is convenient to make a list of the more important activities in which the action of the blood plays a part:

1. Transport of water, the universal solvent in the living tissues.

2. Respiration, by carrying oxygen to the tissues and carbon dioxide back to the lungs.

3. Nutrition, by carrying raw materials for growth and replacement and fuel for combustion in the tissues.

4. Excretion, by transport of waste matter to the kidneys, lungs, or elsewhere for removal.

5. Temperature regulation; by its high specific heat the water of the blood is able to carry heat from regions where it is produced to other parts of the body. Because so much of the body is made of water temperature variations between different regions are slight.

6. Transport of hormones and other chemical stimulants produces a considerable part of the regulation and integration of the activities of the various parts of the body.

7. Protection against infection is largely a function of the blood. Its white cells are able to take up foreign particles and it carries the antitoxins and other antibodies from their places of formation to other organs.

No one of these functions is peculiar to the blood of mammals: for example the properties of water provide some degree of temperature regulation even in amphibia, but in mammals all the activities become intensified. To take one example, protection against infection is more difficult and more necessary in a warm- than a cold-blooded animal.

2. The heart

A great part of the success of the mammals depends on the efficiency of their circulatory apparatus, achieved by complete separation of the main or *systemic vessels*, as a greater circulation, from the *pulmonary* or lesser circulation, supplying the lungs. By this means well-oxygenated blood is delivered to the capillaries at a far higher pressure than can be achieved in a plan such as that of a fish with a single circulation, in which the blood passes through two sets of capillaries under the influence of a single pressure source in the heart. The advantage of the separate circulations is probably especially marked in the case of the muscles, which are regions of high oxygen consumption. By means of this arrangement quick and sustained movements become possible and the whole mammalian organization can reap the advantages of the high body temperature and active chemical processes. It is less important that the interchange between the blood and the internal organs should be rapid and in the liver a *hepatic portal system* still remains, blood passing from the gut in the hepatic portal vein to the liver. After traversing the sinusoids there it is returned by the hepatic vein to the heart.

The separation of the two circulations has been achieved in the mammals by a method quite different from that adopted in the existing reptiles and birds. The original ventral aorta of the fish-like plan of the circulation becomes completely divided into two. The pulmonary artery arises as a single trunk from the right ventricle and supplies the lungs. The aortic arch is also single; arising from the left ventricle it curves over on the left side of the body.

With these modifications the general arrangement of the heart remains in mammals as in lower vertebrates. The organ is formed in the mesoderm below the gut by folding (p. 750) in such a way that it lies in a *pericardium*, whose inner wall (splanchnopleur) adheres closely to the heart surface, while the outer (somatopleur) makes a sac (the fibrous pericardium in the anatomical sense) separated from the inner layer by a small space containing coelomic fluid. The heart in its sac thus lies in a septum, the *mediastinum*, which runs down the centre of the thorax and separates the two lungs. The pericardium is attached to the diaphragm caudally. The surface of the heart and the inner surfaces of the pericardium are covered with smooth layers of mesothelium, allowing freedom of movement. The outer surface of the pericardium is loosely attached to the ventral thoracic wall and to the mediastinum.

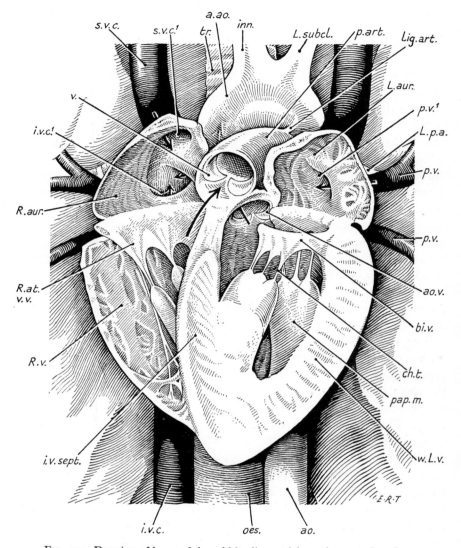

FIG. 122. Drawing of heart of the rabbit, dissected from the ventral surface.

a.ao. ascending aorta; *ao.* aorta; *ao.v.* aortic valves; *bi.v.* bicuspid valve; *ch.t.* chordae tendinae; *i.v.c.* inferior vena cava; *i.v.c.*[1] its opening to R. auricle; *i.v.sept.* interventricular septum; *inn.* innominate artery; *L.aur.* left auricle; *L.p.a.* left pulmonary artery; *L. subcl.* left subclavian artery; *lig.art.* ligamentum arteriosum (ductus arteriosus); *oes.* oesophagus; *p.v.* pulmonary veins; *p.v.*[1] their opening to the left auricle; *p.art.* pulmonary artery; *pap.m.* papillary muscles; *R.aur.* right auricle; *R.v.* right ventricle; *s.v.c.* right superior vena cava; *s.v.c.*[1] opening of left superior vena cava to right auricle; *tr.* trachea; *R.at.v.v.* right atrioventricular valve (tricuspid valve); *v.* semilunar valves in pulmonary artery; *w.L.v.* wall of left ventricle.

The great veins (superior and inferior venae cavae) return their blood to the right atrium, a thin walled chamber, which leads into the right ventricle by an opening guarded by the flap-like right *atrio-ventricular valve* (Fig. 122). This valve (the 'tricuspid' valve of man) allows forward passage of blood but closes during contraction of the ventricle, being prevented from eversion into the auricle by the pull of a number of *papillary muscles*, attached to the valve by fibrous *chordae tendinae*. The opening from the right ventricle to the pulmonary artery is guarded by three *semilunar valves*, arranged to prevent reflux into the ventricle.

Blood returns from the lungs to the left atrium and from here passes through the *left atrio-ventricular (bicuspid* or *mitral) valve* to the left ventricle, the valve being checked by a series of papillary muscles even stronger than those on the right. The left ventricle is by far the most muscular of the four chambers and pumps the blood into the aorta, whose entrance is guarded by semilunar valves.

It is essential to the proper functioning of this double circulation that there should be proper co-ordination of the working of the two sides of the heart. The heart musculature consists of a form of muscle in which there are striations but also much sarcoplasm (Fig. 123); the nuclei lie at the centre of the fibres. Frequent partitions, the *intercalated disks*, cross the fibres, giving the appearance of a division into cells. Another characteristic feature is that the fibres branch and anastomose, so that the whole forms an elaborate net-like arrangement. The contraction of this muscle occurs rhythmically and continues without external stimulation from nerves. Characteristic of the action of heart-muscle is its very long refractory period. Following one contraction no other will take place during the period of relaxation. This enables proper timing of the beat of the various parts. Contraction originates in one centre, the *sinu-auricular node*, a small patch of tissue in the wall of the right atrium, close to the point of entry of the great veins. This corresponds to the position of the sinus venosus of the fish heart, that is to say the posterior end of the region of the sub-intestinal vessel from which the heart has evolved.

In mammals the sinu-auricular node acts as the *pacemaker* of the heart. It consists of a specially modified form of muscle-fibre, inter-mixed with nerve-cells and fibres from the vagal and sympathetic branches that control the heart (p. 398). The beat originates 'spontaneously' in the node but its frequency is controlled by the nerves, the vagal fibres decreasing and the sympathetic increasing the rate (p. 397). The contraction wave spreads away from the sinu-auricular node at about 1 metre/sec. by conduction along the muscle-fibres that fan out from this region. The atria are thus made to contract, approximately together. Transmission to the ventricles does not take place in the same way, there being no muscular continuity; the atria are separated from the ventricles by a ring of connective tissue, the *annulus fibrosus*. Control of the beat is therefore taken up by another special region the *atrio-ventricular node*, from which impulses are transmitted to the ventricles by a strand of tissue, the *atrio-ventricular bundle of His*. This is formed of modified muscle-fibres known as *Purkinje tissue*, which conduct impulses at 5 metres/sec. This bundle spreads out to join the musculature of both ventricles, whose beat is thus initiated nearly simultaneously at all points. After destruction of the bundle of His the ventricular muscle is able to initiate its own beats, but these are not co-ordinated with those of the atria.

3. Regulation of the blood-pressure

The rate of the heart-beat varies greatly in different animals, being lower in larger than in smaller animals (roughly 25/min. in the elephant, 70/min. in man, 740/min. in the mouse). It also varies with activity, with 'emotional' and other factors, and with 'training', being lower in athletes than in sedentary individuals. The means by which the 'basic' rate is determined are not known but the nervous control is reflex, there being receptor systems in the heart itself, in the main blood-vessels, and in the lungs, whose discharge produces alteration of the rate of the heart-beat.

In the rabbit there is a *depressor nerve* arising from the vagus high in the neck and containing afferent fibres from receptors in the arch of the aorta, which discharge when the pressure is raised. The effect of these impulses is then to lower the blood pressure by action through a centre in the medulla oblongata on the efferent sympathetic and vagal nerves. If the depressor nerve is cut stimulation of its central end produces slowing of the heart, stimulation of the peripheral end is without effect. Other receptors are those of the *carotid body* and *carotid sinus*, which lie close to the bifurcation of the carotid arteries and contain cells sensitive to changes of oxygen and carbon dioxide content of the blood, as well as to pressure changes. By the discharge of this complex set of receptors, as well as of others in the lungs, the heart-rate is adjusted to suit the requirements of the moment. For instance when a man rises from the lying to the standing position there is an increase in systolic pressure. While this adjustment is being made

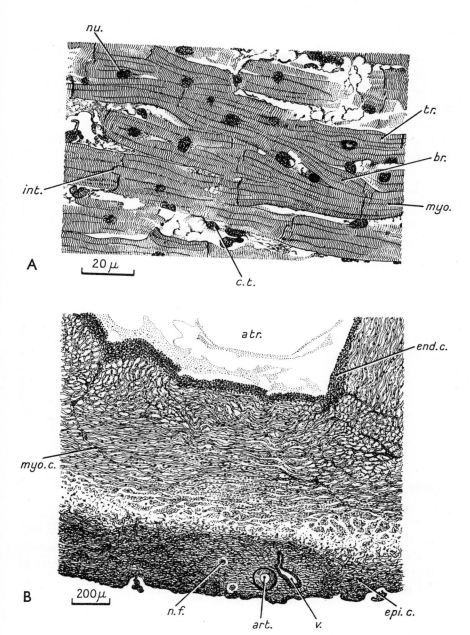

FIG. 123. A, Cardiac muscle of a horse.

br. branching of muscle-fibres; *c.t.* nuclei of connective tissue; *int.* intercalated disk; *myo.* myofibrillae running longitudinally; *nu.* nucleus of muscle-fibre; *tr.* transverse striations.

B, Section of the wall of the right atrium of a horse.

art. artery; *atr.* cavity of atrium; *end.c.* endocardium; *epi.c.* epicardium; *myo.c.* myocardium (the muscle-fibres run in various directions); *n.f.* nerve-fibre; *v.* vein.
(From photographs lent by Mr. K. C. Richardson.)

there may be a temporary reduction of the supply of blood to the brain, which is the reason for the familiar feeling of giddiness.

The contraction of the left ventricle drives the blood along the main arteries at a pressure that is much higher in mammals and birds than in cold-blooded animals. The pressure may be measured by connecting an artery with a column of mercury (manometer) so that the pressure can be recorded with only small changes in the volume of the

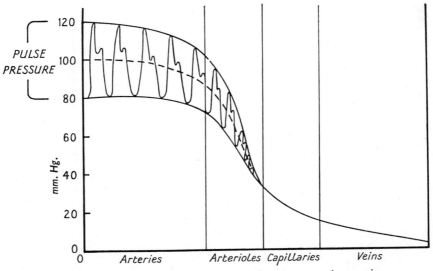

FIG. 124. The pressure of the blood as it passes from arteries to veins.
(After Best and Taylor.)

whole system. The pressure can also be measured without opening any vessel by wrapping round a limb a cuff that can be inflated with air in such a way as to press upon the tissues and stop the blood flow. The restarting of the flow as the pressure is lowered can be heard with a stethoscope and a reading of the pressure in the cuff at that moment provides an estimate of the blood-pressure (sphygmomanometer). The pressure recorded during the contraction of the ventricle is said to be *systolic*, whereas the lesser pressure during relaxation is *diastolic*.

In man the systolic blood-pressure of the young, healthy adult is about 120 mm. Hg., dropping to about 80 mm. at each diastole (Fig. 124). In the dog and horse the pressures are rather higher but the variations are not extreme and for nearly all mammals, large or small, the systolic pressure lies between 100 and 200 mm. Hg., whereas in reptiles, amphibia, and fishes it is about 40 mm.

The pressure falls only slightly as the blood passes along the great and medium arteries, much more rapidly along the arterioles (Fig. 124), until it reaches about 22 mm. Hg., which is the pressure available for driving liquid through the capillary wall (p. 261). The difference between systolic and diastolic pressures gradually disappears along the arteries and in capillaries and veins the flow is uniform. In the vessels immediately beyond the capillary bed there is a pressure of about 10 mm. Hg., and there is a further fall along the veins, so that only a tiny pressure of about 5 mm. *water* remains to drive the blood along the great veins to the heart. Muscle contraction assists the venous return flow but the last portion of the return journey of the blood is effected by a suction pressure exerted on the veins and on the right atrium during inspiration. Enlargement of the whole thoracic cavity in which the heart is enclosed provides a negative pressure of some 6 mm. Hg., falling to 2·5 mm. during expiration. The maintenance of an adequate venous return pressure is a matter of special importance to man because of his upright position and various means are adopted to prevent a fall of this pressure on changing from the horizontal to the vertical position. Quadrupedal animals, which lack means for such adjustment, show greater changes if they are made to stand upon their hind legs.

4. Arteries and veins of the rabbit

The course of the arterial and venous trunks of mammals follows closely the pattern seen in lower vertebrates, with such changes as are made necessary by the presence of special features (single aortic arch and a long thorax). The first vessels to leave the aorta are the right and left *coronary arteries*, supplying blood to the wall of the heart itself. They arise at the level of the union of atria and ventricles. The first large vessel is the *innominate* artery, the root of the right common carotid and subclavian arteries; it represents a portion of the original right aortic arch (Fig. 125). The left carotid arises just beyond this and except for their origins the two *carotid arteries* are similar. Each divides at the top of the neck into a small internal carotid, which enters the skull, and an external carotid. The latter divides into five branches, an occipital artery to the back of the head, lingual to the tongue, external maxillary to the submaxillary gland and masticatory muscles, internal maxillary to the orbit, and superficial temporal to the cheek.

The right and left *subclavian arteries* are also similar except for their origins. Each gives rise to a *vertebral artery* running forward in the foramina of the cervical vertebrae to the base of the brain, where the two fuse to form the *basilar artery*, from which vessels pass to the

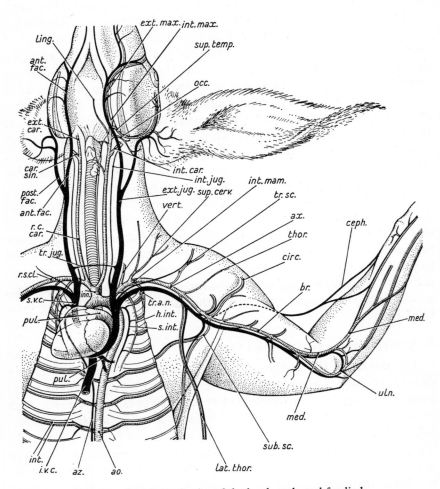

FIG. 125. Arteries and veins of the head, neck, and forelimb.

ao. aorta; *ant.fac.* anterior facial; *ax.* axillary artery; *az.* azygos; *br.* brachial; *car.sin.* carotid sinus; *ceph.* cephalic; *circ.* circumflex; *ext.car.* external carotid; *ext.jug.* external jugular; *ext.max.* external maxillary; *h.int.* highest intercostal; *inn.* innominate; *int.* intercostal; *int.car.* internal carotid; *int.jug.* internal jugular; *int.mam.* internal mammary; *int.max.* internal maxillary; *i.v.c.* inferior vena cava; *lat.thor.* lateral thoracic; *ling.* lingual; *med.* median; *occ.* occipital; *post.fac.* posterior facial; *pul.* pulmonary; *r.c.car.* right common carotid; *r.s.cl.* right subclavian; *s.int.* supreme intercostal; *sub.sc.* subscapular; *sup.cerv.* superior cervical; *sup.temp.* superficial temporal; *s.v.c.* superior vena cava; *thor.* thoraco-acromial; *tr.a.n.* transverse artery of neck; *tr.jug.* transverse jugular; *tr.sc.* transverse scapular; *uln.* ulnar; *vert.* vertebral.

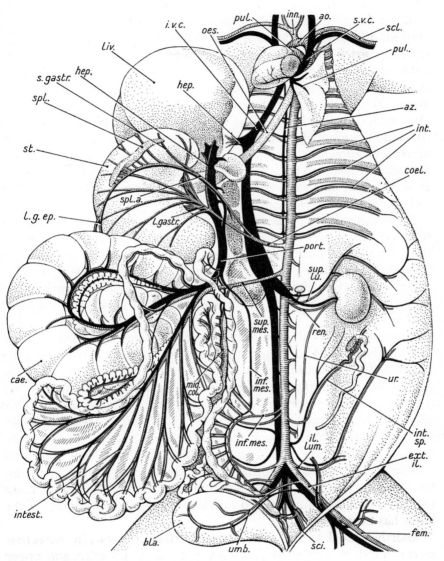

FIG. 126. Arteries and veins of the thorax and abdomen.

ao. aorta; *az.* azygos; *bla*. bladder; *cae.* caecum; *coel.* coeliac; *ext.il.* external iliac; *fem.* femoral; *hep.* hepatic; *il.lum.* iliolumbar; *inf.mes.* inferior mesenteric; *inn.* innominate; *int.* intercostal; *intest.* intestinal; *int.sp.* internal spermatic; *i.v.c.* inferior vena cava; *l.gastr.* left gastric; *l.g.ep.* left gastroepiploic; *liv.* liver; *mid.col.* middle colic; *oes.* oesophagus; *port.* portal; *pul.* pulmonary; *ren.* renal; *sci.* sciatic; *s.cl.* subclavian; *s.gastr.* short gastric; *spl.* spleen; *spl.a.* splenic artery; *st.* stomach; *sup.lu.* suprarenolumbar; *sup.mes.* superior mesenteric; *s.v.c.* superior vena cava; *umb.* umbilical; *ur.* ureter.

medulla oblongata and cerebellum. In front the basilar artery divides again to form two *posterior cerebral arteries*. These join the internal carotids and at the level where they do so they give off *anterior cerebral arteries*, which join in the midline and thus complete the *circulus arteriosus* or circle of Willis. There are considerable differences among mammals in the arrangement of the arteries of the head. In the cat, sheep, and many others the internal carotid artery is very small or absent and the circle of Willis is then mainly supplied with blood from the branches of the external carotid through an abundant plexus of arteries known as the carotid rete. This network lies in a venous lake and is presumed to have some special haemodynamic significance. It is absent in mammals such as the rabbit and man where there is a well-developed internal carotid.

From the subclavian arteries (Fig. 125) there also arise backwardly directed vessels, the *internal mammary arteries*, which run along inside the ventral chest wall and supply its muscles. The main trunk of the subclavian continues as the *axillary* and then *brachial artery*, supplying numerous branches to the muscles of the arm and dividing at the elbow into the *median* and *ulnar* arteries, which pass down the forearm to the hand.

The aorta gives no large branches as it passes through the thorax but a series of small though important *intercostal arteries* (Fig. 126) supplies the muscles of the back and thorax. At the lower end small *phrenic arteries* supply the diaphragm. The first large branch of the aorta is the *coeliac artery*, given off shortly below the diaphragm. This divides almost immediately into (1) the *splenic artery*, with branches to the pancreas, stomach, and spleen, (2) the *left gastric artery* to the stomach, and (3) the *hepatic artery* to the liver, stomach, and duodenum. The stomach, like other organs, thus receives several arteries, whose terminal branches make anastomosis. Blood from one of these may flow into the capillary bed previously supplied by another if the latter has been damaged.

Shortly caudal to the coeliac artery arises the *anterior mesenteric artery*, another large vessel, supplying the small intestine and upper part of the colon. The abdominal aorta continues to give off segmental arteries, similar to the intercostals and here known as the *lumbar arteries*. It also provides paired *suprarenal*, *renal*, and *internal spermatic* arteries, in that order. The internal spermatic differs in its course in the two sexes. In the male it runs caudally and supplies branches to the epididymis and vas deferens and then runs as a much twisted vessel to the testis. In the female it runs more laterally to supply the

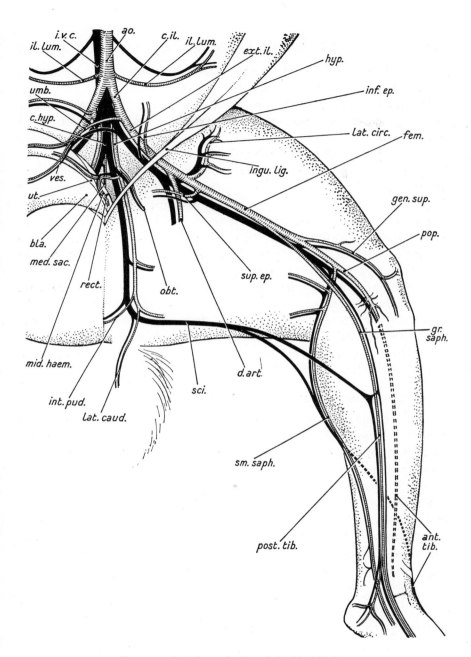

FIG. 127. Arteries and veins of the hind-limb.

ao. aorta; *ant.tib.* anterior tibial; *bla.* bladder; *c.il.* common iliac; *c.hyp.* common hypo-gastric; *d.art.* deep artery of thigh; *ext.il.* external iliac; *fem.* femoral; *gen.sup.* genu suprema; *gr.saph.* great saphenous; *hyp.* hypogastric; *il.lum.* iliolumbar; *inf.ep.* inferior epigastric; *ingu.lig.* inguinal ligament; *int.pud.* internal pudendal; *i.v.c.* inferior vena cava; *lat.caud.* lateral caudal; *lat.circ.* lateral circumflex; *med.sac.* median sacral; *mid.haem.* middle haemor-rhoidal; *obt.* obturator; *pop.* popliteal; *post.tib.* posterior tibial; *rect.* rectum; *sci.* sciatic; *sm.saph.* small saphenous; *sup.ep.* superficial epigastric; *umb.* umbilical; *ut.* uterus; *ves.* vesical.

ovary and uterine tube. A median *inferior mesenteric artery* supplies the lower part of the colon and the rectum.

Within the pelvic cavity the aorta divides into two *common iliac arteries*. There is a small continuation of the aorta, the median sacral artery, which becomes the caudal artery. Near the origin of the common iliac arteries arise the *ilio-lumbar arteries*, but they may originate from the aorta itself. Each common iliac artery divides into an *external iliac artery* supplying the hind leg, and a *hypogastric (internal iliac) artery*, passing caudally to supply the organs of the pelvis, including the uterus in the female. At this division the *umbilical artery* arises from the external iliac. Passing under the inguinal ligament the external iliac emerges as the *femoral artery*, which has three branches supplying the thigh (Fig. 127).

Above the knee the femoral artery supplies the *great saphenous artery*, which continues as the *posterior tibial artery* to the heel. The *genu suprema artery* to the knee arises from the femoral at this level. The femoral artery then continues behind the knee as the *popliteal*, which branches to form the *small saphenous artery* and continues down to the foot as the *anterior tibial artery*.

5. Venous system of the rabbit

The arrangement of veins is more variable than that of arteries and there are considerable differences between the condition in the rabbit and man. Only the veins of the rabbit are described here, except where specific reference is made to man.

The finer divisions of the deeper veins run mostly with the arteries; often there is a pair of vessels one on each side of an artery, hence *venae comitantes*. There is also a system of superficial veins below the skin; these are often quite large and not accompanied by arteries. Such veins are visible on the human forearm and by emptying them with a

---

'If you now press blood from the space above one of the valves, as from H to O (Fig. 2), and keep the point of the finger upon the vein below, you will see no influx of blood from above. The portion of the vein between the point of the finger and the valve O will remain empty. Yet the vessel will continue sufficiently distended above that valve, as at O, G. . . . If you now apply a finger of the other hand upon the distended part of the vein above the valve O (Fig. 3), and press downwards, you will find that you cannot force the blood through or beyond the valve. . . . You will only see the portion of vein between the finger and the valve become more distended, while the portion of the vein below the valve (H, O, Fig. 3) still remains empty.'

'Further, the arm being bound at A, A as before, and the veins full and distended, compress a vein with one finger L (Fig. 4), at a point below a valve or knot. Then with another finger stroke the blood upwards beyond the next valve N. You will now perceive that this portion of the vein L, N still continues empty. . . . But if the finger first applied (H, Fig. 2; L, Fig. 4) is removed, the vein is immediately filled from below, and the arm becomes again as at D, C (Fig. 1).' (Copied from the figure in 'De motu cordis', 1628. Translation from Singer, C. *The Discovery of the Circulation of the Blood*, Bell, 1922.)

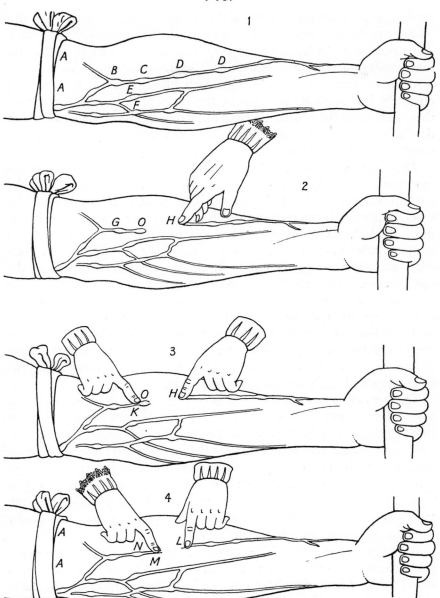

FIG. 128. Harvey's experiment to show the action of the valves in the veins of the forearm.

'Let an arm be tied up above the elbow at A, A (Fig. 1). In the course of the veins, especially in labouring men and those whose veins are large, are certain knots or elevations as at B, C, D, E, and F, which will now be seen. These knots are not only at the places where the veins branch, as at E and F, but also where they do not, as at C and D. These knots are formed by valves, which thus show themselves externally.' [*For continuation see opposite.*]

stroking movement the position of the valves can be made out (Fig. 128). There are communicating vessels between the superficial and deep veins and since the latter accompany their arteries cooling of the skin may produce cooling of the arterial as well as the venous blood.

Veins communicate freely with each other, making a system of channels less regular than that of the main arteries. On account of their thin walls they easily become dilated with blood, especially after death, and it is often difficult to proceed with dissection without breaking them, for instance in the rabbit's neck.

The drainage from the front part of the body is based on the embryonic anterior cardinal veins (p. 759) lying in the dorsal wall of the coelom and represented in the adult chiefly by the large *external jugular veins*. These are connected in the rabbit by a transverse jugular in the neck and each receives smaller *internal jugular veins* from the brain and the large *subclavian veins* from the foreleg. In the rabbit the two vessels enter the right atrium separately as the two *superior venae cavae*, the last portion before the heart representing the *ductus Cuvieri* of the embryo. In man the left ductus disappears (except for some rudiments in the coronary system) and all the blood is passed to the right side by a left *innominate vein*. This joins the right innominate to form the single superior vena cava. The venous drainage of the head and neck is thus mostly into the external jugular veins, though blood from the brain returns largely by the internal jugular.

The venous system of the hind part of the body is based partly on the posterior cardinal (dorsal) vessels found in the embryo (p. 759) but this channel is largely replaced by the great development of the *inferior vena cava*, which proceeds ventrally through the mesentery and past the liver to the heart (p. 761). This very large vessel runs through the whole length of the abdomen and thorax, receiving on its way a number of *lumbar veins* from the muscles of the back and body wall, *testicular* or *ovarian veins*, *renal veins*, *suprarenal veins*, and finally three large *hepatic veins* from the liver.

In the groin the *external iliac vein* (Fig. 127) joins the *common hypogastric vein* to form the inferior vena cava. The external iliac vein receives blood from the abdominal wall and the bladder. On the distal side of the inguinal ligament the external iliac vein is called the *femoral vein*. This receives tributaries from the thigh and the knee. In the region of the knee it is called the *popliteal vein* and receives the *great* and *small saphenous veins* from the foot. In the distal part of the leg the great saphenous becomes part of the posterior tibial vein, a paired vessel lying on either side of the posterior tibial artery.

The common *hypogastric vein* is formed by the union of paired hypogastric veins. Each hypogastric vein receives blood from the uterus, rectum, and abdominal wall via small tributaries and blood from distal parts of the limb by the large *sciatic vein*. Each sciatic vein is joined by one of the posterior tibial branches, anastomosing with the other, and by the anterior tibial vein.

The drainage from the dorsal wall of the thorax and to some extent of the lumbar region still takes place in the adult by dorsal channels directly derived from the embryonic posterior cardinal (p. 789). Only that on the right is continuous, however, forming the *azygos vein*, opening to the right superior vena cava. The left-hand channel is broken into several sections, which cross to join the azygos as the *hemiazygos vein*. These vessels receive the intercostal veins on each side.

6. Regulation of the circulation of the blood

The life of every tissue of a mammal depends upon the maintenance of its blood-supply. Ischaemia lasting for a few minutes leads to paralysis of brain tissue or muscle and if prolonged it is followed by irretrievable damage and necrosis. A most elaborate system of hereditary instructions has been developed to ensure that so far as possible every part shall be provided with an adequate supply of blood. This is possible because the blood-vessels are not a fixed set of tubes but a system of membranes and spaces delicately responsive to changes around them.

These adjustments take place at all levels of time scale from momentary reflex changes of blood-flow occurring within a few milliseconds of the contraction of a muscle to evolutionary changes of arterial pattern requiring thousands or millions of years. The quicker changes depend upon reflex actions that are the result of signals set up by the receptors provided by the hereditary instructions. They lead to changes of heart-rate in response to pressure changes or chemical changes in the main arteries and carotid body (p. 306). When any tissue, say muscle or intestine, becomes active there are corresponding alterations in its blood-supply, produced through the autonomic nervous system under the overriding control of the medullary and hypothalamic centres and perhaps ultimately the cerebral cortex. Proper training of the response of these higher centres is no doubt part of the education that produces a good athlete.

The muscles of the walls of the heart are subject to the effects of use and disuse as are other muscles. After practice it is possible to obtain a much greater output than can be given by the untrained heart. The degree of vascularity of any organ is also influenced by growth processes, operating with a time course of hours or days. If the channels that have been providing blood to a tissue become blocked, or inadequate because of increased demand, others will rapidly be opened from neighbouring vessels. Arterioles may enlarge and new capillaries become established. Little is known about the mechanisms by which these very sensitive adjustments are made. Ultimately they depend upon the growth properties of the tissues, conferred by the hereditary instructions. The vascular system possesses in a high degree the power to acquire in this way a memory or record of the demands that have been made upon it in the past and are therefore likely to be made again in the future. Major changes in the pattern of arteries and veins are of course made by the operation of the processes of mutation, recombination, and natural selection, acting here as in other parts of the body.

Variation in the pattern of the blood-vessels between individuals is familiar in the dissecting room and the surgeon is continually aware of it. Little is known of the underlying genetic basis but there are major differences between the arterial systems of different mammals, for instance in the internal carotid system (p. 292). The supply of blood is an essential feature of every organ and the genetic mechanism is no doubt very sensitive to the advantage conferred by each particular arrangement. On the other hand the capacity for adjustment during the lifetime may to some extent protect the organisms against the effect of genes that produce an unsatisfactory original pattern of blood-vessels. Here as elsewhere we find it difficult to disentangle the effect of genes that produce a particular structural pattern and those that confer the power of reacting to the conditions that the organism experiences. Perhaps the attempt to separate the two is a result of our failure to obtain a single clear picture of the means by which a vascular system is provided that adjusts itself, fast or slowly, to provide for the needs of the organism.

XV

RESPIRATION

1. The significance of respiration

ALL living organisms are steady-state systems in which energy is continually expended to move materials against concentration gradients. Mammals depart widely in composition from the surroundings in which they live and this difference is maintained by the continual expenditure of large amounts of energy. We could express this by saying that mammals have specialized in methods by which energy is exchanged for information. Such a system is only possible if large supplies of energy are available, allowing reactions of the organism to changes in the environment. Regulation of respiration is thus an essential feature of mammalian organization.

The energy requirements of a mammal are all ultimately met by the oxidation of foodstuffs by oxygen taken in from the atmosphere. This process of oxidation takes place within the tissues by virtue of the enzymes found there (p. 22). This *tissue respiration* sets up a change in the haemoglobin of the blood and leads to the uptake of oxygen in the lungs and hence to the process of *external respiration*. The apparatus of the chest and lungs ensures that a supply of air is continually available, which is ensured by regulating the rate of breathing according to the condition of the blood (see Comroe, 1954).

The warm-blooded condition and high level of activity makes mammals, like the birds, acutely dependent on a good oxygen supply. An oxygen debt may be accumulated for a short time during powerful muscular effort (p. 118) but if the tissues are left without oxygen for more than a few minutes they become permanently impaired. In birds the large supply of oxygen is obtained by an arrangement that ensures a complete and continuous change of the air by sweeping it through the lungs into air sacs. In mammals the air is not swept across the respiratory surface into air sacs but is drawn in and blown out of a closed 'respiratory tree', whose terminal portions constitute the region of gaseous exchange. This arrangement is made to function efficiently by the enclosure of the lungs in a chamber, the thorax, whose walls can be expanded to allow air to rush in. The diaphragm closing off the thorax from the abdomen is a characteristic feature of mammals.

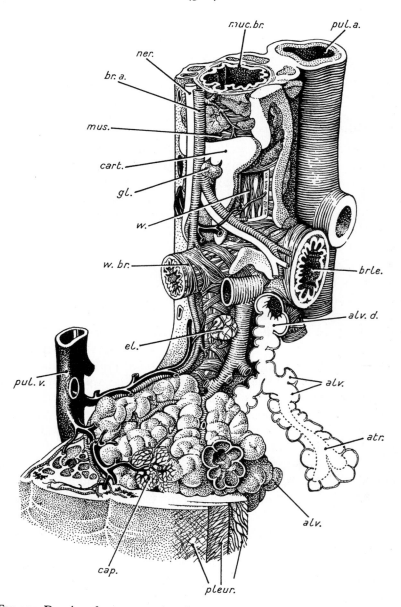

FIG. 129. Drawing of a reconstruction of part of a pulmonary lobule of a young man.

alv. alveoli; *alv.d.* alveolar duct; *atr.* atrium; *br.a.* bronchial artery; *brle.* bronchiole; *cap.* capillaries; *cart.* cartilage; *el.* elastic tissue in wall of alveolus; *gl.* gland; *muc.br.* mucosa of bronchus; *mus.* smooth muscle in wall of bronchus; *ner.* nerve of bronchus; *pleur.* portion of pleural wall, showing three layers; *pul.a.* pulmonary artery; *pul.v.* pulmonary vein; *w.* window cut in wall of bronchus to show elastic network; *w.br.* wall of bronchiole showing elastic fibres and smooth muscle. (After Braus from Maximow and Bloom.)

2. Trachea and lungs

The nasal passages with their vascular membranes for warming and cleaning the inspired air have already been described (p. 195). The

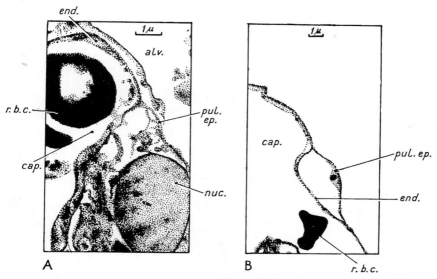

FIG. 130. Copies of electron photomicrographs of sections of rat's lung after fixation in osmium tetroxide.

A, *Alv.* alveolar air space; *cap.* capillary; *end.* protoplasm of endothelial cell; *nuc.* nucleus of pulmonary epithelial cell; *pul.ep.* protoplasm of pulmonary epithelial cell; *r.b.c.* red blood corpuscle.

B, Portion of wall of alveolus in which the endothelium and pulmonary epithelium are closely apposed, but have come apart over a stretch during fixation.

(Low, F. N., *Anat. Rec.* **113**, 1952.)

respiratory system proper may be said to begin where the air enters the *larynx* (p. 205), whose inlet is guarded by the epiglottis.

The *trachea* is a tube strengthened by incomplete rings of cartilage that prevent its collapse during inspiration. At its lower end the trachea divides first into a pair and then into a number of secondary divisions or *bronchi*, leading in turn to smaller divisions the *bronchioles* (Fig. 129). From each bronchiole a system of irregular alveolar ducts leads to the terminal *alveoli*, chambers wider than the bronchioles and each lobed to form a number of *air sacs*. The effect of this branching system of tubes is to allow air to penetrate to every portion of the lung, which is thus a spongy elastic tissue, honeycombed with passages. In the embryo the branching system of tubes is sharply defined and the terminal branches are lined by a definite epithelium. In the adult the finer branches are less regular and the structure of the tree is not apparent in sections.

The walls of the finest chambers are excessively thin, allowing a very close relationship between the air and the blood. There is still

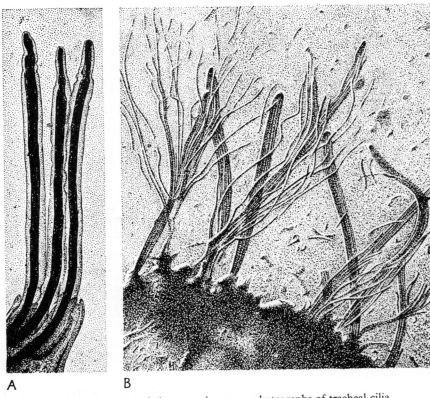

A   B

FIG. 131. Copies of electron microscope photographs of tracheal cilia.

A, intact. B, after ultrasonic treatment by which the axial bundle of fibrils is loosened to various extents. The preparation is heavily shadowed with gold. About 10,000×. (H. Engström, *Acta oto-laryn.* **39,** by kind permission of the author.)

some doubt about the nature of the lining of the alveoli. Electron microscopy shows that outside the capillary wall there is a further thin membranous layer. This is interpreted by some as the protoplasm of flattened pulmonary epithelial cells (Fig. 130), and by others as a supporting material of reticular appearance (see Low, 1952; Swigart and Kane, 1954). It is certainly a very thin layer ($0 \cdot 1 – 0 \cdot 2 \, \mu$) and is closely applied to the endothelium of the capillaries, which form a network around the air sacs. Each sac is of the order of 100 μ across and there are probably more than 700 million of them in the two lungs of man, providing an immense surface (at least 50 square metres) for gaseous interchange. The subdivision of the space is thus enormously greater than in the simple sac-like lungs of the frog. The presence of this great number of tiny sacs and of the elastic tissue between them make the lungs compact organs, very different from the flimsy sacs of the frog, which collapse to almost nothing when punctured.

A striking characteristic of the lung is its elasticity; the walls of the alveoli and bronchioles are abundantly supplied with elastic fibres, giving them the power to contract after they have been dilated, which is important because expiration is otherwise largely a passive process, produced with little muscular effort (p. 58). The walls of the bronchioles also contain smooth muscles. These receive motor innervation from the vagus nerve and inhibitory sympathetic fibres. It is uncertain whether these muscles adjust the proportion of the lung in use according to the requirements at the time.

The trachea and large bronchioles are lined by ciliated cells, which beat in such a way as to transfer substances upwards towards the pharynx, protecting the respiratory tree. Ciliated cells are highly specialized for their functions (Fig. 131). Each hair is a composite structure with an outer sheath and a central core of fibrils, which are attached to basal granules in the cell body.

When necessary the cleansing action of the cilia is reinforced by *coughing*. This action is initiated by the stimulus of particles in contact with receptors in the bronchi. Afferent impulses from these areas produce a sharp expiration, the glottis being at first closed and then suddenly opened to allow the particles to be swept out.

The lungs are covered by the mesothelium of the *visceral pleura*, the layer of splanchnic mesoderm covering the endodermal outgrowth that constitutes the embryonic lung (p. 736). The outer surface of the lung is thus shining and smooth and in life is closely apposed to the *parietal pleura*, the layer of somatic mesoderm that lines the inside of the thorax and has a similar smooth structure. In life these two layers are in contact, with no space between, and this close contact is essential to the working of the lung. If air is present between the pleura the lung does not expand and contract with the movements of the thorax.

3. Respiratory movements

The tidal flow of air is produced by enlargement of the thoracic box, *inspiration*, allowing the air to rush in down the trachea under atmospheric pressure. The movement is the result of contraction of the respiratory muscles, chiefly the *diaphragm* and *intercostals*. When

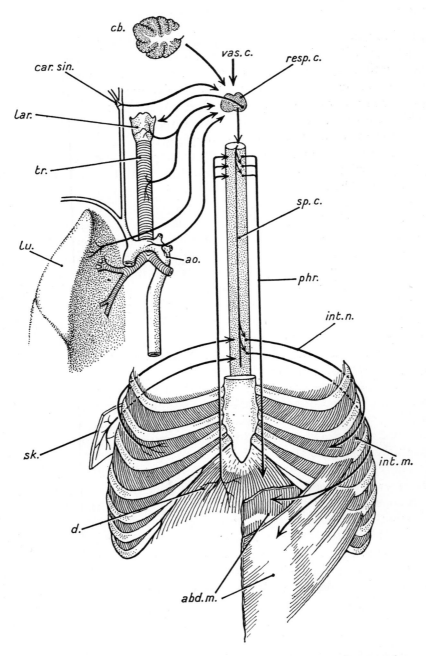

FIG. 132. Diagram of the respiratory muscles and the influences acting upon them.

abd.m. abdominal muscles; *ao.* aorta; *cb.* cerebellum; *car.sin.* carotid sinus; *d.* diaphragm; *int.m.* external intercostal muscles; *int.n.* intercostal nerve; *lar.* larynx; *lu.* lung; *phr.* phrenic nerve; *resp.c.* respiratory centre; *sk.* skin; *sp.c.* spinal cord; *tr.* trachea; *vas.c.* vasomotor centre. (Partly after Best and Taylor.)

this contraction ceases, the movement of expiration follows, largely by elastic recoil, helped by the action of the transverse thoracic and abdominal muscles, tending to make the thorax smaller. These actions are characteristic of mammals and they depend essentially on movements of the ribs. The fibres of the intercostal muscles run from each rib to the rib behind (Fig. 132). The external intercostals pass obliquely ventrally and caudally, the internal intercostals run in the opposite direction. There is also a thin layer of transverse thoracic muscles running from the sternum and to the ribs.

Attached to the upper ribs are the *scalene muscles*, which tend to draw them cranially and thus to fix the whole sternum, so that contraction of the intercostals increases the size of the thoracic cavity. The fibres of the external intercostals are so directed that they have a mechanical advantage in drawing the more caudal rib of each pair cranially. In quiet breathing both external and internal intercostals are chiefly active during inspiration.

An important factor in the inspiratory action is the *diaphragm*, a muscular partition separating the thoracic from the abdominal cavity. It arises during development from muscle-fibres in the septum transversum in which the veins cross from the body wall to the heart (p. 718). This septum lies far forward and becomes invaded by striped muscle, innervated from the ventral roots of the cervical spinal nerves. As the lungs develop and the heart moves caudally the diaphragm also retreats and for this reason the *phrenic nerve* runs a very long course (see p. 84).

The diaphragm is a dome, concave on its abdominal side. It has a central tendinous portion, from which muscle-fibres run to the sternum and ribs and by two cords, the crura, to the lumbar vertebrae. During contraction of these muscles the dome becomes flattened, thus enlarging the cavity of the thorax and pushing the abdominal viscera caudally. This process is limited by the action of the abdominal muscles.

Either the thoracic or the diaphragmatic movements alone are able to maintain respiratory exchange in man, but the diaphragm normally plays the greater part. In very deep inspiration the trapezius, serratus anterior, pectoralis, latissimus dorsi, and other muscles also come into play. The exact details of respiration vary greatly in different animals and even in individual men. In quadrupeds the weight-bearing functions of the thoracic wall (p. 147) tend to fix its parts and the respiration is therefore predominantly diaphragmatic. In these animals the thorax is usually narrow. In bipedal, arboreal, and flying mammals the thoracic muscles play a larger part in respiration and are especially conspicuous in the fully aquatic mammals, where all the weight is taken by the water.

4. Regulation of breathing

The sequence of movements in respiration is maintained throughout life by the rhythmical discharge of impulses in the phrenic and intercostal nerves, producing a series of acts of inspiration. The rhythm is produced by the action of nerve-cells in the medulla oblongata, constituting the *respiratory centre*. Electrical stimulation of the more ventral part of this region produces acts of inspiration and we can thus recognize an inspiratory centre (Fig. 133). Stimulation more dorsally and laterally, however, shows the presence of an expiratory centre, which acts by cutting off the inspiratory action of the main centre. The normal rhythm is produced by a complicated interplay of influences. There are receptors in the walls of the alveoli, which discharge impulses in the vagal nerves when the lungs are inflated (Fig. 132). These receptors are probably smooth muscle spindles scattered throughout the tracheo-bronchial tree, especially at the points of bronchial branching. Impulses from them reach first a vagal receptor centre and thence pass to the expiratory centre and cause the latter to cut off the act of inspiration. Such impulses are not necessary for the maintenance of the rhythm, which may continue after both vagi have been cut. The rhythm stops if the whole brainstem is then cut across in front of the respiratory centre and we must therefore postulate another set of cells farther forward, probably in the pons, which are able to cut off inspiration. The best explanation is that the inspiratory centre sends out its influence all the time ('tonically') not only to the lower motor neurons but also to the expiratory and pontine centres. The two latter together, when sufficiently stimulated, act back on the inspiratory centre, terminating the act of inspiration. In a normal animal this termination is also assisted by the afferent impulses in the vagus, as is shown by the fact that after cutting those nerves the respiratory movements become longer and slower.

It remains uncertain how the central inspiratory centre produces its 'tonic' effect. There are cells in this region that are sensitive to the carbonic acid in the blood. If the amount of this is increased, for instance following muscular activity, the respiratory exchange increases. Receptors in the aorta, carotid bodies, and auricles are sensitive to the pressure and oxygen content of the blood, and their discharges also influence respiration (Fig. 132). Some of the afferents in the vagus influence the inspiratory centre directly, increasing its activity.

There is thus a most elaborate system of chemical and nervous influences acting upon the respiratory centre to ensure that the respira-

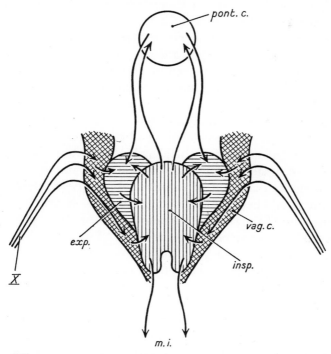

FIG. 133. Diagram of the organization of the respiratory centres of the medulla oblongata.

exp. expiratory centre; *insp.* inspiratory centre; *m.i.* motorneurons producing inspiration; *pont.c.* pontine centre; *vag.c.* vagal reflex centre; *X* vagus, with afferents that inhibit inspiration. (After Wyss, O. A. M., *Gazz. Osp. Clin.*, May, 1950.)

tory movements shall be adequate for the particular level of activity of the organism. Some of these influences may be said to provide a positive feed-back, for example the effect of the carbonic acid in the blood in stimulating the inspiratory centre. On the other hand the flow of impulses from the alveolar receptors provides in the main a negative feed-back, stopping the action of inspiration and producing slowing of respiration and broncho-constriction. Other receptors are present that respond to tactile and chemical influences. Impulses from them set in action the protective cough reflex.

5. The respiratory exchange

The movements of respiration produce in each cycle only a partial change of the air in the lungs. During expiration the lungs are not completely emptied, for the alveoli are maintained distended by the small negative pressure in the thorax. Much of the alveolar air is, however, swept into the bronchioles and mixed with fresh air at the next inspiration. Atmospheric air contains about 21 per cent. of oxygen, 79 per cent. of nitrogen, and 0·04 per cent. of carbon dioxide. By special methods alveolar air can be collected and shown to contain about 14 per cent. of oxygen, and as much as 5·5 per cent. of carbon dioxide, whereas expired air contains 16 per cent. of oxygen and 4 per cent. of carbon dioxide, that is to say, it has a certain admixture of fresh air that has not reached the end of the respiratory tree.

The gases in the air sacs of the alveoli come into equilibrium with the blood by diffusion across the epithelium (if one is present) and capillary walls. On account of the thinness of these membranes the equilibrium is reached rapidly and the oxygen is taken up by the blood-plasma and from this by the haemoglobin of the corpuscles, while the carbon dioxide is given up to the blood. The rates and extents to which these processes take place depend wholly on the partial pressures of the gases in the alveolar air and on the composition of the blood; it is not now thought that any secretion of oxygen across the lung surfaces is involved.

The solubility of oxygen in water is such that only about 0·3 ml. or less is held in simple solution in 100 ml. of blood. However, there are 15 grams of haemoglobin in this volume, and this is able to hold 1·34 ml. of oxygen/gram, that is to say, nearly 20 ml./100 ml. blood. The oxygen carried in simple solution is therefore only about 1 per cent. of the whole and would not be adequate to maintain activity such as that of a mammal except by the very rapid transport of enormous quantities of liquid. The efficiency of the haemoglobin is therefore an essential feature of mammalian life, indeed for that of nearly all chordate animals.

The haemoglobin molecule is formed by the union of protein (globin) with an iron-containing *porphyrin* pigment or *haeme* and it is this latter that gives it a power of loose union with oxygen to form oxyhaemoglobin. Under the conditions in which the haemoglobin occurs in the blood it becomes 95 per cent. saturated with oxygen at the partial pressure of that gas in the alveolar air (100 mm. Hg.). There is therefore little to be gained in man by adding further oxygen to the air breathed under ordinary conditions, though this may be valuable when there is a low oxygen tension, for instance at high altitudes. The haemoglobin remains saturated to as much as 80 per cent.

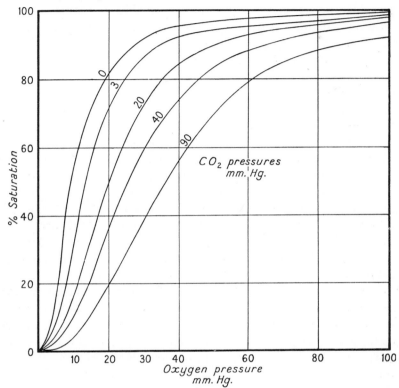

FIG. 134. Dissociation curves of human blood at different pressures of carbon dioxide.

The shape of the curves means that between oxygen pressures of 100–50 mm. Hg., little dissociation of oxyhaemoglobin occurs whilst between 50–0 mm. Hg. oxygen pressure, a small decrease in pressure produces a large fall in the percentage saturation, the oxyhaemoglobin breaking down readily. The effect of carbon dioxide pressure, which is similar to the effect of temperature and is called the Bohr effect, is to decrease the affinity of haemoglobin for oxygen, thus accelerating the dissociation of oxyhaemoglobin. (After Barcroft.)
(By kind permission of the Cambridge University Press.)

if the oxygen tension is reduced to 50 mm. Hg., but below this tension it begins to give up oxygen (Fig. 134) and this normally occurs in the capillaries. Surrounded here by an environment poor in oxygen the haemoglobin yields its oxygen store to the plasma, and through the capillary wall to the tissues. The shape of this *oxygen dissociation curve* of haemoglobin is obviously of great importance for the maintenance of a proper flow of oxygen to the tissues. The particular form of the curve depends on the composition of the blood; for instance the presence of carbonic and lactic acids causes the oxygen to be given off more readily, shifting the curve to the right (Fig. 134). Haemoglobin alone, in simple aqueous solution, retains 80 per cent. of its oxygen down to pressures as low as 20 mm. Hg. and this would not provide an adequate supply. In worms that use haemoglobin as a means of storing oxygen the dissociation curve is flat, considerable quantities of oxygen being retained down to quite low tensions.

6. Tissue respiration

The process of taking oxygen into the lungs and its transport in the blood is only a preliminary to the essential feature of respiration, the using of oxygen by the tissues to provide energy by combustion. We can therefore distinguish between *external respiration* and the *internal respiration* of the tissues. The latter takes place by a system of enzymatic exchanges, probably associated with the mitochondria, making the oxygen able to undertake chemical transformations that would not otherwise occur under these conditions. Ultimately much of the energy of muscular contraction, for instance, comes from the combustion of glycogen to carbon dioxide and water, a reaction that would not take place to any extent at 37° C. in vitro.

A central position in this sequence of changes is taken by *cytochrome*, a haeme-containing substance (or set of substances) resembling haemoglobin, and present in all animal cells. Cytochrome has a characteristic absorption spectrum which, like that of haemoglobin, changes when oxidation occurs. This requires the action of another substance, *cytochrome oxidase*, which activates the oxygen brought to the tissues and transfers it to the cytochrome. The *dehydrogenases* are enzymes able to combine the oxidized cytochrome with the reducing substances produced by the metabolism of the tissues. Thus reactions such as the breakdown of pyruvic to lactic acid are made to proceed by removal of the hydrogen and in this way the whole system of equilibria is shifted so that, for instance, glycogen can break down through the stages of the carbohydrate cycle (p. 116) through pyruvic to acetic acid and ultimately to carbon dioxide and water.

Various poisons act at particular points of these cycles. Thus cyanides inhibit respiration by preventing the action of cytochrome oxidase, leaving the cytochrome in the reduced state. Urethanes, on the other hand, by acting on the dehydrogenases, leave the cytochrome oxidized. Besides this cytochrome system there are other respiratory enzymes present, which are able to change the rate of the reactions in which oxygen is involved. Together these respiratory enzymes make possible the last stages of the flow of oxygen, which goes on throughout life from the air of the lungs to the blood and thence to the tissue fluids and into the cells, where it takes part in the reactions that are the life of the organism.

7. Regulation of respiration

The supply of oxygen to the tissues is essential for their operations and there is an elaborate mechanism for its regulation. Adjustments of the blood-supply of tissues and oxygen-carrying power of the blood have already been discussed. The continuous supply of air in the lungs is so important that it is ensured by a neural system that never comes to rest throughout life (p. 306). The regulation of the rate of operation of this mechanism and hence of gaseous exchange across the lung surface depends upon a system of receptors laid down by heredity and involving positive and negative feed-back. An increase of CO_2 increases the ventilation, acting on the respiratory centre as a 'misalignment signal' activating the 'motor' in such a way as to annul the difference from some standard value. Increased discharge of impulses from the receptors of the lungs acts in the opposite direction, checking the tendency to over-ventilation.

These rapid adjustments of the rate of breathing are the main features of the control of this function. Higher cerebral centres no doubt also influence the process but it is so fundamental to life that it largely escapes the influence of the learning processes of the cortex, which control those operations that can be varied to suit the circumstances.

XVI

EXCRETION AND THE CONTROL OF WATER BALANCE

1. Excretion

THE foodstuffs taken into the body are not used with complete efficiency. Some products of metabolism can be used again, for instance lactic acid, but many others, such as urea, have to be washed out of the tissues and ultimately out of the body by the process of excretion. Most animals are therefore provided with some region in which materials superfluous or harmful to the internal environment can be allowed to escape to the outside. In vertebrates this excretory system originally consisted of a series of funnels leading from the coelom to the exterior. Primitively these served to transport genital as well as excretory products and the urinary and genital systems remain related to each other even in mammals. During development the channels are formed in a series, the pro-, meso-, and metanephros (p. 742), but in a mammal they are never open funnels. Instead each tube is closed at its inner end, where there is a tangle of capillaries, the glomerulus. This arrangement is probably related to the need for a land animal to conserve water (see Keith, 1953). Water and solutes filter out from the blood in the glomerulus and then such part of the filtrate as is needed by the body is reabsorbed during passage down the tube. Thus only unwanted water and solutes are excreted (see Selkurt, 1954). The tubules of this type develop as a metanephros behind and quite separate from the mesonephros, which remains to perform genital functions (p. 742). The urinary system of the adult is therefore entirely separate from the genital system, except where the two open to the exterior.

2. The kidney

The kidney of a mammal consists of a mass of tubules, the nephrons (Fig. 135), each about 35 mm. long, ending blindly internally in sacs known as Bowman's capsules, whose walls are invaginated by special capillary loops, the *glomeruli*. The capsule and glomerulus together are known as a *Malphigian corpuscle*. These closed ends of the tubes lie in the cortical region of the kidney and from each proceeds a tube divided into three regions:

(*a*) the proximal convoluted tubule;
(*b*) the loop of Henle or 'thin segment';
(*c*) the distal convoluted tubule.

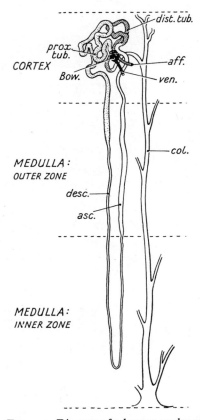

FIG. 135. Diagram of a human nephron.

aff. afferent arteriole; *asc.* ascending portion of loop of Henle; *Bow.* Bowman's capsule; *col.* collecting tubule; *desc.* descending portion of loop of Henle; *dist.tub.* distal convoluted tubule; *prox.tub.* proximal convoluted tubule; *ven.* efferent vessel. (Modified after Peter.)

Finally the lower ends of the distal convoluted tubules unite and thus several nephrons discharge into a common collecting tubule.

The proximal and distal convoluted tubules lie in the cortex and the loops of Henle proceed towards the centre of the kidney and then back again to the surface, each having thus a descending and an ascending portion.

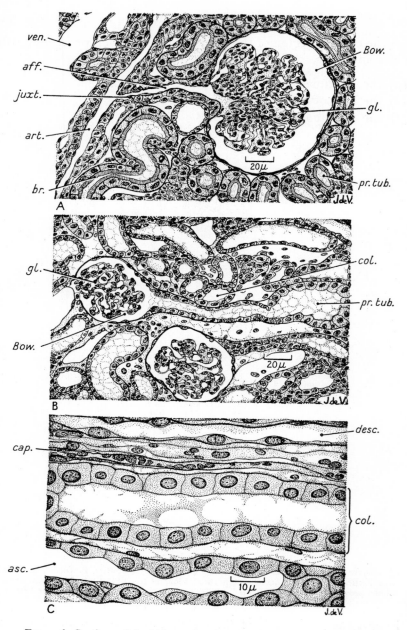

FIG. 136. Sections of the kidney of A. dog, B. salamander, and C. cat.

A, Entrance of an afferent arteriole (*aff.*) to a glomerulus. *art.* arteriole of cortex; *Bow.* Bowman's capsule; *br.* brush border; *gl.* glomerulus; *juxt.* juxta-glomerular cells; *pr.tub.* proximal convoluted tubule; *ven.* venule.

B, Proximal convoluted tubule arising from Bowman's capsule. *col.* collecting tubule.

C, Section passing longitudinally through part of the outer zone of the medulla. *asc.* ascending portion of loop of Henle; *cap.* capillary; *desc.* descending portion.

(From photographs and preparations by Mr. K. C. Richardson.)

3. Filtration in the glomeruli

It is now generally accepted that the kidney functions by a system of filtration in the glomeruli and reabsorption in the tubules (Berliner, 1954). Under the pressure of the left ventricle of the heart there is forced into the Bowman's capsule (the cavity of the corpuscle) a solution containing all the non-colloidal constituents of the blood. As the liquid passes along the proximal convoluted tubule salts, sugars, and other substances not normally found in the urine are reabsorbed, and much of the water is taken back in the loop of Henle, which is specially developed in connexion with life on land. Many features of kidney structure agree with this cycle of filtration and reabsorption and earlier theories ascribing the production of the urine to an active secretion into the tubule are not generally applicable, although it may be that some dyes and other substances can pass from the cells into the lumen of the tube.

The lining of Bowman's capsule is a simple epithelium of flattened cells, invaginated at one point by the glomerulus (Fig. 136). The renal blood-supply is so arranged that nearly all the arterial blood passes first through the glomerular capillaries and then on to the tubules (Fig. 137). The vessels provide for a high filtration pressure; each renal artery arises directly from the aorta and divides rapidly into arterioles, which divide again into some fifty loops, running with little anastomosis through the glomerulus to join again to form an efferent vessel, which then distributes blood to the tubule. The glomerulus thus provides a region where a solution can be forced through the capillary wall into Bowman's capsule, just as liquid normally passes into the tissues (p. 260). The colloid osmotic pressure tends to act in the opposite direction but is lower than the hydrostatic pressure. As a result a concentrated solution is carried away in the efferent blood-vessel of the glomerulus and this aids in reabsorption from the tubules.

Many experiments have confirmed the occurrence of filtration through the glomerular wall, the most direct being those in which fluid is withdrawn by a pipette from the Bowman's capsule of a frog and found to have the composition of blood-plasma free of protein and fat, that is to say it contains substances such as sugar and chloride that are absent from the normal urine. According to the filtration theory a rise in the tubular pressure should prevent urine formation and it can easily be shown that raising the pressure in the ureter will do this, as will also a fall of blood-pressure. Formation of fluid by active secretion, for instance in a salivary gland, does not depend on the maintenance of this difference between blood and duct pressures.

A large portion of the circulating blood flows through the kidney,

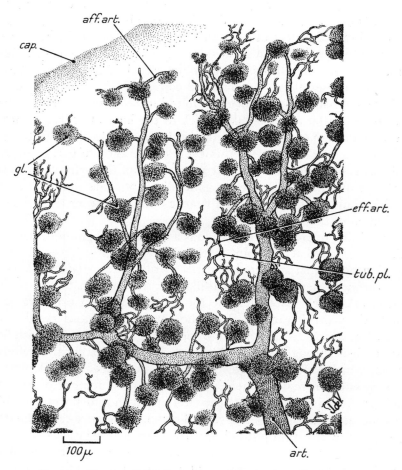

FIG. 137. Portion of the renal cortex after injection of the arteries.

aff.art. afferent artery of glomerulus; *art.* interlobular artery; *cap.* region of capsule; *eff.art.* efferent artery; *gl.* glomerulus; *tub.pl.* capillary plexus around tubules.
(From a photograph and preparation by Mr. K. C. Richardson.)

perhaps a fifth of the output of each discharge from the left ventricle, and as much as 25 per cent. of the liquid entering through the renal artery leaves the glomerular vessels and enters the lumen of the capsules. It is calculated that about 90 litres a day filter across the million glomeruli of a single human kidney. This tremendous flow continues throughout life but is partly controlled by factors regulating the blood-supply of the kidney, such as the nerve-supply to the renal artery and its branches, and chemical influences carried by the blood. These influences may produce a complete cessation of the flow in some of the glomeruli, or conversely the flow may be increased as after drinking excess of water.

4. Reabsorption in the tubules

Each *proximal convoluted tubule* is a much twisted tube 15 mm. long, formed of cells whose inner margin has a characteristic striated structure, the so-called *brush border* (Fig. 137a). Electron microscopy shows that this region contains a number of tubes or ducts extending towards the interior of the cell. These are probably not hollow tubes but special compartments of the cytoplasm, lined with a denser surface structure. The base of the cell is also divided into compartments by folds of the surface membrane (Fig. 137b) and in this region lie many mitochondria (Sjöstrand and Rhodin, 1953). A somewhat similar 'brush border' is seen in the cells lining the small intestine (p. 244) and in other cells where absorption occurs, and it is presumably related to the transport across the membrane of material from the lumen. Phosphatase is abundant in these kidney-cells and is presumably related to the energy used in the transfer. It is supposed that organic constituents (sugar, &c.), water and salts are removed from the filtrate in the proximal convoluted tubule. In the succeeding *descending loop of Henle*, also about 15 mm. long, the walls have a different structure, that of a thin flattened epithelium. In the recurrent ('ascending') loop, however, the cells are of deeper cuboidal form. The significance of the loop of Henle is obscure. The passage of water from the lumen back into the blood-stream is partly operated by the osmotic suction exerted by the concentrated proteins of the blood, as is the return from tissue spaces to venous capillaries (p. 260). The transport of glucose back into the blood has a similar effect. The fluid becomes progressively concentrated as it passes along the nephron and finally produces the urine, which is a liquid hypertonic to the blood and with a minimal content of salt and sugar. The *distal convoluted tubule* is short (5 mm.) and consists of cuboidal cells without a brush border; it leads to the *collecting tubules*, about 20 mm. long, which unite towards the hilum of the kidney to form the ureter. These more distal regions of the tubes probably serve as simple ducts to carry away the liquid.

The 180 litres of glomerular filtrate that are formed each day in man carry as much as 1,100 grams of sodium chloride, 425 grams of sodium bicarbonate, and 145 grams of glucose. 95–99 per cent. of these are reabsorbed, for example only 5–10 grams of sodium chloride appear in the daily output of 1·5 litres of urine (see Smith, 1953).

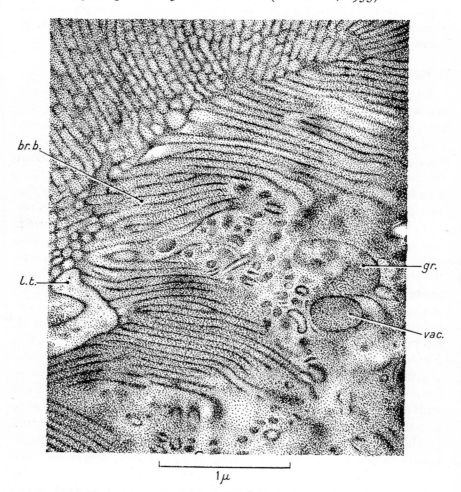

1 μ

FIG. 137a. The structure of kidney tubules as revealed by electron microscopy of high resolution on very thin sections.

Drawing of an electron-micrograph of the brush border and intermediate cell zone with its contained granules and vacuoles.

br.b. brush border; *gr.* granule of intermediate cell zone; *i.c.m.* intracellular cytoplasmic membrane; *l.t.* lumen of tubule; *mit.* mitochondrion of basal cell zone; *nuc.* nucleus; *vac.* vacuole.

(From F. S. Sjöstrand and J. Rhodin, *Exp. Cell. Res.* **4**, 1953.)

These figures give an idea of the magnitude of the changes that take place along the tubules, whose total length if placed end to end would be nearly 50 miles!

5. Ureter and bladder

The ureter is a tube of mesodermal origin, whereas the bladder of mammals is formed as an endodermal pouch of the cloaca (p. 738).

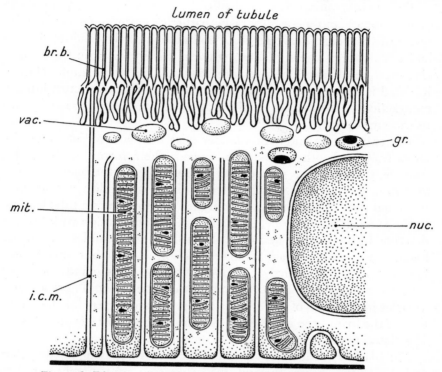

Fig. 137b. Diagram of the kidney-tubule wall. Lettering as on Fig. 137a.
(From F. S. Sjöstrand and J. Rhodin, *Exp. Cell. Res.* **4,** 1953.)

The two organs are, however, of similar structure, being tubes with characteristic lining epithelium and muscular wall. The so-called *transitional epithelium* consists of several layers of cells, not regularly arranged and presumably allowing for considerable increase in area when stretched, especially in the wall of the bladder. The ureters show continual rhythmical peristaltic contractions, by which fluid is passed along into the bladder, the terminal portion acting as a sphincter to prevent reflux.

The smooth muscle-fibres of the wall of the bladder run in various directions and they are able, like other smooth muscle-fibres, to adjust their length so that with distention of the organ the pressure increases only slightly. As fluid accumulates, however, receptors in the wall of

the bladder are stimulated and ultimately by reflex action they produce the rhythmical contractions of the bladder muscle which, together with relaxation of the sphincters of the exit tube from the
bladder, the *urethra*, lead to micturition.

The bladder muscles are controlled by nerves from the hypogastric
(sympathetic) and pelvic (parasympathetic) systems (p. 396). The
fibres of the pelvic nerve produce contraction of the bladder muscle
and relaxation of the sphincter, whereas the hypogastric fibres have
the opposite effects. The pressure at which the micturition reflex is
initiated is about 15 cm. of water in man, but during micturition the
contraction of the bladder wall produces much greater pressures (up
to 130 cm. water).

The two ureters enter the bladder near its lower end at some distance from each other. The line between them forms the base of a
triangle, the *trigone*, at whose apex is the exit from the bladder to the
urethra (Fig. 309). The area of the trigone is recognizable by the smooth,
stretched state of its mucous membrane. The urethra is a tube leading
to the exterior either alone, in the female, or after union with the vas
deferens in the male. The lining of the urethra resembles that of the
bladder in the upper part ('transitional epithelium') but lower down
becomes of the stratified squamous type. Mucous glands occur at
intervals and serve to keep the wall of the tube moist. There are also
muscles in the walls of the urethra to serve as sphincters for the retention of the urine; the more distal portion of this musculature consists
of striated fibres under voluntary control.

The bladder is the most ventral of the structures lying in the pelvis
and the urethra passes through the pelvic ring immediately dorsal to
the pubic symphysis. The male duct (vas deferens) opens into the
urethra on its dorsal side; in the female the vagina runs as a separate
passage above the urethra (Fig. 311). The rectum is the most dorsal
of the structures running through the pelvic ring and lies above the
urethra in the male or vagina in the female.

6. Hormones of the kidney

The kidney produces a hormone that raises arterial blood-pressure
and has been called *renin*. The cells responsible for this are probably
certain *juxtaglomerular cells*, which surround the afferent artery to
each glomerulus, occupying a region between the latter and the distal
convoluted tubule nearby. After partial closure of a renal artery there
is a marked rise in blood-pressure accompanying a hypertrophy of
the juxtaglomerular cells.

7. Control of excretion

The control of the process of urine formation has become very delicate in mammals and plays a large part in the maintenance of the constancy of blood composition that is a characteristic of these animals. Several influences contribute to the control. The secretion of the adrenal cortex is necessary for the absorption of salt from the tubules. The amount of water removed is controlled largely by the influence of an *antidiuretic hormone* secreted by the posterior pituitary (p. 561) and if the pituitary gland is removed there is a greatly increased urinary flow. The pituitary secretion is itself under the control of the hypothalamus, in which there are receptors sensitive to the degree of dilution of the blood (p. 420). These receptors probably provide the ultimate controlling mechanism by which the constancy of concentration of the blood is ensured. The operation of the whole system is, however, much complicated by many other endocrine and metabolic influences that are involved in regulating the amount of water and metabolites leaving the body.

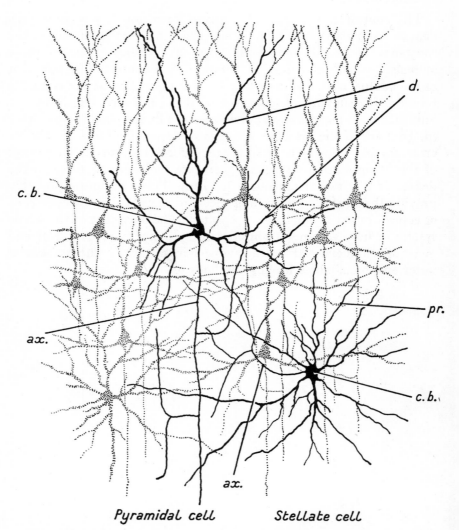

Pyramidal cell   Stellate cell

FIG. 138. Cells of the cerebral cortex of the cat stained by Golgi's method, which colours a few cells but leaves the others unstained.

The pyramidal cell has dendrites (*d*) conducting towards the cell body (*c.b.*) and an axon (*ax.*) conducting away from it. The stellate cell has a number of dendritic processes (*pr.*) radiating from the cell body and a short axon (*ax.*). Its mode of action is not known. (From a preparation by Mr. D. A. Sholl.)

XVII

THE NERVOUS SYSTEM

1. Nervous activity

IN micro-organisms and plants changes in the surrounding conditions influence the metabolism of the cells directly and locally. Higher animals, on the other hand, using the information stored during their long history, operate as wholes in the anticipation of the course of events. They go out and make great efforts to reach the conditions where they can obtain the materials for their life. The various tissues are not controlled directly by the environment but by the nervous system, which regulates the performance of the whole animal. There is an elaborate system of receptors that provides information about events in the world around and converts it into a code. In the central nervous system it is combined with the information stored there and is translated into action by effector organs, especially the muscles. A nervous system thus enables the animal to provide a more perfect and quickly available representation of conditions in the environment than can be produced by changing the hereditary instructions by the slow processes of variation and natural selection. The receptors provide a flow of information from the surroundings, which ensures the production of appropriate immediate actions and also in many nervous systems leaves a record or store of residual information so that future prediction is improved.

The nervous system of mammals thus becomes the main agent regulating activity. In describing its properties we may concentrate from the start on the conception that its characteristic is to *act* and to *regulate*. It has long been usual to lay emphasis on the fact that nerves *conduct* signals (known as *nerve impulses*) from one part of the body to another and thus provide transmission lines that produce the familiar *reflex action*. In higher animals, such as mammals, however, the nervous system is far more than a transmission system or even than a co-ordinating system between the parts; it has become the controlling agent, whose actions regulate almost every aspect of behaviour.

The nerve-cells (*neurons*) are able to act in this way because they have developed the capacity to give discharges that serve as signals. This capacity is a special elaboration of the responsiveness to change that is characteristic of all living systems. It depends on the fact that the surfaces of the cells are electrically charged systems that are sensitive and readily discharge when there is a small change in their neighbourhood. The setting up of the charge by the cell depends upon

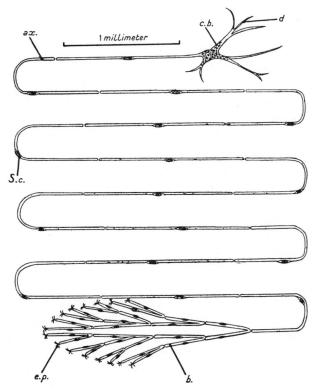

FIG. 139. Diagram of a motor nerve-cell of a rabbit drawn to scale.

The cell is one of the shortest motorneurons in the body, reaching from the spinal cord to the nearby psoas muscle. The cell body (*c.b.*) lies in the ventral horn of the spinal cord. Its dendrites (*d*) conduct towards the cell body. The axon (*ax.*) leaves the spinal cord in a ventral root and finally breaks up into a number of branches (*b.*) reaching end-plates (*e.p.*) in the muscle. The axon is about 17 mm. long and 0·05 mm. in diameter. It is divided into 16 internodal segments (excluding those at the end). One Schwann cell (*S.c.*) is attached to the fibre at the middle of each internode. (From Young, *Advances in Surgery*.)

chemical processes involving the expenditure of energy and the discharge is probably initiated by molecular changes at the surface, followed by ionic movements (p. 338). These movements set up electrical currents that initiate discharge of neighbouring parts of the nerve-fibre and thus make possible the transmission of signals.

Nervous action therefore requires investigation by both biochemical and biophysical methods. In the past there has been some dispute as to whether it should be regarded as essentially chemical or physical.

Clearly several types of change are involved. Each requires investigation with special methods and the results must be combined to provide a coherent analysis of the part that the nervous system plays in main-

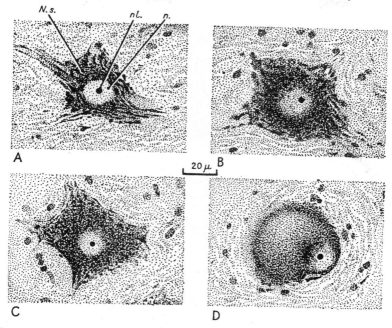

FIG. 140. Stages in the process of chromatolysis of cells of the spinal cord of the cat, seen after fixation in formalin and staining with cresyl violet.

A, Normal cell. *n.* nucleus; *nl.* nucleolus; *N.s.* Nissl substance. B, 6 days after severance of the axon at the ventral root; the Nissl substance begins to break up near the centre. C, Later stage of chromatolysis. The Nissl granules have broken up throughout the cell. D, Severe chromatolysis; Nissl substance reduced to fine granules, cell swollen and rounded, nucleus peripheral.
(Drawn from photographs by Campbell, B., and Novick, R., *Proc. Soc. exp. Biol. Med.* **61**, 425, 1946.)

taining the life of the animal (see *Cold Spr. Harb. Symp. quant. Biol.* xvii, 1952).

2. Nerve-cells

Neurons are cells elongated to form nerve-fibres, in them the effect of the discharge of part of the surface spreads away rapidly, providing transmission of signals to a distance. This elongated form is typical of nervous tissue but many nerve-cells have only short processes and therefore their discharges produce their effect, whatever it may be, in the immediate neighbourhood and not at a distance (Fig. 138).

It is convenient, however, to describe first a neuron of classical

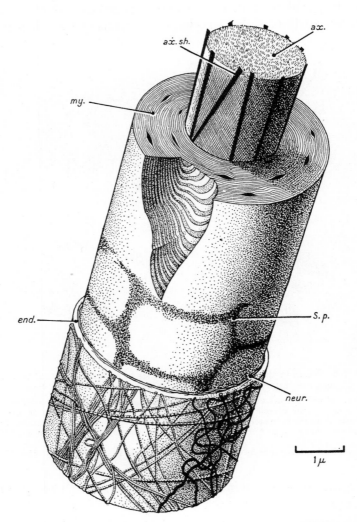

FIG. 141. Diagram of the composition of a nerve-fibre as seen by electron micro-scopy.

ax. axon containing neurofibrils; *ax.sh.* axon sheath in which are a few large fibrils; *end.* endoneural tube (sheath of Henle or of Key and Retzius) composed of connective tissue; *my.* myelin, part of which is shown as if cut away to expose the lamellae; *neur.* neurilemma; *S.p.* Schwann cell protoplasm.

(Modified after Fernández-Moran, H., *Exp. Cell. Res.* **1**, 1950.)

form (Fig. 139), which possesses (1) a *cell body* with nucleus, (2) one or more *dendrites* that receive the signals from the environment or from other neurons, and (3) an *axon* that carries signals away. The whole constitutes a single trophic entity in the sense that any part becoming disconnected from the region containing the nucleus rapidly breaks up and is said to 'degenerate' (p. 333).

The cell body of nerve-cells contains the *Nissl granules* (Fig. 140), composed of material that stains with the basic dyes that also colour nuclei. These granules consist of ribose nucleo-proteins, produced by or under the influence of the nucleus. The fact that nerve-cells, whose cytoplasm is so very large, contain so much nucleic acid outside the nucleus is presumably related to the part that this substance plays in the production and maintenance of the characteristic materials of the cell. It is probable that all the proteins of the nerve-fibre are synthesized in the cell body, under the influence of the nucleo-proteins, and are then passed down the axon. The rate of this transfer has been found approximately by experiments with radioactive phosphorus P^{32}. This becomes incorporated into nucleoproteins only in the nerve-cell body and is transferred thence down the axon at the rate of 2·5 mm./day.

The nerve-cells differ greatly in shape, especially in the length of the dendrites and their method of branching. Little is known about the properties of dendrites, which must be of great importance in determining the conditions under which nerve impulses are set up in each type of cell. The axons differ in size and in the presence and thickness of an outer *myelin sheath* (p. 329). The velocity of impulse conduction is different in the various types of axon, but so far as is known the impulses are all fundamentally alike (p. 343).

The nervous system may therefore be regarded as a transmission network composed of a large number of units all transmitting the same type of signal (but with frequency differences) and with differences in shape, connexions, excitability, and perhaps other features of the units.

3. Nerve-fibres

Axons in mammals range in diameter from less than 1 μ up to 20 μ (including the myelin sheath). They vary in length from a few tenths of a millimetre to more than a metre. The *axoplasm* of which the fibre is composed behaves sometimes as a gel, sometimes as a viscous liquid. This material possesses a considerable degree of organization and in polarized light it shows a weak birefringence. The *neurofibrils*, which can be seen in some fresh nerve-fibres and more clearly after fixation, are a sign of the presence of long, thin particles, 100–200 Å. wide, which can be seen in the axoplasm by electron microscopy

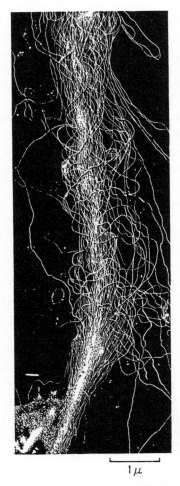

|— 1 μ —|

FIG. 142. Fine unmyelinated nerve-fibre from the lateral funiculus of frog spinal cord. The fibre, which is partly invested with a thin granular sheath, separates into bundles of thin nodular filaments (200 Å diameter) running along independent courses. Osmium fixation. Platinum shadowed. Negative print.

(From Fernández-Morán, H., *Exp. Cell. Res.* **3**, 1952.)

(Figs. 141 and 142). When aggregated together these long particles show as distinct fibrils, which can be traced for some distance within the axoplasm. This organization into neurofibrils within the axoplasm may be related to the transmission system by which the nucleus controls the fibre.

The functioning of a nerve-fibre depends largely on the difference of ionic composition between the inside and outside (see p. 338), but the membrane at the surface of the axon ('axolemma') is so thin that it has not been convincingly revealed by the light microscope. Electron

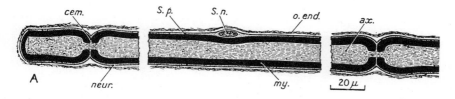

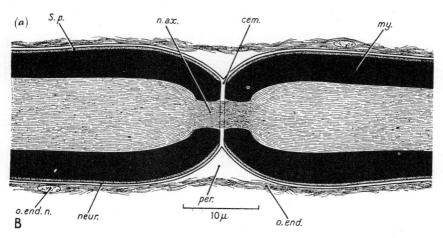

FIG. 143. Diagrams of the structure of a medullated nerve-fibre.

A, in longitudinal section. B, enlarged view of a node. *ax.* axon; *cem.* cementing disc; *my.* myelin sheath; *n.ax.* nodal axon; *neur.* neurilemma; *o.end.* outer endoneurium; *o.end.n.* nucleus of outer endoneurium; *per.* perinodal space; *S.n.* nucleus of Schwann cell; *S.p.* protoplasm of Schwann cell.

microscopy shows a distinct membrane around even the smallest non-medullated nerve-fibres (Fig. 1).

In mammals every fibre greater than about 1 μ in diameter is covered by a myelin (medullary) sheath (Fig. 143), up to 2·5 μ thick on the larger fibres. The myelin consists of layers of material of fatty nature (largely phosphatides), whose molecules are regularly arranged, with their long axes radially. Between these are thinner layers of protein (neuro-keratin). Each lamella (phosphatide+protein) is about 180 Å. thick. This regular arrangement of the molecules gives to the myelin a strong birefringence in polarized light (Fig. 144).

The myelin of the fibres in peripheral nerve trunks is produced at the surface between the axon and a series of satellite *Schwann cells*, which arise mainly from the neural crest during development (p. 769) and apply themselves to the axons. The axon therefore lies within the protoplasm of the Schwann cell and the myelin is formed from the

FIG. 144. Nerve-fibres of a peripheral nerve of a rabbit, teased in Ringer's fluid and seen in polarized light. The fibres have adopted an unduloid outline.

i. incisure; *n.* node.

thickened surface membrane of the satellite cell wound around the axon (Fig. 51, Geren, 1954).

The myelin sheath is easily recognized by the fact that it stains black with osmium tetroxide. Very small nerve-fibres, such as those of the postganglionic sympathetic nerves (p. 385), do not show this sheath with the light microscope and are therefore said to be unmedullated (or non-myelinated). Nevertheless by electron microscopy and other means it can be shown that these small fibres possess a sheath that is not essentially different from that of the larger 'medullated' fibres (Fig. 1). The sheath does not stain darkly with osmium tetroxide because it contains only a small proportion of fatty radicles. We can say therefore that there is a relatively thick sheath around all the fibres of the mammalian nervous system, except at the regions of synaptic contact (see below).

The myelin sheath of the larger fibres is interrupted at intervals, forming the *nodes of Ranvier*, one Schwann nucleus being found between each pair of nodes. The protoplasm of the Schwann cells of adjacent segments is continuous across the node. The internodal lengths vary from 0·3 to 1·5 mm. in mammals and are greater on the larger nerve-fibres. When the nodes are first laid down the distance between them is short, about 200 μ in the peripheral nerves of mammals. As growth proceeds the internodes become stretched and

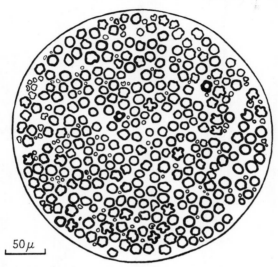

50 μ

FIG. 145. Transverse section of the nerve innervating the gastrocnemius muscle of the rabbit, stained to show the myelin sheaths. Note the presence of fibres of various sizes. The membrane around the nerve is the epineurium.

the final length reached is proportional to the amount of growth that takes place after the time of first myelinization. The number of nodes thus remains constant throughout life.

In addition to this long-period nodal segmentation nerve-fibres examined after removal from the body sometimes also show oblique cracks, spaced at intervals of about 50 microns, the *incisures of Schmidt-Lantermann* (Fig. 144). It is not certain whether these cracks exist in the intact fibre. They correspond to an undulating outline of the myelin and are perhaps an expression of the effect of surface tension, which would tend to make any long cylinder of liquid break into a series of drops. Each internodal segment of myelin may be described as a very elongated viscous droplet, prevented from falling into shorter drops by the outward pressure of the axon (p. 327).

Outside the Schwann cell lies a tough inelastic membrane, the *neurilemma*, which is of scleroprotein nature, probably reticulin, and consists mainly of fine circular fibres. Outside this again is a some-

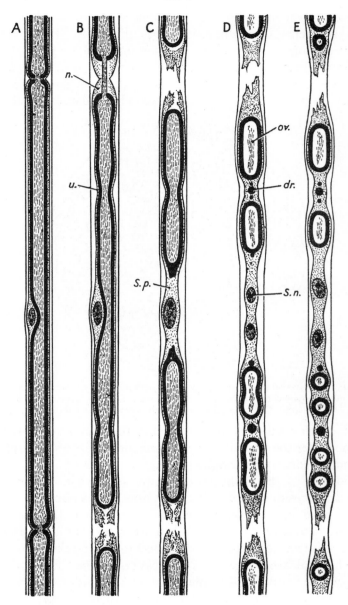

FIG. 146. Stages in the breaking up of a nerve-fibre during the first week after severance from its cell body.

A, normal internode (shown disproportionately wide for its length). B. About 48 hours; the myelin has retracted at the node (*n.*) and shows an unduloid outline (*u.*). C. About 60 hours. The axon is interrupted and the Schwann cell protoplasm (*S.p.*) is increasing. D. About 4 days. The myelin has segmented into ovoids (*ov.*) leaving neck droplets (*dr.*). The Schwann cell nucleus (*S.n.*) has divided. E. About 7 days. Some of the ovoids have now become spherical droplets, the Schwann protoplasm has further increased.

(After Young, *Advances in Surgery*.)

what thicker tube of collagen, the *sheath of Henle*, which is continuous with the connective tissue *endoneurium* that binds the nerve-fibres together. Each fibre thus lies in a tube composed of the neurilemma and endoneurium. Many fibres are held together in a bundle by a sheath known as the perineurium. A complex nerve-trunk, such as the median nerve of man, is composed of many such bundles within a single outer sheath, the *epineurium* (Fig. 145).

Nerve-fibres within the central nervous system differ from those in peripheral nerves in that they do not run in tubes of neurilemma and connective tissue. The white matter is therefore a characteristically soft, almost fluid material. The myelin sheaths of fibres in the central nervous system resemble those of peripheral nerve and are interrupted at regular intervals by nodes of Ranvier (Hess and Young, 1952). The oligodendroglia cells between the fibres (p. 379) probably correspond to the Schwann cells of peripheral nerves and collaborate in the formation of the myelin.

4. Degeneration and regeneration of nerves

Even the most remote parts of a nerve-fibre are maintained intact by the activities of the nerve-cell body; when any part of a nerve-fibre is cut off it undergoes degeneration. The isolated portion breaks up, the axon and myelin first adopting an unduloid outline (Fig. 146) and then falling into droplets. This is the behaviour that would be expected in a long cylinder of liquid under surface tension. It is suggested that the trophic influence that maintains the fibres is the pressure originating in the cell body, which prevents the breaking up under surface tension, somewhat as a sufficient flow of water from a tap prevents breaking up of the outflowing stream (Young, 1945).

The nerve-fibre consists of a cylinder, the axon, inflated by a pressure at one end (from the cell) and pressing the myelin against the inside of an inelastic neurilemmal tube. There are no exact estimates of the pressure and flow along the nerve-fibres. The axoplasm is not a simple Newtonian liquid and indeed may approach the condition of a gel. Yet it certainly has some liquid properties; when a nerve-trunk is constricted the axoplasm becomes dammed up within the fibres behind the obstruction (Fig. 147). The conception of a pressure within the axons provides the best available explanation of the trophic influence of the cell body, but probably transport along the fibres is also involved.

The breaking-up of the part of a nerve-fibre that has become isolated from the nerve-cell body is known after its discoverer as

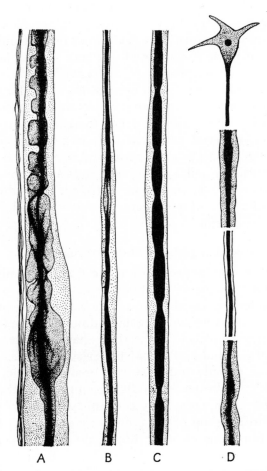

FIG. 147. Effect of chronic constriction on a mature uninterrupted nerve-fibre.

A, B, and C are three sections of the same fibre.
A. Proximal to constriction, showing telescoping and bending of axon.
B. Inside constricted zone: axon narrow.
C. Distal to constricted zone: axon wider.
D. Axon after release of a constriction that had been applied for 25 days, showing cell body and three sections equivalent to A, B, and C.
    (Modified after Weiss, P., and Hiscoe, H. B., *J. exp. Zool.* **107**, 1948.)

Wallerian degeneration. The Schwann cells, however, do not disappear but undergo multiplication. After the remains of the axon and myelin sheaths have been removed the severed part of a peripheral nerve therefore consists of the connective tissue tubes ('Schwann tubes'), now filled with the protoplasm of the multiplied Schwann cells (Fig. 148).

Meanwhile the nerve-fibres of the *central* stump, which are of course still connected with the cell body, begin a process of *regeneration*. The severed end of the fibre swells and streams of axoplasm emerge from the cut ends of the tubes and push out in all directions through the new tissue formed at the site of injury (Fig. 148). The elongated Schwann cells emerge mainly from the peripheral stump and grow in all directions in the scar between the severed stumps. Some of them form bridges between the two cut ends, along which the outgrowing nerve-fibres proceed and are thus led to enter the tubes of the distal stump. There the Schwann cells provide the fibres with favourable conditions for growth and they proceed along the tubes to the original end organs. The tips advance at a rate of as much as 5 mm./day. At first the new fibres are very small but when they reach the end organ they receive a stimulus to grow in diameter (Fig. 149). Some months after the injury they return nearly to their original size, with well-formed myelin sheaths. Only after they have grown considerably do the fibres function like those in a normal body and produce effective sensory and motor discharges. There is therefore a delay between the arrival of the tips of new nerve-fibres at a muscle and the recovery of its normal activity.

Most nerves contain fibres of different types, connected with various end organs, some sensory and some motor (p. 361). During regeneration there is no agency that directs the new fibres into the correct channels and many false connexions are produced. The functions of the limb or other part are therefore often far from perfect after nerve regeneration.

During the process of degeneration and regeneration changes also take place in the nerve-cell body. The Nissl substance at first breaks up and mostly disappears, a process known as *chromatolysis* or retrograde degeneration (Fig. 140). Later the full complement is restored. These changes are presumably connected with the changes in the synthetic activities of the cell consequent on alteration in the length of axon that has to be maintained. They are most marked when the axon is severed close to the cell body.

If the new processes growing out from the cut end fail to make new

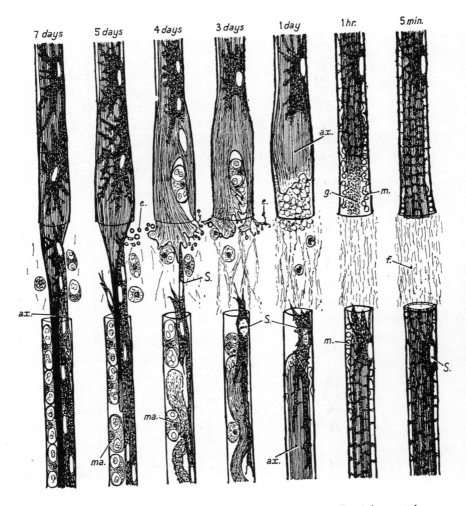

FIG. 148. Changes seen in a nerve-fibre that has been severed. Central stump above, peripheral stump below.

ax. axon; *e.* ends of new fibres formed on central stump; *f.* fibrin clot; *g.* granules formed by degeneration in central axon; *ma.* macrophage; *m.* degenerating myelin; *S.* Schwann cell.
(From Young, 1949, *Advances in Surgery*.)

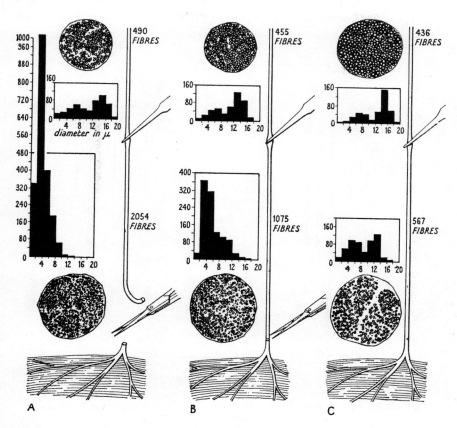

FIG. 149. Effect of peripheral connexion on nerve regeneration. All three nerves were crushed with forceps above but treated differently below. A was cut and left without union; B was cut and sutured; C untouched. All three were then left for 100 days. At the top the sections and histograms of the central stump show the shrinkage of fibres in B and especially in A. Below are shown the conditions of the nerves 1 cm. below the crush; there are very many small fibres in A, a unimodal distribution including some larger ones in B and an almost normal nerve in C.
(From Aitken, Sharman, and Young, *J. Anat.* **81**, 1947.)

peripheral connexions retrograde degeneration may continue until the whole cell atrophies and disappears. Conversely nerve-cells that are cut off from all their sources of normal afferent stimulation may also disappear, a process known as *transneuronal degeneration*. The nerve-cells are therefore said to show *double dependence* (p. 22); they remain

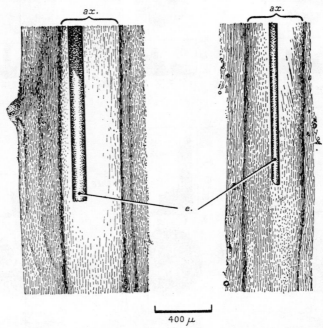

FIG. 150A. Giant axon of the squid (*ax.*) with capillary electrode (*e.*) inside it. The right-hand image is formed directly by the microscope, the left-hand one is a side view obtained by a mirror. The electrode does not touch the side of the fibre at any point.

intact only when they receive proper stimulation at the dendrites and when the axons make proper connexion at the periphery.

5. The nerve impulse

Much is known about the changes that serve for the transmission of signals along nerve-fibres (Katz, 1939; Hodgkin, 1951; v. Muralt, 1954). Studies of the electrical changes in nerve have provided a great part of this information, although propagation of the nerve impulse is not a matter of simple electrical conduction such as occurs in metallic or electrolytic conductors. The essential feature of all nerve activity is discharge of a part of the charged surface of the cell. In a long nerve-fibre propagation is produced because the discharge of each region provokes that of its neighbours.

When a nerve-fibre is at rest there is a potential difference of up to 90 millivolts across its surface, the inside being negative to the outside (Fig. 150B). This *resting potential* can be recorded by placing an electrode on the outside of a nerve and another on its severed end, the latter being then effectively in connexion with the insides of the

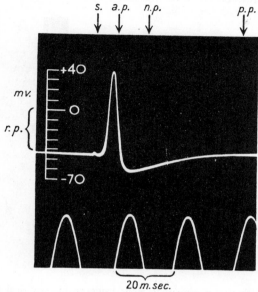

FIG. 150 B. Resting and action potentials reached between an electrode within the giant axon and one outside. The vertical scale indicates the potential of the internal electrode (in millivolts) relative to the sea-water outside. At rest the inside of the fibre is negative (*r.p.*). When the fibre is excited to conduct an action potential the inside becomes positive to the outside. The stimulus artefact shows as a small kink, *s*. The action potential (*a.p.*) is followed by a negative after potential (*n.p.*). The positive after potential (*p.p.*) is beginning to show at the end of the record.
(Hodgkin and Huxley, *J. Physiol.* **104**, 1945.)

nerve-fibres. A more direct demonstration can be obtained in the giant nerve-fibres of the squid. These are as much as 1 mm. in diameter and an electrode can be inserted inside one of them so that the potential difference across the surface is measured directly (Fig. 150). There is a large difference in ionic composition between the contents of a nerve-fibre and its surroundings. The inside is rich in potassium, poor in sodium and chloride, the last two being abundant in the tissue fluids around. The surface membrane is assumed to be moderately permeable to potassium and chloride but not to sodium or to the anions within the cell. The diffusion of the potassium ions would give potentials of the magnitude of the observed resting potential. When an impulse is caused to pass along the fibre a change sweeps over the whole surface. At each point successively the resting potential first disappears and then is reversed. The essence of this change is the breakdown of a barrier or 'membrane' at the surface of the nerve-fibre.

Excitation thus consists of a change such that the surface becomes

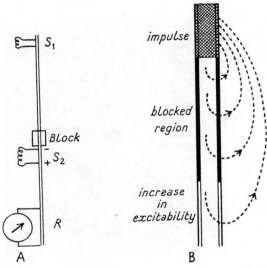

FIG. 151. Hodgkin's experiment to show evidence for electrical transmission in nerve.

A, The sciatic nerve of a frog is laid on two stimulating electrodes S_1 and S_2, and recording electrodes R. Just above S_2 is an apparatus for blocking the nerve by cold or pressure. A sub-threshold stimulus applied at S_2 will only set up an action potential if it is delivered at such a time as to summate with the electrical effects of an impulse arriving at the block. The current responsible is shown in B.
(Hodgkin, *J. Physiol.* **90**, 1937.)

more permeable to sodium ions and the resting potential disappears, making the active surface negative to all neighbouring points and producing a flow of current. This current, *the action potential*, flowing through neighbouring regions, then causes breakdown of other parts of the surface and the process propagates. The current involves an initial phase in which sodium ions move inwards through the membrane, impelled by the differences in concentration and potential. 'This movement of charge makes the inside of the fibre positive and provides a satisfactory explanation for the rising phase of the spike (the action potential). Repolarization during the falling phase probably depends on an outflow of potassium ions and may be accelerated by a process which increases the potassium permeability after the action potential has reached its crest' (Hodgkin, A. L., Huxley, A. F., and Katz, B., 1952).

The change of potential during the passage of the impulse is therefore not simply an abolition of the resting potential of 90 mV. but

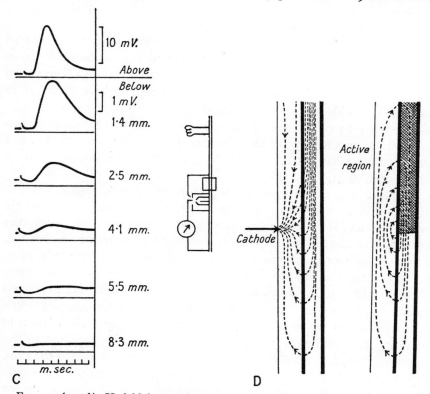

FIG. 151 (*contd.*). Hodgkin's experiment to show evidence for electrical transmission in nerve.

c, Potentials recorded above the block and at various distances below it, the latter with five times greater amplification.

D, Comparison of the stimulating effects of an applied current with those of the local circuits produced by the action potential. (Hodgkin, *J. Physiol.* **90**, 1937.)

involves a change of the order of 120 mV. (Fig. 150). The maximum displacement ('spike') is reached after a rising phase lasting for about 0·7 m.sec. Thereafter the potential falls to the resting value in about the same time. It does not remain steady there, however, but proceeds to a phase of 'negative after potential' lasting some 2·5 m.sec. and succeeded by a smaller 'positive after potential', still recognizable several m.sec. after the passage of the impulse. These later potential changes are associated with the metabolic processes by which the nerve-fibre is recharged, which of course continue long after an impulse has passed. The energy immediately involved in the passage of a single nerve impulse in a medullated nerve-fibre is between 0·5 and 10·0 ergs/gram and the increased heat production, oxygen consumption, and carbon dioxide output involved have been estimated. Much greater amounts of energy are needed during recovery than appear during the actual passage of the impulse.

The evidence that this is the sequence of events that occurs when a nerve-fibre conducts comes from various sources. Sodium has been shown to pass in and potassium to pass out during activity. Nerves can readily be excited by applying an electric current in such direction as would be provided by the above local circuits. Moreover if a nerve be blocked, say by cold, the impulse arriving at the block can be shown to produce effects beyond the block that can summate with applied electrical impulses; in other words, a failing nerve impulse can be augmented electrically (Fig. 151).

We thus have a rather complete picture of the mechanism of nerve propagation as consisting of a discharge that spreads progressively over a surface. It is not known exactly what change in the membrane leads to the discharge, nor by what means the system is recharged. The activity of the enzymes of the axoplasm presumably serves to pump out the sodium that has entered. A suggestion as to the nature of the mechanism by which the changes in permeability are produced comes from the fact that the ester acetylcholine depolarizes some nerves and sets up action potentials when it is applied in minute amounts. In squid nerves it produces no effect when applied to the outside of nerve-fibres but is said to do so when injected into the fibre with a micropipette. It is therefore held by some workers that acetylcholine always produces depolarization when it obtains sufficient access to the cell surface. It is known to be the normal excitant at somatic motor nerve endings (p. 115) and some synaptic junctions (p. 398).

Acetylcholine occurs as a normal constituent of many nervous tissues (perhaps of all) and much is also known of the enzymes cholineacetylase, by which it is synthesized, and cholinesterase, by which it is rapidly removed. These enzymes occur in nervous tissues and drugs that influence their action have profound effects on the functioning of the nervous system. It is not certain that acetylcholine enters into the sequence of changes by which propagation occurs in a peripheral nerve but it may be that its release is concerned in the change by which the fibre suddenly becomes more permeable to sodium. Although the full sequence of events remains uncertain it is clear that the setting up of a propagated nerve impulse depends upon the depolarization of a sufficient area of the surface of the nerve-fibre.

6. The code of the nervous system

The characteristics of conduction determine the method of signalling that is adopted by the nervous system. An essential feature is that activity is broken up into a series of discontinuous signals, the *nerve impulses*. The impulses in any one fibre are all alike, the amplitude of the potential generated at each point depending only on the state of the membrane at that point. Once the membrane has discharged it cannot immediately do so again, it passes through a *refractory period*. There is therefore a maximum frequency of conduction of about 500–1,000 impulses/sec. in a mammal. In normal functioning the fibres mostly discharge at much lower frequencies, for example a motor nerve-fibre will carry about 20 impulses a second when it is producing the contraction involved in a defensive action such as withdrawal of a limb from a painful stimulus (p. 354). Probably motor nerves seldom normally conduct above 100 impulses/sec. This discontinuity of impulses means that all information by nerve signals is carried in a code of similar pulses.

The intensity of the impulse arriving at the end of a nerve-fibre therefore bears no relationship to the intensity of the stimulus by which it was set up. In this respect the nerve-fibre is said to follow the '*all-or-nothing law*'. Transmission in a nerve may be compared with that along a train of gunpowder, where each point fires the next. Variation in the intensity of stimulation may produce variation in frequency of impulses but the intensity of each impulse is determined only by the conditions at the point that is discharging.

Propagation will only occur if there is a sufficient depolarization of the nerve membrane. Experiments with an electrode inside a squid's nerve-fibre show that a depolarization of 15–20 mV. is necessary to set up a propagated impulse. With the application of a potential difference less than this a *local response* occurs. This is especially easy to detect in a nerve-fibre that has been somewhat damaged, so that considerable sections of membrane must become active in order to set up a propagating impulse, the safety factor being below normal (Fig. 152). The existence of a local response suggests that there is a graded relationship between membrane potential and sodium permeability. With a small depolarization the inward current due to sodium entry is less than the outward currents due to movement of potassium and chloride; the membrane therefore repolarizes. With a larger depolarization the inward current is greater than the outward and the membrane continues to depolarize after the stimulating current has ceased. This explains the phenomenon of the threshold.

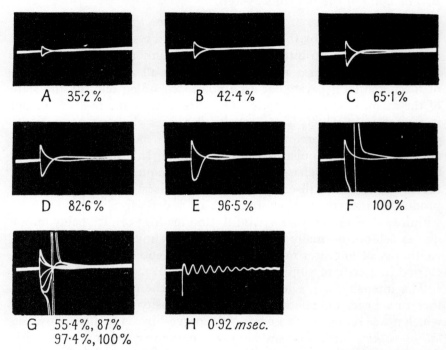

A 35·2 %   B 42·4 %   C 65·1 %

D 82·6 %   E 96·5 %   F 100 %

G 55·4 %, 87%   H 0·92 *msec.*
97·4 %, 100 %

FIG. 152. Records of response of giant nerve-fibres of the squid to cathodal and anodal polarizations. Each record is a double exposure showing the response of the nerve at the stimulating electrode to an anodal stimulus (upwards) and a cathodal stimulus (downwards).

The percentages show the strength of the stimulus in terms of the threshold, which is reached in (*f*). With stimuli of less than half threshold (*a* and *b*) there is no marked difference between the passive anodal and cathodal responses. With stronger stimuli the cathodal response rises rapidly and assumes the characteristic form of the local action potential. In (*g*) the responses to four strengths of anodal and cathodal stimuli are superimposed. The double cathodal responses at 100 per cent. are due to minute variations in threshold; each cathodal and anodal record has a double trace to check constancy.

(From Pumphrey, Schmitt, and Young, *J. Physiol.* **98**, 1940.)

The fundamental property upon which nervous activity depends is the possibility of changing the permeability of the surface, so that the energy stored as a concentration difference between the inside and outside of the cell becomes available to produce activity at some distant place. In a peripheral nerve-fibre a relatively small depolarization (15 mV.) triggers off a response yielding a large potential difference (120 mV.) and the resulting local currents produce propagation over the whole fibre, with a high safety factor. This is the condition required for effective transmission of a signal. There is a high probability that events at one end of the fibre will produce similar events at the other end.

Since the nerve impulses are identical pulses, which can vary only in frequency, the rate of transmission of information by any one nerve-fibre is small. The transmission of large amounts of information is achieved by having large numbers of nerve-fibres and providing arrangements by which the impulses that they carry are allowed to interact within the central nervous system (p. 347).

7. Conduction velocity and the myelin sheath

The velocity of propagation of nerve impulses is not the same in all axons. The largest mammalian fibres, about 22μ in total diameter, conduct at about 120 metres/sec. in man, rather more slowly in the rabbit. Rates grade down to less than 1 metre/sec. for the smallest (non-medullated) fibres. In a cable-conducting system of this sort it is to be expected that velocity will increase with diameter on account of the lowering of resistance in the internal pathway. The increase obtained in this way is, however, only slight. In some invertebrate animals where there is no thick myelin sheath, increased velocity is obtained by diameter increase alone and enormous fibres, up to a millimetre in diameter, are found in squids and some worms. They conduct at about 25 metres/sec.

It would be impossible for reasons of size to produce an elaborate nervous system composed of many of these giant nerve-fibres. The high conduction velocities that make possible the combination of quick reactions and complicated higher nerve centres of mammals and other vertebrates are achieved by the presence of the *myelin sheath*. The sheath functions as an insulator, interrupted at intervals by the nodes of Ranvier (p. 330). The tiny cylinder of axon exposed at the node is the only active portion of the nerve membrane. The depolarization of this cylinder causes a flow of current along the inside of the fibre and out through the next nodal membrane, which is then depolarized. The impulse jumps from node to node. The effect of the insulating sheath is to ensure that the local circuits that produce conduction are spread out along the fibre. Each such unit propagates at high velocity and the whole process therefore proceeds faster than in non-medullated fibres, where the current produced at each point is allowed to leak through the membrane nearby. For the currents to be effective they must be conducted along a large tube and then canalized through a small area of membrane; correspondingly we find that the

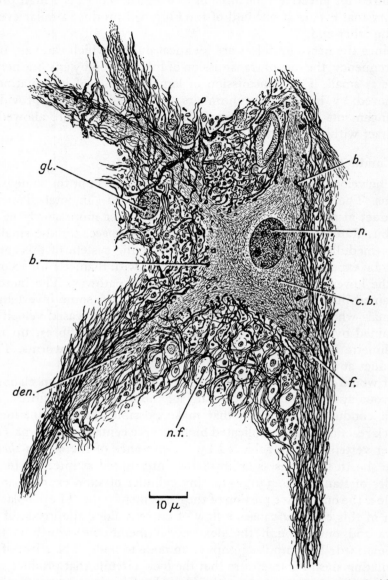

FIG. 153. Cell from the ventral horn of the lumbar spinal cord of a cat, stained with
Cajal's silver stain.

b. boutons terminaux; *c.b.* cell body of neuron containing neurofibrils; *den.* dendrite; *f.* fine
fibres running along dendrite; *gl.* nucleus of glia cell; *n.* nucleus of neuron; *n.f.* larger
nerve-fibres cut in section.

fastest nerve-fibres are of large diameter, but they become narrow at each node (Fig. 143).

The velocity of conduction is an important feature of nerve action since it affects not only the time of arrival of impulses but also the dispersal of volleys in neighbouring fibres. Nerve-fibres for each function possess characteristic diameters (Fig. 145). The motor nerve-fibres to striated muscles are large and medullated, as are the proprio-ceptor fibres that report back the tension on the muscle and play an essential part in producing a steady contraction (p. 366). Pre-ganglionic autonomic fibres are small and medullated, while sympathetic post-ganglionics and some fibres for pain conduction are non-medullated. Fast conduction is necessary for rapid control operations, slower con-duction is more efficient in making the slow changes necessary in the viscera (p. 391).

8. The synapse

Nerve-fibres thus transmit information in the form of a code of nerve impulses. Each impulse propagates over the whole fibre with a high safety factor. At the end of each axon the 'message' has to be 'decoded' and put to use by the receiving system. The study of the way the nerve-fibres transmit their effects to other nerve-cells is therefore of special importance. The same processes that produce propagation are probably used under modified conditions where nerve-fibres excite the next link in the chain at the *synapse* (see Fatt, 1954).

Single nerve-fibres conduct in an all-or-nothing manner but in the intact organism responses are usually produced by the effectors only when groups of nerve-fibres are active in particular patterns. This is ensured by the provision of regions, the synapses, at which the com-bined action of several nerve-fibres sets up impulses in other nerve-cells. We can speak therefore of *presynaptic fibres* conducting towards the synapse and *postsynaptic dendrites*, which, when appropriately activated, initiate nerve impulses in the axon leading to some other nerve-cell or to an effector. The question of the relation of pre- and postsynaptic fibres is obviously of crucial importance for neurology; the processes that go on in this region and lead to excitation of the postsynaptic cell make possible the interaction by addition or sub-traction between the signals in different nerve-fibres. This interaction is the basis of all the 'computations' by which the nervous system ensures appropriate responses to external and internal conditions.

Impulses arriving in a single presynaptic fibre seldom cross a synapse; they produce in the next cell of the chain local responses

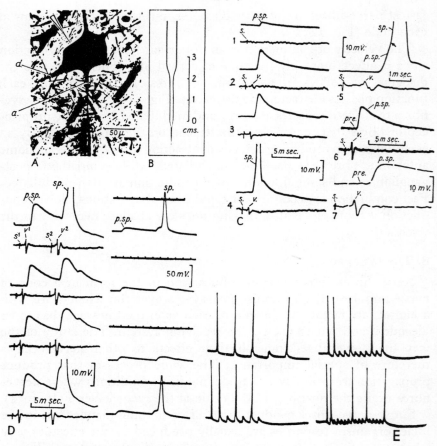

FIG. 154. Electrical changes recorded by micro-electrodes inserted into the spinal cord and presumed to be within spinal neurons.

A, Photograph of neuron with its axon (*a.*) and dendrites (*d.*). Superimposed on it is a drawing of an electrode just before penetration.

B, Drawing of the glass electrode, which is filled with 3 M.KCl.

C, Potentials set up in a neuron by electrical stimulation of the afferent fibres of the nerve in which its axon runs The lower line of each pair shows the response in the dorsal root, the upper line records the intracellular potential. In the series 1–4 increase in strength of stimulus (*s.*) gives larger and larger dorsal root volleys (*v.*) and increasing postsynaptic potentials (*p.s.p.*). In 4 the depolarization is sufficient to generate a propagating spike potential (*sp.*).

5 shows 4 at higher amplification and the arrow indicates the transition from *p.s.p.* to *sp.*, 6 and 7 are slow and fast records of *p.s.p.*'s in another neuron showing the presynaptic spike (*pre.*).

D, Potentials recorded by an electrode inside a motorneuron to two volleys (v¹ and v²) of afferent impulses set up in its own motor nerve. The first stimulus (s¹) is just submaximal, the second (s²) supramaximal. The time between them is the same in all records but since the interval is critical the motorneuron only sometimes fires a spike potential. The two columns show the same responses at different amplification and speed of recording.

E, Potentials recorded by an intracellular electrode in response to a series of volleys of afferent impulses. The first volley always generates a spike, later ones only sometimes. A postsynaptic potential occurs even when there is no spike. The frequencies are 45, 100, 150, and 200 a second. (After Brock, Coombs, and Eccles, *J. Physiol.* 117, 1952.)

(*synaptic potentials*) (p. 351), which can summate with those set up by impulses in other fibres that converge on the same cell. An impulse set up anywhere on a nerve-fibre normally spreads over the whole surface of that fibre. It follows that if excitation is not to spread indiscriminately throughout the nervous system there must be points of discontinuity and these are provided where each cell process makes synaptic contact with some part of another cell. After much controversy it is now agreed that the processes of the individual nerve-cells do not unite completely at these synaptic points, their contents remain separated by the membrane barriers of their surfaces, so that the potassium spaces of the two are not continuous. The effect of an impulse arriving in the presynaptic fibre is therefore not the same upon the postsynaptic cell as it would be upon a further extension of its own axon. The synapses thus provide regions at which the probability of transmission is low; impulses arriving in any one fibre are not here always passed on. The next cell in the chain is only excited when impulses arrive from a number of sources, with suitable timing. In other words the existence of synaptic regions allows for the interaction of signals coming from different sources, so that a properly co-ordinated response is produced.

There is probably great variation in the number of fibres that are involved in the synapses of nerve-cells in different parts of the nervous system but little is known of the details. In some parts impulses in one or a few presynaptic fibres are sufficient to fire the postsynaptic cell; other cells require an input from many sources. The regions of synaptic contact differ in appearance in different parts of the nervous system. Attached to the cell bodies and dendrites of the ventral horn cells of the spinal cord of mammals there are numerous small knobs, the '*boutons terminaux*' or *end feet* (Fig. 153), which are the endings of the presynaptic fibres. There are 2,000 or more of these endings in contact with a large motor cell.

These knobs are surrounded by surface membranes much thinner than those that cover even the smallest nerve-fibres (p. 329). Where the surface of the bouton makes contact with the surface of the nerve-cell body or dendrite the two membranes are in very close apposition and may be united by a special thickening. It is presumably in this region that the exchanges that produce excitation of the postsynaptic cell are initiated.

Some of the presynaptic fibres run for considerable distances along the dendrites before ending as terminal knobs. Others approach the cell surface at right angles. Presumably the effect produced by an

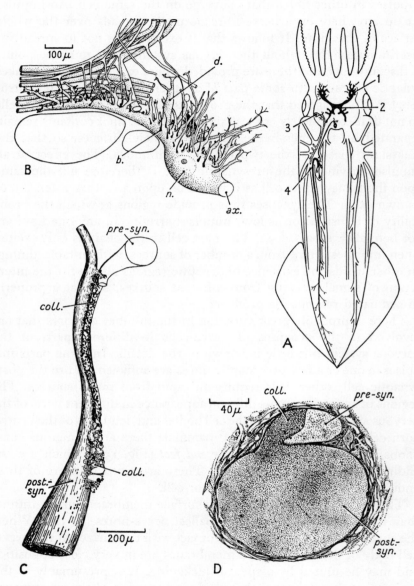

FIG. 155. Synapses in the squid.
(*For Key see opposite*)

incoming fibre depends upon its area of contact with the postsynaptic cell, perhaps also on its position in relation to the cell. In the synaptic region large numbers of mitochondria are present, suggesting that active metabolic processes are involved. This agrees with the fact that if there is shortage of oxygen synaptic transmission fails before conduction along nerve-fibres.

The ventral horn cell is thus brought under a variety of influences, including not only those from afferent fibres entering the cord but also from fibres descending from the cerebrum, cerebellum, and probably other parts of the brain (Fig. 160). There is still much to be learned about how interaction from these sources is ensured. Each presynaptic fibre divides many times and comes into contact with several different parts of the surface of several postsynaptic cells. A single impulse arriving in one fibre does not usually cause discharge of any cell. A series of impulses in one fibre may perhaps do so but excitation is probably usually produced by volleys, arriving dispersed over a short space of time, in several fibres. The nature of this process of *summation* remains in doubt but presumably impulses in each presynaptic fibre produce depolarization of an area of the cell membrane. If these local responses reach a certain value they give rise to a propagated nerve impulse. The local response or *synaptic potential* can be demonstrated by suitable electrical recording (Fig. 154). It is possible that the accumulation of a stimulating substance released by the presynaptic nerve-fibres plays an important part in synaptic conduction (p. 342).

Impulses arriving at a motor cell do not always tend to produce excitation, they may have the opposite effect, *inhibition*. There has been much discussion of how the opposed effects are produced. Excitation is a depolarization and inhibition probably a repolarization. The difference might depend upon different positions of excitatory and inhibitory boutons in relation to the postsynaptic surface or on the accumulation of two substances with antagonistic actions; there is little evidence on the subject. By studies of reflex excitation it can

---

A, Diagram of the system of giant nerve-fibres. 1. The two 1st order giant cells are covered with boutons bringing excitation from optic and other stimuli. 2. The two giant axons fuse across the mid-line. 3. They make connexion with 2nd order cells. 4. These make connexion with 3rd order giant fibres, which are formed by the fusion of the processes of many cells and innervate the muscles of the mantle by which the animal is squirted along.

B, Drawing of the 1st order giant cell. *ax.* axon; *b.* boutons; *d.* dendrites; *n.* nucleus.

C, Low-power view of synapse between 2nd order giant fibre (presyn.) and 3rd order fibre (postsyn.). *coll.* collaterals of postsynaptic fibre wrapping round the presynaptic fibre.

D, Transverse section across this synapse showing the contact between a collateral and the presynaptic fibre. The latter is the more faintly stained with the haematoxylin dye used.

(After Young, J. Z., *Phil. Trans. Roy. Soc.* B. **229,** 1939

be shown that there can be summation of inhibitory as well as of excitatory effects. Sherrington as a result of such experiments spoke

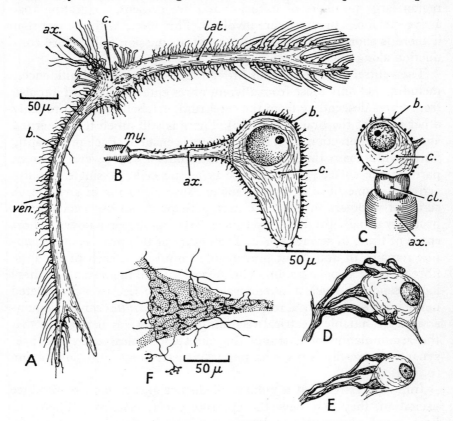

FIG. 156. Various types of synaptic system.

A, A semi-schematic representation of the synaptic apparatus found on Mauthner's cell in the goldfish. The endings on the lateral dendrite are all of vestibular origin while those on the ventral dendrite and cell body come from various other sources.

B, A large motor type cell from the reticular formation of the goldfish showing relatively uniform distribution of homogeneous boutons on the cell body and proximal part of the axon. Mallory-Azan stain.

C, A cell from the reticular formation of the goldfish showing a single large club ending as well as small boutons. Mallory-Azan stain.

D and E, Two cells from the oculomotor nucleus of the goldfish showing a basket-like system of club endings derived from a single large branching axon. Bodian stain.

F, A large interneuron from the spinal cord of a 15- to 16-day-old cat. Golgi method. *ax.* axon; *b.* boutons; *c.* cell body; *cl.* club ending; *lat.* lateral dendrite; *my.* myelin sheath; *ven.* ventral dendrite. (From Bodian, *D. Physiol. Rev.* **22**, 1942.)

of *central excitatory* and *inhibitory states*, without deciding on the physical basis for these (Creed *et al.*, 1932).

The details of synaptic structure are not satisfactorily revealed in the preparations stained with silver that are usually used to stain nerve-fibres. In a few animals there are nerve-cells and synapses that are large enough to be examined after preparation by histological methods suitable for preserving the detailed texture of these fine protoplasmic structures. Such methods reveal that there is always a marked difference in staining between the pre- and postsynaptic regions (Fig. 155). There can be no doubt that the contents of the neurons are separated at these points by one or more boundaries or membranes. Presumably it is this separation that ensures that impulses shall not always pass from the one fibre to the other; the barrier lowers the probability of transmission along the line and thus allows for signals in different fibres to add or subtract their effects. Granules can sometimes be seen at synaptic junctions (Fig. 155), suggesting that the transmission may involve the liberation of unit particles such as are characteristic of signalling systems (p. 22).

At those synaptic junctions where there are few convergent sources of input the area of contact between pre- and postsynaptic units is large. In the case of the stellate ganglion of the squid, shown in Fig. 155, two input fibres co-operate in control of the giant postsynaptic fibres and each makes a large area of contact. Probably much will be learned about the nervous system of mammals when we know more about the extent of the areas of influence at synapses of various types (Fig. 156).

9. Plan of organization of the nervous system; the reflex arc

The nervous system thus consists of a vast set of material, each part triggered to respond to a suitable change in its environment. The special receptor surfaces in eye, ear, skin, &c. are points where cells arranged to respond to small changes in the environment are able to set up impulses in the *afferent nerve-fibres* (Ch. XXIV). All the nerve impulses in any one fibre are alike in amplitude and many fibres are therefore needed in order to transmit information about the variety of changes going on around and within the animals.

Under artificial conditions impulses can pass in either direction along a fibre but on account of the refractory period impulses proceeding in opposite directions are unable to pass. A wholly separate set of *efferent nerve-fibres* is therefore used to carry signals back to the muscles and other effector organs. Throughout life series of impulses pass up the afferent fibres and down the efferent ones. Each act involves the co-operation of tens, hundreds, thousands, or millions of afferent fibres alone, whose impulses provide volleys bombarding the neurons of the central nervous system.

Setting our imagination to work we can now attempt to follow the internal sequence of events that occurs while the body produces a simple *reflex action*, such as the *flexor reflex*, by which the hand or foot is withdrawn on touching a hot object. The change in conditions (*stimulus*—see p. 462) activates a number of receptor organs in the skin, in this case the fine terminal branches of the nerve-fibres for the 'sense' of pain (p. 478). Nerve impulses travel in these fibres to the spinal cord and there initiate activity in a number of *motorneurons*, either directly or after passing through *internuncial neurons*. The motorneurons discharge impulses down to the flexor muscles, by which the limb is withdrawn. This simple movement, one of the most primitive protective or 'nociceptive' responses, thus depends upon connexions within the spinal cord that are determined by heredity. The afferent fibres entering the cord in any one spinal dorsal root may produce flexion in many muscles by the use of intersegmental spinal pathways.

This arrangement, in principle rather simple, is often used as the prototype of all nervous activity. It provides a model and allows us to introduce as it were a causal principle, by which we can seek for the antecedents of all actions of the body. It is important to emphasize the limitations of the picture and the need to use it with caution and with imagination. Sometimes the body may act in this way reflexly, like a simple man-made machine, such as an electric front-door bell. Such simple machines are so designed that they respond only to one aspect of change in the world around and produce only one action. Even the lower parts of the nervous system, however, allow for variation of response as a result of the interaction of input from various sources. Each nerve-cell is acted upon not by one or a few agents, as in a simple machine, but by many. Experiment shows that the pool of motorneurons that controls any muscle can be excited from various afferent sources. Moreover, not all of these sources produce excitatory effects. When we tread on a hot surface with both feet we do not flex both legs. Impulses that excite flexion in one limb *inhibit* it in the other. Indeed these same nerve impulses initiate contraction of the extensor muscles of the opposite leg, producing the *crossed extension reflex*, by which the body is held up. The system is therefore able to work not like a simple bell system but as a computor, like that of a guided missile. Its instructions are to keep the body as nearly as possible upright in the light of the information received from various sources, including feed-back arrangements from the proprioceptors of the muscles (p. 366).

In the higher parts of the nervous system this computing function becomes even more evident, so that only in a general sense is it possible any longer to use comparison with a simple reflex machine. Signals from large numbers of receptors are brought together in the brain centres and allowed to interact to produce elaborate and varied results. Moreover, the control at any moment depends not only on the instructions that are embodied in the hereditary design of the system but on the residual information about past events that has been stored (p. 457). The input interacts with this information store to produce a statistical estimate of the actions best calculated to ensure homeostasis.

These higher parts of the nervous system are composed of an immensely large number of separate units. There are more than 15,000 million nerve-cells in the human brain. Simple electrical machines contain a relatively small number of wires and other parts and we can therefore forecast exactly what will happen when current flows in any one part of the machine. In order to speak about the performance of a system with the immense number of parts found in the brain the best we can do is to use the methods that enable us to forecast the probable course of events. The application of such statistical methods to study of the nervous system is beginning to give us means for speaking about the behaviour of the vast number of cells that is involved.

Finally we must not imagine the nervous system to be in any fixed state of rest before the arrival of afferent impulses. Each part, such as a motorneuron, continually receives impulses from other parts of the nervous system and these impulses affect its excitability and hence its reflex actions. After severance of the spinal cord, cutting off the normal flow of impulses from the brain, a state of *spinal shock* follows and few or no reflexes can be obtained from the motorneurons for some days. In other parts of the nervous system, for instance in the brain, many of the neurons probably do not come to rest at all, but pass through continual cycles of discharge and recharge (p. 455). We understand only little of these central activities, but must continually think of their existence as a background upon which the streams of impulses from the receptor systems produce their effects.

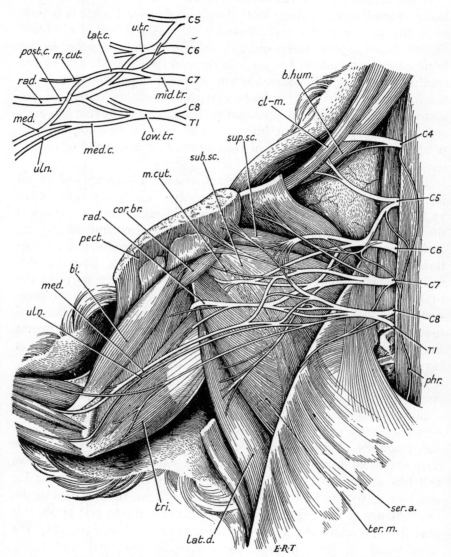

FIG. 157. Dissection of the brachial plexus of the rabbit. The simplified diagram at the top left shows the arrangement of the trunks and cords.

b. hum. basihumeral; *bi.* biceps; C₄–T₁ spinal nerves; *cl.-m.* cleido-mastoid; *cor.br.* coracho-brachialis; *lat.c.* lateral cord; *lat.d.* latissimus dorsi; *low.tr.* lower trunk; *m.cut.* musculo-cutaneous; *med.* median; *med.c.* median cord; *mid.tr.* middle trunk; *pect.* pectoralis; *phr.* phrenic; *post.c.* posterior cord; *rad.* radial; *ser.a.* serratus anterior; *sub.sc.* subscapularis; *sup.sc.* suprascapularis; *ter.m.* teres major; *tri.* triceps; *u.tr.* upper trunk; *uln.* ulnar.

XVIII

THE SPINAL CORD

1. Plan of the spinal cord

HAVING made a preliminary survey of ideas about the parts of the nervous system we can now begin to try to visualize how it works. The nervous system of simpler animals serves mainly for the performance of local reflex actions. In the starfish and other echinoderms there is no central nervous system but a network of nerve-fibres all over the body beneath the skin, thickened in certain regions. The vertebrate nervous system has probably been derived from such a condition, by collection of the nerve-cells and regions of synaptic contact to form the brain and spinal cord. Even in mammals the central nervous system shows by its development that it is essentially a subepidermal plexus rolled up into a tube (p. 767). The advantage of concentration of the nervous system is that it allows the animal to act more efficiently as a whole, bringing together all the information received by the various receptors. With such centralization it is possible for a store or memory of past information to be usefully put into relation with the information arriving at each moment.

The process of centralization has been going on throughout the evolution of vertebrates, with progressive increase in the number of routes that carry impulses up from the spinal cord to the brain and down again from the latter. This process culminates in man, where the main computations that determine the course of action are performed by the operations of the cerebral hemispheres. These are provided with information by all the main receptor systems and are the main stores of past experience. The 'lower' centres of the spinal cord remain of great importance in regulating the performance of each action.

It is convenient to consider the nervous system as consisting of a series of levels. The spinal cord constitutes the lowest level, containing the motorneurons, whose processes pass out to innervate the muscle-fibres, and thus provide the *final motor path*, through which all actions are produced. The motorneurons are mainly set in action by impulses that reach them from the higher levels, but the details of performance are regulated at the spinal level. The degree of contraction of each muscle is determined by the information sent from the receptor organs in the muscles, the proprioceptors (p. 366). This information is used at the spinal level, though it is also transmitted to the brain.

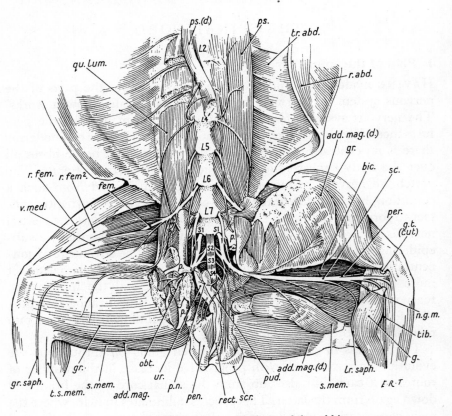

FIG. 158. The lumbo-sacral plexus of the rabbit.

add.mag. adductor magnus; *add.mag.(d.).* adductor magnus (deflected); *bic.* biceps; *fem.* femoral nerve; *g.* medial head of gastrocnemius; *gr.* gracilis; *gr.saph.* greater saphenous nerve; *g.t.(cut)* tendon of medial head of gastrocnemius; L$_2$, L$_4$, L$_5$, L$_6$, L$_7$ lumbar vertebrae with corresponding ventral rami of lumbar nerves; *lr.saph.* lesser saphenous nerve; *n.g.m.* nerve to medial head of gastrocnemius; *obt.* obturator nerve; *p.* pelvis; *pen.* penis; *per.* peroneal nerve; *p.n.* pelvic nerve; *ps.* psoas major; *ps.(d.)* psoas major (deflected); *pud.* pudendal nerve; *qu.lum.* quadratus lumborum (psoas major removed); *r.abd.* rectus abdominis; *rect.* rectum; *r.fem.* rectus femoris; *r.fem.2.* rectus femoris, second head; S$_1$, S$_2$, S$_3$, S$_4$ sacral nerves; *sc.* sciatic nerve; *scr.* scrotum; *s.mem.* semi-membranosus; *tib.* tibial nerve; *tr.abd.* transversus abdominis; *t.s.mem.* tendon of semi-membranosus; *ur.* urethra; *v.med.* vastus medialis.

The spinal cord therefore consists of the motorneurons, the pathways by which they are controlled, mainly from the proprioceptors, and the pathways for certain quick defensive actions, such as the reflex withdrawal from a painful stimulus. The cord also contains numerous fibres ascending to the brain and descending from it. In all its actions the cord is profoundly influenced by the operations that go on at higher levels.

2. The spinal nerves

The spinal cord of mammals is built on the same plan as in other vertebrates, giving off a dorsal and a ventral root on each side in each

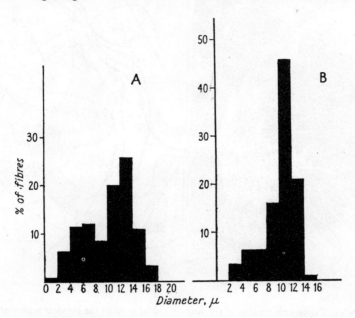

FIG. 159. Histograms showing the sizes of the fibres of two muscle-nerves in the rabbit.

A is an antigravity muscle (gastrocnemius) with many spindles and a bimodal set of nerve-fibres. B is the sterno-thyroid with few or no proprioceptors and a unimodal distribution of fibres in the nerve. (From Fernand and Young, *Proc. Roy. Soc.* B. **139,** 1951.)

segment (Fig. 160). The spinal dorsal roots are wholly afferent and each carries a ganglion containing the cell bodies of the nerve-fibres. The ventral roots contain the efferent fibres, whose cell-bodies lie within the spinal cord. Passing outwards the two roots join and then immediately divide into dorsal (posterior) and ventral (anterior) primary rami, each carrying motor and sensory fibres to the periphery. In many segments one or more rami communicantes join the sympathetic nervous system (p. 387).

In the cervical region the spinal nerves serve the muscles and skin and the more caudal ones (4, 5, and 6 in the rabbit) give rise to the phrenic nerve. The forelimb is served by parts of the ventral primary rami of a number of segments, usually C_4–T_1, which anastomose in a complex *brachial plexus* (Fig. 157) and distribute their fibres to form the nerves of the arm. The chief of these are the *radial nerve*, running mainly to the flexor muscles of the arm and forearm, and the *ulnar*

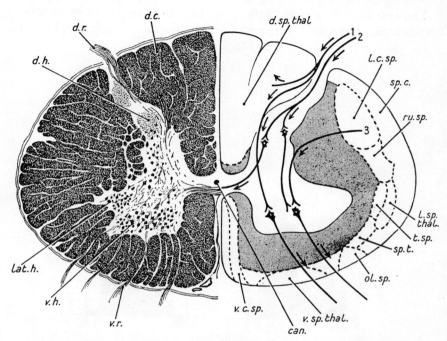

FIG. 160. Transverse section of the human spinal cord in the cervical region showing on the left the histological appearance with the medullated nerve-fibres and the nerve-cells stained. On the right a diagrammatic representation of some fibre connexions and pathways.

1. Pathway of the monosynaptic proprioceptor reflex. 2. Pathway of the flexor and crossed extensor reflexes. 3. Corticospinal pathway.

can. central canal; *d.c.* dorsal column; *d.h.* dorsal horn; *d.r.* dorsal root; *d.sp.thal.* dorsal spinothalamic tract; *lat.h.* lateral horn; *l.c.sp.* lateral cerebrospinal tract; *l.sp.thal.* lateral spinothalamic tract; *ol.sp.* olivospinal tract; *ru.sp.* rubrospinal tract; *sp.c.* spinocerebellar tract; *sp.t.* spinotectal tract; *t.sp.* tectospinal tract; *v.c.sp.* ventral cerebrospinal tract; *v.h.* ventral horn; *v.r.* ventral root; *v.sp.thal.* ventral spinothalamic tract.

and *median nerves*, to the muscles and skin of the forearm and hand.

In the thoracic region the ventral primary rami form the intercostal nerves, which supply the muscles and skin of the chest. Caudal to the thorax are the lumbar nerves, whose more cranial members innervate the abdominal muscles and skin. The more caudal lumbar nerves unite with those emerging in the sacral segments (usually L_4–S_3) to form the *sciatic* or *lumbo-sacral plexus*, which gives rise to the *femoral, obturator*, and *sciatic nerves*, innervating the hind limb (Fig. 158). Caudal nerves are well developed where there is a tail but are reduced to small coccygeal nerves in man.

The fibres in the spinal roots and spinal nerves and their branches vary greatly in diameter and therefore in velocity of conduction (p. 347). The nerve to each muscle or part of the skin carries fibres showing a characteristic 'spectrum' of diameter (see Fernand and Young, 1951). Thus the nerves innervating the main muscles of the body contain numerous large and small fibres but few of intermediate diameter and are hence said to be 'bimodal' (Fig. 159). It is not certain what factors determine the fibre sizes (p. 345). Some of the large fibres of a muscle-nerve are afferent (proprioceptor), others are motor. The small group contains the motor fibres that regulate the muscle-spindles and also some afferent fibres. Probably the diameters are important because the proper functioning of the whole system depends upon the correct timing of arrival of impulses at the spinal cord or muscles. The complicated organization of the nerve to a single muscle shows the great elaboration involved in the control of bodily activities. The afferent nerves of the skin are no doubt equally complex but even less is known about them.

3. Structure of the spinal cord

The spinal cord terminates in mammals in the lumbar region, even if there is a tail. The roots for the hinder segments therefore run back for a considerable distance within the vertebral canal and form a bundle, the *cauda equina*, in the middle of which is a narrow *filum terminale*, the non-nervous continuation of the cord.

The spinal cord itself is composed of central *grey matter*, in which lie the nerve-cell bodies, and an outer *white matter*, composed of ascending and descending tracts, whose medullated fibres give the white colour (Figs. 160 and 161).

The afferent fibres that enter the grey matter sometimes make direct contact with ventral horn cells, thus establishing two-neuron or *monosynaptic reflex arcs* (p. 365). More usually they end in connexion with cells in the dorsal portion of the cord and from these *internuncial neurons* axons run either to the ventral horn or else in other pathways, such as the spinothalamic tract, to the brain. There is some evidence that the fibres responsible for each modality of sensation have a characteristic pathway, running in a certain portion of the white matter of either the same or the opposite side. Thus the fibres entering from the muscle-spindles (proprioceptors) run in the dorsal

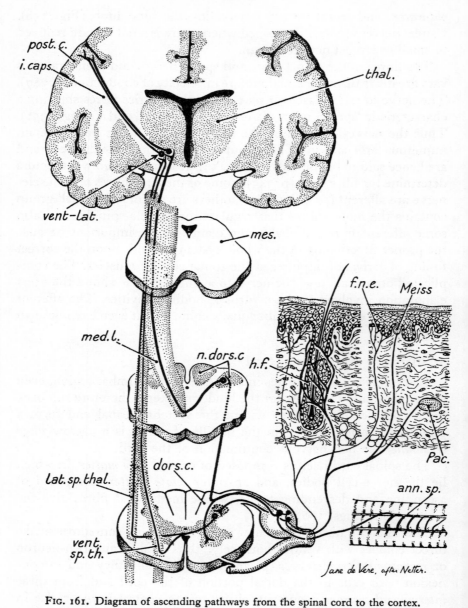

FIG. 161. Diagram of ascending pathways from the spinal cord to the cortex.

ann.sp. annulo-spiral ending of muscle-spindle; *dors.c.* dorsal column; *f.n.e.* free nerve endings; *h.f.* hair follicle; *i.caps.* internal capsule; *lat.sp.thal.* lateral spinothalamic tract; *med.l.* medial lemniscus; *Meiss.* Meissner's corpuscle; *mes.* mesencephalon; *n.dors.c.* nucleus of the dorsal column; *Pac.* Pacinian corpuscle; *post.c.* post-central gyrus; *thal.* thalamus; *vent.-lat.* ventro-lateral nucleus of the thalamus; *vent.sp.th.* ventral spinothalamic tract. (Modified from original illustration by F. Netter, M.D., from Ciba Collection.)

columns of the same side, those for pain in the opposite spinothalamic tract, lying more ventrally (Fig. 161).

The white matter also contains numerous descending fibres, by which the brain controls the actions of the spinal cord. Among the more important of these tracts are the cerebrospinal (pyramidal) and reticulospinal tracts (p. 438). Much remains to be learned of how they influence the cord. Their fibres mostly do not end directly on the ventral horn cells but among the internuncial neurons of the dorsal horn.

Within the grey matter it is possible to recognize an arrangement in four columns, concerned with separate functions (Fig. 160). From the ventral side upwards these are the somatic motor, visceral motor, visceral sensory, and somatic sensory columns of cells. The most ventral nerve-cells are those that innervate the striated muscles of the somatic motor system, constituting the *ventral horn*: they provide the motorneurons for the whole body musculature. Above these are the visceral motorneurons, which are smaller cells. This column is well marked only in the cord segments in which preganglionic autonomic fibres are found (p. 387), namely those of the thoracic and upper lumbar region and sacral region, in which a *lateral horn* of grey matter is present.

Where there are special cells of the grey matter connected with visceral afferent functions these lie in or just above the lateral horn. The regulation of the discharge of these cells is by afferents arising in the viscera and entering over the dorsal roots. Influences also reach the lateral horn cells from the autonomic regulating centres in the medulla oblongata and hypothalamus (p. 419).

The whole mass of neurons of the *dorsal horn* of the cord is concerned with appropriate routing of the afferent impulses but the details of how this is achieved are still unknown. The effect of these connexions is to produce the pattern of spinal reflexes, the basal units of the organization of behaviour.

4. The reflex control of movement

Throughout life a continual stream of nerve impulses proceeds from the spinal cord to the muscles, serving for the regulation of posture and the initiation of movement. Many influences play upon the ventral horn cells, increasing and decreasing the frequency of the impulses that are sent to particular muscles. The pattern of these discharges is set by the afferent impulses arriving from the many receptors. For example maintenance of the standing posture depends upon impulses from the labyrinth of the ear, eyes, proprioceptors of the neck and limbs, and tactile organs in the feet (Ch. XXI). Again, the initiation of walking movements may depend upon change affecting any of the afferent fields (say in the nose and eyes) and the combination of this information with that stored in the cerebral cortex.

All muscular contraction, whatever its ultimate source of initiation,

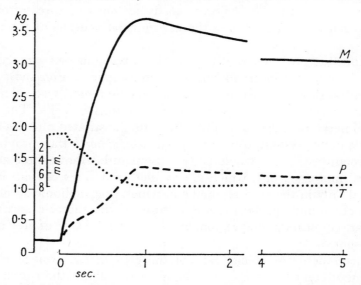

FIG. 162. Recording of stretch reflexes in a decerebrate cat. The quadriceps muscle is attached to a lever whose point moves upwards when the muscle contracts, recording the tension in kilograms.

The table on which the animal lies is dropped as shown by the line T, stretching the muscle. M shows the tension change with the nerve intact, P when it has been cut. (After Liddell and Sherrington, *Proc. Roy. Soc.* B. **96**, 1924.)

requires to be performed in an orderly manner and this is ensured by mechanisms situated primarily at the spinal level. The muscles are capable of producing very great forces. A maximal discharge of nerve impulses reaching the muscles of the human arm as a synchronous volley would produce a tension approaching one ton in 20 m./sec. on the short arm of the lever (Ruch, 1951). This would produce a very jerky start and an enormous kinetic energy in the arm, followed by an overfling. Effective movements depend upon proper limitation and control of these great forces that the muscles can produce. Actions must start and stop gradually or be steadily maintained. All of this is ensured by a control system based fundamentally on feed-back from the proprioceptor organs within the muscles, which record the length and/or tension within the muscles. The impulses they discharge pass to the spinal cord and brain, allowing comparison to be made between the state of the muscles and the instruction provided by the brain, which is itself dependent on the impulses received from the outside world by the receptors.

The system for making this comparison is elaborate and imperfectly

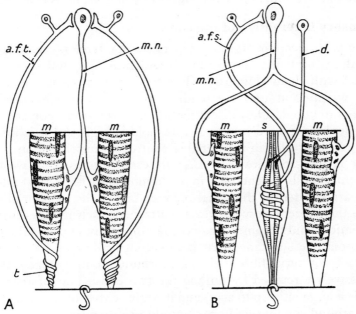

FIG. 163. Diagram of the two types of receptor in skeletal muscle.

A, Tendon organs (*t.*) are arranged in series with the muscle-fibres (*m.*). The afferent fibres from them (*a.f.t.*) enter the spinal cord through the dorsal root and influence the motor-neurons (*m.n.*). It is not certain whether the pathway is monosynaptic as shown.
B, The muscle-spindles (*s.*) are in parallel with the muscle-fibres. The afferent fibres from them (*a.f.s.*) run direct to the motorneurons, making a monosynaptic reflex. The small motor nerve-fibres (*d.*) control the bias of the spindle. (Partly after Fulton and Pi-Suner.)

understood; at the spinal level it constitutes the *stretch reflex* (myotactic reflex), which ensures that a muscle contracts when the tension upon it is increased. This tension can be shown to depend upon receptors in the muscle by an experiment in which the effect of the brain on the spinal cord is first removed by transection to eliminate the influence of the higher centres (decerebration). The quadriceps muscle is then attached to a myograph to record its tension (Fig. 162). The table on which the cat lies is quickly lowered, as indicated by the line *T*, and the tension in the muscle increases markedly (line *M*). If now the nerve to the muscle is cut the increase of tension is only about one-fifth of that with the nerve intact (line *P*). The remaining four-fifths of the tension must be the result of nerve impulses set up in the muscle by the stretch, producing increased discharge of the motorneurons. That this is so is confirmed by cutting the dorsal roots, which has the same effect as severing the whole nerve-supply to the muscle. There must therefore be proprioceptor organs within the muscle that are able to provide impulses when the muscle is stretched.

5. Sensory innervation of muscle

The proprioceptor organs are of two sorts, tendon organs in series with the contracting muscle-fibres and muscle-spindles that are in parallel with them (Fig. 163). The tendon organs consist of nerve-fibres wrapped around the tendinous fibres by which muscles are attached to bones. They discharge when the tension upon the muscle is suddenly increased but their threshold is high and it is uncertain what part they play in the detailed control of muscle action.

The muscle-spindles (Fig. 164) are each composed of two to four small muscle-fibres, enclosed in a common sheath. At the ends these fibres are striated in the usual manner but at the equatorial region, where the afferent nerve-fibres are attached, each muscle-fibre loses its striations and becomes a bag containing many nuclei embedded in a sarcoplasmic substance that is non-contractile (see Barker, 1948). The receptor nerve-fibre is therefore wound around a region that can be passively stretched by pulling the two ends. The afferent nerve-fibre is a large one (up to $20\,\mu$) and it begins either by a series of spiral turns around the muscle-fibre ('annulo-spiral endings') or as a series of branches ('flower spray ending'). Various simpler types of muscle receptor are also found, for instance in the eye-muscles there are sprays of nerve-fibres attached to the surface of muscle-fibres that are otherwise little modified.

Studies of the discharges in single afferent nerve-fibres have shown that the basic response of the muscle-spindle is a volley of impulses discharged when the muscle is stretched or the spindle itself contracts. This discharge is responsible for the stretch reflex, thus ensuring that a muscle contracts when it is pulled upon. The large afferent fibres from the annulo-spiral endings enter the dorsal horns and send branches that reach directly to the ventral horn cells (Fig. 164a). By this *monosynaptic reflex* impulses are set up in the ventral horn cells with a delay shorter than is found in any other reflexes. Ascending branches of the annulo-spiral afferents pass in the dorsal columns to the cerebellum, which also plays a large part in the regulation of muscular action (p. 408).

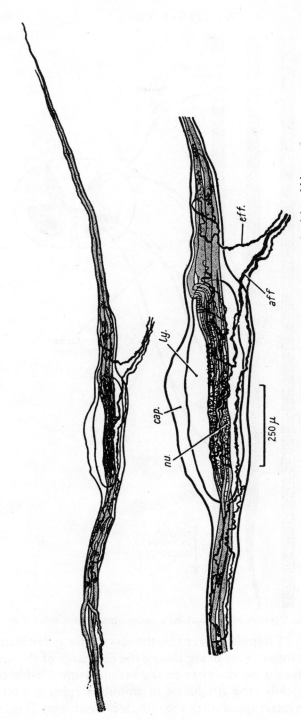

Fig. 164. A single muscle-spindle from the vastus intermedius muscle of the rabbit.

Note the tapering muscle-fibres, striated over most of their length (stippled) but forming bags of nuclei (*nu.*) in the equatorial region, where the afferent fibres (*aff.*) wrap around them. The efferent fibres (*eff.*) end outside the capsulated region (*cap.*). A space (*ly.*) intervenes between the muscle-fibres and the capsule. (Modified from Barker, *Quart. J. micr. Sci.* **89,** 1948.)

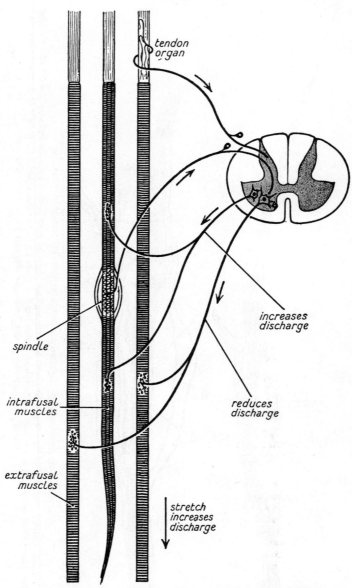

tendon
organ

spindle

intrafusal
muscles

extrafusal
muscles

increases
discharge

reduces
discharge

stretch
increases
discharge

FIG. 164a. Diagram of action of the monosynaptic stretch reflex.

The discharge of impulses over the monosynaptic reflex pathway
is a factor of first importance in regulating the discharge of the motorneurons. If the motor nerve-fibres to the ordinary muscle-fibres are
stimulated electrically, the discharge of impulses from a stretched
muscle-spindle is interrupted while the muscle is shortening (Fig. 165).

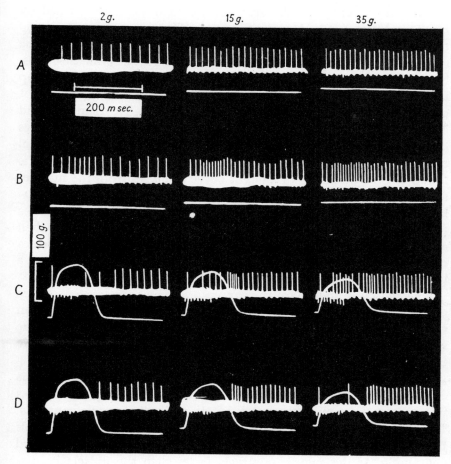

FIG. 165. Discharge of nerve-impulses in a single nerve-fibre from a muscle-spindle of the cat. The motor nerve has been cut so that there is no reflex discharge through the spinal cord. The white line below records the pull of the muscle upon a strain gauge.

Line A shows the increasing frequency of discharge under three levels of tension. In line B is shown the effect of electrical stimulation of a single small motor nerve-fibre; no tension is produced but the afferent discharge is increased. In line C large and small motor nerve-fibres are stimulated together and the muscle contracts. Under 2 g. load there is a pause in the discharge but under the higher loadings the spindle discharge is maintained throughout. In line D only the large motor nerve-fibres are stimulated: during the contraction there is a pause in the afferent discharge. (From Hunt and Kuffler, *J. Physiol.* 113, 283, 1951.)

The effect of this 'silent period' is to reduce the flow of excitation reaching the muscle over the monosynaptic pathway during any period in which it is shortening. This is the basis of the method of control by which the tension in the muscle is adjusted to the task it is called upon to perform.

The muscle-fibres of the spindles are themselves innervated by motor end-plates at both ends (Fig. 164). The nerve-fibres supplying these 'intra-fusal' end-plates emerge in the ventral roots with the motor fibres that innervate the ordinary ('extra-fusal') muscle-fibres, but whereas the nerve-fibres to the latter are large 'alpha' fibres (up to 20 μ) and conduct rapidly (50–110 m./sec. in the cat), those that control the spindle muscle-fibres are smaller (3–8 μ diameter) and conduct at between 15 and 20 m./sec. These small nerve-fibres ('gamma' fibres) can be stimulated electrically under experimental conditions without stimulation of the larger fibres and the result is found to be a discharge of afferent nerve impulses from the muscle-spindles (Fig. 165B). If the small and large nerve-fibres are stimulated together there is a continuous discharge of afferent impulses (Fig. 165C). This is presumably the condition that occurs in life when a muscle contracts against resistance and the flow of afferent impulses over the monosynaptic pathway serves to maintain the muscle in a tetanically contracted state.

The muscle-spindles are thus receptors for a servo system. They discharge when the muscle is stretched, this discharge ceasing when the muscle itself contracts, unless the small motor nerve-fibres to the spindles come into action and maintain the tension on the spindle even in the tensed muscle.

The nerve-fibres producing contraction of the spindles are thus able to control the 'bias' of the receptor in such a way that it fires impulses at the same rate at each length while the muscle contracts. In other words when the gamma fibres are active the spindle signals the difference between the muscle shortening and the intrafusal shortening. If the spindle contracts faster than the muscle its discharge accelerates and vice versa. Observation in man shows that the spindle discharge always accelerates during a 'voluntary' contraction. Since the effect of the afferent impulses is to produce contraction through the monosynaptic reflex, this means that the gamma fibres are the agents that drive the muscle.

6. Control of muscles through their afferents

According to this conception, therefore, the influence of the brain on the muscular system is exerted not so much by fibres that control the motorneurons directly as by control of the rate of discharge of the smaller motorneurons that innervate the spindles. Evidence for this hypothesis can be obtained by inserting stimulating electrodes into regions of the brain-stem (p. 412) and recording their effects on the afferent discharge of spindles. Stimulation of some points produces increase of frequency, others decrease, at all levels of extension of the muscle. There are therefore systems in the brain that are able to vary the bias of the spindles over their whole physiological range. In this way it is ensured that the instruction proceeding from the higher levels of the brain is translated into movements that are effectively adjusted to the resistance that is met with at each phase of the action. The system involves many further components at both spinal and cerebral levels, ensuring minimum transient errors and absence of oscillation (Ch. XXI).

The functioning of a feed-back system of this sort must depend upon the proper timing of the arrival of the signals. If the information about the tension in the muscle is to be effective it must be quickly available and the afferent nerve-fibres of the muscle-spindles are among the largest in the body and therefore the fastest-conducting. The gamma fibres that control the bias of the spindles are smaller but it is not clear whether their slower conduction has any special significance.

7. Reciprocal innervation

The stretch reflex is able to hold the limb in a constant position for long periods and for this purpose the red muscle-fibres (p. 121) are used. The motorneurons for these fibres discharge impulses at a low rate (5–10/sec.) and the muscle-fibres relax only slowly, making possible the maintenance of tension for long periods at low cost.

The afferent fibres from the stretch receptors also cause inhibition of discharge of impulses in the flexor motorneurons. This *reciprocal innervation* is obviously necessary for effective functioning and is an example of a simple pattern of motor activity determined by the hereditary arrangement of connexions within the spinal cord.

The stretch reflex and flexion reflex have opposite effects upon the limbs and are therefore said to be *antagonistic reflexes*. When stimuli evoking two such reflexes occur together the response to one of them dominates the other—usually nociceptive (protective) reflexes dominate all others. The inherited patterns of the spinal cord thus provide a simple system for computing appropriate responses.

Many other reflex actions can be performed by an animal with an isolated spinal cord and the basic patterns of standing, walking, and many visceral activities such as micturition and the sexual acts are laid down there. Most of these actions normally come under the control of centres in the brain (p. 424).

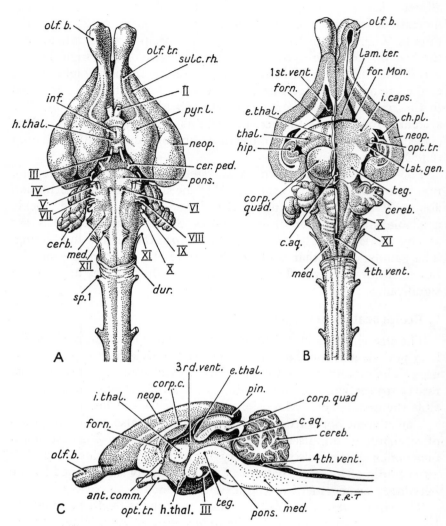

FIG. 166. Views of the rabbit's brain.

A, Ventral; B, partially dissected from dorsal surface; C, sagittal section.

II, Optic nerve; III, oculomotor nerve; IV, trochlear nerve; V, trigeminal nerve; VI, abducent nerve; VII, facial nerve; VIII, acoustic nerve; IX, glossopharyngeal nerve; X, vagus nerve; XI, accessory nerve; XII, hypoglossal nerve.

ant.comm. anterior commissure; *c.aq.* cerebral aqueduct; *cereb.* cerebellum; *cer.ped.* cerebral peduncle; *ch.pl.* choroid plexus; *corp.c.* corpus callosum; *corp.quad.* corpora quadrigemina; *dur.* dura mater; *e.thal.* epithalamus; *for.Mon.* foramen of Monroe; *forn.* fornix; *hip.* hippocampus; *h.thal.* hypothalamus; *i.caps.* internal capsule; *i.thal.* interthalamus; *inf.* infundibulum; *lam.ter.* lamina terminalis; *lat.gen.* lateral geniculate body; *med.* medulla; *neop.* neopallium; *olf.b.* olfactory bulb; *olf.tr.* olfactory tract; *opt.tr.* optic tract; *pin.* pineal body; *pons.* pons Varolii; *pyr.l.* pyriform lobe; *sp.1* first spinal nerve; *sulc.rh.* sulcus rhinalis; *teg.* tegmentum; *thal.* thalamus; *1st, 3rd, and 4th vent.* first, third, and fourth ventricles.

XIX

THE ORGANIZATION OF THE BRAIN

1. The functional columns in the brain

THE presence of the four functional columns provides a convenient frame of reference around which to organize knowledge of the brain. The brain is the part of the neural tube that is modified by development of the various columns at places where there is an inflow of fibres connected with special receptor systems or where there are special motor centres. The general arrangement into the four functional columns seen in the spinal cord is preserved but the higher ('suprasegmental') centres, such as the cerebral cortex and cerebellum, cause much distortion of the simple tubular plan.

In the *medulla oblongata* (Fig. 170) the spinal plan can be clearly seen but the nervous tissue is spread out laterally, leaving an extensive roof of thin non-nervous tissue, the *choroid plexus*. In front of it the *cerebellum* represents a great development of the somatic sensory column, connected with the inflow of nerve-fibres of the auditory nerve concerned with balance. The medulla and cerebellum constitute the *hind-brain* (*metencephalon*).

In front of this lies the *midbrain* (mesencephalon). Here the somatic sensory columns form the *corpora quadrigemina*, which are higher centres concerned with impulses from the optic and auditory nerves. They are less developed in mammals than in lower vertebrates. The somatic motor column is especially developed in the floor of the midbrain as the *tegmentum*, a region that has important influences in controlling the pattern of motor behaviour (p. 411).

The *forebrain* is greatly developed in all mammals and includes the unpaired between-brain (*diencephalon*) and the cerebral hemispheres (*telencephalon*). The more dorsal part of the diencephalon includes the *thalamus*, where fibres from the various receptor systems make synapse on their way to the cerebral cortex. The ventral part of the diencephalon (*hypothalamus*) represents the front end of the visceral sensory and visceral motor columns and serves to regulate many of the internal (visceral) activities. The *pituitary body* (hypophysis) is attached to the lower side of the hypothalamus by a stalk (infundibulum).

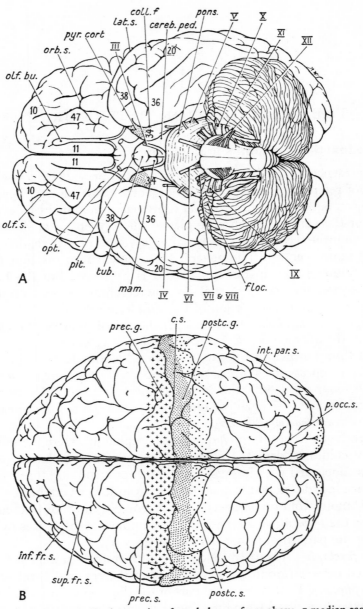

FIG. 167. The human brain seen in A from below, B from above, C median sagittal section, and D from the side. The numbers of the areas are those used by Brodmann. Primary afferent areas close stipple, secondary areas dotted. Crosses indicate motor cortex.

III, Oculomotor nerve; IV, trochlear nerve; V, trigeminal nerve; VI, abducent nerve; VII and VIII, facial and auditory nerves; IX, glossopharyngeal; X, vagus; XI, spinal accessory; XII, hypoglossal.
ant. c. anterior commissure; *ca.s.* calcarine sulcus; *c.call.* corpus callosum; *cereb.ped.* cerebral peduncle; *cing.s.* cingulate sulcus; *c.s.* central sulcus; *coll.f.* collateral fissure; *cun.* cuneus; *floc.* flocculus; *forn.* fornix; *inf.fr.s.* inferior frontal sulcus; *inf.t.s.* inferior temporal sulcus;

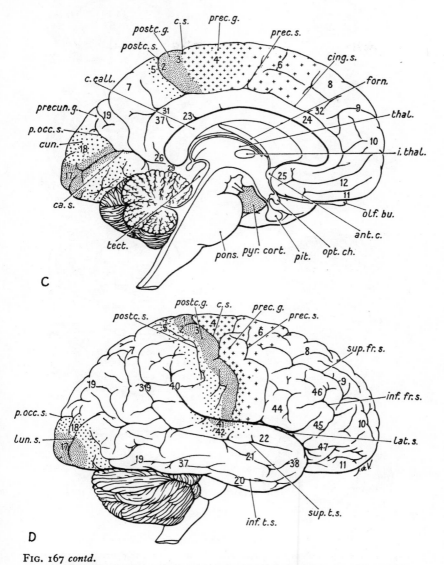

C

D

FIG. 167 *contd.*

int.par.s. intraparietal sulcus; *i.thal.* interthalamic connexion; *lat.s.* lateral sulcus; *lun.s.* lunate sulcus; *mam.* mamillary body; *olf.bu.* olfactory bulb; *olf.s.* olfactory sulcus; *opt.* optic nerve; *opt.ch.* optic chiasma, *orb.s.* orbital sulcus, *pit.* pituitary stalk; *p.occ.s.* parieto-occipital sulcus; *pons.* pons Varolii; *postc.g.* postcentral gyrus; *postc.s.* postcentral sulcus; *prec.g.* precentral gyrus; *prec.s.* precentral sulcus; *precun.g.* precuneate gyrus; *pyr.cort.* pyriform cortex; *sup.fr.s.* superior frontal sulcus; *sup.t.s.* superior temporal sulcus; *tect.* tectum; *thal.* thalamus; *tub.* tuber cinereum.

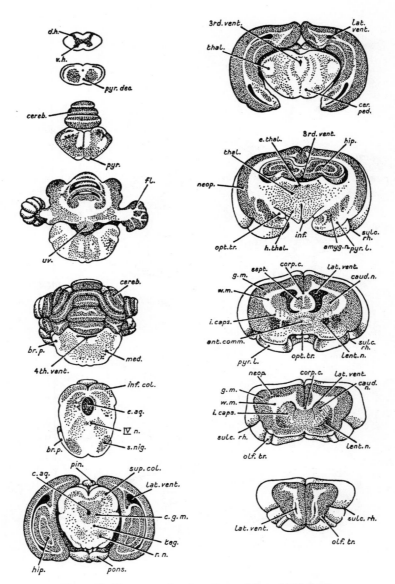

FIG. 168. Transverse hand sections of the rabbit's brain.

amyg.n. amygdaloid nucleus; *ant.comm.* anterior commissure; *br.p.* brachium pontis; *c.aq.* cerebral aqueduct; *caud.n.* caudate nucleus; *cereb.* cerebellum; *cer.ped.* cerebral peduncle; *c.g.m.* central grey matter; *corp.c.* corpus callosum; *d.h.* dorsal horn; *e.thal.* epithalamus; *fl.* flocculus; *g.m.* grey matter; *hip.* hippocampus; *h.thal.* hypothalamus; *i.caps.* internal capsule; *inf.* infundibulum; *inf.col.* inferior colliculus; *lat.vent.* lateral ventricle; *lent.n.* lentiform nucleus; *med.* medulla; *IV n.* nucleus of trochlear nerve; *neop.* neopallium; *olf.tr.* olfactory tract; *opt.tr.* optic tract; *pin.* pineal body; *pons.* pons Varolii; *pyr.* pyramid; *pyr.dec.* pyramidal decussation; *pyr.l.* pyriform lobe; *r.n.* red nucleus; *sept.* septum pellucidum; *s.nig.* substantia nigra; *sulc.rh.* sulcus rhinalis; *sup.col.* superior colliculus; *teg.* tegmentum; *thal.* thalamus; *uv.* uvula; *3rd (4th) vent.* third (fourth) ventricle; *v.h.* ventral horn; *w.m.* white matter.

The *cerebral hemispheres* represent an immense development of the front end of the somatic sensory column. This region was originally concerned with olfactory functions (as it still is today in fishes and amphibians). In mammals the olfactory centres are limited to the more ventral parts of the cerebral hemispheres. The remainder, the cerebral cortex proper, is made up of a vast number of neurons receiving impulses from the various receptor fields (eye, ear, skin, &c.) and serving to analyse the information that arrives from these receptors and to compute appropriate responses in the light of the memories of past events that are recorded there. The efferent pathways from the cerebral hemispheres reach to many parts of the brain (hypothalamus, tegmentum, cerebellum, spinal cord) and they dominate the whole action system of the animal. The characteristic of the mammalian brain is thus that instead of local centres, each concerned mainly with one receptor system, there is developed a very large cerebral cortex, which deals with afferent impulses of many sorts and has direct control of the muscles and other effectors.

The general plan of the brain is similar in all mammals but the cerebral hemispheres are relatively larger in the 'higher' forms. This development must have occurred independently in several distinct lines of mammals. In the living mammals that remain close to the earliest mammalian type, e.g. shrews, the cerebral cortex is small, especially its more anterior (frontal) part, but there is a relatively large development of the olfactory parts of the forebrain. The brain of the rabbit (Fig. 166) shows some further development of the cortex but this remains relatively much smaller than in man (Fig. 167).

2. Ascending and descending pathways

Throughout the brain and spinal cord of mammals there is a great development of long pathways leading upwards from the primary sensory centres to the cerebral hemispheres and downwards from the latter towards the spinal cord. Some of the lower centres become reduced as their functions are taken over by the forebrain. For example, the optic lobes of the midbrain, which are large and important in pre-mammalian forms such as the frog, are relatively small in mammals. On the other hand, some stations along both the ascending and descending pathways become greatly developed in mammals, for instance, the walls of the diencephalon (thalamus) are thickened because all the ascending pathways make synapse there. Similarly the red nucleus of the tegmentum and the inferior olive in the medulla, which are parts of the brain concerned with motor functions, become increased rather than reduced as the cortical control develops, and all of these reach an exceptional size in the higher primates (see Brook-hart, 1954).

The long pathways of the brain run in the white matter, which in the lower parts of the brain lies, as in the cord, around the grey matter. In certain parts these long tracts make thick strands that influence the external form of the brain. Thus the descending cortico-spinal fibres form a marked pair of columns, the *pyramids* (Fig. 168) along the lower side of the medulla oblongata. Beneath the cerebellum these join the tracts of the *pons Varolii*, which unite the cerebellum with the cerebrum. Together they form beneath the midbrain and between-brain an even larger pair of bundles, the *basis pedunculi*. The tracts ascending from the cord are externally visible as the nuclei of the dorsal columns above the hind end of the medulla, but above this level they run within the medulla and midbrain as large bundles close to the midline, known as the *medial lemniscus* (p. 427), eventually reaching the thalamus.

3. The cerebral ventricles, cerebro-spinal fluid, and meninges

The development of special thickenings gives to the brain its curiously irregular shape. The central canal is also not simple. In the medulla oblongata the canal forms the large *fourth ventricle*, then narrows again as the *cerebral aqueduct*, passing through the midbrain to the *third ventricle*, which occupies the centre of the diencephalon. From this cavity paired *interventricular foramina of Monro* lead to the cavities of the lateral ventricles. The ventricles are occupied by the *cerebrospinal fluid*, produced by the *choroid plexuses*. These latter are thin, vascular, folded membranes, formed from the roof of the ventricles. The anterior choroid plexus is an extensive membrane pushed through the foramina of Monro into the lateral ventricles. Here most of the cerebrospinal fluid is produced and passes through the foramina and backwards to the third and fourth ventricles. It leaves the fourth ventricle through three foramina beneath the cerebellum, which lead to *arachnoid spaces* between the inner membrane or *pia mater* that closely covers the brain and spinal cord and an outer, more loosely attached *dura mater*. The arachnoid space is crossed by a fine web of fibres, from which it gets its name, and here there are special regions (arachnoid villi) in which the cerebrospinal fluid is absorbed back into the venous system.

4. Neuroglia

The tissue of the brain is not made up wholly of neurons. It contains many blood-vessels and also a set of cells, the *neuroglia*, that are presumed to act in a supporting and nutritive capacity. These cells are of three types, *astrocytes*, *oligodendrocytes*, and *microcytes* (Fig. 169).

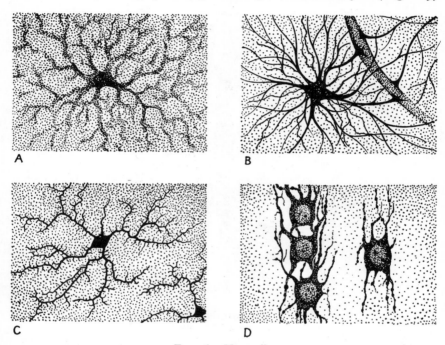

FIG. 169. Neuroglia.

A. Protoplasmic astrocyte.   B. Fibrous astrocyte with vascular feet.
C. Microcytes (microglia).   D. Oligocytes (oligodendroglia).

Together they make a packing tissue that fills up all the spaces between the nerve-cells and fibres in the central nervous system. Their protoplasm is in close relation to the surfaces of the neural elements and may play a part in nourishing the latter and perhaps also in the specific functions of conduction and synaptic excitation. The glial protoplasm contains numerous mitochondria and is evidently an actively metabolizing tissue.

The astrocytes are much-branched cells; some of the processes being attached to the walls of the blood-vessels. Oligodendrocytes (= oligocytes) have elongated processes, often wrapped around medullated nerve-fibres; they may be regarded as the equivalent in the central nervous system of the Schwann cells of the peripheral nerves and they probably play a part in the production of myelin (p. 329). These two types of cell are derived from ectoderm. The microcytes (microglia cells) have numerous short branches and are of mesodermal origin. They correspond to the histiocytes found in other tissues

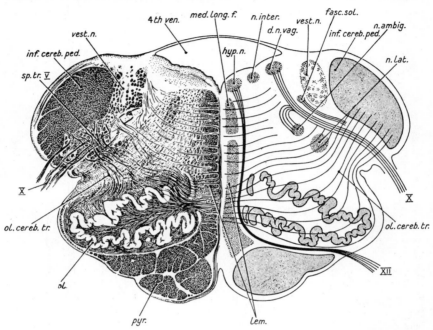

FIG. 170. A transverse section through the medulla oblongata of man below the middle of the olive.

x, Vagus nerve; XII, hypoglossal nerve; *d.n.vag.* dorsal nucleus of vagus; *fasc. sol.* fasciculus solitarius; *hyp.n.* hypoglossal nucleus; *inf.cereb.ped.* inferior cerebellar peduncle; *lem.* medial lemniscus; *med.long.f.* medial longitudinal fibres; *n.ambig.* nucleus ambiguus; *n.inter* nucleus intercalatus; *n.lat.* nucleus lateralis; *ol.* olive; *ol.cereb.tr.* olivo-cerebellar tract; *pyr.* pyramid; *sp.tr.V.* spinal tract of trigeminal nucleus; *4th ven.* fourth ventricle; *vest.n.* vestibular nucleus (descending root).

(p. 58) and when the brain is damaged they withdraw their processes and become phagocytic.

5. The medulla oblongata. Regulation of visceral activities

The medulla oblongata is the region of origin of the cranial nerves that innervate the muscles of the head and the viscera (p. 392). These nerves bring information from the viscera and send back motor impulses to them after appropriate synaptic action by the nerve-cells aggregated as 'nuclei' within the medulla. This region thus has important receptor and effector functions and it shows the four main functional columns clearly. Indeed it retains more nearly the primitive organization than does any other part of the brain. Its roof is thin and non-nervous but the functional columns can be recognized in the sides and floor (Fig. 170). The somatic sensory column is represented at the caudal end of the medulla by the large *nuclei of the dorsal columns* and more cranially by the nuclei connected with the somatic sensory systems of the cranial nerves, especially the trigeminal. The visceral sensory system is largely developed where the gustatory and other afferent fibres of the vagus and glossopharyngeus enter.

The motor nuclei of the medulla are complicated by the fact that in this region the dorsal and ventral roots do not join, and, moreover, the dorsal roots besides their afferents also carry efferent fibres to the musculature that is derived from the branchial arches (see p. 733). The somatic motor column is present in the hind- and midbrain, lying medially as the sets of cells giving rise to the fibres of the ventral cranial roots, III, IV, VI, and XII. The cells of the fibres to the lateral plate musculature of the visceral arches arise in a special column somewhat lateral (dorsal) to the somatic motor nuclei, the axons running in the dorsal roots V, VII, IX, X, and XI. This column may be regarded as a special part of the somatic motor column and is sometimes called the *special visceral efferent* or branchial motor column. Its cells are large, like those of the somatic motor column in the cord. The similarity of function is emphasized by the collaboration of some of these muscles (sterno-mastoid and trapezius) with true somatic muscles in producing movement of the shoulder in man (p. 161).

The (general) visceral efferent column is represented in the medulla and the midbrain by the cells of origin of the preganglionic autonomic fibres that run in nerves III, VII, IX, and X (p. 390).

The detail of the organization of the medulla shows a bewildering variety of nuclei concerned with various functions. The appropriate level of activity of the heart, lungs, alimentary canal, and other viscera is computed by these nuclei in the light of signals received in afferents from these organs and from the hypothalamus and other parts of the brain. Local injuries in the medulla produce irregularity of many activities. There are groups of cells concerned with control of respiration, heart-rate, diuresis, sugar metabolism, and other functions. The medulla, being the centre of origin of the fibres of the cranial nerves, has developed into a most elaborate system for the regulation of the life of the whole animal. No doubt it also provides, by interaction between these various centres, for the proper integration of many of the internal functions of the body. It is a region of the brain absolutely indispensable for the life of a mammal and its cells are deeply involved in the production of the rhythm of action that dominates the life of every animal (p. 471). We can only dimly imagine the complicated activities that produce these various drives. Afferent impulses from the stomach, heart, and lungs and elsewhere produce reflex effects in the medulla, but this region cannot be adequately described as a 'reflex centre'. Many of its cells do not come to rest, in particular those of the respiratory centres discharge rhythmically from birth to death (p. 306), though their periodicity is influenced by afferent discharges. Such rhythmical changes going on in the medulla and in other parts of the brain are as much a part of the 'life' of the animal as is the heart-beat.

XX

THE AUTONOMIC NERVOUS SYSTEM

1. The control of internal activities

THE somatic part of the nervous system controls those organs of the body that are in contact with the outside world. It serves to bring the body to places where food and drink can be obtained and enemies avoided; the striped musculature is the agent through which it works. For the continued maintenance of the body there is necessary also a mechanism by which the actions of the internal parts can be controlled and co-ordinated. In the simpler Metazoa the co-operation of the cells is mainly ensured by the effects that the working of each has upon others, but as the specialization of tissues proceeded during evolution an internal co-ordinating mechanism became developed, serving to ensure that there is proper adjustment of the functions of the organs to each other, the heart being made to beat faster when the muscles require more oxygen, the movements of the gut being accelerated during digestion and so on.

The visceral nervous system that accomplishes this co-ordination is already present in *Amphioxus*; throughout the chordate series it has become progressively elaborated, allowing more and more detailed control of the workings of the special parts that became developed as the animals colonized more and more 'difficult' habitats. This visceral nervous system works with an endocrine co-ordinating system of increasing complexity (Ch. XXXIII). Study of the evolution of these two parts of the body therefore gives some indication of the nature of the change by which animals have become 'higher' or more complex.

The separation between outer (somatic) and inner (visceral) nervous systems is obviously largely artificial; they work together for the maintenance of the integrity of the body and can only do so effectively if their actions are co-ordinated. When the somatic nervous system sets the muscles into action the heart and blood-vessels must adjust their output to provide a suitable flow of blood; moreover this blood must be made to carry enough sugar for fuel and enough oxygen to burn it. Nevertheless the visceral motor section of the nervous system forms a rather distinct anatomical unit and this separation has been

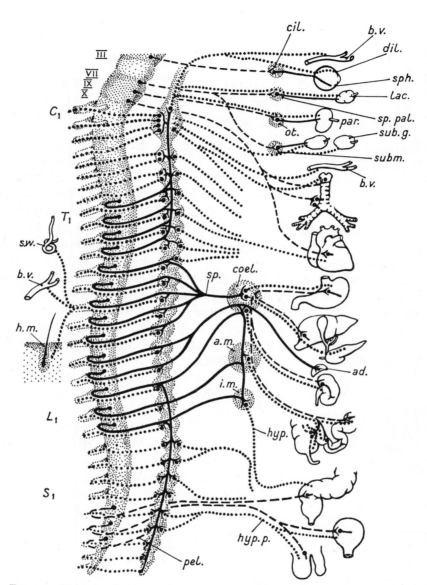

FIG. 171. Diagram of the autonomic nervous system. Preganglionic sympathetic pathways are shown as solid lines, postganglionic sympathetic pathways as dotted lines. Preganglionic parasympathetic pathways are shown as broken lines, post-ganglionic parasympathetic pathways as solid lines. The parasympathetic pathway to the gut passes mainly in the gut wall, partly through the coeliac ganglion as illustrated.

(*For Key see opposite*)

recognized by calling it the *autonomic nervous system*, although, in spite of its name, it is not independent in its working. According to the classical view it does not even allow the performance of reflex actions but is simply an arbitrarily separated portion, the visceral motor system (see p. 400). It receives its activation, as does the somatic motor division, from the central nervous system. The term 'involuntary nervous system' is also often used for this set of visceral nerves. It is true that we do not usually speak of exerting conscious control of the activities that it regulates, but by suitable training some people can obtain 'voluntary' control of these powers, for instance, they can narrow the pupil or quicken the heart-beat 'at will'. Conversely many somatic actions are 'involuntary' (the knee jerk).

2. Preganglionic and postganglionic cells

The characteristic feature of the arrangement of the visceral motor nervous system is that the cell bodies of its final motor neurons are outside the central nervous system (Kuntz, 1946; Mitchell, 1953), not within it as are the ventral horn cells of the somatic system (p. 401). The cells are aggregated into ganglia, which lie either along the course of the nerves or actually within the organs that they control. These peripheral autonomic motorneurons are controlled by nerve-cells lying within the central nervous system. On every autonomic pathway we can therefore distinguish *preganglionic neurons* in the central nervous system, which send axons to make connexion with the *postganglionic neurons* of the peripheral ganglia (Fig. 171). In mammals the preganglionic axons are usually small medullated nerve-fibres, whereas the postganglionic fibres are unmedullated. A convenient means of locating the point at which the break (synapse) occurs is provided by the alkaloid nicotine; if applied to an autonomic ganglion this drug first excites the cells to activity and then paralyses all the synaptic junctions. We can therefore discover whether a given set of fibres ends in a ganglion by seeing whether the effect produced by stimulating them is abolished by painting the ganglion with a 1 per cent. solution of nicotine. For example, preganglionic fibres that produce contraction

---

Key to Fig. 171:

III, Oculomotor nerve; VII, facial nerve; IX, glossopharyngeal nerve; X, vagus nerve; *ad.* adrenal gland; *a.m.* anterior mesenteric ganglion; *b.v.* blood-vessel; *cil.* ciliary ganglion; *coel.* coeliac ganglion; *dil.* dilatator muscle of iris; *h.m.* hair muscle; *hyp.* hypogastric nerve; *hyp.p.* hypogastric plexus; *i.m.* inferior mesenteric ganglion; *lac.* lacrymal gland; *ot.* otic ganglion; *par.* parotid gland; *pel.* pelvic nerve; *sp.* great splanchnic nerve; *sph.* sphincter of iris; *sp.pal.* spheno-palatine ganglion; *sub.g.* submandibular sublingual glands; *subm.* submandibular ganglion; *s.w.* sweat gland.

(Modified from original illustration by F. Netter, M.D., from Ciba collection.)

of the dilatator muscle of the iris of the eye of a mammal leave the spinal cord in the ventral roots of the upper thoracic region, run forwards in the cervical sympathetic trunk and make synapse in the superior cervical ganglion with postganglionic nerve-cells whose fibres ultimately reach the eye. Nicotine interrupts this pathway only when it is applied to the superior cervical ganglion.

The functional significance of the fact that the visceral motor-neurons lie outside the central nervous system is not clear. According to orthodox beliefs the visceral ganglia are not reflex centres (see, however, p. 395). Visceral afferent nerve-fibres do not end in the autonomic ganglia but proceed through the dorsal roots (where their cell bodies lie) to make connexions in the brain or spinal cord. All activation of the visceral motor system is on this view through the preganglionic fibres, unless, of course, the postganglionic neurons show rhythmic spontaneous activity of their own or are directly stimulated by local influences. Each preganglionic fibre is connected with many postganglionic neurons and this diffusion of the effects may be the reason for the presence of a cell on the motor pathway but there may well be some further recoding or other change that at present escapes us.

3. Divisions of the visceral motor system

The classical analysis of the visceral motor system, developed by Gaskell and Langley (Langley, 1921), recognizes two major divisions *sympathetic* and *parasympathetic* (Fig. 171). These are distinguished by the fact that they are (1) anatomically distinct, (2) physiologically opposite or 'antagonistic' in their actions, and (3) mimicked by the action of two distinct sets of drugs. We have therefore three separate criteria for decision as to whether any given visceral nerve or ganglion is to be called sympathetic or parasympathetic. We may decide by its anatomical position and connexions, by its physiological effects, or by pharmacological study of the substances that stimulate it or imitate its action. There is sufficient agreement between these criteria to encourage us to believe that there are two different sets of nerve-fibres but there are divergences, suggesting that the nerves responsible for the control of the viscera are not simply divisible into two sharply distinct systems.

4. The sympathetic system

The chain of sympathetic ganglia extends in mammals from the neck to the end of the abdomen (Fig. 171). The head and tail are supplied by fibres originating in ganglia of the neck and trunk. The preganglionic neurons that control this system leave the cord as medullated fibres in the ventral roots of about segments T_1 to L_2, forming the *white rami communicantes*, which run from the spinal nerves to the ganglia. The non-medullated (grey) axons of the postganglionic cells pass from the ganglia to the muscles of the blood-vessels and of the viscera, and to various glands. Some of these fibres reach their end organs by passing back from the ganglia to the spinal nerves as the *grey rami communicantes*. The muscles and glands of the abdominal viscera receive their nerves mainly not from the ganglia of the sympathetic chain itself but from certain splanchnic or collateral ganglia, including the coeliac and anterior mesenteric ganglia of the *solar plexus* and the inferior mesenteric ganglia. These collateral ganglia are connected with the sympathetic chain by a series of *splanchnic nerves* (Fig. 172), the most important being the greater splanchnic, which arises in the thorax and runs to the solar plexus.

The most cranial member of the sympathetic chain is the *superior cervical ganglion*, lying dorsal to the carotid artery, approximately at the level of its division into internal and external branches. This ganglion supplies postganglionic fibres to numerous structures in the head. It receives its preganglionic fibres from the white rami communicantes of the upper thoracic segments and for this reason interruption of these spinal nerves by injury or operation produces many signs in the organs of the head, such as narrowing of the pupil and drooping of the eyelid.

The sympathetic ganglia of the neck do not show a regular segmental arrangement. Besides the superior cervical ganglion there is also a large *inferior cervical (stellate) ganglion* and often also a small middle cervical. From the three cervical ganglia grey rami communicantes pass to the cranial nerves, to the cervical spinal nerves and to the heart, lungs, and other organs of this region.

In the thoracic and lumbar regions the sympathetic ganglia are more regularly arranged, one to each spinal nerve. There are white rami communicantes in the thoracic and upper lumbar segments and these usually run obliquely, especially lower down, so that each ganglion receives a white ramus from the spinal nerve of a different (higher) segment (Fig. 172). The grey rami on the other hand run transversely.

The splanchnic nerves arise from the sympathetic chain in the lower thoracic and upper lumbar regions. They consist mainly of small medullated fibres, which pass from the white rami through the ganglia of the sympathetic chain to end in the solar plexus, where they make synapse. Non-medullated postganglionic axons proceed from the coeliac and anterior mesenteric ganglia to the stomach, intestines, and other viscera. They pass through the plexuses of the gut wall (p. 239) to end on the smooth muscles, glands, and blood-vessels.

The viscera of the lower abdomen (bladder, rectum) receive their sympathetic fibres from the *inferior mesenteric ganglion*, whose pre-ganglionic fibres leave the chain in several lesser splanchnic nerves in the lumbar region. The system in this region forms a complicated network of fibres on either side of the aorta, which is known as the *hypogastric plexus* and continues downwards at the side of the rectum as the *pelvic plexus*; this is also connected with the sacral parasym-pathetic system (p. 391).

The sympathetic chains continue through the lower lumbar and sacral regions as thin strands with segmental ganglia, sending grey rami to the nerves. The two chains lie close together on either side of the aorta and are joined by transverse commissures.

The sympathetic system can be described as consisting of a set of ganglia but the ganglia are only denser aggregations of cells within a rather irregular network of cells and fibres. Postganglionic cells are found at numerous places along the sympathetic chains and the rami communicantes, splanchnic nerves, and plexuses; the whole set con-stitutes a network of cells and fibres lying on either side of the aorta and extending among the viscera.

5. The parasympathetic system

The fibres whose actions are in general opposite to those of the sympathetic system run in nerves of the head and sacral region and are less easily characterized as an anatomical entity than are the sym-pathetic fibres. The sympathetic preganglionics all leave the central nervous system in ventral roots but the parasympathetic fibres leave in both ventral and dorsal roots. Fibres regarded as parasympathetic are found in the oculomotor, facial, glosso-pharyngeal, and vagus nerves and in the ventral roots of the sacral segments at about the level of the third sacral spinal nerves.

6. Cranial parasympathetic system

The preganglionic fibres in the oculomotor nerve run to the ciliary ganglion, in the orbit. They make synapse with postganglionic cells there, and these in turn send fibres in the short ciliary nerves to pro-duce contraction of the muscles of accommodation and the sphincter

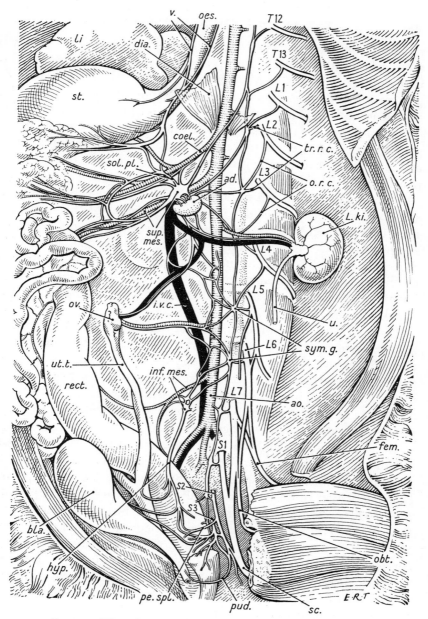

FIG. 172. Dissection of the autonomic nervous system of the cat.

ad. adrenal; *ao.* aorta; *bla.* bladder; *coel.* coeliac artery; *dia.* diaphragm; *fem.* femoral nerve; *hyp.* hypogastric nerve; *inf.mes.* inferior mesenteric artery and ganglion; *i.v.c.* inferior vena cava; *L. 1–7*, ventral rami of lumbar nerves 1–7; *li.* liver; *l.ki.* left kidney; *obt.* obturator nerve; *oes.* oesophagus; *o.r.c.* oblique ramus communicans; *ov.* ovary; *pe.spl.* pelvic splanchnic nerve; *pud.* pudendal nerve; *rect.* rectum, *S 1–3*, sacral nerves 1–3; *sc.* sciatic nerve; *sol.pl.* solar plexus; *st.* stomach; *sup.mes.* superior mesenteric artery and ganglion; *sym.g.* sympathetic ganglion; *T 12 & 13*, thoracic nerves 12 & 13; *tr.r.c.* transverse ramus communicans; *u.* ureter; *ut.t.* uterine tube; *v.* vagus nerve.

muscle of the iris (Fig. 171). This system is therefore connected with a ventral root (oculomotor) and it carries a ganglion (the ciliary). Thus it resembles the sympathetic nerves and the only clear reason for placing it in a distinct system is that the action of the sphincter iridis muscle is 'antagonistic' to that of the dilatator muscle, which receives its motor fibres from the superior cervical ganglion. Yet we do not place flexor and extensor muscles of the elbow in opposite 'systems' and it is difficult to see the justification for doing so in this case. The pharmacological criterion, however, provides a further test (p. 398).

The *ciliary ganglion* is a minute body lying in the orbit. It may be said to have three roots, short, long, and sympathetic. The short root runs from the oculomotor nerve and carries the preganglionic parasympathetic fibres that end in the ganglion. The postganglionic fibres then pass in the short ciliary nerves to the eyeball. The long root of the ciliary ganglion contains sensory fibres from the trigeminal nerve. They pass through or near the ciliary ganglion into the long ciliary nerves running to the eyeball.

The sympathetic root of the ciliary ganglion consists of postganglionic fibres arising in the superior cervical ganglion and passing along the carotid plexus (p. 387). They pass with branches of the trigeminal nerve through the ciliary ganglion without synapse and are distributed in the long ciliary nerves to the dilatator iridis muscle.

The main bulk of the parasympathetic system consists of fibres in the seventh, ninth, and tenth cranial nerves, controlling the secretion of the salivary glands and the actions of many of the viscera. The preganglionics in the seventh nerve run a complicated course to reach the submandibular and sphenopalatine ganglia. The *sphenopalatine ganglion*, which controls the lacrimal gland, lies just below the exit of the maxillary branch of the trigeminal nerve but fibres reach it from the facial nerve. It also receives sympathetic fibres from the plexus around the internal carotid artery and ultimately from the superior cervical ganglion (p. 387). The sphenopalatine like the other parasympathetic ganglia of the head is therefore said to have two motor roots but of course the sympathetic fibres, being postganglionic, run through the ganglion without synapse. These ganglia also have sensory 'roots', in the case of the sphenopalatine from the maxillary nerve. The *otic ganglion* receives its preganglionic fibres partly from the facial, partly from the glossopharyngeal nerve; it controls the parotid gland. The facial fibres for the *submandibular ganglion* pass through the chorda tympani and lingual nerves and control the submandibular and sublingual salivary glands.

The *vagus* is a large nerve (see p. 208) containing numerous small medullated preganglionic fibres, in addition to many sensory ones. The preganglionic fibres run to the heart, lungs, walls of the stomach, small intestine and colon, and the alimentary glands, such as the pancreas. The fibres end in contact with postganglionic cells lying close to the muscles or glands of these organs. In the gut wall there are two plexuses of cells and fibres, an outer *myenteric* or *Auerbach's plexus*, between the circular and longitudinal muscle layers, and an inner *submucous* or *Meissner's plexus*, beneath the mucosa (Fig. 239). The cells of these plexuses are the postganglionic parasympathetic neurons that have migrated out during development along the vagus, but the details of their development, arrangement, and functioning are still obscure and Langley suggests that it would be wise to regard them as belonging to an enteric nervous system, distinct from the remainder of the autonomic. Their axons run to the smooth muscles and glands of the gut.

7. Sacral parasympathetic system

The ventral roots of certain sacral segments contain preganglionic fibres that run to the viscera in the pelvic splanchnic nerves. These *pelvic nerves* join the hypogastric plexus to form the pelvic plexus, from which branches pass to the neighbouring organs. The pelvic plexus therefore contains both sympathetic fibres (through the hypogastrics) and parasympathetic fibres (through the pelvic splanchnic nerves). The parasympathetic fibres are preganglionic and make synapse with cells lying either in the pelvic plexus or in the walls of the uterus, bladder, external genitalia, lower colon, and rectum. This sacral parasympathetic system has effects opposite to those of the sympathetic fibres that reach these viscera.

8. Functions of the two parts of the autonomic nervous system

It is sometimes said that the function of the autonomic nervous system is the regulation of the *milieu intérieure*, or internal environment, which is maintained constant in the higher animals. Cannon expresses a similar idea in his conception that the autonomic nervous system maintains the homeostasis by which the internal environment is kept constant (p. 18). It is true that the autonomic system is involved in many regulatory actions. For instance, the sympathetic system, by its control of the blood-vessels of the skin, regulates temperature. But the maintenance of the integrity of the organism is the 'function' of *all* its parts. The characteristic by which we recognize a creature as alive is that its actions tend to promote its own con-tinuance (p. 15). It is necessary, therefore, to keep a sense of propor-tion and not ascribe to the autonomic system any particular mysterious influence on homeostasis not possessed by other organs, say the brain, the bladder, or even the less active parts like the hairs or the bones.

The autonomic nerves have indeed actions that regulate the activi-ties of many internal organs and the sympathetic and parasympathetic parts of the system often act in opposite directions, setting up a balance. It is convenient to generalize these activities by saying that the sympathetic nerves make the body ready for action in an emer-gency whereas the parasympathetic ones promote the restorative activities, which go on while the animal is at rest.

9. Effects of sympathetic nerves

The effects observed on stimulating sympathetic nerves electrically are found to be such as would be expected for the purpose of pre-paring the body for action in attack or defence. Thus the sympathetic fibres running to the lungs produce dilatation of the bronchi, allow-ing increased ventilation. The nerves from the cervical sympathetic ganglia to the heart are known as the *nervi accelerantes*, because they increase the frequency and strength of the heart-beat. The action on the coronary arteries of the heart is, however, to produce relaxation, providing an increased blood-flow. In other parts of the body the sympathetic nerve-fibres to the blood-vessels usually produce con-striction. The diameter of each artery or arteriole can be increased, when necessary, by inhibition of the sympathetic tonus, allowing a greater blood-flow. The state of the vessels thus comes under a com-plicated set of reflex and hormonal influences, which ensures that the blood-supply to any organ is made large when the organ becomes active. When the whole body is in action the sympathetic (constrictor) tone of the vessels to the viscera is increased, depriving them of blood, which is transferred to the muscles, whose arteries dilate. Conversely during digestion the blood-supply of the gut is increased. In some active animals (dog, hare, and perhaps man) there are sympathetic nerve-fibres that actively dilate the blood-vessels in the muscles, but usually the blood-flow is controlled by variation in sympathetic con-strictor tone. This is exercised in such a way as to make the most efficient use of the blood by transferring it to whatever part of the body needs it at the time. This mechanism for effective use of the blood is probably a major factor in allowing the success of the higher vertebrates.

The list of sympathetic controls that prepare the body for action is very long. Many details of metabolism are controlled by these nerves. The sympathetic fibres cause the spleen to contract and pass out its store of red corpuscles into the circulation (p. 279). Glucose is mobilized from glycogen stores by sympathetic action upon the liver. Activity of the viscera uses a large supply of blood and is reduced in an emergency; the sympathetic nerve-fibres passing from the coeliac and anterior mesenteric ganglia to the gut therefore mostly inhibit the movements of peristalsis, but they cause contraction of the pyloric and ileo-colic sphincters, preventing movement of food along the canal. Similarly there is constriction of the blood-vessels of the pelvic viscera and external genitalia and relaxation of the wall of the urinary bladder.

The muscles in the walls of the male reproductive tract (vas deferens, seminal vesicles, and prostate) are caused to contract by their sympathetic nerves during ejaculation. The sympathetic nerves to the uterus vary in effect according to the state of the organ, producing relaxation when the uterus is empty, contraction at the end of pregnancy. There is probably no antagonistic parasympathetic innervation of the internal reproductive organs.

Finally, in addition to these internal regulatory activities the sympathetic also has effects on organs at the periphery of the body that make preparation for action. The pupil of the eye dilates because of sympathetic action on the radial dilatator muscle, perhaps to allow more light to enter (though this would not necessarily always increase the usefulness of the eyes!). The dilatation of the pupil may serve to produce a sudden presentation of dark, round, eye-spots eliciting a flight reaction in the opponent.

The sudden bristling of the hairs (associated with arching of the back) is another action controlled by sympathetic nerves, whose effect in apparent size increase can be seen in any cat and dog fight. The control of the hair position also has the effect of regulating the heat loss. The flow of sweat, which is produced by impulses in sympathetic fibres, is another action that may be necessary during the stress of battle.

10. The sympathetic system and the adrenal glands

Many of these actions of the sympathetic nervous system are also performed by adrenaline (p. 542). The association between the sympathetic and the adrenal medulla is certainly close and there is evidence that sympathetic postganglionic nerve-fibres produce their excitatory and inhibitory effects by secretion of a substance like adrenaline, probably *nor*-adrenaline, close to the muscles or glands that they innervate (p. 399). The adrenal medullary cells develop, like sympathetic cells, from the neural crest and they are to be regarded as postganglionic sympathetic cells that pour adrenaline into the bloodstream instead of producing it in the peripheral tissues.

l-nor-adrenaline and some *l*-adrenaline occur in postganglionic sympathetic neurons and nerve-trunks and in larger amounts in the organs that these nerves innervate. These substances disappear from an organ after degeneration of its nerves, but reappear as the nerves regenerate. Amine oxidases present in the tissue are able rapidly to inactivate these mediators. Evidently the sympathetic system and the adrenal medulla act together in the regulation of many parts of the body. The sympathetic nerves act by carrying signals to particular tissues, where they cause liberation of adrenaline-like substances. The adrenal medulla liberates similar substances into the blood so that they influence tissues throughout the body.

Groups of gland-cells of the same type as those in the adrenal medulla occur within many sympathetic ganglia. Presumably their secretion assists in the regulation of the activities of the postganglionic cells. This is a further sign of the close relationship of the two systems, which should repay further investigation.

11. Effect of removal of sympathetic chains

The part played by the sympathetic system in the life of the animal can be investigated experimentally by removing the entire sympathetic chain. The arduous operations involved were performed by Cannon and his colleagues at Harvard, where cats and dogs were kept alive for many months without any sympathetic nerves. Providing that the surrounding conditions were not severe the animals showed no gross abnormalities. When they were exposed to conditions of stress, such as extremes of temperature or lack of oxygen, they died sooner than did normal animals. The cats were found to be considerably less active after the operation but this was less evident in the dogs.

In summary then we may say that the sympathetic division of the autonomic nervous system produces effects throughout the body that tend to make preparation for strenuous action.

12. The functions of the parasympathetic system

The parasympathetic nerves form a less compact unit anatomically than the sympathetic and functionally they control a number of separate activities; the system seldom acts as a whole. Nevertheless one can say that in general its actions are such as to assist in restoring the energies of the body after action, in preparation for further efforts. Thus parasympathetic nerves play a large part in promoting digestion. Fibres in the seventh and ninth cranial nerves control the secretion of the salivary glands, including vasodilator fibres that cause the blood-vessels of the glands to relax and produce a flow adequate to allow a copious secretion of saliva. Throughout the gut the rule is that the parasympathetic nerves increase peristalsis and promote secretion of the glands, whereas the sympathetic fibres inhibit these actions but cause contraction of the muscles of the sphincters. Thus the flow of gastric and pancreatic juice, succus entericus and bile is increased by stimulation of the vagus. The nerve-cells in the myenteric and sub-mucous plexuses of the gut wall are probably all postganglionic para-sympathetic cells, which have moved out during development along the vagus nerves. Their function is presumed to be simply the motor one of distributing the impulses for reflexes whose pathway is from afferent fibres of the gut or elsewhere through the spinal cord and brain and the preganglionic parasympathetic fibres.

It has often been suggested that these plexuses can perform reflex actions when isolated from the central nervous system. Co-ordinated peristaltic movements continue in isolated pieces of intestine suspended in a suitable liquid and stimulation of one point in such a preparation may produce effects at a distance. Some of these pheno-mena may be due to 'axon reflexes'; the cells of these plexuses have many long and branching processes and impulses set up anywhere in one cell will thus become widely distributed. Further work is needed on the action of this rather isolated portion of the nervous system, to determine whether its cells are capable of initiating action either by their own rhythmic properties or reflexly.

There may well be shorter autonomic reflex chains besides those through the spinal cord and preganglionic fibres. It has recently been shown that very small nerve-fibres (0.2μ diameter) leave the gut and make synapse in the inferior mesenteric ganglion (Brown and Pascoe, 1952; McLennan and Pascoe, 1954). These may perhaps be repre-sentatives of a whole set of nerve-fibres mediating short chain reflexes in the enteric plexuses and sympathetic system.

The parasympathetic system has less general influence on the vascular system than has the sympathetic but produces effects in cer-tain parts. The nerves from the vagus to the heart slow the rate of beat and there is usually a tonic discharge in the vagus restraining the heart. Doses of atropine, which paralyses this vagus action (p. 399), may produce a doubling of the rate of heart-beat in man. The dilatation of vessels in the salivary glands has already been mentioned and the sacral parasympathetic fibres passing in the pelvic nerves cause relaxation of the vessels of the external genitalia, producing erection of the penis or clitoris.

Many other more or less isolated functions throughout the body are controlled by nerves classed as parasympathetic. Thus the muscles of accommodation of the eye and the sphincter muscle of the iris are caused to contract by impulses passing through the third nerve and ciliary ganglion. The lachrymal gland is made to secrete by fibres of the facial nerve that synapse in the sphenopalatine ganglion. The effect of the vagal nerve-fibres to the lungs is to cause constriction of the bronchi, an action clearly opposite to that of the sympathetic nerves.

The sacral parasympathetic nerves produce the reflex contraction of the wall of the urinary bladder in micturition, the internal sphincter muscle being caused to relax.

13. Antagonism of sympathetic and parasympathetic systems

Evidently the two sets of autonomic nerves often work in opposite directions on an organ and this is clearly brought out in Table A. The sympathetic and parasympathetic nerves to the heart, blood-vessels of the salivary glands and external genitalia, and to the musculature of the gut clearly work in such a way that when the one excites muscular contraction the other inhibits it. In other organs, especially in the iris (p. 388) the antagonism is between muscles that pull in opposite directions and does not involve the presence of nerve-fibres that actively promote relaxation. Moreover, it is important to recognize the large number of cases in which there is no clear 'antagonism' between the two systems. These exceptions are of two sorts. Some organs are innervated by one system only, thus the sweat glands, hair muscles, and many blood-vessels receive only sympathetic, while muscles of accommodation, salivary glands, and all the glands of the gut only parasympathetic fibres. Conversely the nerves from one system may in some organs produce both excitatory and inhibitory effects. Thus the sympathetic nerves to the blood-vessels of the limbs contain in some animals vasodilatator, as well as vasoconstrictor fibres (p. 392). Again, electrical stimulation of the splanchnic nerves of the cat may produce contraction of the stomach musculature instead of the more usual relaxation, depending on the duration and frequency of the shocks used.

TABLE A. *Table of Actions of Autonomic Nerves in Man*
(*Partly after Best and Taylor, 1955*)

Organ	Sympathetic	Parasympathetic
HEART		
Rate	Increased	Reduced
Auricular Muscle	Stronger contraction	Weaker contraction
Ventricular Muscle	Stronger contraction	No innervation
BLOOD-VESSELS		
Cutaneous	Constriction	No innervation
Muscular	Constriction (usually, dilatation also in some)	No innervation
Visceral	Constriction	No innervation
Coronary	Dilatation	Constriction
Cerebral	Constriction	Dilatation
Pulmonary	Constriction	Dilatation
Salivary glands	Constriction	Dilatation
External genital	Constriction	Dilatation
LUNGS		
Bronchial muscles	Relaxation	Contraction
ALIMENTARY CANAL		
Muscles		
Oesophagus	Relaxation	Contraction
Stomach	Relaxation (sometimes contraction)	Contraction
Intestine	Relaxation	Contraction
Pyloric sphincter	Contraction	Relaxation
Ileo-colic sphincter	Contraction	Relaxation
Internal anal sphincter	Contraction	Relaxation
GLANDS		
Salivary	Some mucous secretion	Secretion
Gastric	No innervation	Secretion
Pancreas	No innervation	Secretion
Intestinal	No innervation	Secretion
LIVER	Glycogenolysis	Flow of bile
URINOGENITAL SYSTEM		
Bladder muscle	Relaxation	Contraction
Bladder sphincter	Contraction	Relaxation
Vas deferens, seminal vesicles and prostate	Contraction	No innervation
Uterus (non-pregnant)	Relaxation	No innervation
(pregnant)	Contraction	
EYE		
Iris sphincter	No innervation	Contraction
Iris dilatator	Contraction	No innervation
Ciliary muscle	Relaxation	Contraction
Muscles of Eyelids	Contraction	No innervation
Lachrymal gland	No innervation	Secretion
SKIN		
Hair muscles	Contraction	No innervation
Sweat glands	Secretion	No innervation
ADRENAL MEDULLA	Secretion	No innervation

It is clear that the visceral nervous system cannot be divided into two separate and antagonistic divisions and it is possible that this attempt at a classification has obscured the outstanding fact that *visceral nerves sometimes act by inhibiting muscular contraction, whereas the somatic nerves always promote it.* Thus in the heart the effects of the sympathetic are abolished by the action of the vagus. There is a similar antagonism in the nerves to the blood-vessels of the salivary glands, external genitalia, and the coronaries of the heart, as well as of the muscles of the lungs and the gut wall.

Consideration of these interesting peripheral inhibitory effects is made difficult because some of the organs contain nerve-cells and we do not know how the two sets of nerve-fibres end in relation to them. For instance, the effect of the sympathetic nerves in causing inhibition of the movements of the gut may possibly be produced by action upon the nerve-cells in the myenteric plexus, rather than directly upon the muscle of the gut wall but there is no evidence about this. In the heart the problem is even more obscure since the inhibitory (vagal) pathway makes synapse there, whereas the excitatory (sympathetic) one does not.

14. Pharmacology of the autonomic nervous system

The whole subject is made especially interesting by the fact that the nerves produce their opposite actions by secreting different active chemical mediators. The study of these 'neurohumors' and of drugs that mimic or inhibit their actions has already shed much light on the nature of the action of this part of the nervous system (and indeed of other parts too).

The transmission of the nerve impulse depends on a series of electrical discharges (p. 338) but the effect of nerve-fibres on their muscles or glands is produced by chemical mediators liberated by the nerve-fibres close to these effector cells (p. 115). It has been known for some time that the ester acetylcholine is able to produce contraction of some smooth muscles (for instance, those of the gut or bladder) at extremely great dilutions (1 part in 100 million). It has now been satisfactorily demonstrated that this substance is produced at the endings of many autonomic nerve-fibres. All preganglionic fibres (whether sympathetic or parasympathetic) produce it where they connect with their postganglionic cells. Further, parasympathetic postganglionic fibres produce acetylcholine at their nerve-endings in muscles and glands and the sympathetic postganglionics to the sweat glands also operate by its action in man, though in the horse they liberate an adrenaline-like substance, as do other sympathetic post-ganglionic fibres (p. 394). Dale has suggested that synapses and motor endings where acetylcholine is produced shall be called *cholinergic*. Wherever they are found there is also present the enzyme, *cholineste-rase*, which rapidly removes the acetylcholine and prevents the spread of its action.

Certain alkaloid drugs, such as *pilocarpine* and *arecoline*, imitate the action of acetylcholine and they are said to be parasympathomimetic in action. Other substances, notably the alkaloid *atropine*, inhibit the action of acetylcholine and of parasympathomimetic drugs. A third interesting set of substances inhibits the action of cholinesterase and thus makes the effects of acetylcholine more pronounced; these include the alkaloid eserine and the synthetic substance di-iso-propyl fluorophosphonate (D.F.P.).

The interactions of these various substances, especially those produced naturally in the body, has provided a fascinating study, which is also of great practical importance because of the valuable medicinal effects of the drugs. Thus atropine (belladonna) has long been known to quicken the heart-beat and dilate the pupil. The inhibitory drugs probably act by competing with the acetylcholine for places on the sensitive or 'receptive' parts of the effector cells. The situation is complicated by the fact that not all of the actions of acetylcholine are inhibited by atropine. Thus although atropine inhibits the effects of the parasympathetic postganglionic fibres on the heart, pupil, urinary bladder, and muscles and glands of the gut it has no action on the preganglionic fibres (including those to the adrenal medulla) or on motor nerve-fibres to striped muscle.

It is interesting in view of the antagonism of effects between different autonomic nerves that the postganglionic sympathetic nerve-fibres produce their effects not by means of acetylcholine but by a substance similar to adrenaline known as *sympathin*, which is probably *l-nor*-adrenaline (p. 394). In Dale's terminology such synapses are *adrenergic* (Dale, 1933). The similarity between the actions of adrenaline and sympathetic stimulation was one of the early clues that led to the discovery that nerves act by the liberation of chemical mediators. As in the case of the parasympathetic we can recognize a series of sympathomimetic drugs, many of them chemically related to adrenaline (e.g. *benzedrine*). Moreover there are substances that can prevent the motor action of adrenaline on its effectors, the best known being the alkaloid *ergotoxine*, found in the fungus ergot, which attacks rye and wheat.

The recognition that distinct substances are produced by visceral nerves and that they may act in opposite directions upon effector tissues opens up large possibilities for development of understanding of the way in which the activities of various parts of the body co-operate to maintain the whole. Sufficient has been said to show something of the great advances that have been made recently, and enough exceptions have been quoted to warn against the attempt to classify all autonomic nerves too simply into two systems. Reactions to particular drugs do not provide safe means of identifying sympathetic or parasympathetic nerves. The great sensitivity of the tissues to these substances provides a means for exploring the nature of the activities by which the balance of action of the various visceral motor nerve-fibres ensures that the tissues play their proper parts in maintaining the homeostasis of the body.

15. The autonomic nervous system and homeostasis

The visceral motor nerves thus play a part in a variety of actions by which the steady state of the body is maintained. These actions are mostly slower adjustments than those mediated by the somatic nervous system but they are faster than the chemical changes and growth processes that are regulated by endocrine systems (p. 572). Correspondingly autonomic nerve-fibres are small, often non-medullated and they conduct slowly. Such fibres may be more effective than larger more rapidly conducting ones for producing long-sustained influences. It may also be significant that some autonomic effects are produced by liberation in the tissues of mediators that are destroyed relatively slowly.

The activities of the autonomic nervous system show clearly the predictive character common to many living activities. Upon receipt of suitable signals from the central nervous system the sympathetic nerves prepare the body for an impending emergency. The parasympathetic nerves on the other hand operate when a period of recuperation is available, during which digestion and other restorative processes can proceed.

By definition the autonomic nerves constitute only an effector system, they include no afferent or computing mechanisms. They are therefore only activated by signals from the central nervous system and are not truly autonomous. They serve to distribute throughout the body the signals that ensure that the behaviour of the internal organs is consonant with the condition of the environment and the needs of the rest of the body. In this sense they assist the other parts in ensuring that the organism adequately represents the changing conditions of its surroundings. Their capacity to do this is largely dependent upon the hereditary instructions, which control the arrangement and functioning of the nervous pathways and allow them to receive information through the preganglionic fibres from the central nervous system. There is no evidence that the autonomic nerves themselves carry memories of their past history but it may be that, like other nerve-fibres, they are influenced by use.

In the autonomic system the pattern of nerve impulses sent out over the preganglionic pathways is transformed and transferred to the effector tissues. The details of the transformation are not understood but it always involves passage through a synapse. There are known to be as many as twenty postganglionic cells for every preganglionic one, but it cannot be assumed that wide diffusion is the only significance of these autonomic relays. Research over many years has given us much detailed information about the autonomic nervous system but it would be well not to assume that it consists of simple chains of neurons. There are hints that its ganglia and plexuses mediate transformations of information in ways that we do not yet understand.

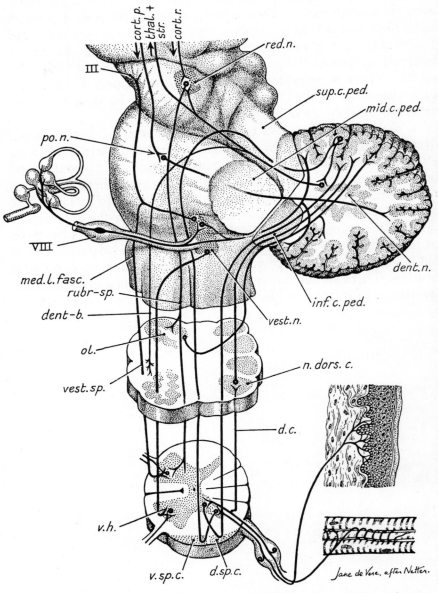

FIG. 173. The main afferent and efferent connexions of the cerebellum of man
seen from the left side.

(*For Key see opposite*)

XXI

THE CONTROL OF POSTURE AND MOVEMENT. THE CEREBELLUM AND MIDBRAIN

1. Representation of movement patterns in the brain

THE basic mechanism for the control of posture and movement lies in the spinal cord. Each muscle is controlled by its pool of motor neurons and the firing of these is under the influence of local input, especially the impulses arriving from its own proprioceptors (p. 366). These set the muscle into action when it is put under tension and by suitable arrangements for reciprocal inhibition some quite complex effective movements can be produced by the operation of the spinal cord alone. Yet in normal life the patterns of behaviour of a mammal are not produced only by these spinal responses of the muscles but are called into action in a well-organized time series by the brain.

The mechanism by which posture and movement are produced is only partly understood. Ultimately all action depends upon the pattern of stimulation that falls upon the receptors, especially on the main exteroceptors, eye, ear, and nose. Impulses from these organs, after suitable combination with memories stored in the cerebral cortex, are able to produce action by stimulation or inhibition of groups of neurons in the basal portions of the brain. Electrical stimulation has shown that the neurons of these basal regions play upon the spinal centres to produce patterns of movement. For example, activity of a centre in the hypothalamus of a cat will produce all the actions appropriate to rage (p. 421).

Each muscle participates in many different actions and in each action it requires to be co-ordinated in a different way with other muscles. For example, flexor carpi ulnaris and radialis muscles work together

---

Key to Fig. 173:

III, Nucleus of oculomotor nerve; VIII, vestibular nerve and ganglion; *cort.p.* cortico-pontine tract; *cort.r.* cortico-rubral tract; *d.c.* dorsal column of spinal cord; *dent.-b.* dento-bulbar tract; *dent.n.* dentate nucleus; *d.sp.c.* dorsal spino-cerebellar tract; *inf.c.ped.* inferior cerebellar peduncle; *med.l.fasc.* medial longitudinal fascicle; *mid.c.ped.* middle cerebellar peduncle; *n.dors.c.* nucleus of the dorsal column; *ol.* olive; *po.n.* pontine nucleus; *red.n.* red nucleus; *rubr.-sp.* rubro-spinal and rubro-olivary tracts; *sup.c.ped.* superior cerebellar peduncle; *thal. & str.* cerebello-thalamic and cerebello-striatal fibres; *vest.n.* vestibular nucleus; *vest.sp.* vestibulo-spinal tract; *v.h.* ventral horn of spinal cord; *v.sp.c.* ventral spino-cerebellar tract. (Modified from original illustration by F. Netter, M.D., from Ciba collection.)

in some actions but antagonistically in others (p. 129). Such co-ordination is the result of the action of cells in the basal centres of the brain, which may be called the *representatives* of the spinal motor-neurons. The whole basal region, from the corpus striatum to the medulla, is involved in this production of patterns of action, but there is little knowledge available as to how the co-ordination is achieved.

2. Gravity and the control of posture

At the front end of the medulla oblongata enter the fibres of the *eighth (auditory) nerve*, carrying impulses from the inner ear. The ear contains several different receptors, all of them serving to record minute movements. These mechanoreceptors provide the brain with information about small changes in the position of the body relative to gravity and of the surrounding air relative to the body (Ch. XXVII). The response to air movements by the receptors of the cochlea has led to the apparatus for discrimination of tones. This information is mainly of value in providing clues about changes in the outside world, often at a distance, and the associative processes involved take place in the cerebral cortex. The fibres of the *cochlear nerve* end in the cochlear nucleus, whose cells send fibres, along with some direct cochlear fibres, forward in the lateral lemniscus to the opposite medial geniculate body of the thalamus and thence to the cortex.

We are here concerned more with the fibres of the *vestibular nerve* (Fig. 173), arising in the semicircular canals, utricle, and saccule, which serve to provide information about changes in the position of the body in relation to gravity (p. 514). This information is obviously of first importance in the regulation of standing and of movement. The fact that it enters at this level has led to the development nearby of a series of organs concerned with the nervous operations involved in control of movement and posture. These include the vestibular nucleus, the cerebellum, the red nucleus, and other centres known as the reticular formation of the midbrain and the inferior olivary nucleus in the medulla. The vestibular nucleus and cerebellum are developments of the dorsal columns and may be regarded as computing centres that work with the input provided by the proprioceptors, vestibular receptors, and impulses from the cerebral cortex and other parts of the brain (p. 438).

The red nucleus and the other centres in the base of the midbrain, on the other hand, lie near the front end of the somatic motor column (p. 411) and their cells provide higher representations of the various segmental motor nuclei. Activation of relatively few cells in these midbrain centres sets into operation whole patterns of activity in the muscles.

The dorsal and ventral portions of this region together control the muscles in such a way as to give the animal a *posture* suitable to the environment in which it lives. The organization of the neurons of the vestibular nucleus, cerebellum, and midbrain base provides the appropriate representation that ensures that a cat stands on four legs, or a man on two, while the sloth hangs upside down. It is not easy to reach an adequate idea of the nature of this neural organization. It involves a flow of afferent impulses from various receptors, passing through the system in such a way that they set the appropriate muscles into action. We can analyse the system by considering the various afferent channels and central pathways, and the effect of interrupting these by transection of the brain at various levels. Electrical stimulation of these higher motor centres often leads to the adoption by the animal of characteristic postures or to complicated sequences of movements, for example, those of walking. The stimulus activates not merely a few nerve-cells or fibres but the whole representation that produces the movement pattern.

In life these higher motor centres operate under the control of the instructions proceeding from the computations that go on in the forebrain, which thus regulates motor activity, although itself consisting of a special development of the more dorsal and hence receptor part of the brain (p. 784). The cerebral cortex produces its effects by calling into action the various motor patterns of the higher motor centres, combining them in the many and changing ways that characterize the behaviour of each individual animal. If the cortex is removed the parts that remain show simple stereotyped actions, *postural reflexes*, *righting reflexes*, *placing reactions*, and various others, which will shortly be considered (p. 412).

3. The cerebellum

The cerebellum is an important part of this system for control of movement and posture. It receives afferents from the vestibular and proprioceptor systems and sends impulses to the motor centres of the midbrain base. In mammals there has also developed a large two-way system of interchange between the cerebellum and the cerebral cortex (Jansen and Brodal, 1954).

The fibres of the vestibular nerve end partly in the vestibular nucleus at the base of the cerebellum and thence there is a projection to the cerebellum and to various motor centres; other vestibular fibres enter the cerebellum directly. The cerebellum is a huge extension of the somatic sensory column, overlying the front end of the medulla oblongata. Its mass of tissue, of tree-like form, is connected with the rest of the brain by three *cerebellar peduncles* or brachia, the inferior peduncle (restiform body), middle peduncle (brachium pontis), and

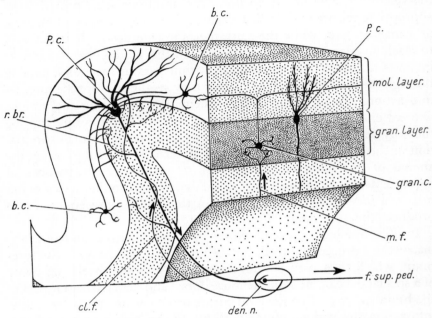

FIG. 174. Diagram showing principal cell types of the cerebellar cortex and their connexions.

b.c. basket cell; *cl.f.* climbing fibre; *den.n.* dentate nucleus; *f.sup.ped.* fibre of superior peduncle; *gran.c.* granule cell; *gran.layer*, granular layer; *m.f.* moss fibre; *mol. layer*, molecular layer; *P.c.* Purkinje cell; *r.br.* recurrent branch from Purkinje axon.

superior peduncle (brachium conjunctivum). To the primitive vestibular connexions of the cerebellum, running in the inferior peduncle, there have been added in mammals large projections: (*a*) from sensory, mainly proprioceptor, systems through the spinocerebellar tract, passing in the inferior and superior peduncles, (*b*) from the cerebral hemisphere, passing in the middle peduncle. These latter fibres form the *pons Varolii* on the under side of the brain, a large mass of fibres and cells at the point where the fibres turn forwards to run up in the cerebral peduncle to the hemisphere.

The cerebellum has throughout a uniform histological structure (Fig. 174). The cells have moved away from the primitive position to form a cerebellar cortex, with outer molecular and inner granular layers. The incoming fibres from proprioceptor, vestibular, and other sources end as coarse *mossy fibres* in the inner granular layer (Fig. 174). Here they make synapse with the *granule cells*, each of which has about four dendrites and a single axon that ascends into the molecular layer, where it branches and runs along the length of the cerebellar fold (folium). In this way it crosses the dendrites of many of the cells of the molecular layer, the *Purkinje cells*. These have large cell-bodies

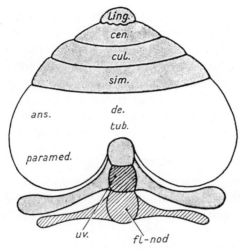

FIG. 175. Parts of the primate cerebellar cortex. The hatched region receives vestibular, the stippled proprioceptor, and the white cerebral afferents.

ans. lobulus ansiformis; *cen.* lobulus centralis; *cul.* culmen; *de.* declive; *fl.-nod.* flocculo-nodular lobe; *ling.* lingula; *paramed.* lobulus paramedianus; *sim.* lobulus simplex; *tub.* tuber; *uv.* uvula. (After Larsell and Fulton.)

and an elaborate system of dendrites branching in a plane at right angles to the length of the folium. The axons of the Purkinje cells pass towards the centre of the cerebellum to end in the *cerebellar nuclei*. From the large cells of these nuclei fibres carry impulses in the superior cerebellar peduncle to the thalamus and striatum, the red nucleus, and the medulla oblongata.

Recurrent collaterals from the axons of the Purkinje cells and from those of the cerebellar nuclei re-enter the molecular layer as the *climbing fibres*, which make close contact with the dendrites of the Purkinje cells. The system of connexions in the cerebellum thus ensures that impulses in the entering mossy fibres are relayed through the granule cells to many Purkinje cells. Impulses in the axons of these latter activate the efferent fibres of the cerebellar nuclei but also stimulate further Purkinje cells by the collateral pathways of the climbing fibres. A set of small *basket cells*, with short axons in the molecular layer, serves for further diffusion of effects.

This system of 'avalanche conduction' seems to be designed for the spreading of influences from a few input sources to produce an output in many fibres. But it is probable that the effect is much more subtle than a mere amplification. It may involve alteration of the patterns of the input impulses ('re-coding') or the interaction of the effects of impulses from different sources.

The cerebellum is divided externally into a great number of lobes. The vestibular fibres all end in the posterior part of the cerebellum, the flocculo-nodular lobe (Fig. 175). The proprioceptor (spinocerebellar) fibres end here and also in the four most anterior lobes. These front and back parts are present in all vertebrates and may be called the *paleocerebellum*. They have become divided into anterior and posterior sections by the development at the centre of a region with pontine (cerebral) connexions, the *neocerebellum*.

4. Functions of the cerebellum

The cerebellum is essentially an organ concerned in the control of movement but the manner in which it enters into the activities of the muscles is difficult to summarize. Injury to the organ in man and other mammals shows that the paleocerebellum is concerned with equilibrium; if the flocculo-nodular lobe is damaged there is swaying and staggering. Electrical stimulation of the paleocerebellum (especially its anterior section) inhibits the anti-gravity reflexes. After removal of the anterior region there is overaction of the postural mechanisms (stretch reflexes, &c., p. 412). Moreover, through the cerebral cortex each portion of the musculature is related to a particular part of this anterior region of the cerebellum. Electrical stimulation of any one cerebellar point either inhibits or facilitates movements that are produced by stimulation of the corresponding cortical motor area (Figs. 176 and 177).

After removal of the neocerebellum, the man or animal is unable to perform properly the 'voluntary' movements initiated by the cerebral cortex. The actions are done with too much or too little force; for instance, movement may be in great leaps and progress once started cannot be quickly stopped or deflected (Fig. 178). Parts of the body may show a continuous tremor.

The cerebellum thus provides in general an inhibiting or restraining mechanism. It regulates the activities of other parts of the nervous system either by making them active or by damping them down. In

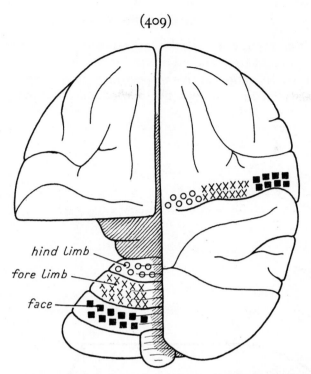

FIG. 176. The interrelation between the representations in the motor cortex and cerebellum. Stimulation of points in the cerebellum alters the response to stimulation of the correspondingly marked cerebral points. (After Adrian, *Brain*, **66**, 1943.)

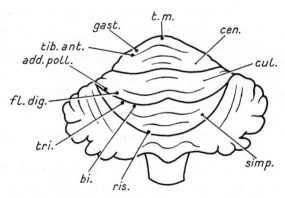

FIG. 177. Functional localization in the anterior lobe of the cerebellum of the macaque. Electrical stimulation of the points indicated inhibits or facilitates cortically induced movements of the muscles shown.

Add. poll. adductor pollicis; *bi.* biceps; *cen.* lobulus centralis; *cul.* culmen; *fl.dig.* flexor digitorum; *gast.* gastrocnemius; *ris.* risorius; *simp.* lobulus simplex; *tib.ant.* tibialis anticus; *t.m.* tail muscles; *tri.* triceps.
(From Fulton, after Nulsen, Black, and Drake, *Fed. Proc.* **7**, 86, 1948.)

particular it allows the feed-back that comes from the proprioceptors of the muscles and from the vestibular regions to influence the force of contraction. Its action in this respect may depend upon amplification, signals in a few afferent fibres producing discharge in many

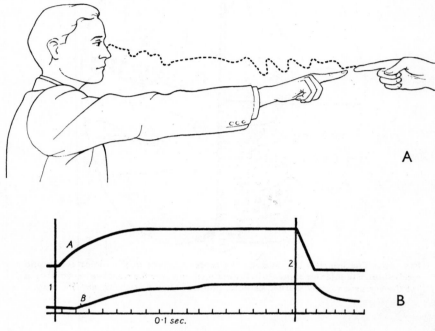

FIG. 178. Effect of cerebellar lesion on voluntary movement.

A. Diagram showing how a man with a cerebellar lesion moves his hand. The patient is asked to move an index finger from his nose to the examiner's finger held at arm's length from the patient. The dotted line represents the course along which his hand moves and shows the typical tremor, most marked at the beginning and end of movement.
(After Lyman, *Medical Diagnosis*, Philadelphia: Saunders 1950.)
B. Voluntary muscle contraction in A the normal and B the affected arms of a man with unilateral cerebellar lesion. At 1 the signal to contract was given and at 2 the signal to relax. In the affected arm the latency is longer, the contraction slower and weaker, and relaxation is delayed. (From Holmes, *Lancet*, **202**, 1922.)

Purkinje cells through the mediation of the granule cells and axonal collaterals.

Any system as complicated as the body is likely to show oscillatory responses when activated by external stimuli; damping mechanisms are therefore introduced to ensure smoothly limited action. Thus when extra tension is put upon a muscle its proprioceptors produce discharges that elicit compensatory tension (the stretch reflexes, p. 366); the cerebellum ensures that the action is suitably damped and not followed by oscillations. We cannot see in detail how this control is effected but it is reasonable to suppose that the numerous similar cells constitute a source by which a few suitably placed incoming impulses can cause large volleys to be directed for control of the appropriate parts. It is significant that the cerebellum is especially highly developed in the higher primates and man, whose survival depends so largely on manipulating the environment by means of well-controlled and delicate movements.

5. The midbrain

The dorsal and ventral parts of the midbrain are large and important in lower vertebrates but in mammals the visual and auditory computational functions of the dorsal parts have been transferred to the cerebral cortex. The roof (tectum) is divided into four hillocks, the *superior* and *inferior corpora quadrigemina* (Figs. 166, 167). The superior are optic centres and receive some direct fibres from the optic tract; injury to them in man causes disturbance of eye movements. The inferior corpora quadrigemina receive, through the lateral lemniscus, fibres ascending from the cochlear nucleus of the medulla. Their exact function is unknown but they are probably concerned with hearing. Some of their neurons send axons forward to the medial geniculate body of the thalamus (p. 427).

The floor of the midbrain contains the nuclei of origin of the third and fourth cranial nerves, which are portions of the somatic motor cell column (Fig. 179). The greater part of this region is made up of a mass of grey matter, the *tegmentum*, including the *red nucleus* and neighbouring cell masses, which are part of the *reticular formation*. This area receives fibres from the forebrain and cerebellum and sends fibres downwards to the spinal cord. It is an important higher motor centre and because it is additional to the direct or pyramidal motor pathway (p. 438) this region, together with the corpus striatum, inferior olive and other parts working with it, is known as the *extra-pyramidal pathway*.

As already mentioned, the midbrain base constitutes morphologically the front end of the somatic motor column and contains the representational neurons whose activities produce movement by large groups of muscles. Stimulation or lesions of the tegmentum produce curious aberrations of locomotion. For instance, there has been described in the cat a 'syndrome of obstinate progression'. Following an injury to the tegmentum the animal persistently walked forward until it damaged itself by battering against the wall. The effect of the lesion was evidently to release one of the motor patterns that are represented here. We can analyse these further by investigating the patterns of 'reflex' nature that are seen after isolation of this region from the influence of the higher nervous centres.

6. Postural reflexes

The basic mechanism for the control of the posture of a mammal is the stretch reflex, which has already been described (p. 366). If a

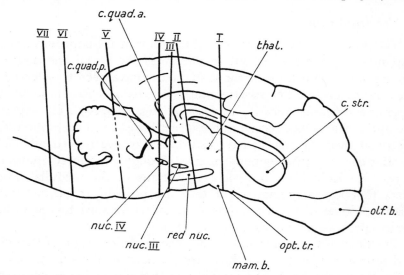

FIG. 179. Effect of section of the brain of the cat at various levels (I–VII), see text.

c.quad.a. & *p.* anterior and posterior corpora quadrigemina; *c.str.* corpus striatum; *mam.b.* mamillary body; *nuc. III* & *IV*, nuclei of 3rd and 4th nerves; *olf.b.* olfactory bulb; *opt.tr.* optic tract; *red nuc.* red nucleus; *thal.* thalamus.

cat whose spinal cord has been cut caudal to the medulla (Fig. 179, VII) is suspended off the ground the limbs hang limply. If one of them is now pressed against the ground it will extend, as if to bear the weight. This response is due to the setting up of nerve impulses by the proprioceptors of the extensor muscles. Such a *spinal animal* is not able to stand, the anti-gravity reflexes operating independently cannot produce a pattern of contraction that ensures the balance of the animal.

If a cut is made across the midbrain behind the level of the red nucleus (Fig. 179, III) an exaggerated form of standing known as *decerebrate rigidity* is seen. When such an animal is hung with a sling round the belly the limbs are held stiffly, thrusting downwards and backwards. The tail and head are held up in spite of their weight. The animal maintains this rigidity for days, but it disappears if a second cut is made at a level caudal to the vestibular nucleus (Fig. 179, v); the limbs then hang flaccid, as in a spinal animal. Moreover, if the dorsal roots to a limb are severed the decerebate rigidity disappears from that limb, showing that a supply of proprioceptor impulses is necessary for the phenomenon.

In decerebrate rigidity we see an exaggerated form of part of the organized set of nervous patterns by which posture is maintained. Freed from the inhibitory influence of higher cerebral centres the vestibular nucleus uses the signals provided by the proprioceptors of the anti-gravity muscles to produce a combined action of all these muscles. This is a manifestation of the pattern of interactions in the nucleus that represents the posture of the animal. The rigid position adopted is a sort of exaggerated standing but it does not serve to support the animal properly. With care a cat showing decerebrate rigidity may be propped up on its limbs, but it is readily pushed over.

The proper maintenance of position depends upon the discharge of receptors that provide the information that ensures adjustment of the tension of the muscles to meet the changing environmental conditions. Four main sets of receptors are involved. (1) Those in the skin of the feet and the proprioceptors of the small muscles of the toes. (2) The proprioceptors of the anti-gravity muscles of the neck. (3) The gravity receptors in the labyrinths. (4) The eyes. This information is assembled in the centres in the midbrain and medulla oblongata and a dog or cat with the brain-stem severed in front of the midbrain (Fig. 179, I or II) stands normally, indeed it can walk. In primates such a lesion produces abnormal posture and no walking is possible; in these animals, therefore, the representation that controls posture lies mainly in the forebrain.

The skin of the feet provides part of the information for the postural reflexes. Gentle pressure with a finger on the skin of the foot of a dog after decortication is followed by extension of the limb to meet the finger. This *magnet reaction* or supporting response is due primarily to stimulation of the skin but slightly stronger pressure causes separation of the toes and stimulation of the proprioceptors of their small muscles, which also play a part in the phenomenon.

The *neck reflexes* can be investigated if the labyrinths are first removed. Passive turning of the head to one side then produces a thrust of the limbs of that side. In a mammal the head carries most of the main exteroceptors and slight changes in its position occur continually as eyes, ears, or nose are directed towards some change in the surroundings. All of these movements produce corresponding changes in the posture of the limbs, preparing for subsequent advance or retreat. Similarly, if the head of an animal without labyrinths is turned dorsally, the forelimbs extend and the hind ones become flexed. The converse movements are seen if the head is turned downwards.

In order to study the effects of the labyrinths on posture the animal is decerebrated and the neck reflexes also eliminated by cutting the dorsal roots of the three upper pairs of cervical nerves. It is now found that for every position of the head relative to gravity contractions appear in the muscles of the back and limbs, these contractions being such as would be appropriate to maintain the head and back in a horizontal position. The contractions are elicited by the two sets of receptors in the labyrinths, those of the semicircular canals, which discharge when there is angular acceleration of the head in any direction and those of the maculae of the utricle and saccule, which by the pull of the otoliths upon the hairs provide positional information (Ch. XXVII).

Every movement of the head relative to gravity thus sets in action a series of *righting reflexes*, which tend to keep the head the right way up. In life these are combined with further righting reflexes initiated by the pull upon the muscles that follows movement of one part of the body upon another. These ensure that the rest of the body follows the head into the correct relation to gravity. This relation will, of course, differ according to whether the animal walks upon four legs or two and, as mentioned already, in the sloth, which hangs from branches, the 'correct' position is 'upside down'.

Posture and righting thus depend upon the interplay of a large set of afferent impulses from the skin, muscles of the legs and neck, and the labyrinths. In life the eyes provide a further most important contribution. All of this information is assembled in the nuclei of the vestibular region and brain-stem, whose neurons compute at every instant the output to the muscles that will ensure correct posture. In lower mammals this can be assured by these brain-stem centres working alone, but in primates the appropriate representation also involves action by the cerebral hemispheres.

This whole complicated system of receptors, nerve impulses, and centres is obviously a predictor that is of fundamental importance to the maintenance of the life of the animal. It is mainly the product of heredity, at least in non-primate forms, though in the present state of knowledge it would be difficult to deny that learning plays a part in the establishment of the representation.

During the normal life of a mammal this whole apparatus is continually at the service of the associational systems of the forebrain. These compute in any situation the output that is likely to be effective in the light of past experience. This output passes over the fibres of the cerebrospinal, cerebrorubral, and other motor pathways, calling into action appropriate parts of the motor systems that they contain.

XXII

THE FOREBRAIN

1. General plan of the forebrain

THE region of the third nerve marks the anterior end of the somatic motor column and the whole forebrain consists of an expansion forwards of the dorsal portion of the neural tube. In the main this represents a vast extension of the somatic sensory region, developed originally as a computer for the signals from the olfactory receptors, but coming later to dominate all the rest of the brain.

In mammals the olfactory system is still connected with the forebrain separately from all the other receptor systems and by a simpler pathway (p. 430). It occupies only the basal region of the anterior portion of the hemispheres. The greater part of their bulk is made up of the tissue of the cerebral cortex, which receives signals from nearly all the receptor systems of the body. It records the patterns in which these signals have been associated and so stores a representation of the external environment. This information store is then used to compute outputs that produce anticipatory actions adequate to maintain the life of the animal. In other words the cerebral cortex is the part of the animal particularly devoted to the establishment of stores of information received during the life of the animal, rather than from heredity.

In order to understand how the pathways and centres concerned are arranged we may consider that the forebrain develops from a simple tube (Fig. 323). Near the front end a pair of lateral pouches, the *cerebral hemispheres* (*telencephalon*) develops and their cavities are the first and second ventricles, communicating by the *interventricular foramina* with the median third ventricle, whose walls form the unpaired between-brain or *diencephalon*, connecting the hemispheres with the rest of the brain. The pathways from the receptor organs to the cortex pass through the dorsal part of the diencephalon, the *thalamus*. The cortex exerts its effects on the rest of the brain by a number of pathways lying more ventrally. Some of these proceed directly to the spinal cord (the *pyramidal tract*) but others pass through centres in the base of the forebrain, including the *corpus striatum*, which have an obscure connexion with the production of co-ordinate movements. The *hypothalamus*, the part of the diencephalon ventral to the thalamus, is concerned with the production of co-ordinated visceral and other activities and is also connected with the cortex by fibres passing in both directions.

These *basal ganglia* of the forebrain constitute a series of groups of cells that set into operation elaborate patterns of motor activities. There is little understanding of how they do this but we may consider that there is a hierarchy of levels from the spinal cord up through the medulla, midbrain, hypothalamus, and corpus striatum. The cells at each level control groups of cells at lower levels, so that the higher levels produce the more elaborate and more highly co-ordinated movements. All operate under the control of the cerebral cortex.

The whole forebrain forms an immensely complicated apparatus and it is absurd to expect to be able to understand it in simple terms. All that can be done here is to give an account of the main masses of tissue and their connexions, with some indications of the results of removing them or of activating them by electrical stimulation. No language is available with which to speak of the details of the functioning of the forebrain; suitable terms will probably only evolve gradually as men make machines that imitate these complicated actions more closely.

2. Transverse connexions in the forebrain

The front wall of the tube, between the hemispheres, is the *lamina terminalis*, through which fibres run between the two sides to form the *anterior* and *hippocampal commissures*. In the human brain the enormous growth of the cerebral hemispheres results in a backward displacement of the hippocampal commissure and in the adult only the anterior commissure can be seen in its original position in close relationship to the lamina terminalis at the front end of the third ventricle.

As the hemispheres grow large they bulge forwards and backwards and come to lie over the diencephalon. The floor of the evaginated hemisphere, the corpus striatum, thus lies immediately lateral to and in contact with the thalamus (Fig. 337). New commissural fibres come to join the hemispheres, forming the *corpus callosum*.

3. The pineal body

The unpaired portion of the forebrain is directly continuous with the midbrain. It has a thin non-nervous choroidal roof, to which is attached the *pineal body*, a solid mass of peculiar neuroglial tissue. In mammals the pineal shows no trace of the eye-like structure that is seen in lampreys and some reptiles. Its significance is completely

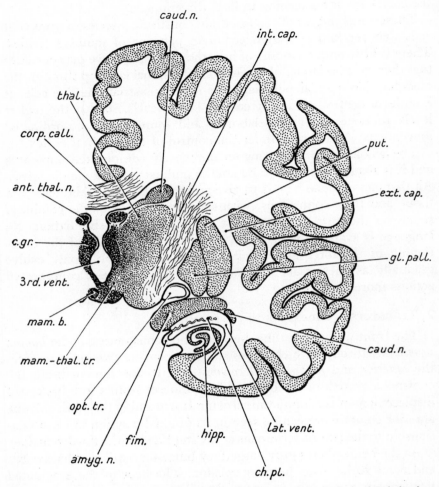

caud. n.

int. cap.

thal.

corp. call.

ant. thal. n.

c. gr.

3rd. vent.

mam. b.

mam. - thal. tr.

opt. tr.

fim.

àmyg. n.

hipp.

lat. vent.

ch. pl.

caud. n.

gl. pall.

ext. cap.

put.

FIG. 180. Diagrammatic transverse section of half a human brain in the thalamic region.

amyg.n. amygdaloid nucleus; *ant.thal.n.* anterior thalamic nucleus; *caud.n.* caudate nucleus; *c.gr.* central grey matter; *ch.pl.* choroid plexus; *corp. call.* corpus callosum; *ext.cap.* external capsule; *fim.* fimbria ; *gl.pall.* globus pallidus; *hipp.* hippocampus; *int.cap.* internal capsule; *lat.vent.* lateral ventricle; *mam.b.* mammillary body; *mam-thal.tr.* mammillo-thalamic tract; *opt.tr.* optic tract; *put.* putamen; *thal.* thalamus; *3rd vent.* third ventricle.

obscure. Some of its cells have branched processes ending in knobs and resemble neuroglia, others have acidophil, basophil, or fatty granules. After puberty characteristic granules of phosphates and carbonates ('brain sand') appear in the pineal. A further indication of some connexion with phosphorus metabolism is that radioactive phosphorus (P^{32}) injected into the blood-stream appears in greater amounts in the pineal than anywhere else in the brain.

There have been reports that removal of the pineal affects the onset of puberty but no changes have been demonstrated to follow removal of the pineal from rats, even when young. Changes of rate of growth and of sexual development are found in connexion with tumours of the gland in man but they may be secondary effects due to disturbance of the hypothalamus (p. 421). Extracts of the mammalian pineal produce no known effects when injected into mammals, but they cause contraction of the melanophores of amphibia.

4. Hypothalamus

The thick walls of the diencephalon form the *thalamus* above and *hypothalamus* below (Fig. 180). The floor is pushed out into a stalk, the *infundibulum*, which is continuous with the pars nervosa of the pituitary (p. 559). The hypothalamus is well developed in mammals, as in all vertebrates, and may be considered as the anterior end of the visceral sensory and visceral motor columns. It contains groups of cells that serve to activate combinations of lower centres to control many visceral activities. Electrical stimulation of a localized region of the hypothalamus calls forth a whole pattern of action that is based upon some internal need—say for water or food. Although such actions have prominent visceral components they also involve somatic movements. The hypothalamus thus contains groups of cells that set into operation quite complicated patterns of behaviour, for example, those of aggression or of sleep (see below). The presence of these centres is obviously one of the features that gives to a mammal the capacity to perform a variety of complicated actions, involving muscles and glands dispersed throughout the body. The representations in the hypothalamus thus stand at a level above those of the medulla and midbrain. They integrate the visceral and somatic activities of these latter into elaborate behaviour patterns that can be called upon by the output of the overlying thalamo-cortical system.

The hypothalamic region lies dorsal to the optic chiasma and infundibular stalk and is marked externally by a pair of white protuberances, the *mammillary bodies* and a lobe, the *tuber cinereum*, lying between these and the optic chiasma. The hypothalamus receives fibres from the hippocampus of the cerebral hemispheres in a special bundle the *fornix* (Fig. 181) and it also receives fibres from many other parts of the forebrain. Its efferent tracts pass forwards to the thalamus and backwards to the motor centres in the tegmentum and probably also to the medulla and perhaps spinal cord. A tract of nerve-fibres passes down the infundibular stalk from the hypothalamus to the pituitary body, whose secretion it helps to control (p. 559).

The cells of the hypothalamus are scattered in groups, so-called nuclei, which may be significant in providing each for the control of a different set of motor centres lower in the hierarchy. The cells are mainly large, with irregular dendrites interlacing with the incoming fibres in a pattern that is not understood. Some small cells with short axons are present but the hypothalamus is not characterized by numerous small cells as are centres with computational functions such as the cerebral cortex. Where quantitative data are available (as in the mammillary bodies) it is found that the number of fibres entering a part of the hypothalamus equals that of the cells and output axons. It remains to be discovered how these centres transpose or recode various input patterns into outputs that activate the appropriate motor centres.

5. Activation of the hypothalamus through the blood

Experiments by extirpation and stimulation of parts of the hypothalamus have shown that this organ influences a wide range of internal activities, such as temperature regulation, sugar metabolism, heart-rate, and blood-pressure, motility of the gut, sleep, sexual functions, salt balance, and water excretion. In many of these activities it works in conjunction with the pituitary gland, and secretory cells are found within the hypothalamus itself (p. 559). The anti-diuretic hormone, which controls the output of the kidney, is found both in the posterior lobe of the pituitary and in the hypothalamus. The hypothalamic region is more richly supplied with blood than is any other part of the brain and the control of its functioning is probably partly a direct response to changes in the composition of the blood. Such direct effects have been shown in the goat by means of a syringe implanted so that its tip lay in the hypothalamus. Injection of minute amounts of sodium chloride solution then caused an animal that previously refused water immediately to drink copiously. Cells are therefore present that are sensitive to change in the concentration of salt around them. When stimulated they initiate the search for water. Cells with large vacuoles are present in some parts of the hypothalamus and they send their axons down the infundibular stalk to the posterior lobe of the pituitary. Probably these cells serve as osmoreceptors and the signals they convey regulate the concentration of the blood by controlling the output of the anti-diuretic hormone of the pituitary (p. 561). The signals may take the form of chemical substances carried along the axons (neurosecretion).

6. Electrical stimulation of the hypothalamus

The representations of motor activities within the hypothalamus have been investigated by Hess (1948 and 1954) by the method of implanting a small pair of electrodes in the head of a cat and activating these by remote control through an induction coil. In this way complicated behaviour patterns were produced in the unanaesthetized animal. The effects varied according to the position of the electrodes (Fig. 181). When they were in the periventricular grey matter of the caudal or dorsal parts of the hypothalamus (or the front part of the midbrain) visceral changes concerned with control of energy expenditure, such as rise or fall of blood-pressure, alteration of heart-beat, or respiratory rate were seen. These changes are mediated through the sympathetic division of the autonomic nervous system, which prepares the body for attack or defence (p. 392). The hypothalamus may be regarded as the head centre controlling all the activities of that system (v. Euler, 1954). More elaborate preparatory actions were also seen. Following some stimulations the cat would snarl and its fur bristle and pupils dilate (Fig. 182). If approached when in this state it would readily scratch or bite. Many of the phenomena of this defence reaction are also controlled through the sympathetic system.

The hypothalamus also contains the head centre for the other division of the autonomic nervous system, the parasympathetic, concerned with setting into action processes that conserve the body and build up its internal resources (p. 394). Electrodes placed more cranially, in the pre-optic and supra-optic regions of the hypothalamus, produced movements involving groups of muscles concerned with the conservative functions mediated by the parasympathetic system. These include a whole range of activities of the gut, and others concerned with the finding and intake of food. Stimulation of different points produced defaecation, peristalsis, or vomiting.

From the most cranial parts of this region elaborate behaviour patterns were elicited, including sniffing, licking, and chewing, any of which might be seen after stimulation of points quite close together.

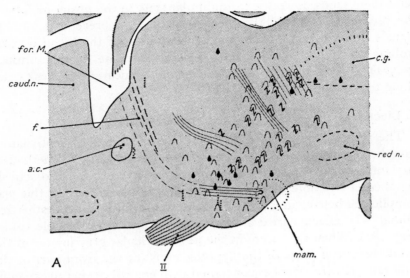

FIG. 181 A

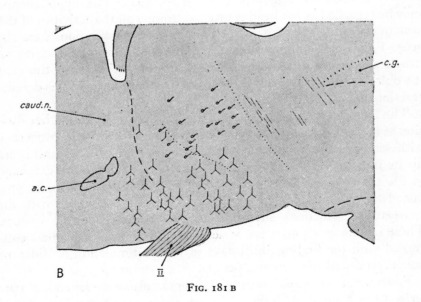

FIG. 181 B

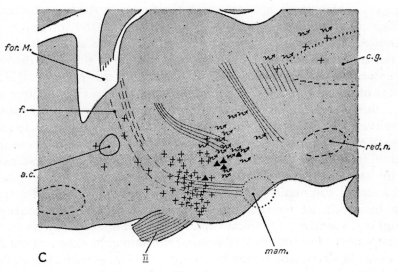

FIG. 181 C

∧ *Blood-pressure rise*
↘ *Increase in respiratory activity*
● *Salivation*
⋮ *Defaecation*
≷ *Micturition*
◡ *Vomiting*

λ *Sniffing*
⌒ *Licking*
+ *Defensive responses*
▲ *Eating*
ⁿ *Escape movements*

II, Optic nerve; *a.c.* anterior commissure; *caud.n.* caudate nucleus; *c.g.* central grey; *f.* fornix; *for.M.* interventricular foramen; *mam.* mammillary body; *red.n.* red nucleus. (After Hess.)

FIG. 181. Sites in the hypothalamus from which various responses were obtained on electrical stimulation.

They are similar to actions seen after stimulation of the hippocampus (p. 431), which sends fibres through the fornix to the hypothalamus.

Evidently this whole region is concerned with the integration of activities for detection, intake, and digestion of food and with control of the amount taken. The olfactory system, one of the chief distance receptors for the finding of food, lies cranial to this region and is no doubt often responsible for activating first the sniffing actions and then those of eating. The gustatory receptors then assist with control of salivation (also elicited from stimulation of the hypothalamus) and at each of the later stages of digestion appropriate receptors come into action, for instance, by providing information of the state of distension of the stomach or rectum.

Electrical stimulation shows that many other co-ordinated actions can be produced by the cells of the hypothalamus, for example, coughing, sneezing, and micturition. Stimulation at some sites in the hypothalamus has the effect of causing the animal to close its eyes and lie down to sleep, which may be considered as an extreme form of the parasympathetic conservative behaviour (Fig. 182).

These elaborate behaviour patterns evidently involve actions of somatic motor as well as visceral systems and the fact that such complex movements can be elicited from activation of single points warns us that only an artificial separation can be made between internal and external actions.

Some of the actions of the hypothalamus are purely somatic, for example, Hess showed that following stimulation in the region shown in Fig. 181 c the animal began to walk up and down and to make vigorous efforts to escape. These are somatic activities at a still higher level than those of the midbrain base (p. 411) and in life they are presumably under the direct control of the cerebral cortex.

The output of the cortical computing system no doubt produces its effects largely by stimulating appropriate sets of cells in the hypothalamus and other higher motor centres. More complicated processes are also involved, for the hypothalamus sends fibres forwards to the thalamus and cortex. From the mamillary bodies fibres pass to the anterior nucleus of the thalamus and thence others pass to the cingulate area on the medial surface of the frontal lobe of the cortex. This area probably has connexions with the hippocampus, which in turn sends fibres in the fornix to the mamillary bodies. The possible significance of this circuit is discussed on p. 433.

Fig. 181 shows that many of the responses described can be elicited from stimulation of a wide area of the hypothalamus. This may be

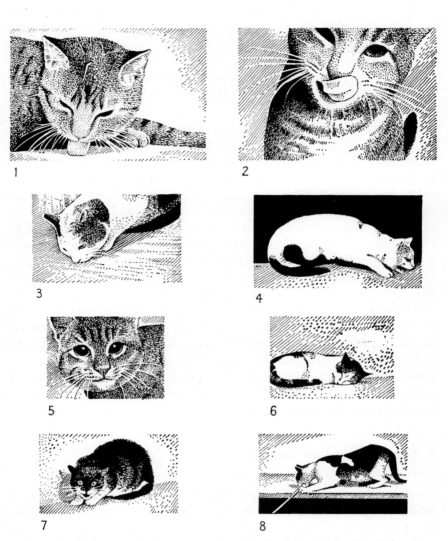

FIG. 182. Actions induced in cats by electrical stimulation in the hypothalamus.
1. Lapping; 2. licking; 3 and 4. sniffing; 5. dilatation of pupils; 6. sleep; 7. snarling; 8. persistent gnawing. (After Hess.)

because they follow excitation of afferent or efferent pathways as well
as of groups of cells. Yet the occurrence of such varied actions following stimulation of points so near together emphasizes the coupling
action of these networks, by which the operations of so many motor
systems are combined in diverse patterns.

It is not easy to find words to describe adequately the part that the
hypothalamus plays in mammalian life and this difficulty is a sign of
the primitive state of the terminology available. The fact that 'centres'
for so many distinct functions lie close together suggests that the
significance of the whole region is that the actions of relatively few
cells integrate those of many lower centres. The hypothalamus itself
sends fibres up to the cortex and down to the tegmentum. The pattern
of control is produced by a balance of interaction between all these
various centres. Moreover, elaborate vascular and chemical interactions are involved. The cells of the hypothalamus are influenced by
the composition of the blood and through their nerve-fibres they assist
in control of the secretions of the pituitary gland (p. 561). This in turn
influences the composition of the blood and the action of many
glandular and metabolic systems throughout the body. The hypothalamus and pituitary together constitute a control centre for much
of the life of a mammal, influencing many parts and itself responsive
to a wide variety of influences. This part of the brain is very sensitive
to infections of the meninges, which lead to pressure changes of the
cerebrospinal fluid. Meningitis may produce a variety of abnormal
states, such as sleeping sickness or errors of metabolism (excessive
fatness or emaciation) as a result of action upon this region.

7. The corpus striatum and septum

The floor of the forebrain in front of the hypothalamus is one of the
most obscure regions of the brain. The corpus striatum constitutes the
lateral portion of the floor. On account of the evagination and backward direction of the hemisphere it lies immediately lateral to the
thalamus (Fig. 180). The fibres of the internal capsule, proceeding
to and from the cerebral cortex, run through it and divide it into
several parts.

The *caudate nucleus* and *putamen* of the corpus striatum receive
fibres from the medial nuclei of the thalamus and from the cortex.
These afferent fibres end among the numerous small cells of the
caudate nucleus, whose axons excite larger cells with axons proceeding
to the *pallidum*. This latter is the motor region of the corpus striatum

and from it fibres proceed to the hypothalamus, red nucleus, and other midbrain regions and to the medulla.

The part that the corpora striata play in the control of movement is not understood. Lesions affecting this region in man are said to produce tremor during voluntary movement and various other motor disturbances (Parkinson's disease and chorea) but experiments by excision and stimulation have not succeeded in reproducing these symptoms in animals. These regions constitute the highest level of the hierarchy of motor representations and it is not surprising that it is difficult to analyse and describe their activities.

8. The thalamus

The walls of the diencephalon are especially developed in mammals as the station for ascending sensory pathways, from which relay is made to the cerebral cortex. The projections from thalamus to cortex and in the opposite direction are so abundant that it is evident that the two form one interacting reciprocal mechanism. The thalamus is therefore far more than a mere relay station on the way upwards, but it is not yet clear how its interactions with the cortex are involved in the computation of appropriate responses to the afferent input.

The thickening of the diencephalic walls is so great that they come together in the midline to form a mass, the interthalamic connexus, above and below which are distinct portions of the third ventricle (Fig. 180). Numerous separate 'nuclei' are recognized in the thalamus. Many of these receive the termination of a particular part of the ascending fibres of the lemniscus system of ascending projections. The *ventral nucleus* receives the exteroceptive and proprioceptive fibres of the medial lemniscus and spino-thalamic tract, and its cells send fibres to the parietal cortex (p. 442). The *medial geniculate body* receives auditory impulses and sends fibres to the temporal lobe, while the *lateral geniculate body*, a complicated laminated region, receives the fibres of the optic tract and projects to the hind end of the occipital lobe of the hemisphere. Besides these projection systems from receptors the thalamus also receives fibres from the cerebellum, in the *lateroventral nucleus*, and there is a forward projection from this to the motor portion of the frontal cortex (areas 4 and 6, see p. 438).

Some of the thalamic nuclei receive no fibres from outside the thalamus and these send fibres to the parts of the cortex that are associated with no particular receptor. Thus the *dorsomedial thalamic nucleus* receives fibres from other thalamic centres (the nuclei of the midline) and projects to the hypothalamus and to the prefrontal *cortical areas* (9–12). The *dorso-lateral nucleus* projects to the posterior parietal regions (areas 5 and 7) and the *pulvinar* to the occipital areas (18–22) that lie in front of the main optic projection area. A fourth set of thalamic centres (the *nuclei of the midline*) sends fibres to the hypothalamus and other subcortical regions, as well as to the corpus striatum and medial cortex; they are large in lower animals and may be named palaeothalamus to distinguish them from the neothalamic centres that relay only to the cortex.

We may recognize then, four sorts of thalamic nuclei: afferent projection nuclei, cerebellar projection nuclei, association nuclei, and a fourth set projecting to the basal parts of the forebrain. Nearly every part of the forebrain receives some thalamic connexions and this region plays a central part in the functioning of the system. There are abundant connexions between the various thalamic nuclei.

The axons of the thalamic neurons mostly proceed laterally in the *internal capsule* (Fig. 180) to radiate out to the appropriate regions of the cerebral cortex, but some fibres also pass down into the hypothalamus and backwards into the tegmental region of the midbrain.

XXIII

THE CEREBRAL CORTEX

1. General plan of the cortex

IN mammals centralization of the control of action has proceeded so far that almost every single act is influenced by the cerebral cortex. This region receives information directly or indirectly from nearly all the receptors in the body and every muscle and gland-cell is influenced by the impulses that originate in it. It may be considered as containing the most complete representation of the environmental conditions that is available to the animal. This representation is used in the operations of a vast computing system, which devises at each moment the behaviour that is most likely to provide for survival in view of the present situation and the experiences of the past.

We still have too little knowledge to say how this computation is performed, but it evidently depends on a display of the signals from the various receptors over a vast number of cells, which are arranged as a 'cortex' (= rind, also known as 'pallium' = mantle) so as to provide for the spread of influences in many directions through the system. This opportunity for interaction between many afferent impulses presumably makes it possible to preserve a record of the various patterns of input that have occurred in the past and hence to make those solutions of the animal's problems that we characterize as 'intelligent'.

The cerebral hemispheres, within which this computing system has developed, serve in lower vertebrates as purely olfactory centres (see Young, 1950, p. 329). Sherrington suggested that their development into discriminating centres came about because the nose is the distance receptor that initiates the actions of hunting and finding a a mate. If smell thus provides the 'drive' for behaviour it is obviously likely to be efficient for the 'smell brain' to receive impulses from the optic, tactile, and other receptors that are furnishing the detailed information with which the chase is pursued. Moreover, chemical changes in the environment will often give valuable clues from past experience as to the presence of food, mates, and other conditions.

The cerebral cortex became large when numerous afferent systems came to discharge forwards into the hemisphere. In all mammals we can still recognize the original 'smell brain' (*rhinencephalon*), although it is now overshadowed by the great development of the non-olfactory part, the *neopallium*. In premammalian animals all parts of the hemispheres were pervaded by olfactory fibres. Already in amphibians, however, it is possible to recognize a lateral *pyriform cortex* and medial *hippocampal cortex*, both receiving only olfactory fibres, as distinct from the more dorsal *general somatic cortex*, which in addition receives from the thalamus forward projections associated with optic and other impulses.

In mammals a similar division into three sorts of cortical tissue can still be recognized. The lower lateral portion, which receives secondary olfactory fibres from the olfactory bulbs, is known as the *pyriform cortex* or *palaeocortex*. The lower medial cortex, the *hippocampus* or *archi-cortex* was also for long considered to be concerned with olfactory activities, but this now is not thought likely (p. 432). These two regions have a relatively simple structure and are known as *allocortex*. The complete layered cortical structure (*isocortex*) is seen only in the main dorsal portion of the cortex, the *neopallium*.

2. The smell-brain

The olfactory nerve-fibres (p. 521) end in the olfactory bulbs in tangled bundles, the *glomeruli*. As many as 26,000 olfactory axons end in each glomerulus and here they become associated with the dendrites of the *mitral cells* and *tufted cells* (Fig. 183). Each mitral cell makes connexion with a single glomerulus and in the rabbit 24 mitral cells and 68 tufted cells send dendrites to each glomerulus. These mitral cells and tufted cells have intertwining collateral dendrites, which may also be influenced by recurrent axonal collaterals. Moreover, there are periglomerular and granule cells that further complicate the neuronal chains. The setting up of impulses in the axons of a given mitral or tufted cell presumably depends upon the stimulation of a particular set of olfactory receptors.

The mitral-cell axons proceed in the olfactory tract to the front part of the *pyriform lobe* (Fig. 183), occupying the lower lateral portion of the hemisphere. This palaeocortex (palaeopallium) has a structure simpler than that of the main cortex. It probably sends its output to higher cortical centres and is concerned in the more elaborate learned olfactory reactions. After ablation of this area olfactory conditioned reflexes that had been previously learned are lost.

The axons of the tufted cells pass to nuclei lying in the floor of the forebrain (amygdala), in the region of the anterior commissure. Experiments suggest that these fibres and centres mediate the simpler

reflex responses to olfactory stimuli, probably by activating the hypothalamic centres that lie caudal to them. Electrical stimulation of the

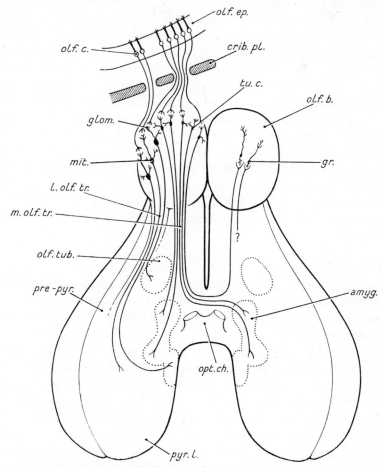

Fig. 183. Diagram of the secondary olfactory pathways in a mammalian brain.
amyg. amygdaloid nuclei; *crib.pl.* cribriform plate; *glom.* glomerulus; *gr.* granular cell;
l.olf.tr. lateral olfactory tract; *mit.* mitral cell; *m.olf.tr.* medial olfactory tract; *olf.b.* olfactory
bulb; *olf.c.* olfactory cell; *olf.ep.* olfactory epithelium; *olf.tub.* olfactory tubercle; *opt.ch.*
optic chiasma; *pre-pyr.* pre-pyriform area; *pyr.l.* pyriform lobe; *tu.c.* tufted cell.
(After Allison, *Biol. Rev.* 1953.)

prepyriform cortex or the amygdala in animals gives rise to actions
related to feeding, such as retraction of the lips, sniffing, licking,
chewing, and salivation, which are also seen after stimulation of the
hypothalamus (p. 421).

Fibres pass from the pre-pyriform region to other parts of the cortex
and it is probable that the function of this part of the olfactory system

is more complicated than the simple initiation of feeding actions. The association of particular smells with situations useful or dangerous for the animal is one of the most important determinants of behaviour, especially in mammals, which were originally nocturnal animals. The apparatus for forming association between olfactory and other afferent impulses is therefore one of the most important regions of the brain. Even in man, where visual clues are more important than olfactory ones, we still find that particular smells may suddenly arouse complicated memories of past visual and other situations with which they have been associated, particularly if these situations were connected with the satisfaction of a strong biological need, such as food or sex. We express this in another way when we say that the olfactory sense has strong emotional value. It is not unlikely that the action of these parts of the rhinencephalon has an important influence on the rest of the cerebral cortex, which has become developed, it must be remembered, in an area that was originally wholly devoted to olfactory functions.

3. The hippocampus

The *hippocampus* of mammals is the lower medial portion of the cortex. Its cells have migrated away from the ventricle and hence constitute a cortex, but this cortex differs from that of the rest of the hemisphere and is known as the *archicortex* (archipallium). The hippocampus was long considered to be functionally related to the pyriform cortex (palaeocortex) and hence to the sense of smell; these more basal parts of the cortex are therefore often spoken of together as the *rhinencephalon*. It is now doubtful whether the hippocampus has any close relationship with olfaction. It receives fibres from the hinder (non-olfactory) part of the pyriform cortex (known as the entorhinal area), and probably also from other sources. The axons of its cells pass downwards in a special bundle, the *fornix*, to the hypothalamus and especially to the mamillary bodies (p. 420). Experiments in which the hippocampus is removed or electrically stimulated do not show any signs that it has an olfactory function but suggest that it may be related to the production of 'emotional' responses, for example, searching movements and signs of anxiety and anger. Stimulation of the hippocampus and nearby medial cortical areas has been achieved in cats by implanting electrodes and applying electrical pulses through them when the animal was unrestrained (Kaada, Jansen, and Andersen, 1953). The effect of the stimulus was regularly to make the animal give 'quick glancing or searching movements to the opposite side, while the facial expression changed to one of attention accompanied by surprise, bewilderment, and anxiety. The reaction to external stimuli was decreased and the animal's attention became intensely fixed on "something" in the environment that they seemed to experience. Some cats showed signs of fear, anger and fury.'

When the temporal lobe and hippocampus were removed on both sides from monkeys profound changes in behaviour were seen (Klüver, 1951). The animals picked up and examined every object within sight, without exercising any discrimination, and often transferred the objects to the mouth. They would touch snakes and other objects that produce signs of terror and avoidance in normal monkeys. When these parts of the brain were absent the visual systems of the cortex called forth investigating reactions to all objects indiscriminately, the normal mechanisms of avoidance are not evoked. These monkeys ate voraciously and males showed almost continued sexual activity.

It seems, therefore, that the hippocampus is concerned with control of elaborate action patterns appropriate to investigation of unknown objects, including reactions of attention, anxiety, and defence. In this it is associated with the hypothalamus and perhaps the prefrontal cortex. The mamillary bodies send fibres through the anterior thalamic nuclei to the prefrontal cortex (p. 424). From that area influences can reach to the hippocampus, which is thus involved in a circuit. The function of this circuit is sometimes expressed by saying that it is concerned in the regulation of 'emotional behaviour' (Papez, 1929), which is another attempt to describe the part that it plays in producing actions of investigation and protection, suppressing the appearance of others that are irrelevant. This function may have arisen at first in relation to olfactory changes, but in modern mammals it is no longer limited to these. The hippocampus is large in primates and whales, in spite of the reduction of the olfactory system in these animals. It evidently plays some important part in the functioning of the whole forebrain apparatus.

4. The neopallium

The special characteristic of the mammalian brain is the expansion of the mid-dorsal portion of the roof of the cerebral hemispheres, the region that receives ascending projection fibres from all parts of the body and is known as the general somatic cortex, neopallium, neocortex, or isocortex. The function of this tissue is to allow association between patterns of signals coming from the various external receptors and those within the body that record the state of the various

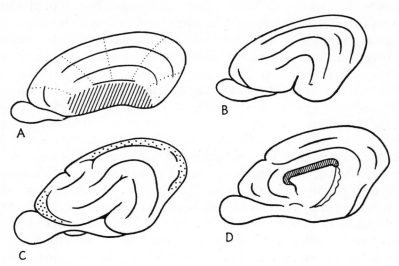

FIG. 184. A. Diagram showing the tendency for longitudinal folds to develop in the cerebral cortex at right angles to the lines of stress, shown by dotted lines, which are set up by expansion of the thinner pallium on the thicker basal ganglia. B. Effect of ventral flexure of the hemisphere in producing arcuate sulci. C and D. Lateral and medial view of cat's cerebral hemisphere, showing arcuate sulci. The frontal and visual areas are stippled.

(Figs. 184–7 from Le Gros Clark, *Essays on Growth and Form*, Oxford, 1945.)

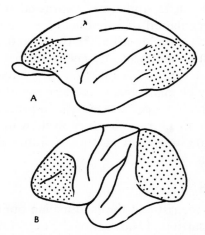

FIG. 185. Cortex of A *Lemur* and B the monkey *Cercopithecus* to show transition from pattern of longitudinal to transverse sulci as the frontal and visual areas became developed.

organs and hence the needs of the organism. It thus carries a store of information about the relevance of various patterns of events that have occurred. Subsequently, as new combinations of inputs arrive, it computes appropriate actions to suit each occurrence. It assembles and reacts to information from a variety of sources and provides a representation of the events that have occurred in the environment.

The essential feature of the cortex is that a great number of pathways converge into it and the probability of a given response to input along any particular channel is initially low. The information of heredity provides in the cortex a system that is able to make predictive actions only after it has been trained. It produces few or no complete 'hereditary' responses to the environment, but has great capacities for building up representations as a result of the information transmitted by the receptors. Such information is of course a more 'up to date' and complete record of the environment than can be provided by heredity alone. It is the capacity to form this information store that gives to mammals their special ability to survive even in 'improbable' situations, that is to say those that are apparently unpropitious for life.

5. The cerebral sulci and areas

The reaction to patterns of inputs, which is the characteristic feature of the activities of the cerebral cortex, seems to depend on the presence of a relatively thin sheet of tissue, within which the cells are arranged in layers. The development of this extensive sheet leads in all larger mammals to folding of the surface of the cerebral hemisphere. The area available increases of course only with the square of the linear dimensions, whereas the volume of underlying white matter increases as the cube. The proportions are kept constant by folding of the surface to give the *sulci* and *gyri*; these are found in all large mammals, irrespective of affinities, whereas the hemispheres of their smaller relatives are smooth.

Le Gros Clark has shown that the pattern of the sulci depends on the way the stresses fall during the expansion of the brain roof. The basal ganglia form a solid mass along the floor of the hemisphere and expansion of the thinner pallium produces the *lateral (Sylvian) fissure*, the most constant of all the sulci (Fig. 186). Similarly the *rhinal fissure* laterally and *hippocampal fissure* medially separate the pyriform lobe and hippocampus from the neocortex above them.

The expanding sheet is attached to fixed points laterally and medially (the basal ganglia and corpus callosum) and as it enlarges it

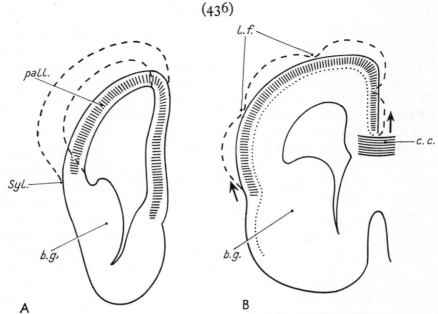

A   B

FIG. 186. A. Diagram of the developing cerebral vesicle of a mammal in transverse section showing how the Sylvian fossa (*Syl.*) is formed by expansion of the thin-walled pallium (*pall.*) on the thicker basal ganglia (*b.g.*).

B. Showing how the tendency to form longitudinal folds (*l.f.*) is produced by expansion of the pallium against the resistance of the corpus callosum (*c.c.*) and basal ganglia (*b.g.*).

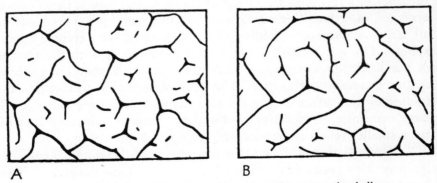

A   B

FIG. 187. A. Patterns formed on the surface of a contracting balloon (after Bull, A. J., *Geol. Mag.* **69**, 73, 1932).

B. Sulcal patterns from the parietal lobe of a human brain, showing tri-radiate patterns, some of them linked, as in A.

falls into the longitudinal folds that are commonly found in lower mammalian brains (Fig. 184). Lesser furrows form when the brain becomes still larger, and often these take triradiate patterns (Fig. 187), such as can be imitated by allowing contraction of the surface of a sphere, say, by coating a balloon with gelatin or collodion and then allowing it to collapse. In primate brains the longitudinal folds are found only among the earlier types (lemurs), in the later forms the sulci are mainly transverse (Fig. 185). This is probably a result of the great expansion of the posterior (visual) and anterior (frontal) parts of these brains, which would have the effect of causing the crumpling to occur in the transverse rather than the longitudinal direction.

The longitudinal furrows of the earlier brains bear little relation to functional areas, but in primates some of the major sulci occur along lines that demarcate functionally distinct regions. Thus the *central sulcus* is a rather constant groove that divides the motor cortex in front from the sensory areas behind. In man there is a reduction in thickness of the cortex from 3·5 to 1·5 mm. between these areas and this makes a line of weakness at which folding occurs.

The visual cortex surrounds the *calcarine fissure*, and the frontal gyri are separated by fissures that are probably produced by similar factors. The detail of the pattern of the sulci is not sufficiently constant to be a reliable guide. For purposes of description the surface of the hemisphere is divided into four main lobes, frontal, parietal, occipital, and temporal and a finer division is made into numbered areas (Fig. 167). Each of these areas was originally distinguished by Brodmann on a basis of supposed differences in neuronal structure. The numbers have been retained for the areas, although in most cases no exact criteria by which the neuronal structure of the areas can be recognized have been agreed (p. 453).

6. Localization within the cortex

The cortex is an organ for allowing association between signals arriving from many sources. Obviously in such a system there is in a sense no localization: it is the very fact of bringing together and allowing interaction that is important (v. Bonin, 1950; Sholl, 1956). Experimental studies confirm this, showing that removal of particular parts of the cortex from rats does not lead to the loss of any single learned habit but to a diminution of the effectiveness of many of them (Lashley, 1950). Yet the cortex is far from being a uniform field in which all parts receive and give out similar influences. The input from each of the thalamic centres proceeds mainly to one particular part of the cortex. We can therefore recognize a *sensory cortex*, consisting of separate receptor areas where the impulses from the visual, auditory, tactile, and some other systems arrive. Efferent fibres proceed from many, perhaps all, parts of the cortex to lower centres, but the main pathway for direct control of the activities of the spinal cord is from the *motor cortex*. The parts of the cortex not directly identifiable as sensory or motor areas are sometimes called *association areas*: they receive fibres from the receptor areas and send them to the motor areas. These association areas also receive fibres from the thalamus and send them back there.

As information about cortical structure accumulates it appears that all parts are based upon a common plan (p. 448). The differences in structure in various areas have been the subject of much study, the 'architectonics' being minutely described. For instance, the occipital cortex, which receives the visual projection, is characterized by a special band or stripe of medullated fibres and is hence known as the *striate area*; the motor cortex contains numerous large cells and so on. Such broad differences undoubtedly exist, but there has been much controversy about the division of the cortex into smaller areas. Lack of quantitative methods of analysis has made decisions about differences highly arbitrary.

7. The motor cortex

The areas of the primate brain were numbered by Brodmann about the central sulcus as a reference point (Fig. 167). The system is arbitrary and the distinctions between the areas are not easy to define accurately by histological or other methods. Nevertheless, the divisions are convenient and the areas are often referred to by these numbers. Immediately in front of the central sulcus is area 4, the motor cortex, characterized histologically by the presence of the very large *Betz cells* (p. 453), whose axons enter the *pyramidal tract* (hence 'area giganto-pyramidalis'). Stimulation of a point in the motor cortex by electrical or other means produces a twitch of a localized group of muscle-fibres. All parts of the body are represented within the area, the lower parts nearer to the mid-dorsal line and the others spread out in a series over the side of the hemisphere (Fig. 189). The extent of motor cortex that is related to any part of the body is proportional not to the bulk or power of the muscles concerned but to the complexity and variety of the movements in which they become involved. Thus the hand and face have an especially large representation in man, corresponding to the large number of possible actions among which selection can be made.

Above the main motor area is a second set of points representing

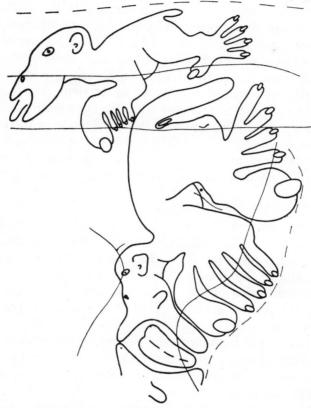

FIG. 188. Motor areas of the cerebral cortex of the monkey. The 'simiusculi' show the areas from which movements of the parts concerned can be elicited by threshold stimulation with a 60 cycle A.C. stimulator and unipolar electrode 0.5 mm. in diameter applied to the surface for 2 sec. The main motor area lies in the pre-central gyrus laterally and there is a secondary area on the medial surface of the cortex. The diagram is inadequate in so far as it does not indicate that areas activating neighbouring muscles overlap. (After Woolsey.)

the muscular system and extending on to the medial surface of the hemisphere (Fig. 188). The significance of the presence of two sets of motor points is obscure.

Removal of a portion of the motor cortex produces partial paralysis of the part concerned, fine movements can no longer be made by this part but other functions are not impaired. Habits learned before operation are performed imperfectly but are not always completely lost; their performance may be difficult because of the motor defect, but with practice alternative methods are usually found.

Stimulation of the region in front of area 4 also produces movements but these usually involve large groups of muscles and it may be that this *premotor area* (area 6) is concerned in the elaboration of complex acts and that it operates by activation of selected groups of cells in area 4. After removals in area 6 there are disturbances of skilled movements and of posture but usually no single movement is affected and the disturbances rapidly pass off, unless area 4 is also damaged.

Stimulation of parts of the cortex other than area 4 or 6 may produce movements and there are many 'extrapyramidal motor connexions' of the cerebrum, although normally much of the movement is controlled through the pyramidal system. In man there is a special region (Broca's area) at the front end of area 6, usually on the left side only, whose removal produces severe disturbances of speech.

8. The prefrontal areas

The prefrontal areas at the anterior end of the hemisphere are 'silent areas', that is to say electrical stimulation of them does not lead to any obvious movements. Their functions are still not well understood but studies by ablation show that they are concerned with selecting the direction of the activities of the whole organism; they are 'motor' centres that control activity by inhibition as well as excitation. Their connexions include fibres coming from the red nucleus, and impulses pass in both directions between the prefrontal areas and the cerebellum through the ventro-lateral nucleus of the thalamus. Once again one gets an impression of mutual interaction, which suggests possible oscillatory actions or a system of damping, but no words are available that will properly characterize these actions.

Removal of these prefrontal areas (8–12) in chimpanzees was found to produce striking change in personality. Normal animals when given problems too difficult to solve become highly enraged; after removal of the prefrontal areas performance in tests was below normal but the apes seemed to be resigned to their failures. Following the clue of these experiments, neurosurgeons have produced cures of some types of severe depressional state in man by the operation of prefrontal leucotomy, cutting the white fibres that connect the prefrontal areas with the rest of the brain.

Evidently the influence of this tissue controls in some way the balance of forces that regulates the 'drive' of the individual. Similar personality changes can be produced without any actual surgery by

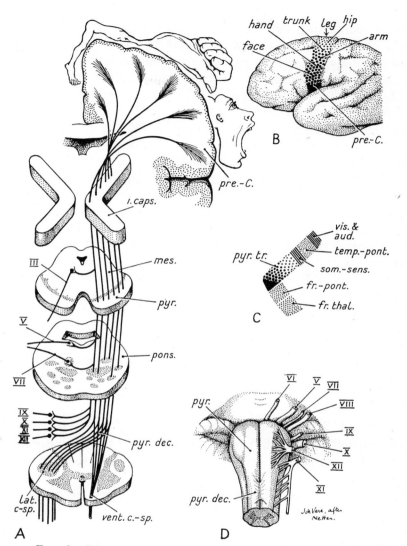

FIG. 189. Diagram illustrating the connexions of the motor cortex.

A. Shows the parts of the precentral gyrus concerned with movements of different parts of the body and the course of the pyramidal tracts; B, lateral view of cerebral cortex with motor centres indicated on the pre-central gyrus (*pre-c.*); C, horizontal section through the internal capsule showing the arrangement of the principal tracts; D, ventral view of the medulla showing the decussation of the pyramids and some cranial nerves.

III, Oculomotor nerve; v, trigeminal; vI, abducent; vII, facial; vIII, auditory; IX, glosso-pharyngeal; x, vagus; xI, accessory; xII, hypoglossal.

fr.-pont. fronto-pontine fibres; *fr.-thal.* fronto-thalamic fibres; *i.caps.* internal capsule; *lat.c.-sp.* lateral cerebro-spinal tract; *mes.* mesencephalon; *pons.* pons Varolii; *pre.-c.* pre-central gyrus; *pyr.* pyramid; *pyr.dec.* pyramidal decussation; *pyr.tr.* pyramidal tract; *som. sens.* somatic sensory fibres; *temp.-pont.* tempero-pontine fibres; *vent.c.-sp.* ventral cerebro-spinal tract; *vis. & aud.* visual and auditory fibres.

(Modified from original illustration by F. Netter, M.D., from Ciba collection.)

passing stimulating currents through the areas. There are various forms of this shock treatment, all based on the idea that after some drastic change the activity of cerebral systems that had been functioning wrongly may restart on more normal lines.

The lower parts of the frontal lobes, areas 13 and 14 on the orbital and 24 and 25 on the medial surfaces, also play a large part in influencing the 'personality'. Under suitable conditions various internal activities such as respiration or heart-rate can be influenced by electrical stimulation of area 13 and damage to this region in animals or man produces phenomena of 'sham rage' somewhat similar to those found after lesions in the hypothalamus.

Great development of this extreme front part of the brain is characteristic of the higher apes and man, and it seems that its influence is largely one of inhibition. Higher primates, like other mammals, are active and investigating animals but they pursue their inquiries in a restrained and orderly way. One can often notice a marked difference between the ceaseless, if somewhat aimless, activity of the 'monkey house' at a zoo and the more dignified quiet of the corner occupied by chimpanzees, gorillas, or orang-outangs. Again, listening with several thousand other human beings to a speech or concert one cannot but be impressed at the astonishing restraint that characterizes the behaviour of man and may be a result of the great development of the pre-frontal lobes.

9. Afferent projection areas

Immediately behind the central sulcus is an area in the parietal lobe that receives projections concerned with the general somatic afferent systems for touch and pressure and perhaps also for heat and cold and proprioceptive senses. There is an accurate projection forward by fibres arising in the ventral nucleus of the thalamus and connected with particular areas of the body surface. The arrangement resembles that of the motor area, the lower part of the body being represented on the upper portion of the hemisphere (Fig. 190).

When a touch stimulus is given to any portion of the body surface electrical activity can be detected by electrodes placed upon the appropriate part of these areas at the front end of the parietal lobe, which are numbered 1, 2, and 3 on architectonic maps. This region thus constitutes the cortical receptor organ for touch, heat and cold, taste and proprioception (Fig. 190). Caudal to the main somatic sensory area lies a second area in which electrical activity is also recorded after suitable peripheral stimulation. Each of the primary receptor areas of the cortex is accompanied by such a secondary area (and a third set may also be present). The significance of this arrangement is not yet apparent but it is clear that we cannot analyse the actions of the cortex on the assumption that input from any given receptor area occurs only through a single channel.

Electrical stimulation of areas 1, 2, and 3 in a man under local

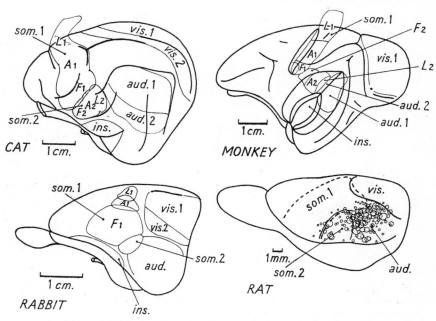

FIG. 190. Primary and secondary receptor areas of the cortex.

Aud. 1 & 2. auditory areas; *som.* 1 & 2. somatic areas; *vis.* 1 & 2. visual areas; *ins.* insula; *L, A* & *F* refer to the leg, arm, and face portions of the somatic areas. In the rat the areas giving auditory and somatic responses overlap.

(After Woolsey, *The Biology of Mental Health and Disease*, 1950.)

anaesthesia produces reports of feelings (usually of touch), referred to the appropriate part. It is interesting that such procedure is not said to be painful, nor does it elicit referred pain (Penfield and Rasmussen, 1950). The thalamocortical projection system is concerned with the formation of associations between complex patterns of stimulation and with the computing of suitable responses. The impulses of the pain system operate primarily at a lower level, producing responses that are accurately predictable, and by a mechanism that is simpler than that of the cortex (p. 478). Yet the operations of the cortex are certainly often influenced by pain impulses, acting as indicators of the undesirable nature of particular situations.

The area of the brain that is devoted to each part of the body varies with the importance of that part of the life of the animal. Thus in cats the limbs are used in varied ways and they have quite a large cortical representation, but in ungulates the limb area is small, perhaps because of the limited sensitivity of the hooves. In both horses and pigs

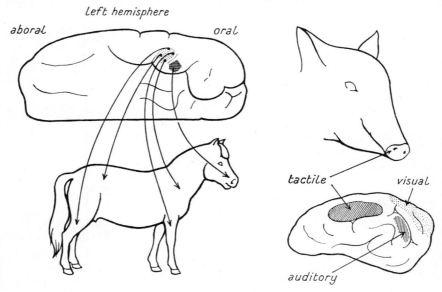

FIG. 191. Diagrams of the receiving areas in the brains of a horse and a pig. The anterior part of the receiving area in the horse brain is concerned entirely with the detailed representation of the nostril. In the pig the tactile area is connected with the opposite half of the snout. (After Adrian, 1943, *The Lancet*, and 1946, *Brain*, **69**.)

the area concerned with the snout and lips is much larger than that of all the rest of the body (Fig. 191).

Behind the areas 1, 2, and 3 is a large part of the parietal lobe, known as areas 5 and 7, that is concerned in a less direct way with general somatic sensation. These areas receive projections from the association nuclei of the dorso-lateral region of the thalamus, which are only indirectly connected with the ascending sensory systems (p. 427). Injuries in areas 5 and 7 in apes produce temporary impairment of powers of localization of touch or discrimination of weights, and similar symptoms have been recorded in man.

The occipital lobe of the cortex contains the *striate area* (area 17), which receives the fibres from the lateral geniculate body of the thalamus, the end station of the optic tract (Fig. 192). There is a rather precise localization all along this optic pathway, so that when any

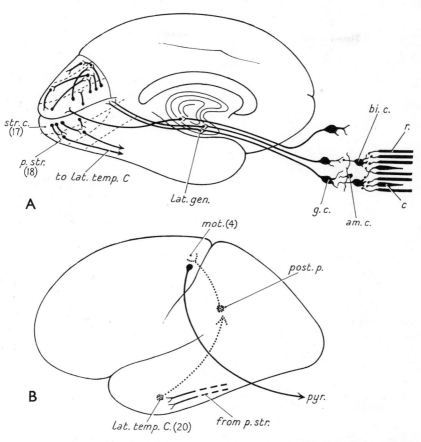

FIG. 192. Diagram of the visual pathway in the monkey. There are opportunities for local cross connexions within the retina. From the retina to the lateral geniculate and from the latter to the striate cortex topographical relations are preserved, but are lost in the projections from the striate to the parastriate area (A). The further connexions involved in visual cortical activity are not well known but are shown diagrammatically for completeness in B. The pathway proceeds to the temporal lobe and thence probably through the parietal cortex to the motor areas. Many other parts of the cortex are no doubt involved even in simple visual cortical responses.

am.c. amacrine cell; *bi.c.* bipolar cell; *c.* cone; *g.c.* ganglion cell of retina; *lat.gen.* lateral geniculate; *lat.temp.c.* lateral temporal cortex, *mot.* motor cortex; *post.p.* post-parietal cortex; *pyr.* pyramidal tract; *p.str.* parastriate cortex; *r.* rod; *str.c.* striate cortex.

(Diagram prepared by Mr. D. A. Sholl from various sources of evidence.)

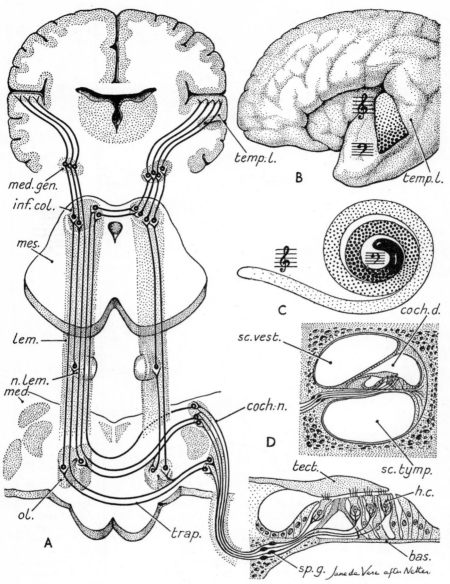

FIG. 193. Diagram showing the nervous pathways involved in hearing in man.

A, Connexions of the organ of Corti with the cerebral cortex; B and C, the cochlea and the representation of frequency discrimination in the auditory cortex; D, section of the cochlea showing the disposition of the organ of Corti.

bas. basilar membrane; *coch.d.* cochlear duct; *coch.n.* cochlear nerve; *h.c.* hair cell; *inf.col.* inferior colliculus; *lem.* lateral lemniscus; *med.* medulla oblongata; *med.gen.* medial geniculate body; *mes.* mesencephalon; *n.lem.* nucleus of lateral lemniscus; *ol.* superior olivary complex; *sc.tymp.* scala tympani; *sc.vest.* scala vestibuli; *sp.g.* spiral ganglion; *tect.* tectorial membrane; *temp.l.* temporal lobe; *trap.* trapezoid body.

(Modified from original illustration by F. Netter, M.D., from Ciba collection.)

small part of the retina is stimulated, activity is aroused in certain
distinct thalamic cells, which in turn activate a small portion of area 17.
Removal of part or all of area 17 produces various degrees of blindness in different animals. In man complete removal of the area leads
to complete blindness but in lower primates and other mammals form-
discrimination alone is affected and animals completely deprived of the
occipital cortex can still react to changes of intensity and illumination.

In man a greater area of the brain is devoted to sight than to any

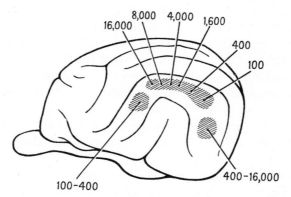

FIG. 194. The auditory area in the dog's brain.

The figures indicate the frequency of the sounds that produce the maximum potential
change in different parts of the area. The two lower regions are not further localized to
different frequencies; all parts of them respond maximally to the frequencies to which they
do respond. (After Tunturi, *Amer.J.Physiol.* **141**, 397, 1944.)

other sense. The primary cortical (striate) area is much greater than
that of the peripheral receptor itself. Thus whereas the area of the
pig's brain devoted to the snout is only a tenth of the receptor surface,
the cortical receiving area for the macula of the human eye is 10,000
times greater than the macula itself. If the retina is illuminated by a very
faint narrow beam of light, electrodes on the cortex record localized
activity. The focus of maximum activity moves with the beam, a shift
of 1° producing a movement of 1 mm. in the cat, more in the monkey.
Stronger illumination produces more widespread activity.

As in the case of other senses the primary area for vision (17) is
surrounded by a secondary visual area (18). This receives fibres from
the primary area and also from the pulvinar, one of the association
nuclei of the thalamus. Area 19, lying farther forward, receives few
thalamic fibres but many fibres reach it from other parts of the cortex.

The relative position of fibres and cells is preserved along the pathway retina—lateral geniculate body—striate cortex (Fig. 192). Excita-

tion of a set of retinal elements in the form of (say) a square therefore produces an approximately square area of activity in the cortex. In the connexions of the striate area with its surroundings this arrangement is no longer continued. Two cells that are close neighbours in area 17 may send axons to widely different parts of area 18 and vice versa. This mixing and interlacing of fibres provides the opportunities for the setting up of the associations by which the cortex exercises its functions (p. 453).

The auditory system projects through the medial geniculate body of the thalamus on to area 22 in the temporal lobe of the cerebral hemisphere, essentially in the same way as the other sensory systems (Fig. 193). The thalamic fibres come from the medial geniculate body to area 22 and there is a point to point representation between the parts of the organ of Corti and the cortex. In the dog each octave is represented by a strip of cortex about 2 mm. wide (Fig. 194). Besides the main sensory area there is a secondary area of cochlear representation, lying below the first. The vestibular receptors also have a cortical representation.

Electrical stimulation of area 22 in patients under local anaesthesia produces reports of roaring, and after its removal there is a reduction in auditory acuity (but not complete deafness); sometimes there are also defects of recognition of words and of speaking.

10. Structure of the cerebral cortex

Studies by stimulation, electrical recording, and extirpation, such as we have been considering, give an idea of the variety of functions that are under cortical control but they do not tell us in detail how the influence is exercised. Indeed it is very difficult to specify the nature of the 'functions of the cortex' and neither histologists nor physiologists have yet found convenient units in terms of which the organ may be adequately considered.

There is considerable controversy about the best means of describing the structure of the cortex and classifying its variations in different parts. The thickness of the grey matter is filled only partly with cells, the intervening space contains interlacing nerve-fibres, the *neuropil* or nerve felt, and much neuroglia. The neuropil is composed of incoming and outgoing axons and of the dendrites of the cells, but it is uncertain how all these fine fibres are related to each other and to the processes of the neuroglial cells. It may be that transmission is mainly from the incoming axons to dendrites, indeed synaptic boutons, such as those seen on ventral horn cells of the spinal cord (p. 349), have been described, and are probably numerous throughout the cortex. They are small and cannot usually be stained by the methods that reveal boutons in the spinal cord. It is possible that the parts of the fibres that are interlaced in the neuropil influence each other directly, in ways at present little understood.

Our ignorance of the method of working of the cortex makes it

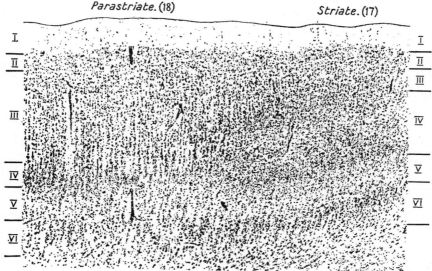

FIG. 195. The cells of the striate (visual) cortex (17) to right and parastriate (visuo-psychic area (18)) to the left as seen after staining of the Nissl substance. The layers are labelled as by von Economo but not all are equally distinguishable.) (After von Economo and Koskinas.)

difficult to decide how to arrange a description of its parts, but it is conventional to recognize six layers (Fig. 195). The cells vary greatly in size and length of dendrites. The fact that cells of different sizes occur close together suggests that the size of each cell and the length of its processes may be determined by the specific activities in which it has been engaged (p. 458). Two main types can be distinguished, pyramidal cells and stellate cells (Fig. 138). The *pyramidal cells* have a triangular cell body with *basal dendrites*, proceeding in all directions, and a main *apical dendrite*, stretching out towards the cortical surface, where it gives off many branches. The pyramidal cell has a single axon that proceeds towards the white matter and conducts either to some other cortical area or to a region outside the cortex. The axon often gives off collateral branches, which run back to the more superficial layers. These collaterals thus provide the possibility for the setting up of self-re-exciting chains of activity each time that the pyramidal cell discharges.

The *stellate cells* are often small (but not always) and they have many dendrites proceeding in all directions. Some of them have axons that break up at no great distance from the cell body. Others may be

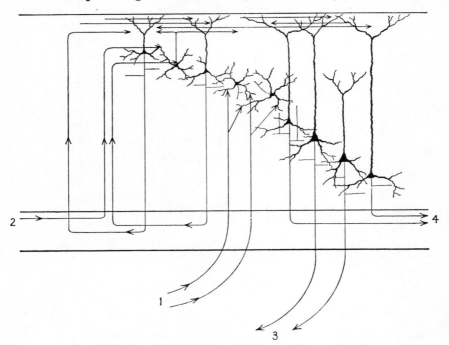

FIG. 196. Arrangement of cells and fibres in the cerebral cortex.

1 and 2 show the main afferent pathways, 1 being extrinsic fibres from the thalamus, 2 fibres from other parts of the cortex near or far. 3 are the main efferent fibres leaving the cortex. 4 shows fibres going to other cortical areas.
(Figure kindly supplied by Mr. D. A. Sholl.)

multipolar cells with no axon. The function of such cells has never been investigated. It is not even certain whether the dendrites conduct impulses only towards the cell body, or indeed whether impulses are propagated along them at all. The fact that the processes proceed at random in all directions suggests that the function of these cells is to spread the activity of a given excited region (see p. 460).

The proportions of pyramidal and stellate cells differ in different parts of the cortex. In the areas where the main afferent fibres arrive from the thalamus there are concentrations of stellate cells in the middle portion of the cortex, where the thalamic afferent fibres end (Fig. 196). The presence of these numerous small cells produces a 'granular layer' in such areas. In the 'association' and 'motor' regions the stellate cells are found at all levels and these areas are therefore often referred to as 'agranular cortex'.

Each afferent fibre that arrives from the thalamus branches several times and the limits of the final branches lie as much as 650 μ apart in the visual area of the cat (Sholl, 1953). Each single afferent fibre there-

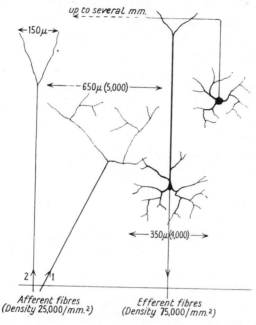

FIG. 197. Diagram to show the extent of the afferent axons and dendritic fields in the primary visual area of the cortex of the cat.

1. Thalamic afferents; 2. intra-cortical afferents. (Figure kindly supplied by Mr. D. A. Sholl.)

fore excites neurons lying within a considerable volume of cortex (about 0·1 mm.³). Such a volume would contain about 5,000 neurons, most of them stellate cells (Fig. 197). There is therefore very great overlap between the volumes that are innervated by neighbouring afferent fibres. At present it is not possible to visualize the patterns in which the cortical neurons will be set into action by these overlapping inputs. The dendrites of each cortical cell extend over 350 μ and they share a volume of tissue with the dendrites of over 4,000 other cells.

It is even harder to say how excitation will proceed away from the primary foci of excitation. The number of possible pathways provided by the axons of the stellate cells and the recurrent axons and collaterals of the pyramids is very great. Moreover, influences are continually reaching each section of the cortex from other cortical areas near and far, as well as from the thalamus. The intracortical afferents (set 2 of Figs. 196 and 197) reach mostly to the surface layers and each divides into branches extending over at least 150 μ. Each therefore may influence many cells, because the majority of the pyramidal cells send apical dendrites to the surface layers.

The total number of afferent fibres reaching any region of the cat's visual cortex is 25,000/mm.[2], whereas there are 75,000 efferent fibres leaving it to proceed to other parts of the cortex or to non-cortical regions (Fig. 197). At present we can only form a vague idea how the output of impulses along these fibres is related to the input. In order to obtain a clearer picture we need more knowledge of the synaptic arrangements by which the incoming fibres influence the cortical cells. If we knew the means by which effective contacts are made in the intricate neuropil that occupies so much of the space within the cortex we might be able to understand how particular input patterns interact with the activities already going on that constitute the cortical information store.

11. The layers of the cortex

The branches of the cortical cells are arranged in different ways in different parts of the cortex. No doubt the particular patterns are related to the functions performed but at present we have no clear understanding of the relationship. It is convenient to describe each section of cortex as composed of layers of cells and fibre plexuses with differing directions and densities. The boundaries between some of the layers are sharp but others grade into each other and the number of layers recognized is arbitrary. Layer 1 at the cortical surface consists of fibres only, including the apical dendrites of pyramidal cells, and fibres that probably originate from other cortical cells, near and far. Layers 2 and 3 are known as the supragranular layers and they consist of cells with dendrites ramifying near the cell body. Their axons mostly form association fibres proceeding to other parts of the cortex.

Layer 4, the granular layer, is the region of termination of many of the afferents that reach any given area from the thalamus. They break up into fibres interlacing with the numerous horizontal basal dendrites of the cells of the layer, which are mostly stellate cells, with some pyramidal cells among them. The axons of these latter proceed down into the white matter, mainly to other parts of the cortex; recurrent branches from them proceed to the more superficial layers.

There is a sharp break between layers 4 and 5 and the latter (sub-granular layer) contains large pyramidal cells, whose axons constitute the main efferent pathway of the cortex. Their apical dendrites proceed to layer 1 and the axons give off collaterals also reaching upwards. These cells are especially well developed in the motor cortex, where they are known as the *Betz cells* (p. 438).

The innermost part of the cortex (layer 6) contains some stellate cells with very short processes, others have dendrites reaching to the surface and there are axons conducting both inwards and outwards.

Different parts of the cortex show considerable differences in structure. The archicortex and palaeocortex lack the granular and supragranular layers, presumably in connexion with the fact that they receive cortical and olfactory fibres, the missing layers being those that in other parts of the cortex receive the afferent fibres from the thalamus. The granular and supragranular regions are well developed in the parts of the cortex that receive the specific afferent thalamic fibres, for instance the striate cortex (area 17) of the occipital pole, which receives the optic radiation. Conversely in the motor area (precentral gyrus, area 4) the subgranular layers and the Betz cells are well marked.

12. Functioning of the cerebral cortex

Such a description only gives the main types of cell and others are found; the cortex has a network of fibres of confusing complexity. We still understand too little of its mode of operation to decide which of the many possible connexions are significant. The cerebral cortex exercises profound effects directly or indirectly on the activities of nearly all parts of the body. It is not too much to say that it is responsible for guiding the whole system of actions by which the life of a mammal is maintained. Changes in the outside world or within the animal set up patterns of disturbance within the cortex, which initiate activities that continue until the disturbance ceases. The flow of information from the receptors combines with that stored in the cortex, producing by continual trial and error a stable life for the individual.

Any analysis of cortical function in terms of single neuronal chains is misleading since the whole sheet of tissue is essentially a mechanism for reacting to patterns of stimulation rather than to localized influences. The arrangement provides the possibility not only of direct excitation of the efferent fibres by the afferents but also for the setting up, through the smaller neurons, of subsidiary chains of excitation, which may continue for a long time (see Burns, 1955).

Some progress can be made by studying the electrical activity that can be recorded in the cortex after stimulation of afferent fibres (see Cragg, 1954). A single microelectrode placed within the pia of the visual cortex records first a positive then a negative wave after stimula-

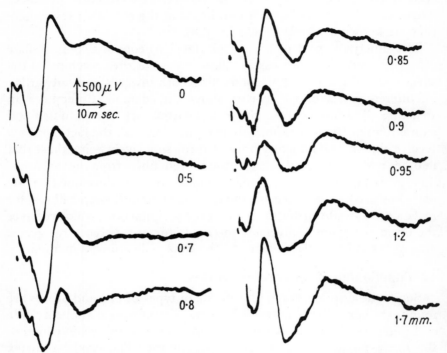

Fig. 198. Electrical changes recorded in the visual cortex of the cat, following electrical stimulation of the optic nerve. A single steel microelectrode with tip diameter about 5μ is inserted to the depths shown. When this electrode becomes positive with respect to an indifferent electrode the trace records downwards. There is therefore a reversal of response as the electrode moves through the cortex.
(Figure kindly supplied by Dr. B. G. Cragg.)

tion of the optic nerve (Fig. 198). A deeper electrode records an opposite sequence of events. The afferent fibres entering from the thalamus branch mainly in the fourth layer; those from other cortical cells in the more superficial layers. The first response recorded following optic nerve stimulation is probably the synchronized synaptic potential of the first neurons activitated, but no exact interpretation is possible.

It is too early yet to describe the means by which the cortex functions. It may be altogether wrong to try to analyse its activities in terms of conduction along individual pathways, which are isolated only in our imagination. The densely interlaced fibres of the neuropil between the cells may work in ways that cannot be summarized in terms of simple conduction from place to place. Signs of the activity of the cortex are provided by electrodes in contact with the surface, which record rhythmical changes of potential known as the electro-encephalogram (E.E.G.). These waves can be recorded even through the skull of an intact human individual and they show striking changes with the activity of the brain. In a man asleep or resting with the eyes shut there is recorded from the region of the occipital cortex a rather regular rhythm (α rhythm) at about ten beats a second. On waking or the beginning of intellectual activity, especially of a visual sort, this rhythm breaks up into less regular changes, varying with the person and the type of computation that is involved. These electrical changes give a valuable means of following the brain's activities but we cannot at present say in detail what they mean. When a stimulus is fired into a known area of the cortex, say the visual by illumination of a small retinal area, it produces a local change of electrical activity, followed by irradiation to neighbouring areas. Evidently the system depends in some way on the projection of patterns of impulses on to a surface that is itself already in a state of activity and hence acts as a selector.

13. Learning and conditioned reflexes

By some means the cortex allows mammals to select appropriate responses corresponding to fine differences between the patterns of change around, and to record past sequences that have been of significance for life (Hebb, 1949; Malmo, 1954). These faculties of discrimination and learning are linked. The brain selects for attention the features of the world that past experience has shown to be important for the needs and interests of the individual. Yet most of the study of the properties of the cortex has concentrated not on its powers of selection but on the learning process and especially on the formation of simple associations of stimuli, as in the *conditioned reflex* of Pavlov. A stimulus producing a particular effect is said to be an *unconditioned stimulus*, thus the presence of meat in the mouth produces salivation in the dog, by a set of cerebral connexions that are established very early in life. The sound of a bell does not normally produce salivation, but if on a number of occasions a bell is rung shortly before the giving of meat, then it will be found that salivation follows when the bell is rung alone, the sound has become a *conditioned stimulus* for the response.

By his careful technique for quantitative study of the amount of saliva produced Pavlov was able to throw much light on the circumstances in which this association or 'conditioning' occurs. He showed that in addition to the *simultaneous conditioned response*, in which the conditioning stimulus continues during application of the unconditioned it is possible to set up *trace conditioned responses*, in which there are intervals, even of several minutes, between the stimuli. When the conditioned stimulus was given alone the response later occurred with a delay equal to that which had elapsed between the stimuli during training. Loss (inhibition) of the association follows either from repeated failure to reinforce it (*experimental* or '*internal*' *inhibition*) or by presentation of some strong third stimulus such as a loud noise ('*external*' *inhibition*). The response may again be elicited some hours later after either sort of inhibition has died away. A conditioned reflex established to a particular stimulus will also extend to other similar stimuli, a phenomenon called generalization, but if only one specific stimulus is reinforced then discrimination occurs.

Pavlov interpreted his results by postulating a series of hypothetical brain processes. Any afferent stimulus is supposed to set up excitation at a cortical focus, followed by irradiation to neighbouring areas. The excitation then 'concentrates' back to the excited point and is followed everywhere by a phase of lowered excitability. Conditioning is supposed to be possible because the concentration will occur not only to the originally excited point but to any other point that is active at the time, for instance the point excited by the unconditioned stimulus. After several repetitions this somehow ensures that the excitation 'flows' so readily from the conditioned to unconditioned locus that it produces the response appropriate to the latter. The various phenomena of inhibition are explained by appropriate timing of the excitatory and inhibitory processes and there is a 'top effect' of unpredictable behaviour to explain any residual occurrences not otherwise forecasted by the theory!

This set of hypotheses reduces the observed phenomena to order but it makes no serious attempt to correlate them with known cerebral events. There is no experimental evidence that repeated excitation of any two loci together leads to any 'flow' between them such as Pavlov postulates. The attempt to 'explain' the phenomena of association in terms of such a simple hydrodynamic analogy fails to make use of all the recent advances in physics and communication engineering.

14. Response to formed stimuli

Moreover, Pavlov's theory at best will only cover the association of 'stimuli' of simple unitary form, such as ringing a bell and tasting meat. It is not obvious what such associating has in common with the acts of discrimination and selection by which, for instance, a man learns to respond to spoken or written symbols. In such acts the response is not to a single 'stimulus' but to a particular ratio of such excitations, say, to a given pattern of light and shade or to a tune. Moreover, the discrimination is not necessarily performed on any particular part of the sensory surface. A figure is recognized as that of man whether it is seen near or far away and when it is cast on various parts of the macula of the retina. A man or animal can learn with one eye and hand to do some act and can then perform it with another limb. The representation that is set up must occur in some portion of the nervous tissue that is accessible from all parts.

The fact that so many fibres reach the cortex from different sources suggests that its function is to allow interaction between the signals in all these fibres. This implies that opportunities are allowed for the interaction of the impulses arriving along various lines from different parts of one receptor system, say the parts of the retina, or from different receptors. It is this interaction that enables us to respond appropriately to the distributions or pattern of changes around, that is to say to shapes or configurations. Along the pathways from the receptors many opportunities for such interaction are provided, for example, in the retina and the thalamus. It is probable that at these lower levels the interaction helps to ensure that a particular pattern of distribution of excitation is appropriately reproduced on the cortex. Within the cortex opportunity is probably provided for each excited point to interact with a wide variety of other points. Thus it has been shown that activation of any one small region in the primary visual area (striate) of the monkey is followed by activity in all parts of the surrounding parastriate area (Fig. 192). Obviously since each point spreads its influence in this way there are wide possibilities of interaction.

15. The nature of the cortical information store

Until some more powerful methods for study of the brain are available it is only possible to speculate about the way in which the organism selects and responds to shapes, tunes, or other *'formed stimuli'* (*'Gestalten'*). During learning some change occurs that gives the power to act in a way that was not possible before. It is the business of neurologists to discover the nature of this change. It will probably be found by consideration of the changes in more than one part of the cortex, perhaps dispersed throughout it and perhaps in other parts of the brain as well. The fact that so many centres exchange sets of fibres suggests some type of reciprocating system as part of the basis of memory.

The study of association perhaps tends to obscure the fact that learning is the selection of the responses that are of value to the organism by satisfying its needs. The ringing of the bell, not by itself of significance, only becomes firmly established as a provoker of salivation if it proves to be useful as a sign of approaching food. We can imagine that the occurrence together of a particular set of attributes and of a 'satisfactory' result may set up conditions within the central system that would enable the conditioned stimulus alone to produce a response not given before. Although we cannot specify in detail how this happens it is not impossible that the process of learning begins with the starting up of cycles of activity within the brain. It seems likely that the memory consists in part of some form of deposit or 'print' left upon the cerebral tissue by past events. It is not easy to see exactly what form such a print may take but there is some evidence that the size of nerve-cells and fibres is influenced by their activity (p. 337). The cortex at birth is a system within which many pathways are equally possible. It is by virtue of this large range of possibilities that it is able to receive and store such a wide range of information from the environment. To say that it does this is indeed another way of stating that it has few capacities determined by the information received by heredity.

The patterns that are cast upon the cortex cannot at first be 'interpreted'. A baby does not discriminate between shapes and if a person who has been born blind later receives his sight by an operation he is at first unable to make proper use of his eyes. The capacity to give distinct responses to particular configurations of stimuli has to be learned. It is possible only after the cortex has acquired a store of information, perhaps by the growth of some of its cells and fibres and thus the formation of sets of preferential pathways for excitation. Particular patterns of excitation occur in association with the achievement of biologically satisfactory results and in some way the 'memory' of these is preserved. We may suppose that each set of attributes occurring in such a way as to produce a satisfactory pattern causes the setting up of particular types of reverberating circuit. These may last only for a few seconds or minutes but they leave behind them some trace of changed metabolism in particular sets of cells. Such 'growth' changes, even if very small, will alter the probable course of future activity in the presence of any particular stimulus configuration. So the brain gradually loses its first randomness. The animal learns from the information it has received to act in the particular ways that are likely to ensure survival if the future resembles the past.

The information thus stored in the cortex provides the animal or man with 'knowledge', that is to say with a system for forecasting the probable result of each situation as it arises. The cortex after it has learned contains a sort of model of the situations that have been experienced. The model represents the particular world in which the animal has lived and provides a means by which, as each configuration of stimuli is presented, behaviour can be initiated that is appropriate to the probable outcome of events.

16. The comparison of brains with machines

We find it difficult to visualize how such a system operates because we cannot yet make machines that can store information of comparable complexity and calculate probabilities from them. Yet the development of calculating machines has made it possible to imagine that machines for the recognition of patterns could be produced. The machines that have been built hitherto have mostly served to perform the limited operations of addition and subtraction. Their special powers have been due to the fact that they can work very fast and hence perform calculations that would take many years without them. For example, electronic computers can calculate the probable outcome of the progress of a series of partially correlated events, such as are involved in making forecasts of future weather conditions. These machines already provide us with useful comparisons that help in analysis of brain action. However, the principles that they use are certainly not identical with those of the brain.

A major difference between these machines and the nervous system is that the latter uses a great number of channels. The memory of most calculating machines depends on the exact specification of the positions of events in a time series, such as is provided by sending impulses very fast round a self re-exciting channel. Conduction in the nervous system is slower and less precisely timed. In the brain large amounts of information are received and stored by the presence of very numerous channels, each alone carrying information at a low rate. Appropriate response by the whole assembly depends upon displaying the information of these multiple channels in space, on the cortical surface, allowing suitable patterns to develop. No means are at present available for describing how this occurs. The processes involved may be comparable to those by which the molecules in a magnet influence each other to produce domains in which the state of each depends upon the others (Cragg and Temperley, 1954). A pattern of domains consisting of cells in a particular state of excitability may be set up following the occurrence of each set of impulses from the periphery. The domain would then move through the whole system in a way that would depend upon the properties remaining from previous events, including patterns of particular cell sizes and lengths of dendrites and axons. The output of impulses from the precentral and other motor areas would then depend upon the particular courses that are taken by the movement of the domains of membrane potentials, and hence of excitability and capacity to set up propagated action potentials.

It is not possible at present to make this picture specific but it may provide a model that is on the right lines. The electro-encephalogram shows that waves of change of state move about within the cortex. Knowledge about specific pathways is very meagre but there is evidence that the adult cortex is not an unspecified diffuse network. The cells are of different sizes and shapes, and the fact that a large cell occurs among small ones suggests that the properties of each have been determined by local influences rather than by the position of a cell in a field. Although all the cells have a common pattern each has a distinct arrangement of its dendrites.

Sholl and Uttley (1953) have recently shown that a machine for the recognition of patterns can be constructed on the surprisingly simple principle of the connexion of all its input channels with all the units that store memories of actions in the past. Such wide connexion would involve an enormous number of interconnecting fibres, greater even than is present in the brain. Nevertheless it is probable that the making of particular connexions within systems that are at first randomly related is the basis for the setting up of memories in the brain. It is interesting to find along the pathways of the receptor system arrangements that ensure wide dispersal of effects. Thus an axon arising in a given part of area 17 can end in any part of area 18. This system does not ensure that each input channel to area 18 is connected with all units but it allows any channel to be connected with any unit at random. Moreover, it is suggestive that at the points of arrival of input channels in the cortex there are numerous stellate cells, whose influence may be to spread activity widely from any point. From these clues we cannot fully understand the workings of the cerebral calculating machine; but we can see some indications that by using very large numbers of units, connected at random, there can be registration of the various combinations of afferent impulses that occur and this provides an information store with which future presentations can be compared so that useful forecasts are made.

At present this is little more than a formal account of cerebral activities. We know nothing of the details of the cerebral patterns or how they are established. However, this account takes into consideration the facts that we do know about the cortex, for instance that there are great numbers of input channels, leading to great numbers of cells, among which there are vast possibilities of interconnexion. Moreover, by dealing with probabilities, such an account gives us some hope of being able to speak more satisfactorily in statistical terms about this system with its large number of components. It is perhaps as well at present not to try to be too specific, the arrangement in the brain is so utterly different from that of any man-made machine that attempts at close comparison may be only misleading unless great care is taken in the choice of words, of logical methods, and of models.

XXIV

RECEPTOR ORGANS

1. Living measuring instruments

THE problem of finding terminology adequate to describe the actions of the sense organs is obviously especially difficult—for they themselves provide the information by which this and all other questions are decided. It has been usual to define the activities of these organs in terms of the sensory experiences to which they give rise. This is a form of the 'person language' used for describing living activities (p. 4) and it may be that for some purposes it is useful. However, following the principles laid down in Chapter I, we shall try to describe the actions of the 'sense organs' in the language that is used for description of artefacts that have been devised to supplement them—namely *measuring instruments* (see Granit, 1955). Every sense organ serves to measure some condition in the environment or to measure a change in a condition. In everyday language we say that our sense organs 'tell us' (note the person language) about the intensity, say of a light, or that the intensity has changed, constituting a 'stimulus'. Put otherwise we may say that the function of the receptors is to measure either the intensity or the extent of change of conditions. This is a more useful way to start than by saying that 'sense organs respond to stimuli'.

The eye measures intensity of light and its wave-length and also the distribution of patterns of change of light intensity, enabling the body to react to shapes. The skin measures mechanical movement and the ear is also a mechano-receptor, able to detect the minute air movements that we call sounds. The nose and tongue measure chemical concentrations, the skin measures temperature, and so on.

The measuring instruments that man has invented provide us with powerful extensions of our own receptors and also with a complete new language for the description of living measuring instruments. In the first place these artefacts give us a set of standards to which we can refer. We can speak much more precisely about weights, movements, or light changes if these are measured in c.g.s. units by instruments than if they are assessed only by the human receptors. Moreover, with the very exact measuring instruments, such as electronic valve amplifiers, we can record the changes that go on within the body accompanying the operation of the receptors themselves. It is now known, from the work of Keith Lucas, Adrian (1953), and many others, that the receptors all operate by setting up distinct signals, the nerve impulses, in the afferent nerve-fibres (p. 338). These nerve impulses are, as a first approximation, all alike in any one nerve-fibre, but they differ in frequency according to the state of affairs at the receptor cell surface. We can therefore centre our study of all receptors around investigation of the conditions under which the receptor cells set up nerve impulses. Whether the animal or man actually responds by moving or speaking is, however, very seldom determined by the actions of a single receptor fibre. The receptor surfaces are served by numerous nerve-fibres and the impulses in them interact at various levels as they pass through the nervous system.

We can therefore ask the following questions about any receptor system:

1. Under what conditions does it set up nerve impulses in the nerve-fibres leading away from it?
2. What are the frequencies of the nerve impulses under various conditions?
3. What are the spatial relations of the various receptors and their afferent nerve-fibres, and what opportunities are provided for interaction of impulses within the nervous system?

As we become more adequately informed about these matters we begin to be able to give a satisfactory account even of the most complicated feats of measurement, such as the reaction to minute differences between sounds or shapes that we employ in hearing or reading.

2. Response to environmental change

Living organisms are composed of polyphasic physico-chemical systems whose steady states are responsive to changes in the external environment. Colloidal solutions are easily changed by such factors as stirring, shaking, heating, illumination, or the actions of small amounts of other chemicals. Similarly even unicellular organisms are affected by changes in the mechanical, photic, or chemical conditions of their surroundings. The responses of organisms differ from those of non-living systems in that they are in the main such as will lead to a continuation of life; they are adaptive. During the course of evolution there has been produced from the responses of simple living systems an amazingly sensitive arrangement by which minute changes, occurring perhaps at a great distance from the surface of the animal, are measured and lead to readjustments that ensure its continuance. A hawk swooping to seize a lizard that has moved in the grass below shows one extreme development of the system by which the changes in the incident pattern of light have been linked up with the action system of the whole animal to produce forecasts that are effective in maintaining life.

Jennings (1906) has drawn attention with some surprise to the fact

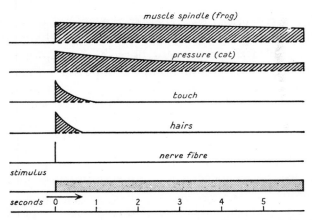

FIG. 199. Duration of firing of impulses by various types of end-organ, and a single nerve-fibre, to a continuous stimulus. (Adrian, *Basis of Sensation*, London, 1928.)

that *Amoeba* reacts to nearly all the types of change that affect a man. It is sensitive to heat, light, touch, vibration, and to chemical change. Yet light is a 'stimulus' for a man in a more extended sense than for *Amoeba*. The reaction of a protozoan when there is a change in intensity of some factor in its surroundings is usually limited to the setting in action of the motor system that operates to produce random avoiding reactions, which ultimately lead it to optimum conditions. The protozoan may be said to be a system that can receive only a minimal amount of information from its surroundings. If the only action that it can give is the avoiding reaction then it is certain that every effective change in the surroundings will produce that response. The only alternative is whether or not the avoiding reaction will be produced and only one unit or 'bit' of information passes through the system at a time.

Proceeding up the animal scale there is a great increase in the number of possible alternative actions and correspondingly an increase in the amount of information that can be transmitted. When a change occurs in the neighbourhood of a man he may move in various ways, either towards or away from the place where the change occurred. Instead of reacting only to a change in intensity he may respond in particular ways to differing patterns of intensities; the significance of a diamond is not only in the fact that it reflects light. Decision is made between a great variety of possible responses. In other words much information flows rapidly through the organism.

3. The peripheral receptors.

The invention of electronic valve amplifiers has revolutionized knowledge of the receptor organs by showing that each receptor functions by sending to the nervous system a report of some condition in terms of a code of nerve impulses (p. 343). Each receptor thus consists of cells specialized in their sensitivity to one of the types of change to which all living tissues respond. The response of the receptor cell then serves to set up impulses in the nerve-fibre or fibres connected with it.

Thus the muscle spindle whose response is shown in Fig. 200A sets up a train of nerve impulses whose frequency provides a measure of the load (or length) of the spindle. Detailed study shows that the frequency is proportional to the decadic logarithm of the load. Many receptors discharge continuously in this way, the frequency serving to report the level or intensity of some external condition. In other receptors the discharge increases when the intensity at the receptor surface increases but the new high rate of discharge is not maintained. This decline in frequency is known as *adaptation* and is, of course, prominent in those receptors that signal a change of condition ('stimulus'). Following bending of a single hair the subject reports the sensation of touch only for a short period: the receptor system adapts rapidly. Conversely the muscle-spindles discussed above adapt very slowly (Fig. 199).

The relations of the receptor cells to the nerve-fibres vary. The 'free nerve-endings' in the skin are not accompanied by any specially sensitive cells. Here the ends of the nerve-fibres themselves are the receptor organ. Nerve-fibres can be activated by mechanical and chemical changes and some at least of these free nerve endings send impulses that serve as the signals reporting a trauma; accompanying the sensation we identify as pain (p. 478). The receptor cells in the olfactory epithelium themselves give rise to nerve-fibres running into the brain (p. 521). On the other hand the cells in the tongue that are responsible for 'taste' have no nerve-fibres themselves, but around them are the endings of nerve-fibres whose cell bodies lie in the cranial ganglia (p. 521). The rods and cones of the retina show yet another arrangement. They have short processes that connect with the dendrites of nerve-cells lying close to them. The sensitive cells are in this case derivatives of the brain, from which the eye develops (p. 782), and they make immediate connexion with other nerve-cells in the retina.

4. Mode of activation of receptors

The changes to which the mammalian receptors respond may all be classified as (a) mechanical, (b) chemical, (c) thermal, or (d) photic. Each receptor system contains a terminal apparatus sensitive to change of one of these four types. Thus the receptors for touch, pressure, and sound all depend upon mechanical deformation. Chemical means of excitation are employed by the receptors for smell and taste and in certain internal organs sensitive to changes in the composition of the blood. Thermal energy changes stimulate the receptors that serve to measure temperature, and change of electromagnetic vibrations of a certain wave-length are the basis of vision, the light changes in that case serving to alter the condition of suitably photosensitive molecules in the rods or cones.

The next question is how does the mechanism that provides the specific sensitivity of the end-organ to its adequate stimulus serve to set up nerve impulses? Although the answer is not fully known it is probable that the impulse discharge is initiated and maintained by a depolarization of the receptor cells. This depolarizes the fine nerve terminals nearby so that they propagate nerve impulses. Such *generator potentials* have been recorded from many receptors. Thus in the muscle-spindle Katz has recorded a depolarization within the end-organ itself, which increases with the load. The number of impulses per second in the associated nerve-fibres is proportional to this depolarization (Fig. 200 B). As we have seen above the frequency of impulses is proportional to the logarithm of the load on a muscle-spindle. Presumably, therefore, the generator potential is also proportional to the logarithm of the load, though this has not been satisfactorily demonstrated experimentally.

Generator potentials are probably also involved in the setting up of nerve impulses by photoreceptors (p. 497) and in the cochlea of the ear (p. 518) and it may be that all receptors function by translating the external change first into a given level of depolarization of the receptor cell.

It is not yet certain whether the phenomenon of adaptation indi-

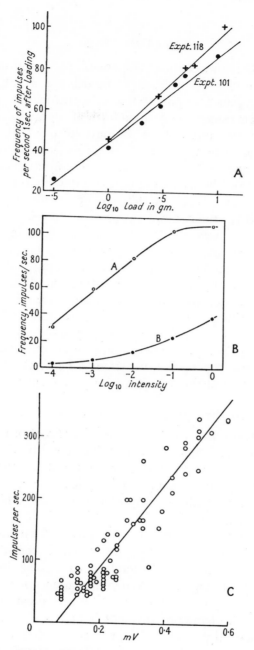

FIG. 200. A. Discharge of frog muscle-spindle under different loads.
(Matthews, *J. Physiol.* **71**, 64, 1931.)

B. Relationship between frequency of impulses and intensity of stimulating light in the frog.
(Hartline and Graham, *J. cell. comp. Physiol.* **1**, 277, 1932.)

The intensity is in arbitrary units. *A*, initial maximal discharge; *B*, 3·5 sec. after illumination.

c. Frog muscle-spindle. Relation between frequency of impulses and local depolarization.
(Katz, *J. Physiol.* **111**, 261, 1950.)

cates a change in the mechanism responsible for the specific sensitivity of the receptor (for example, the photochemical substance in the retina) or in the generator potential or other mechanism by which this specific change is transformed into a form of energy capable of setting up impulses in the nerve-fibres. It may be that both are involved. Nerve-fibres themselves show a process of accommodation, so that the impulse frequency declines under constant conditions (p. 464). Each impulse is followed by a process that counteracts the setting up of a fresh impulse. Yet a single stretch receptor may discharge 300 impulses a second for many seconds. Clearly there is some mechanism in receptors that maintains firing in the nerve-fibres in spite of accommodation. This is indeed necessary if the receptor is to provide a measure of a given level of intensity. One suggestion is that the numerous terminal branches that are often found at the ends of the afferent nerve-fibres provide the mechanism. In a muscle-spindle each afferent terminal twig generates small non-propagating local potentials, which summate at the points where they join (see Fatt and Katz, 1951). Even if there is accommodation of some of the nerve terminals under the generator potential, yet there are enough of them to allow repeated excitation at the junction point, on a statistical basis.

5. Stimulus and threshold

Receptor organs are thus able to signal a report of the condition in their neighbourhood or a change in that condition. In the current phrase they are said to show responses to stimuli. A stimulus may thus be defined as a change that is of sufficient magnitude to produce variation in the frequency of impulses in the nerve-fibres connected with a receptor.

The lowest intensity at which a receptor will change its discharge is called the *threshold*, but the rate at which the intensity change takes place affects this level. Generally speaking the slower the change the less the stimulating effect. When operating under suitable conditions the sensitivity of receptors may be very great. The human eye can respond to a change of incident light from zero to only a few photons per second per mm^2. One rod can probably be activated by a single photon and is thus at the maximum possible sensitivity for any light detector (p. 494). The ear is also able to respond to exceedingly minute forces (p. 515).

In any receptor field the degree of intensity change that can be discriminated varies with the absolute intensity at which the discrimination is made. In general at greater intensities the receptors become less sensitive, so that the differences needed to allow discrimination are greater. This relationship was first noticed by Weber and later investigated by Fechner (1862), who expressed it that if I and $I+\Delta I$ are the intensities that can just be discriminated, then

$$\frac{\Delta I}{I} = k \, . \, \Delta S.$$

Fechner believed that ΔS can be regarded as a minute unit of sensation S, such that $S = a \log I + b$. In fact, that as stimulus strength increases in geometrical progression some feature of sensation increases arithmetically. There has been much criticism of this law and there are exceptions to it, but it still holds good as an approximation and can be related to modern studies of the receptors. Thus we have seen above that the rate of discharge of a muscle-spindle afferent nerve-fibre increases with the logarithm of the load.

6. The frequency code

Nerve impulses have now been recorded in single fibres proceeding from muscle-spindles, cochlea, retina, touch organs, pain organs, and many other receptors. It is safe to say that receptors function by reporting external conditions in terms of a frequency code of nerve impulses. Changes in incident intensity are thus not recorded by the body as changes in the amplitude or duration of the signals set up by the receptor. The nerve-fibre connected with a given receptor cell carries impulses that are essentially all alike and vary only in frequency. The maximum frequency reached may be 1,000 impulses per second for some receptors recording vibrations, but is usually considerably less.

Each nerve-fibre can carry only one sort of signal and therefore it is clear that response to a wide variety of types of change is achieved only by having many different types of receptor, each 'tuned', as it were, to respond to a particular change and sending signals in its own nerve-fibre. This is the 'doctrine of specific nervous energies'; it may be stated in the form that any given nerve-fibre, however excited, gives rise only to its own characteristic type of activity in the central nervous system. The activation of each receptor is therefore reported by man as yielding a characteristic sensation. When the elements of the retina are stimulated by a blow we record a sensation of light, not of pressure. It is gradually becoming apparent, however, that the particular response produced by the brain following arrival of impulses from any given receptor cell varies according to the activity in neighbouring cells, and is greatly influenced by the memory system that the organism has acquired (p. 457). The doctrine of specific nerve energies is true in so far as each single channel from the receptor cells is only normally activated by one form of external energy. But the multiplicity of channels and of their modes of combination is so great that it is not easy to forecast the response to activity of any one channel. Here, as elsewhere in biology, we have to find ways not only of acquiring knowledge about the activity of single units but also of forecasting the actions of many of them in combination.

Responsiveness to the details of the changes in the world around is ensured by the presence of several quantitatively different types of receptor within each of the main modalities. Thus the eye includes the rods, sensitive to low intensities of light, also cones of several types, with maximum sensitivity at various wave-lengths, which enable us to distinguish colours (p. 501).

The specific effects of the discharge of the nerve-fibre connected to a given receptor surface therefore depend on the central connexions rather than on any particular quality of its impulses. Yet there are characteristic differences between the impulses set up in different afferent nerve-fibres. The peripheral nerve-trunks contain fibres of a wide variety of sizes (p. 347) and the impulses of each sensory (and motor) system are conducted in fibres of a particular size and therefore travel at a characteristic velocity. The afferent impulses differ in other respects besides velocity, for instance, in duration. The characteristic patterns of response are produced by variation in the combinations that result when the impulses reach central neurons. The significant features of the impulse discharges from receptor surfaces are mainly the frequency and velocity and these, together with the spatial distribution of their connexions peripherally and centrally, determine the result of bombardment of the nerve-centres following any particular peripheral change.

7. Overlap and the information content of the channels

A characteristic feature of the organization of the nervous system is the overlap between conducting pathways, both peripherally and centrally. Thus many retinal elements are connected with a single optic nerve-fibre. In man there are about 6 million cones and 125 million rods, but only 1 million optic nerve-fibres. At the other end of the system each nerve-fibre arriving in the visual cortex may stimulate any among some 5,000 neurons in whose dendritic fields its terminations lie. Clearly the operation of the nervous system does not depend upon a technique of reproduction similar to that of photography or television, where the image is transmitted piecemeal. The overlapping would be highly deleterious to such a system.

In the simpler parts of the nervous system a motor response may be produced when impulses are set up in relatively few afferent fibres. Moreover, the magnitude of the response may be determined by the frequency of the impulses. Thus the amount of contraction produced in the flexor reflex (p. 354) depends on the numbers of motor neurons activated and the frequency of their firing, which in turn depend upon the number of afferents excited and *their* frequencies. In this case, therefore, the organism may be said to measure the stimulus intensity by interpreting the frequency code in the afferent fibres.

This occurs in the parts of the nervous system in which the afferent fibres are connected with relatively few efferent channels. Impulses in the afferent channels thus decide only the extent to which a given reflex mechanism with which they are connected is operated. In other words the channels carry relatively little information because they control decision between few alternatives. The more elaborate receptor systems, such as the eye, may influence many effector systems. Any one of many responses may be made following input to the C.N.S. from the retina. We can therefore say that the optic nerve-fibres carry a great deal of information, because they participate in the making of decisions between many possible alternatives.

This greater complexity of response to environment is made possible by the specialization of certain parts of the body of the metazoan for response to particular stimuli and the linking of the changes produced in these receptor organs with an elaborate pattern of activity already going on in the brain of the animal. Thus the light from the diamond interacts with the optical and nervous system of the man, causing him to react in devious and subtle ways such as shall lead him to acquire the jewel.

8. The probability of a response and the rhythm of life

Such specialization of response has been achieved by the setting aside of areas of tissue that have high sensitivity to certain of the changes around the organism. At the same time there has been a development of suitable central mechanisms allowing response to elaborate patterns of change. This appears clearly in the case of the set of signals that accompany pain. The hereditary system provides receptors of rather simple structure, which discharge when conditions occur that grossly damage the tissues (p. 478). If these conditions continue, the reaction of the body is such as to produce, if possible, a cessation of the trauma. These reactions often consist in a series of sudden jerks and writhings in various directions, often at random, comparable with the avoiding reaction of protozoans. When impulses signalling the occurrence of trauma arrive at the central nervous system the result is that the part or limb concerned is drawn away from the source of trauma. The probability that this avoiding response will be given is so high that we can forecast accurately that it will be shown by any intact individual of the species. The amount of information conveyed by the nerve-fibres under these conditions is therefore low. Yet in higher animals the response is not completely invariant and may depend upon the circumstances, especially in man. In social animals sounds may be produced when a pain stimulus is applied and the sounds may serve to warn other individuals and in the case of man to bring others to the rescue. It is interesting that trauma is not accompanied by sound production in species that lack the appropriate social organization, for example, grasshoppers or frogs. In races of men with well-developed communication systems the 'response' to pain even includes discussions and the writing of books on the problem of pain, helping in the preparation against future damaging agents.

In higher animals life consists of a continual series of readjustments, many of them rhythmic. Study of these sequences of action is the essential requisite for investigation of the action of the receptors and measurement of the amount of information that they provide. Unfortunately we have at present few investigations of this sort and little knowledge of the rhythms of animal lives or of the way in which differences between them may be classified. Receptor action heralds each new phase, for example, nerve impulses are set up in the walls of an empty stomach. These impulses serve to initiate the search for food, but since this is a regular occurrence we may say that these impulses, like those of pain, provide only a small amount of information. The way in which food is sought may also follow a regular pattern, but there is probably more variability here than in the recurrence of food-seeking. The great amounts of information that ensure stability in spite of this variation come from the receptors that signal the presence of objects likely to provide food even when they are at a distance from the body. As we study species with more and more complex ways of life we find greater and greater variation in the way the rhythm of life is controlled. More and more information is used to maintain stability by minor or major changes in routine. It becomes more and more difficult to forecast the course of behaviour of any given individual.

As each reaction runs its course, for example, as the animal seeks its food and eats it, the initial discharges die down and are replaced either by inactivity or perhaps by discharges that lead the organism to remain in the condition it has reached. Such impulses could be called those of 'pleasure', but to remain in a favourable state is in general to be inactive and there is a connexion between pain and change, the stimulants of activity. There is a contrast between these and pleasure and repose, the negative state of inactivity in which the organism is satisfied. Life tends to those conditions in which its continuance is most easily and completely ensured and the degree of activity is adjusted to this end; the organism reacts to threats to its continuance, produced either from within or from without.

It must be remembered that the receptor systems themselves are not passive agents that are only set into action in response to external change. Many of them discharge trains of impulses continually into the nervous system, for example, receptors both in the eye and the ear are continually active in this way and the effect of a 'stimulus' is to change their activity rather than to initiate it. The recognition of this 'spontaneous' activity of the receptors considerably alters one's view of the nature of the whole system. Together with the 'spontaneous' activity within the brain (p. 455) this may be the basis of much of the 'drive', which, as psychologists have long recognized, comes from within the organism (see Young, 1938). Indeed, there is now direct physiological evidence that the discharges of the receptors operate along specific pathways in the reticular system of the brain (p. 411) to 'arouse' the cortex. Cases have been reported of people whose afferent input became limited to very few sources (say one eye and one ear). When these channels were not stimulated the person fell asleep.

A still further complication is that there are *efferent* fibres running from the central nervous system to the receptors. The best-known example is the muscle-spindles, whose sensitivity is varied by discharges reaching them along efferent nerve-fibres (p. 370). But there are efferent fibres also in the optic nerve and they have been shown to alter the sensitivity of the retina.

If the receptors activate the C.N.S. and the latter sensitizes the receptors we obviously have a very complicated set of loops to consider. The effect of any pattern of external change will vary greatly according to the internal condition of the system; a fact with which we are all familiar. It is indeed hard to forecast the behaviour of living systems, but we can now begin to see the principles upon which they operate.

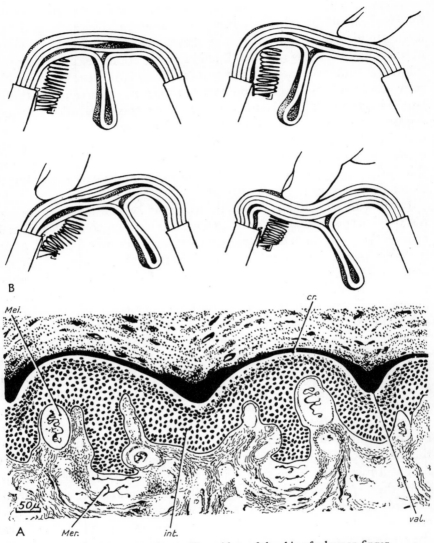

FIG. 201. A, Section across the papillary ridges of the skin of a human finger.

Cr. crest with soft keratin, *int.* intermediate ridge projecting into dermis; *Mer.* plexus of nerve-fibres including Merkel's corpuscles; *Mei.* Meissner's corpuscle in dermal papilla; *val.* valley composed of harder keratin.

B, Rubber model to show how the intermediate ridge may act as a magnifying lever and the Meissner's corpuscle as a receptor sensitive only to pressure along its axis. (After Cauna.)

XXV

RECEPTORS IN THE SKIN AND VISCERA

1. Information from the body surface

IT is obviously important for the body to provide appropriate reactions to events occurring close to the surface. Some of these are likely to be traumatic and a system of 'pain' nerve-fibres is present, whose central connexions, probably mainly laid down by heredity, determine that when such events occur there is withdrawal of the part or avoidance behaviour by the whole animal. On the other hand, some types of light touch produce movements that maintain the contact, for example, in animals that follow solid contacts in the dark, or in some forms of social and sexual behaviour. Moderate warmth may also elicit movement towards the source. The portions of the limbs that are in contact with the ground or other means of support provide information that is important for the maintenance of posture. Responses to the detailed pattern of contact are made possible by the special sensitive areas on the limbs (and sometimes tail) of primates and perhaps by other areas, such as the lips. Such reactions to the 'shape' of the object depend upon a more elaborate central organization than is involved in the responses to stimulation of pain receptors.

2. Receptors in the skin

The classification of the 'skin sensations' and identification of the receptors involved is in an unsatisfactory state (see Bishop, 1946, and Sanders, 1947). In man it is usual to recognize a number of different 'sensations', such as touch (light pressure), deep pressure, warmth, cold, quick pain, slow pain, and some others. Recent studies of the histology of the skin recognize only three types of nerve-fibre there. (1) The free nerve endings are fine fibres ending in the superficial layers of the dermis and perhaps extending into the epidermis. (2) The hair follicles are surrounded by nerve-fibres. (3) The organized nerve endings are whirls of nerve-fibres in the dermis, surrounded by a more or less elaborate capsule (Fig. 201). There is a continuous series from very simple whirls to large and elaborate ones.

The free nerve endings probably occur in all parts of the human skin. The hairy skin has hair endings but few or no organized endings.

The hairless skin of such regions as the lip or finger pad has numerous organized endings, which may perhaps be regarded as consisting of modified hair follicles. Until recently it was thought that each of the 'qualities' of sensation recorded by the skin depended upon a particular type of organized nerve ending. Further study has shown that many of the appearances that had been recorded are artefacts produced by the histological technique (Weddell and Sinclair, 1953).

The problem of skin receptors is that all of the qualities of sensation may be reported from an area such as the lobe of the ear that contains only free nerve endings and hair follicles (Hagen, *et al*, 1953). It is possible that there are differences in threshold between organs that look alike. An alternative and more probable view is that the response that is 'reported' depends upon whether a few isolated endings or those of a whole area are stimulated, in fact upon the pattern of activity that is set up. The nerve-fibres reach the skin through an elaborate plexus; individual fibres may supply a wide area and there is a complicated pattern of overlapping.

A further fact to be explained is that different areas of the skin appear to give different responses. Thus there are distinct 'spots' sensitive to touch, warmth, cold, and pain. Moreover, operations in which part of the spinal cord is severed show evidence that impulses for the different 'sensations' travel up distinct pathways. Pain can usually be prevented by severance of the lateral spino-thalamic tract (p. 427), leaving the other senses unimpaired.

No general solution of these difficulties is possible at present. They are partly due to dependence upon human subjective criteria for describing activity in the nervous system. Progress may come from considering the actual nerve impulses that are set up by particular sorts of change, and correlation of these with the behaviour that they produce.

3. Touch

On the hairy areas of the skin of man response to touch depends upon nerve-fibres wrapped around the base of the hairs; these act as levers to increase the effect of small movements near the skin surface in distorting the ends of the nerve-fibres. A measure of their efficiency in this respect is the fact that in order to stimulate the exposed end of a nerve-fibre in a nerve-trunk with an object weighing 0·2 gm. it is necessary to move the weight at 140 mm./sec., yet the skin can detect the same object moving at only 0·2 mm./sec. The sensitivity of such organs reaches its extreme development in the vibrissae of many mammals. These may be sufficiently sensitive to respond to small air movements and they thus become 'distance receptors', like the eye, nose, or ear.

A different aspect of the sense of touch is the power to distinguish patterns and qualities of incident movement. A distribution of receptors sufficiently dense to allow discrimination between patterns differing in fine details is achieved in some skin areas of primates, such as the fingers, where there are special organized nerve endings consisting of a few epidermal cells, associated with the nerve-fibres. The skin of these regions has a thick stratum corneum, which is folded into ridges. The keratin is soft over the crests of the ridges but harder in the valleys. From each crest a core or 'intermediate ridge' of keratin extends down into the dermis (Fig. 201). These ridges are probably connected with the receptor functions of the skin and two types of end organs are found. *Meissner's corpuscles* lie in papillae extending up into the ridges. They consist of a spiral arrangement of nerve-fibres that branch and end in knobs. Underneath the intermediate ridge lies a plexus of nerve-fibres with simpler knob-like endings (*Merkel's discs*). It is suggested that the soft skin of the ridge is readily deformed, producing movements of the intermediate ridge, which thus acts as a magnifying lever (Fig. 201). The Merkel's discs could therefore provide high-sensitivity touch receptors. The Meissner's corpuscles, on the other hand, are protected by the hard keratin from deformation except by pressure that coincides with their axes. They may thus provide the basis for tactile localization (see Cauna, 1954). Probably only a few of these corpuscles are innervated by the branches of each nerve-fibre, but the plexus is complicated and details of the pattern are not known. The power of 'two point discrimination' is so high that contacts one or a few millimetres apart are recognized as distinct by the finger tips. On the hairy portions of the skin the minimum distance at which points can be discriminated increases to a centimetre or more and presumably the branches of a single nerve-fibre here innervate a large area of skin.

The nerve-fibres in the skin pass through an elaborate plexus and the way in which the fibres in this plexus are arranged must be of great importance in determining the pattern of impulses projected centrally from stimulation of a given set of receptors in the skin.

The sense of pressure is not always easy to distinguish subjectively from touch; it depends on organs lying deeper in the dermis. Various special types of touch receptor occur on particular parts of the body surface, for example, the lips and the genitalia. Stimulation of these produces particular types of reaction, for instance, erection of the penis or clitoris.

4. Temperature receptors

The response to increase of temperature can be shown to be localized to discrete 'warm spots' in the skin and it is often said that the receptors involved are certain encapsulated endings, the 'corpuscles of Ruffini' (Fig. 3) (see Zotterman, 1953). Similarly the cold spots have been supposed to contain 'end bulbs of Krause'. Recent investigations have shown that areas of skin that contain no encapsulated endings may show responses to heat and cold as well as to touch and pain. The only nerves in the skin of the human external ear end either around the bulbs of the hairs or as fine 'free nerve endings'. Yet tests show the ear to be as sensitive to touch, pain, cold, and warmth as is the skin of the forearm or the front of the ring finger (Sinclair et al, 1952; Lele, 1954). The question of the occurrence and nature of specific receptors for each modality of skin sensation therefore remains open. It may be that the structures described by Ruffini and Krause are artefacts, tangles of nerve-fibres produced during the processes of fixation and staining.

5. Indicators of trauma, pain

It is necessary for homeostasis that the body be provided with receptors that report the occurrence of events likely to cause it damage (Weddell and Sinclair, 1953). These are abundant at the surface and are also found in many internal organs. The study of the 'sense of pain' is in a confused state, perhaps it may be clarified by considering that the body has two distinct ways of forecasting that a given situation is likely to be traumatic. The hereditary mechanism provides a set of pain fibres activated by any disruptive change, mechanical, electrical, thermal, or chemical. These fibres are connected with the motor system at the spinal level and signals in them produce withdrawal movements of the affected part with a high level of probability (p. 354). But the signals set up by traumatic events also reach to higher, cerebral, levels and there become associated with the visual, auditory, and other attributes of the situation, so that this may be avoided in the future. In man this latter type of forecasting of the likelihood of trauma is especially highly developed. The word 'painful' is used to describe all situations that are to be avoided, including those that the organism has learned to avoid as well as those depending directly upon stimulation of pain receptors, which produce withdrawal reactions.

The receptors of pain wherever they occur are fine nerve-fibres without special terminal capsules. They discharge when there is a mechanical, chemical, or thermal change of sufficient magnitude. In the skin there are numerous very fine fibres reaching to the outermost layers of the dermis and perhaps into the basal layers of the epidermis. Pain impulses are often conducted in fibres of low velocity, very small and non-myelinated. It may seem anomalous that the signals responsible for producing an avoidance reaction, say withdrawal of the hand from a hot object, travel more slowly than the signals of the proprioceptors of the muscles (p. 370). But the conduction-time in the nerve-trunks is a relatively small fraction of the total reflex time, even in a quick flexion reflex. It may be that the low velocity and long duration of the pain impulses has the advantage of ensuring that even when only a small skin area is traumatized impulses continue to arrive over a considerable period and produce changes in sufficient nerve-cells to produce flexion. There are also some faster-conducting pain-fibres and in man it is possible with care to distinguish the arrival of fast and slow pain following say a pin-prick. Impulses produced by trauma are transmitted to the brain by a special set of fibres in the lateral spino-thalamic tract. They reach the thalamus but have not been traced to the cortex, although they certainly influence some of its activities!

6. Enteroceptors

The receptors in the internal organs serve to assist homeostasis by initiating and stopping many actions. They provide an essential feed-back system ensuring stable life, particularly in the young mammal, before a system for regulating rhythmic activity has been built up in the brain. Some of the receptors in the viscera set up discharges whose effects are familiar enough, for instance, those of hunger (p. 253). Probably there are many other systems present that regulate the action of the body, even though we are not accustomed to describing their effects. Many of the hollow organs contain receptors that discharge when the state of distension of the organ changes. Thus the lungs set up impulses when they are inflated and these impulses travel up the vagus nerve and inhibit the discharge to the muscles, cutting short the act of inspiration (p. 306).

The impulses associated with hunger are often quoted as an example of initiation of action of the organism by an internal driving system, but little is known of them in detail. They probably arise from receptors in the muscular stomach wall, which are stimulated by the 'hunger contractions' of the organ, but the conditions that make the stomach contract are largely unknown. Hunger normally comes on rhythmically, at a given time after meals, at a certain stage of emptying of the stomach. Once again we see the difficulty of finding the beginning or ending of any phase of living. Still less is known of the mechanism of thirst but it presumably involves stimulation of receptors by dryness of the membranes of the pharynx. There are receptors within the hypothalamus sensitive to changes in the concentration of the blood (p. 420).

Receptors able to respond to distension are probably present in the bladder, uterus, seminal vesicles, and other internal organs. It is often suggested that discharges from these organs produce 'drives' controlling behaviour. Distension of the bladder may be a factor leading to urination, as filling of the rectum is for defaecation, but the conception that filling of the prostate or seminal vesicles is the chief influence controlling male sex behaviour is probably an oversimplification.

Many viscera are painful when distended, though not when cut or pinched. Important enteroceptors are present in the vascular system, including organs sensitive to increase of blood-pressure (in the carotid sinus and arch of the aorta) and to reduction of oxygen tension (in the carotid body) (p. 286).

XXVI

THE EYE

1. Sensitivity to radiant energy

THE eye of man is a region specialized to provide the body with information about changes in the flux of radiant energy between wave-lengths of about 380 and 760 $m\mu$. It is interesting to speculate why organs for dealing with this particular range should have become well developed. Radiant energy of greater and lesser wave-lengths is abundant around land animals, yet changes outside the visible range are either undetected by the human body or else produce only poorly localized responses (as to heat) or slow alterations such as the pigmentation of the skin by ultra-violet light.

Organs for detecting radiation in the visible range have probably become developed because there is here a larger variety of easily collected relevant information than would be available elsewhere in the spectrum. Radiation of longer or shorter wave-length is also significant for some animals. Organs for accurate detection of the direction of heat radiation are found; for example the special receptors on the head of pit vipers are used to detect the warm-blooded prey. Man-made direction-finding devices that employ a reflected beam of waves of 1–10 cm. length show that this radiation could be 'useful' if the body had means for producing and detecting it; but these wave-lengths are not continuously present in the sun's radiation.

At the other end of the spectrum ultra-violet radiation of wave-lengths less than 300 $m\mu$ is abundant in nature and is made use of for direction-finding by bees and perhaps other animals, but so far as is known not by any mammal. Whether a particular type of change provides 'information' for an animal type depends upon whether such change provides a basis for selection among the various actions that the animal can make.

Changes that occur within the visible range have the advantage that they act as signals for many events that are important for the survival of an animal. Detection of the mere difference between light and darkness or of the intensity of illumination is itself of value, providing, for example, signs that can be used for the selection of appropriate habitats or niches out of the many that are available. In many animals the eyes allow more information than the mere intensity of illumination to be extracted. Often they enable the animals to react specifically according to the position of a change in the visual field, for example, to snap at the movement of some lighter or darker spot. The periphery of the human retina is used in this way when we see dimly 'in the dark' (p. 496). In some animals different reactions can be performed according to the wave-length of the light, in other words colour can be discriminated (p. 501). In a few species the eye and the associated parts of the brain allow 'form vision', the performance of distinct reactions chosen in relation to a combination of many features of the incident flux of radiation. This is especially true of man, who is able to respond differently to minute differences between objects having light-reflecting surfaces, that is to say recognizing their texture and shape. We probably extract more information with our eyes than do any other animals and it is largely on a basis of this visual information that the great variety of human actions is based. The eye is the chief means by which man makes in the brain a 'representation' of the occurrences around him that is useful for determining appropriate reactions to situations as they occur. This faculty more than any other provides us with the 'picture' of a world filled with objects, and this is the basis of much of our communication system and of our technology and way of life.

In all animals, eyes operate by translating a change in the incident radiation into nerve impulses in the fibres of the optic nerve (Chang, 1953; Granit, 1955). These are then 'analysed' by the brain to produce appropriate reactions. In studying the eye, therefore, we have to inquire how the light-sensitive surface is arranged and how the changes in it come to set up nerve impulses. Moreover, we can investigate the methods by which the energy is collected and focused by a lens system and how the whole eye is moved to enable the individual to scan over the world around and report upon the changes going on there.

There are marked differences between the eyes of different animals according to the type of information required; that is to say the type of decision that the animal can make between different actions. Nocturnal animals require a high sensitivity, which would be a disadvantage in very strong light. Hawks require to localize minute movements and men can act differently according to the shape of small objects. The hereditary mechanism of each species provides the means of collecting the appropriate information. By studying the differences we learn to recognize the significant features of the visual process (Walls, 1942).

2. Development and structure of the eye

Embryologically we may distinguish three main parts in the eye, (1) the optic vesicle, which grows out from the brain, (2) the meso-

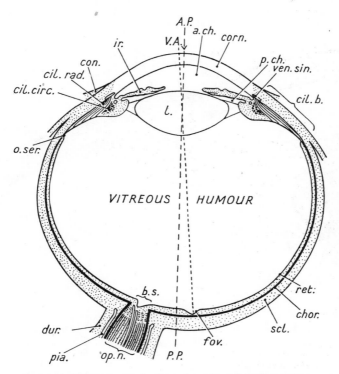

FIG. 202. Diagram of a horizontal section of the human eye.

a.ch. anterior chamber; *A.P.* anterior pole; *b.s.* blind spot; *chor.* choroid; *cil.b.* ciliary body; *cil.circ.* ciliary circular muscle; *cil. rad.* ciliary radial muscle; *con.* conjunctiva; *corn.* cornea; *dur.* dura; *fov.* fovea centralis; *ir.* iris; *l.* lens; *op.n.* optic nerve; *o.ser.* ora serrata; *p.ch.* posterior chamber; *P.P.* posterior pole; *ret.* retina; *scl.* sclera; *V.A.* visual axis; *ven.sin.* venous sinus of the sclera (canal of Schlemm).

dermal tissues that later surround the outgrowth, and (3) the lens, formed from the overlying ectoderm (Fig. 332). The wall of the diencephalon becomes evaginated and then makes a cup; the inner wall of the cup differentiates into the retina. The lens separates two chambers, the outer filled with a liquid *aqueous humour*, the inner with a more viscous substance, the *vitreous humour* (Fig. 202). The outer wall of the cup becomes the pigment layer covering the retina and where the two layers are continuous at the margin of the cup there differentiate the pigmented inner side of the iris and the iris muscles (Fig. 204).

The mesoderm around the retina makes a vascular layer, the *choroid*, corresponding to the pia arachnoid. The choroid layer expands at the front of the eyeball to form the ciliary body, containing

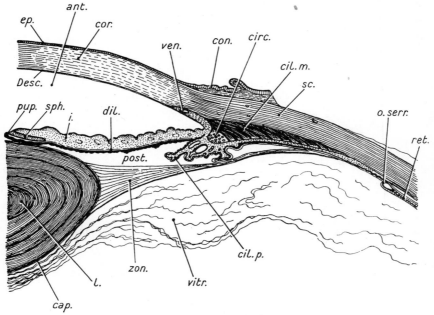

FIG. 203. Section through meridian of eye of man.

ant. anterior chamber; *cap.* capsule of lens; *cil.m.* radial fibres of ciliary muscle; *cil.p.* ciliary processes; *circ.* circular fibres of ciliary muscle; *con.* conjunctiva; *cor.* cornea; *Desc.* Descemet's membrane; *dil.* dilatator; *ep.* epithelium of cornea; *i.* iris; *l.* lens; *o.serr.* ora serrata; *post.* posterior chamber; *pup.* pupil; *ret.* retina; *sc.* sclera; *sph.* sphincter; *ven.* venous sinus of sclera (canal of Schlemm); *vitr.* vitreous; *zon.* zonule.
(Modified after Schaffer.)

'hair-like' secretory ciliary processes and the ciliary muscles, which operate the mechanism of accommodation (p. 486). The mesodermal layer is then continued to make the outer layer of the iris, whose inner lining is the ectodermal tissue of the optic vesicle. Outside the choroid is a tough coat of modified connective tissue, the *sclera*, showing in front as the white of the eye. The part of the sclera in front of the lens forms the outwardly convex, transparent *cornea*. The cornea is covered on its outer surface by ectoderm continuous with the *conjunctiva*, the lining of the lids. Over the surface of the cornea, the skin is very sensitive to pain, stimuli here serving to elicit lid reflexes and a flow of *tears*, by which foreign bodies are removed. The tears contain some organic matter and probably assist in the nourishment of the cornea, which contains no blood-vessels of its own.

Behind the cornea there is a split in the mesodermal tissues, making a space, the anterior chamber of the eye, lined in front by a mesothelial layer covering the back of the cornea (Fig. 203). Internally the mesodermal tissue unites with the margin of the optic cup to form the *iris*. The iris is therefore a fold of tissue closing the front of the optic cup except for a circular aperture, the *pupil*, whose diameter is adjusted by circular (sphincter) and radial (dilatator) muscles. These

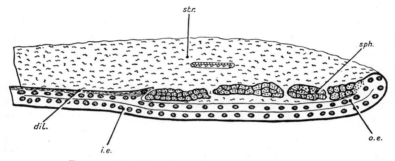

FIG. 204. Radial section of border of iris of newborn.
dil. dilatator muscle-fibres; *i.e.* inner epithelium; *o.e.* outer epithelium of optic cup; *sph.* sphincter muscle-fibres; *str.* stroma of iris. (After Szily.)

are said to be formed by the development of muscular processes at the outer side of the epithelial cells of the outer ectodermal layer of the iris (Fig. 204). The *sphincter iridis* muscle is a circular ring of fibres thrown into contraction by the action of postganglionic nerve-fibres of the short ciliary nerves. These arise from the cells of the ciliary ganglion, activated by the preganglionic fibres leaving the brain in the oculomotor nerve (p. 388). The *dilatator muscles of the iris* consist of numerous radial bundles, receiving their motor innervation from the sympathetic system. Preganglionic fibres leave in the ventral roots of the upper thoracic region and run cranially to make synapse in the superior cervical ganglion with cells whose processes pass with the internal carotid artery to join the fifth cranial nerve, whence they pass to the eyeball in the long ciliary nerves.

Behind the iris lies the posterior chamber of the eye, communicating with the anterior chamber around the margin of the pupil. The ectodermal layers at the periphery of the iris are thrown into a series of ridges, the *ciliary processes* (Fig. 203), projecting into the posterior chamber. Both chambers are filled with the *aqueous humour*, a solution resembling cerebrospinal fluid and containing 98 per cent. of water,

some sodium chloride, and traces of protein. It is either secreted or
filtered from the surfaces of the ciliary processes and is removed into
a series of spaces leading to the circular *canal of Schlemm* (venous
sinus of the sclera), which runs round parallel to the outer edge of
the cornea and communicates with the veins, though it is not itself
normally filled with blood. The amount of the aqueous humour controls the intra-ocular pressure, which determines the shape of the
eyeball. Any obstruction of this circulation leads to excessive intra-
ocular pressure, the condition of *glaucoma*.

3. The lens and accommodation

The *lens of the eye* is a biconvex body produced by the metamorphosis of the cells of the original ectodermal lens vesicle into
special lens-fibres of keratinous nature. The anterior surface of the
lens is less curved than the posterior. The shape of the whole depends
partly on the arrangement of the lens-fibres, partly on the action of
the elastic lens capsule that encloses them, which is thicker in front
than behind. The lens is attached all round to the edges of the optic
cup, along a line known as the *ciliary ring*, by a suspensory ligament,
the *zonule*, composed of radially arranged fibres. The elasticity of the
sclera causes this ligament to pull upon the lens all round and hence
to flatten it. The process of *accommodation* is produced by the *ciliary
muscle*, resisting this elastic force of the sclera. The muscle consists
of two parts, one with fibres directed radially (Brücke's muscle) and
the other circularly (Müller's muscle). Contraction of either muscle
relaxes the pull on the suspensory ligament. The radial fibres run
from the ciliary ring of the lens to the scleral spur, a thickening close
to the union of sclera and cornea. Their action is thus to draw the
lens outward, relax the tension on the suspensory ligament, and hence
allow the capsule of the lens to mould the plastic material to a more
rounded form, giving it a shorter focal length. The circular fibres of
Müller's muscle exert a similar effect by their sphincter action.

The refraction by which an image is thrown on the back of the
retina takes place at the various surfaces across which the light passes.
The anterior surface of the cornea, in contact with the air, provides
a large part of this refraction. The cornea and aqueous humour have
similar refractive indexes but the lens differs in refractive index from
both humours.

The measure of the power of a lens is the *diopter*, which is the
reciprocal of the focal length, a lens with focal length 1 metre having
therefore refracting power 1 diopter. The total refraction of the human

eye is about 58 diopters, 42 at the corneal surface, the rest at the surfaces of the lens. Variations in the focus of the whole lens system are
produced by alteration of the tension of the ciliary muscles, allowing
the pull exerted by the suspensory ligament to vary the curvature of
the lens, especially at its anterior surface. The central part of the lens
becomes more curved than the peripheral and the pupil narrows

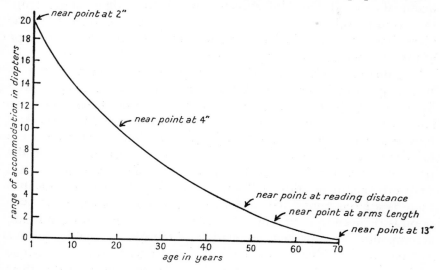

FIG. 205. Graph showing the decrease of human accommodation with age.

during accommodation for near vision, thus masking off the flatter
outer portion of the lens.

When the eye is accommodated for distant vision the ciliary muscle
is relaxed and the suspensory ligament pulls on the lens, reducing its
curvature. The act of accommodation for near vision consists in contraction of the ciliary muscle, taking the tension of the ligament off
the lens and allowing the latter to become more curved by virtue of the
elasticity of the lens capsule. The range through which accommodation is possible thus depends on the power of the muscles and the
elasticity of the lens. These factors become reduced with age, especially
the second. The lens capsule loses its elasticity and the substance of
the lens its plasticity; the whole therefore fails to round up when the
tension upon it is slackened, and the subject finds himself unable to
focus upon near objects. This change takes place in nearly all people
with advancing age. The full range of accommodation is about 16
diopters at puberty but falls to about 5 between 30 and 40 and is as
low as 1 diopter in most persons of 60 years old (Fig. 205).

The mammalian method of accommodation has presumably been derived from some arrangement such as that found in amphibia, where the lens does not change its shape but is moved forward by protractor lentis muscles attached to the periphery of the zonule fibres (Young, 1950, p. 332). With the development of a soft lens and an elastic capsule the muscle would, with modifications, be able to take on the mammalian condition. Unfortunately we obtain little evidence about the evolution of this mechanism from the living reptiles. Like the birds they have striped ciliary muscles, acting by changing the shape of the soft lens by squeezing it.

The degree of accommodation varies greatly in different mammals and is high only in some ungulates, most carnivores, and in primates. Many rodents (mice) and ungulates such as the pig, sheep, and horse have little or no accommodation, the eye is permanently long-sighted. Special arrangements are found in amphibious and aquatic mammals to increase the refracting power of the lens in order to focus on the retina under water. In otters there is a very strong ciliary muscle and a powerful sphincter iridis that squeezes the lens. In seals and sea-lions there is a large, round lens and powerful iris sphincter, so that the pupil is reduced to a slit when the eye sees in the air. This condition, accompanied by a marked astigmatism of the cornea, enables the eye to focus on the retina both in air and in water without undue change in the shape of the lens; the performances of sea-lions show that their vision in air is quite efficient. The circular fibres of the ciliary muscle (Müller's muscle) are well developed only in seals, whales, some ungulates and the higher primates, especially man; all being animals that require extensive accommodation, though for different reasons.

4. The retina

The inner layer of the optic cup is composed of the light-sensitive cells themselves, together with a complicated arrangement of nerve-cells (see Granit, 1947, 1955). The retina is not strictly a peripheral receptor but an evaginated portion of the brain (p. 782). The photo-chemical changes go on in the rods and cones, which are the *outermost* cells of the retinal layer and therefore lie with their outer (sensitive) ends in contact with the pigment-cell layer derived from the outer wall of the original optic vesicle (Fig. 332), the space between the two layers being obliterated. The pigment actually surrounds the outer portion of the rods and cones, separating the individual cells from each other. In bright illumination the pigment spreads out but contracts again in the dark. The pigment layer is also necessary for the regeneration of visual purple (p 494).

The rods and cones point away from the centre of the eye and the

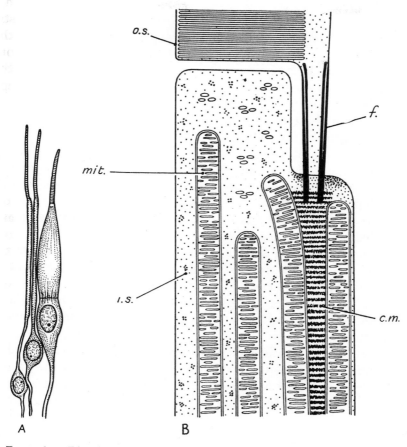

FIG. 206. A, Diagrammatic views of two rods and a cone from the eye of rhesus monkey (*Macacus*); B, schematic presentation of the connexion between the inner and outer segments of a rod from the guinea-pig retina, as seen by electron microscopy. (From Sjöstrand, *J. Cell. comp. Physiol.* **42**, 1953.)

i.s. inner segment, containing mitochondria (*mit.*) and other bodies; *o.s.* outer segment, filled with double disks; *c.m.* cross-striated material; *f.* bundle of fibrils connecting the two segments.

light passes through the nerve-fibres and cells to reach the actual sensitive region. In the human retina it is usual to distinguish two types of photoreceptor cell. The *cones*, occurring mainly in a circular area, the *fovea centralis*, are responsible for fine discrimination. The *rods*, covering the rest of the retina, have a lower threshold and are therefore able to respond to changes at low light intensity. The two types of sensory cell are fundamentally alike and are not always easy to distinguish. Both types are elongated cells and may be considered to have four parts (Fig. 206). (1) a long outer segment, which is the receptive portion, (2) an inner segment, called the myoid because in some animals it can contract, (3) a rounded cell body containing the nucleus, and (4) a short rod-fibre or axon pointing towards the centre of the eye. The rods and cones are held firmly in place by a 'limiting membrane' between the inner segment and the cell body.

The outer segment has parallel sides in the 'rods' but is usually expanded at its base in the 'cones', giving them their characteristic shape, but many of the 'cones', of the fovea are elongated and shaped like rods. The outer segment has an elaborate internal organization of layers of phosphatide and protein material. Electron microscopy shows that the structure consists fundamentally of a pile of disks, each with a double membrane at its upper and lower surfaces (Fig. 206B). Each disk is 140Å. thick and between them are 100Å. spaces, across which the disks are joined by stalks.

The outer and inner segments are joined only by a very narrow stalk, which contains fibrous bundles and presumably serves to carry signals from the light-sensitive outer segment to the rod-fibre. This latter has itself an elaborate organization with many large elongated mitochondria. It serves to transmit the signal to the nervous elements in the retina.

The cell bodies of the rods and cones form a well-marked outer cell layer in the retina, inside which their axons make a narrow almost cell-free 'outer plexiform layer' (Fig. 207). Here the terminal portions of the visual cells end by making synapse with *bipolar ganglion cells*, constituting the layer inside the outer plexiform layer. Each bipolar cell has a short outwardly directed dendrite, a cell-body, and a short axon, which breaks up in an 'inner plexiform layer', anastomosing with dendrites of larger *ganglion cells*, which make the innermost cell layer of the retina and send their axons into the optic tract. Axons from all parts of the retina converge to leave through a *blind spot*, which contains no rods or cones.

At its simplest therefore the conducting system of the retina would allow one visual cell to transmit impulses to one bipolar cell and this to connect with one ganglion cell. Counts show that there is one bipolar cell for each cone of the human fovea and it may be that this allows the projection on to the lateral geniculate body of the thalamus, where the optic tract ends, of an exact representation of the pattern of excitation falling upon the retina. In other parts of the retina each bipolar cell connects with many visual cells, often with both rods and cones.

Even in the fovea there are other complications in the retina and

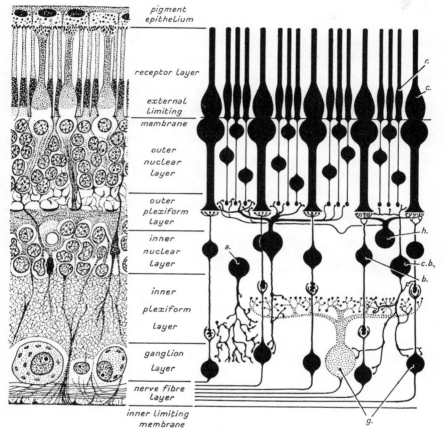

FIG. 207. The human retina showing the arrangement of cells and a schematic 'wiring diagram' of their connexions.

a. amacrine cell; *b.* bipolar cell; *c.* cone; *c.b.* centripetal bipolar cell; *g.* ganglion cell; *h.* horizontal cell; *r.* rod. (After Walls and Polyak.)

it is doubtful if the transmission ever occurs along isolated lines. The inner nuclear layer contains, besides the bipolar cells, many small *amacrine cells*, which send short branching processes into the plexiform layers and have often no single axonic process. In terms of usual ideas of the nervous system as a set of conducting pathways it is difficult to understand the function of these cells, but it should not be assumed that a nerve-cell only functions by conducting impulses from one place to another (p. 450). The amacrines provide nervous tissue that makes up part of the web of neuropil filling the plexiform layers and no one knows what processes go on in that tissue. It should be added that some amacrine cells have single processes projecting into the bipolar layer and they may perhaps conduct centrifugally.

Other nerve-cells in the retina are the *horizontal cells*, with processes spreading widely in the outer or inner plexiform layer. The presence of the amacrine and horizontal cells suggests that it would be unwise to assume too much about the mosaic of impulses transmitted in the optic nerve from the fact that there are equal numbers of cones, bipolar, and ganglion cells in the fovea. Study of the discharges in the optic tract fibres in the cat and other mammals shows that a considerable variety of cross connexions occurs. Rods and cones may be connected to the same bipolar cell and the horizontal and amacrine cells provide opportunities for interaction (Fig. 210). There are also efferent fibres in the optic tract, ending within the retina. Their function is not fully known but they can alter the responses following illumination and thus provide a feed-back or reciprocating system such as occurs in so many other parts of the nervous system (see Granit, 1955).

5. The duplicity theory of vision

Although the rods and cones are fundamentally alike there is evidence that their particular characteristics enable man to use the eye in two ways so different that they may almost be said to provide two distinct receptor organs. It was first noticed by Schultze in 1866 that the eyes of nocturnal animals contain mainly or only rods, whereas in related diurnal forms there are either both rods and cones or cones alone. According to the *duplicity theory*, which he put forward, the rod retina is responsible for *scotopic* or dim-light vision, having a high sensitivity but poor powers of discrimination, whereas the cones are responsible for *photopic* or bright-light vision, involving fine discrimination, including that of colour and shape.

6. Scotopic vision. Dark adaptation

It is easy to find evidence of this double function in our own eyes. Everyone is familiar with the fact that the eyes gradually become 'accustomed to the darkness'. This process of dark adaptation can be investigated by first making the eyes fully 'light-adapted' by looking at a bright light and then testing the sensitivity of the retina by finding the weakest light that can be seen after various subsequent times in the dark (Fig. 208). By this method it is found that the threshold of the eye falls rapidly; after half an hour in the dark it responds to light 10,000 times less intense than at first; the eye has become 'dark-adapted'. The curve of dark adaptation shows a sharp kink and the usual interpretation of this is that during the first six minutes the cones are rapidly increasing in sensitivity, threshold of the rods falling only later but continuing for a much longer period. Investigation of

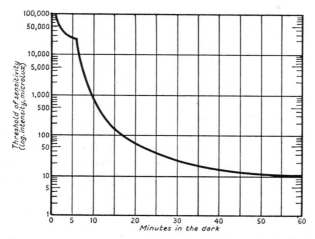

FIG. 208. Course of dark adaptation in the human eye. The cones are completely adapted after about six minutes. The rods then begin to be adapted. The change over from cone adaptation to rod adaptation is marked by the sharp change in direction of the curve.
(After Wright and Granit, 1938, *Brit. J. Ophthal.*, Monogr. Suppl. No. 9.)

many visual processes shows kinks of this sort, providing evidence in favour of the duplicity theory.

Anyone can confirm that the greater sensitivity of the retina is in its peripheral part; when fully dark adapted and using low intensities of illumination we can only vaguely discern the presence of objects, but *we see them better if we do not look directly at them*; that is to say by using the periphery of the retina rather than the fovea.

As the visual threshold drops during dark adaptation the visual acuity falls: it is a commonplace that when things are seen in a dim light they are indistinct. Moreover, they then have no colour; only very bright moonlight is sufficient to allow the cones to function, hence in dim light we see things in shades of grey or silver. Red light has no effect on the rods, a fact that allows us to use the two parts of the visual system separately when we want both to make fine discriminations (say for reading) and yet remain able to use the eye at low threshold. Instruments on the dashboard of a motor-car or an aero-plane can be read easily at night-time by use of the cones, if illuminated with red light, allowing the rods (unaffected by red light) to develop their maximum sensitivity for peering out of the vehicle into the darkness.

7. Visual purple

It is not certain whether the rod or cone type of vision appeared first in the vertebrate series, but the scotopic (rod) type is somewhat the simpler to consider and may be described first. The incident light sets up nerve impulses in the rods by a process involving change of the substance *visual purple* (rhodopsin). This substance is found in the retina of man and of all animals except those that have only cones. A fully light-adapted retina is colourless but retinae removed as dark-adaptation proceeds show a purple tint, which disappears quickly on exposure to light. This can be readily verified with frogs' eyes.

Rhodopsin has a molecular weight of about 270,000 and is com-posed of a protein, opsin, associated with the carotenoid substance retinene, derived from vitamin A. Deficiency of this vitamin therefore produces night-blindness. The maximum sensitivity of rhodopsin is to blue-green light ($500\,m\mu$) and this is approximately (but not exactly) the region of maximum sensitivity of the dark-adapted eye ($510\,m\mu$). The pigment is not decolorized by red light.

The simplest hypothesis is that in scotopic vision the light changes rhodopsin to an unstable substance that breaks down into opsin and retinene, the process of break-down stimulating the rod to the activity, perhaps a generator potential, by which the next link is activated. Dark adaptation consists in the enzymic resynthesis of rhodopsin.

8. The absolute threshold of vision

The remarkable nature of the photochemical process appears when we consider the extraordinarily high sensitivity of the retina. Much energy is absorbed by the refracting media as light passes through the eye. Therefore in order to determine the minimum light energy needed to initiate the visual process it is necessary to find what is the smallest amount falling upon a given corneal area that will stimulate. After calculating how much of this light is absorbed by the lens, &c., we can find how much actually reaches the retina. Hecht and his col-leagues (1942), having made careful determinations with minute spots of light, exposed for 1 m.sec., decided that a very small light source is just reported as seen when between 5 and 14 light quanta fall upon an area containing 500 rods (see Pirenne, 1948). Simple statistical considerations show that there is only a 4 per cent. probability that 2 quanta will be taken up by a single rod. These results therefore mean that one quantum falling upon a rod is able to set up changes in the rod and that between 5 and 14 rods must be stimulated for reports of vision to occur.

If this is so it must follow that a very faint light, near the threshold, is sometimes seen and sometimes not. This phenomenon can in fact easily be observed by asking subjects to say whether or not they see a faint flash. As the light intensity is increased with an optical wedge the frequency with which the flash is reported increases in exactly the manner that would be expected as the chances rise that enough rods will be struck by single quanta. No setting of the wedge can be found such that at lower intensities the light is *never* reported while at higher ones it is *always* reported. These fluctuations in the apparent threshold had previously been supposed to be due to changes in the eye, or in the observer. Hecht's work shows that in reporting that a very dim flash is only sometimes visible an observer is directly recording the quantal nature of light. A retinal rod reaches the absolute limit of sensitivity set by the quantum and molecular theories. Observers of the visual threshold had therefore noticed that light is a quantal or discontinuous phenomenon long before that fact was indirectly established by physical analysis. That the facts had not forced themselves on the attention of physicists is an interesting comment on modern man's distrust of his own recording apparatus. The importance of the clues provided by faint light sources in deciding human actions agrees with the discovery that we are provided with a system capable of collecting information from the smallest possible change in the emission of radiant energy at these wave-lengths (see Pirenne and Denton, 1952).

One quantum of light energy can only transform a single molecule of visual purple or other receptor substance. There must therefore be some mechanism by which the products of this molecule can affect others and produce a sufficient change to fire off activity in the rod. The only suggestion we have at present about how this occurs is that the rods have an elaborate internal organization, as shown by their cross striation and birefringence (p. 490). Perhaps a change in any part of this system leads to extensive reorientations throughout. The great length of the rods and large number of their plates, especially in nocturnal animals, presumably increases the chance that any photon will be effective in disturbing the state of the whole.

9. Special adaptations for nocturnal vision

The relative degree of emphasis on photopic and scotopic vision varies greatly in different species. Many animals that are mainly nocturnal are also able to achieve quite good visual discrimination in the day-time, for instance the cat. These animals have cones as well as rods in the retina. Some completely nocturnal creatures have abandoned cone vision altogether and developed rod retinae, with a very high sensitivity to light. The retina is completely free of cones in bats, armadilloes, and probably in hedgehogs, lemurs, guinea-pigs, whales, and seals; rats and other nocturnal rodents have only very few of them. As many as 1,000 rods connect with each bipolar cell in such rod retinae. The other cells of the retina are reduced and the whole is therefore thinner than in diurnal animals, and the optic tract is slender. Many other special features can be recognized in these night eyes. They are usually very big, allowing for a wide pupil and necessitating a large anterior chamber and large round lens. This often gives the eye a tubular form, which may restrict its movement within the orbit to such an extent that the animal can only change its line of sight by means of a mobile neck. It is no accident that owls as well as tarsiers can turn round and look backwards.

Protection of the very sensitive retina from bright light is afforded in nocturnal animals by the presence of pupils capable of wide excursions. Animals that are mainly nocturnal but also come out in the day often have a pupil that closes to a narrow slit and the edges of the iris may even come together to leave one, two, or in the case of the gecko, several tiny apertures. Such pupils may be horizontal, as in the dogfish or vertical as in cats. Presumably the narrow cracks allow the formation of pin-hole ('stenopaic') images independently of the use of the lens. In lower vertebrates the rods may also be protected by appropriate migration of pigment around them and by photomechanical movements of the 'myoid' segments of the rods themselves, pushing the sensitive outer segment into the pigment layer. It is not certain whether such movements also occur in mammals.

The sensitivity of the eye at low intensities is increased in many animals by a reflecting or diffusing arrangement, the *tapetum lucidum*. This usually lies in the choroid but may be formed in various ways, for instance, from a layer of connective tissue shining as does the tissue of a tendon (ungulates), or from a special layer of cells filled with granules of guanin, as in carnivores, prosimians, and especially in elasmobranch fishes. In the semi-diurnal *Mustelus* and other sharks the guanin can be covered or uncovered by movement of pigment cells of the choroid. This device may be used by animals living in dimly lit situations, as well as by those that come out at night. Thus there are tapeta in the eyes of seals and of whales and they have been developed independently in various species of fish living in the turbid shallow waters of lakes.

10. Impulses in optic nerve-fibres

Knowledge of the working of the eye has been greatly advanced by

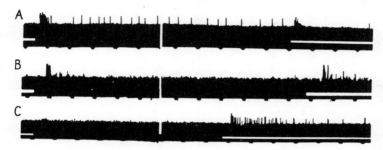

FIG. 209. Responses of the three types of intraocular nerve-fibre of the frog.

A, On-fibre, responding with an initial burst of impulses followed by a maintained discharge during illumination with no response at 'off' (the apparent off-response in the record is partly due to the retinal potential and partly to the reaction of the fibre); B, on-off-fibre, responding only to onset and cessation of illumination; C, off-fibre, responding only to cessation of illumination.
Time marking: ⅕ sec.
(From Hartline, *Amer. J. Physiol.* 121, 1938.)

study of the electrical changes produced in the retina and nerve-fibres of the optic tract during changes of illumination. The electroretinogram, recorded by electrodes placed on the intact eye, shows complicated changes of potential, which may be interpreted as indicating that the outer segment of each visual cell becomes electrically negative to the inner on change of illumination. Presumably this is a generator potential by which the visual cells activate the nerve-cells of the retina (see Granit, 1955).

In an animal such as the guinea-pig, whose eye contains only rods, study of the action potentials of optic tract fibres show discharges when the intensity of illumination is increased (Fig. 209). These may be called 'on effects'. Eyes that contain cones (for example, those of the cat) also show discharges with decrease of illumination ('off effects'). Fibres in the optic tract may therefore discharge either when the intensity of illumination is increased or when it is reduced. It is presumed that the fundamental photochemical process occurs when the light intensity is increased but that to produce the off effects the results of light increase are 'stored', as it were, presumably by synaptic processes in the retina such that the ganglion cells are inhibited while their visual cells are illuminated and discharge when the light intensity is reduced.

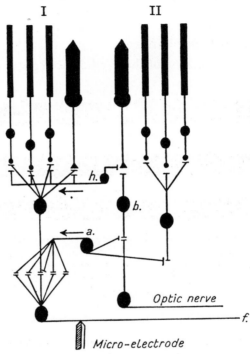

Fig. 210. Diagram of retinal structure illustrating possible pathways by which one set of receptors (II) could produce excitation through the amacrine cells (*a*) in the fibre (*f*), recording through a microelectrode, while also inhibiting through the horizontal cell (*h*) the response of the same fibre (*f*) to stimulation by another set of receptors (I). *b*. bipolar cell.
(From Granit, R., and Tansley, K., *J. Physiol.* **107**, 1948.)

It is also significant that fibres of the optic tract often show a continuous rhythmic discharge.

In an eye that contains cones there are therefore some 'on' elements, some 'off' elements, and some that are both 'on' and 'off'. Moreover, individual elements may change their state according to the condition of the retina and the action of their neighbours. The horizontal cells provide a mechanism by which the discharge from a cone could act to inhibit the impulses set up in nearby rods and cones (Fig. 210). It is possible that the amacrine cells provide a similar means by which rods can set up inhibition.

11. Photopic vision

The cones of the eye provide a mechanism of low sensitivity but high acuity, suitable for obtaining information in the bright light of day-time. Cones are found in the retinae of nearly all diurnal animals, either mixed with rods or in a special central fovea. In some purely diurnal creatures (squirrels, many birds, many lizards, snakes, and turtles), they are the only visual cells in the eye. The differences between the photochemical processes in the two types of visual cell are not well understood. Cones contain no visual purple and it is not certain what substance is responsible for their photosensitivity. Extractible cone-substances have been reported but their nature is still in doubt. The shortness of the outer segment of typical cones is presumably connected with their low sensitivity. In some animals they perform photomechanical movements opposite to those of rods, becoming elongated in brighter, contracted in duller illumination.

Vision at high luminosities permits collection of much information and development of elaborate behaviour patterns. Firstly, there is the possibility of using great resolving power to discriminate fine detail and small movements, thus of taking correspondingly detailed action. Secondly, the eye and brain together can recognize and react to a great variety of significant patterns and shapes from the varied changes of light intensity around. Thirdly, photopic vision is often associated with a high degree of wave-length discrimination, producing the phenomenon we know subjectively as colour vision.

12. Resolving power

A greater degree of resolution is possible at high than at low luminous intensities because there is so much light that the summation mechanism present in the rod system can be dispensed with. Fine movements can then be discriminated and remarkable feats of resolution are performed by animals such as birds and primates when they are picking out small seeds or insects, or detecting movements at great distances (Pirenne, 1948). These achievements depend on the presence of a high density of cones. The central fovea of man is a circle about 500 μ across, containing 30,000 narrow cones. The cells are so densely packed that not even capillaries intervene. Outside this area is an outer fovea, where there are some rods and capillaries. The cones of the central fovea are elongated and thus resemble rods anatomically, though not in sensitivity. They are so arranged that the light reaches them directly from the vitreous, their connexions with bipolar cells being made round the margin of the fovea. The retina of the central fovea is therefore slightly thinner and that around it thicker than the retina elsewhere. The amacrine layer associated with the foveal region is especially thick.

The resolving power of the eye is defined as the angle at which two outlines can just be discriminated, and may be as little as 10 seconds of arc subtended at the eye. The acuity varies with the intensity of illumination. These facts imply that acuity discrimination is not limited, as might at first be supposed, by the condition that two cones are stimulated with one unstimulated between them. The cones are about $3 \cdot 2 \mu$ across, which would only allow for resolution down to 44 seconds of arc. The fact that finer discrimination is possible, for example when setting the lines of a vernier to coincide, implies that the individual retinal elements do not function in isolation. This indeed is clear from the complexity of cross connexions provided in the retina, some of whose effects are now becoming apparent in the studies made by Granit (1947, 1955) and others of the nerve impulses set up in fibres of the optic tract (p. 498).

We can obtain some idea of the processes at work by considering, as Hartridge has done, that on account of the chromatic aberration of the eye the image of a very narrow bright line on a dark background will affect a number of retinal elements. Slight shifts in the position of two lines, as in setting a vernier, will be detected by their effects on the whole pattern of stimulation of many cones.

13. Form vision

Vision in daylight allows a far greater perfection in the recognition of shapes than is possible at night. This power is one of the most developed human attributes but its basis is little understood. Human actions are controlled by information about the great variety of objects provided by the natural environment and by our artefacts. This information allows a much more detailed set of choices than does the information about flashes, patches of light and shade, or hints of movement that are available to other animals.

The recognition of shape depends on the picking out of certain significant outlines from the many that are presented in the visual field. Some shapes seem to force themselves upon us, for instance, the startle pattern of round eye-spots shown by many animals: yet to a large extent we have to learn to recognize shapes. Probably the process goes on in the cerebral cortex and the necessary requirements as far as the eye are concerned are that there should be a system able to register a pattern of light and shade and to project it to the cortex, where its features can be matched against those stored in the memory system as a result of previous experience (p. 457). The significant processes presumably occur at the boundaries between areas that are illuminated to different extents. It is possible that events in the retina itself play a part in detecting these boundaries, perhaps by sharpening them or increasing their contrasts. Retinae rich in cones (and the central areas of mixed retinae) are associated with very thick inner retinal layers and especially with numerous amacrine cells. There is at present little but speculation as to whether and how these may be concerned in the process of form vision. It is significant that these pathways that carry large amounts of information also allow much overlap (see Granit, 1955).

Study of the impulse discharges in the optic-tract fibres has shown that variation in the intensity of illumination of the retina produces several different types of changes in the discharge of the cones. Cone units put out complicated patterns of discharge and these may be important for recognition of spatial phenomena such as the dominance of contour and shape. Minute fluctuations in the position of the eye-ball must produce an elaborate mosaic of on-and-off effects and these provide the cortex with some of the material for form discrimination, though eye movements are not necessary for the latter to occur.

14. Colour vision

Any animal whose photo-sensitive cells have a range of maximum sensitivities could respond differently to illumination by light of different wave-lengths. In practice only eyes working at high luminous intensities allow colour vision and only a limited number of animals make use of this information. Accurate investigation of colour vision is difficult because it must take account of the possibility that the differential sensitivities of the animal enable it to distinguish wave-lengths as if they were of different intensities. Many animals, for instance dogs, show themselves able to discriminate one colour from another but will yet confuse each colour with some tint of grey. True colour vision, the discrimination of wave-length independently of brightness, is known with certainty to occur in some teleostean fishes, in turtles, lizards, birds, and primates, all being diurnal animals with high visual acuity. It may be present in some other groups but is probably absent from elasmobranchs and amphibians, and from most mammals.

Human reaction to colour consists in giving a series of names to light between wave-length about 760 $m\mu$ (red) and 380 $m\mu$ (violet). All the visible wave-lengths presented together, or certain combinations of them, we call colourless, white, or grey; removal of certain wave-bands leaves the remainder coloured. Thus coloured paper reflects only some wave-lengths and coloured liquid or glass transmits some. Absorption of all wave-lengths produces black. It is found that white, grey, and all the colours visible in the spectrum can be obtained by mixing three 'primary' colours. Within limits any three colours can be chosen, provided they are from widely separated parts of the spectrum. For mixing lights it is usual to take blue, green, and red as 'primaries', but with pigments, blue, yellow, and red are chosen. There has been much discussion as to whether the phenomena of colour vision depend essentially on the presence in the retina of three types of receptor with maximum sensitivities at different wave-lengths, say blue, green, and red, as was suggested by the trichromatic theory of vision proposed by Thomas Young and later developed by Helmholtz.

Study of the impulses set up in the optic nerve-fibres has shown that there are great differences between the maximum sensitivities of the visual cells. The cells of pure rod eyes have a maximum sensitivity close to the wave-length of maximum absorption by visual purple, but they will respond to light of a considerable wave-band (Fig. 211), the threshold at each wave-length corresponding closely to the absorption by visual purple. Granit calls this rod element of the retina the *scotopic dominator*, it is the system functioning in dark-adapted eyes.

In light-adapted cone-containing or mixed eyes the responses of individual visual elements were found to be more complicated, but some evidence has been collected that there are actually three types of receptor, with maximum sensitivities in the red, green, and blue, as suggested by Young's theory. Granit calls these elements the *modulators* and their characteristic is that each is sensitive to a narrow wave-band, with a peak lying away from that of the dominator. It may be that there are also distinct photopic dominator elements, but the modulator elements working together would produce the photopic visibility curve. The effect of this arrangement is that the dominators make a broad wave-band available for vision while the modulators provide for discrimination of wave-length.

There is therefore some evidence that the distinct types of receptor required by the three-colour theory actually exist, but we are far from a full understanding of colour vision, or from identification of the separate receptors. Studies of the excitability of the human eye to electrical stimulation have shown evidence of the presence in the fovea of three kinds of process. Following illumination with a given wave-length the electrical excitability is changed in a characteristic way. R, G, and B processes with preferential sensitivities at 590, 550, and 460 $m\mu$ can thus be identified (Motokawa, 1949).

A further interesting suggestion is that the blue modulator is provided by the rods. It has long been suspected that the bleached visual

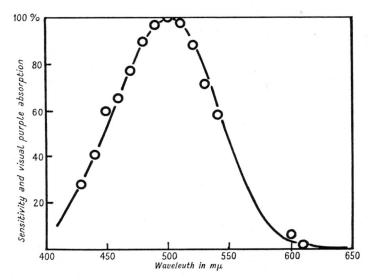

FIG. 211. Comparison of the visual absorption curve with the scotopic distribution of sensitivity of various vertebrate eyes deprived of their lens and cornea.

The values plotted as circles are the average thresholds at different wave-lengths of a spectrum of equal intensity obtained by the micro-electrode technique from 4 cats, 10 rats, 20 guinea-pigs, and 3 frogs.

The curve (solid line) is Lythgoe's for visual purple absorption.

(From Granit.)

purple of the light-adapted eye may work as a visual receptor and, moreover, the central fovea is blue blind. If this identification proves correct it is necessary to find only two types of cone in the fovea. As Granit points out, the essence of Young's theory is that colour vision depends on the presence of a number of receptors with distinct thresholds and evidence that this is true has already been obtained.

Willmer (1946) has suggested that many phenomena of colour division depend on the mixture of two effects only, corresponding to the actions of the rods and cones. Thus the rods have their maximum sensitivity towards the blue end of the spectrum, the cones towards the red end. Each wave-length therefore has a characteristically different influence on the two receptors, and this allows of the possibility of discrimination of colours (Fig. 212). There are some phenomena that demand the postulation of a third receptor; Willmer suggests that perhaps this may be a non-adapting type of rod, present in the fovea, which is unable to accumulate visual purple. Evidently we have not

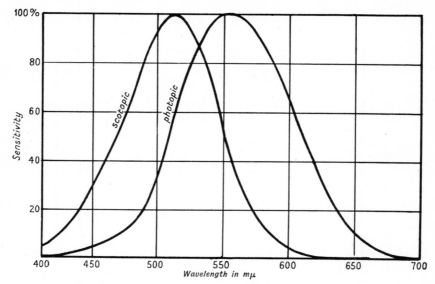

FIG. 212. Photopic and scotopic luminosity curves of man.
The curves show the sensitivity at different wave-lengths expressed as percentage of the maximum sensitivity. The scotopic sensitivity is obtained from the threshold at different wave-lengths using a spectrum with equal energy throughout. The photopic sensitivity curve is obtained by finding the intensity at each wave-length that is matched as being of brightness equal to a standard at 550 $m\mu$.
The difference between the two curves is a quantitative expression of the Purkinje shift, namely that colours elicited by shorter wave-lengths appear brighter in poor illumination and that those elicited by longer wave-lengths appear brighter in good illumination. (From Granit.)

yet enough evidence to identify precisely the receptors by which colour is discriminated.

15. Colour blindness

Variations from the 'normal' range of colour vision are common and can be interpreted on the dominator-modulator version of the three-colour theory. Total congenital colour blindness (*achromasy*) is very rare and is presumably due to absence of the whole photopic system. Dichromats are more common and may be of two sorts, confusing either red and green or yellow and blue. Inherited *dichromasy* is usually a red-green blindness and in the people known as *deuteranopes* the photopic luminosity curve is normal, suggesting that the dominator is unimpaired but the red and green modulators are deficient. *Protanopes* are unable to see the red end of the spectrum at all and there is presumably a marked atrophy of the red modulator and of its contribution to the dominator system. Whatever mechanism is suggested for colour vision must explain the fact that some colour-blind individuals (deuteranopes) can yet see well over the whole range of the spectrum and the simple three-colour theory is unable to do this. The dominator-modulator theory can do so because it provides for a mechanism of brightness discrimination partly linked with that for wave-length analysis. The key to understanding the retina is probably to be found in recognition that visual cells with differing thresholds may interact in influencing each ganglion cell.

16. Special adaptations for diurnal vision

The eyes of diurnal animals are mostly arranged to allow fine discrimination at the expense of a high level of sensitivity, they are cone rather than rod eyes. The high acuity is differently used according to whether the animal is insectivorous (swallows) or feeds on seeds (many birds) or is a predator, such as the hawks, or a shy herbivore, like the ungulates, which use their large eyes to keep a look-out for enemies. Animals that move swiftly also have large eyes, allowing high resolution for the avoidance of obstacles.

Eyes used during the day-time show various characteristics that appear to be associated with their use for fine discrimination. They are often large, allowing a large retinal image. In small diurnal animals this may make the eye relatively large (Fig. 213) but it is the absolute size that is important and large animals may have relatively small eyes ('Haller's Law'), which are yet very effective, as in the horse. The cornea-lens system usually lies farther from the retina in diurnal than in nocturnal eyes, allowing for a larger image (Fig. 213). Correlated with this, the cornea and lens are less sharply curved in diurnal animals, giving the necessary longer focal length. The pupil is often small in the eyes of purely diurnal animals.

In the retina it is found that the proportion of cones to rods is relatively higher the more completely the animals keep to day vision. Completely rod-free eyes are found in lizards and snakes, many birds, and squirrels. The presence of rods would, of course, be a disadvantage if it interferes with the photopic system by interposing blind spots between the cones. Human sensations in very bright light show the disadvantage of possessing a high-sensitivity system in day-time and it is not surprising that sun-loving reptiles, such as lizards and snakes, possess only the less sensitive cones. Presumably it is partly for this reason that where, as in man, the eye is used both by day and night, the rods occur at the periphery and there is a central area of cones.

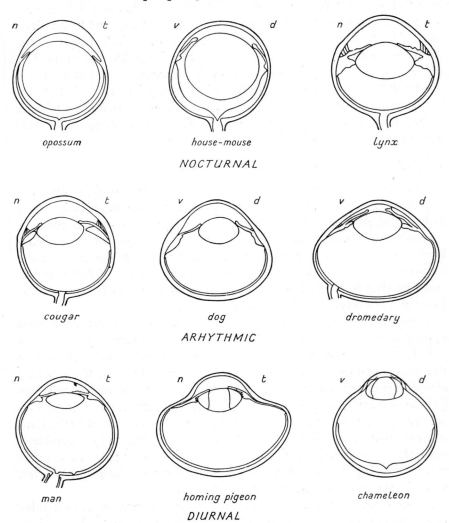

opossum   house-mouse   lynx

NOCTURNAL

cougar   dog   dromedary

ARHYTHMIC

man   homing pigeon   chameleon

DIURNAL

FIG. 213. Diagrams showing the relations between intra-ocular proportions and environmental light intensity. (After Walls, *The Vertebrate Eye*.)

d. dorsal side of eyeball; *n*. nasal side; *t*. temporal side; *v*. ventral side.

The effect of the blind spot might well be serious in the absence of binocular vision, which ensures in man that no part of the visual field falls on both blind spots. In squirrels and some fishes the optic tract leaves the eyeball not at one point but as an elongated line, so that the blind spot is a thin horizontal stripe along the upper border of the eye and does not interfere with vertical discrimination of the approach of enemies from above (Fig. 214). Nocturnal squirrels have the more usual round blind spot. In birds the blind spot is associated with a vascular membrane, the pecten but the method of working of the arrangement is uncertain (see Young, 1950, p. 465).

The central area is developed to varying degrees. The depression

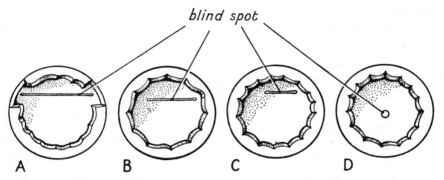

FIG. 214. Diagrams showing the blind spot in various members of the squirrel family. (After Walls, *The Vertebrate Eye.*)

A, Prairie-dog, *Cynomys* (inhabits open spaces, very bright light); B, wood-chuck, *Marmota* (inhabits less bright spaces); C, grey squirrel, *Sciurus* (inhabits dense woods); D, flying squirrel, *Glaucomys* (nocturnal, with a nearly pure-rod retina). The drawings are not to the same scale and the anterior segments have been cut away.

(fovea) is not always present and it has been suggested that since the vitreous humour and the retina differ in refractive index the steep curvature of the walls of the foveal pit may produce a magnification of the image in some reptiles and birds, such as the swallows, and some primates (marmosets). More probably, as Pumphrey suggests, the aberration produced by this curvature gives changes in the apparent size or other characteristic of an image as it crosses the fovea, thus allowing fixation and assisting in providing the high visual acuity found in these animals (Young, 1950, p. 463). The presence of a central area of special visual cells does not necessarily mean that the animal is diurnal. In crocodiles there is a patch of cells probably of high sensitivity rather than high acuity.

The yellow pigmentation that gives the human central area its name of *macula lutea* is probably a colour filter, providing an increase of visual acuity by eliminating chromatic aberration. The images of objects reflecting the various parts of the spectrum occur at different levels and although the great length of the central cones reduces the disadvantages of this effect, a yellow filter, cutting out especially the violet end of the spectrum, should act to reduce the blurring. Many birds have yellow or orange oil droplets in the cones, and the cornea and lens are distinctly yellow in some diurnal animals (especially in squirrels and to some degree in man).

Colour filters in the eye may also serve to increase contrast in important regions of the spectrum, for instance, yellow filters by eliminating the blue element would assist in distinguishing between various greens. In pigeons the lower part of the retina has yellow droplets, increasing the contrast of objects seen against the sky, whereas the upper part, with mostly red droplets, is suited to see objects against the green of the world beneath the bird. The red droplets in the cones of turtles may serve to reduce glare and it is perhaps significant that they are also abundant in the retina of kingfishers.

It is difficult to be sure of the exact significance of these as of many other details of the optic system, but it can hardly be an accident that the lenses of squirrels and some primates are yellow, that pigment granules are found in the sharp-sighted birds, and that colour filters are completely absent from the mainly nocturnal or crepuscular ungulates and carnivores. The yellow pigment of the human macula has a significant effect in absorbing blue light (when it is especially dense it may make its possessor blue blind). Riflemen and others have long known that the use of extra-ocular yellow filters produces a significant increase in visual acuity.

Thus the eye shows a great range of variation in different animals and many of the variants are correlated with the habits. Even after discounting all the dangers of speculation on such themes it can hardly be denied that the structure of the eyes is appropriate to the way in which they are used, by whatever process this result may have been achieved.

XXVII

RECEPTORS FOR SPACE ORIENTATION AND AIR-BORNE VIBRATIONS

1. Orientation in space and hearing

DETECTION of changes in orientation in space is of fundamental importance for the maintenance of stability and regulation of position. Throughout the vertebrates the apparatus of the inner ear shows a remarkably constant organization, providing receptors that respond to slight mechanical deformation and give information (1) about the position of the head in relation to gravity, (2) of the angular acceleration of movement of the head in various directions, (3) of the direction and frequency of incident sound-waves.

The first two functions, mediated by the utricle and saccule and the semicircular canals, are universal in vertebrates; the third function, hearing, occurs from fishes to mammals but is absent in some animals, for instance tortoises. The connexion of gravity receptors with those for hearing depends on the fact that both rely on detection of mechanical deformation by small forces. Yet the information is used in very different ways. The impulses originating in the gravity receptors serve mainly for reflex control of posture. Changes in the pattern of incident sound-waves provide signals for the occurrence of a wide variety of events associated with the animal's food, enemies, and mates. Full use of this information involves its assessment by the elaborate computing system of the higher nerve centres, therefore responses to sounds vary with past experience and are often not forecastable for all individuals of a species.

2. Parts of the ear

The mammalian inner ear consists of three distinct receptor systems (Fig. 215), (1) the semicircular canals and their *cristae*, giving response to rotational movements of the head in space; (2) the *maculae* of the utricle and saccule, providing tonic gravitational receptors; and (3) the *organ of Corti* for measuring intensity and frequency of sound-waves between limits about 20 and 15,000 per second. All of these receptors are formed by division of an original ectodermal sac, the *otic vesicle*. This becomes embedded in the otic bone (petrous portion of the temporal bone as it is known in man). The reception of sound-waves is mediated by the outer and middle ears and the tympanum, parts not directly connected with the otic vesicle but developed from the first branchial (hyoidean) gill slit (p. 733). The tympanic membrane stretched across the canal marks the outer end of the middle ear. The region external to the tympanum is the

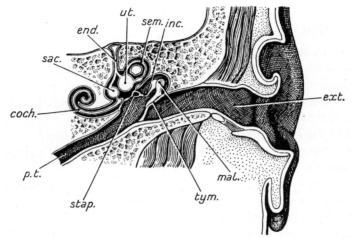

FIG. 215. Section through the ear of man.
coch. cochlea; *end.* endolymphatic duct; *ext.* external auditory meatus; *inc.* incus; *mal.* malleus; *p.t.* pharyngotympanic tube; *sac.* sacculus; *sem.* semicircular canal; *stap.* stapes; *tym.* tympanic membrane; *ut.* utriculus. (Modified after Cunningham.)

outer ear, terminating in the pinna, which is variously adapted to reflect sound-waves and to assist in the localization of sound.

3. The middle ear

The middle ear communicates with the pharynx by the *Eustachian tube* (pharyngo-tympanic tube). This is normally closed by a muscle, the tensor palati, but is opened during swallowing, allowing equalization of pressure on the two sides of the ear drum.

The *tympanic membrane* consists of a thin core of connective tissue, covered externally by skin of the outer ear, internally by mucous membrane of the middle ear. It is not round and its shape is such as to make it nearly aperiodic, that is to say, to reduce its tendency to vibrate especially readily at certain frequencies. Vibrations are transmitted from the large ear drum (85 sq. mm.) to the inner ear by the *auditory ossicles, malleus* resting on the drum, *incus* in the middle, and *stapes* touching a membrane covering a small hole, the *fenestra ovalis* (3·2 sq. mm.) in the petrous temporal bone. There are joints between

the ossicles, and the whole system ensures that every inward movement of the centre of the tympanic membrane produces a movement
of about one-third the extent in the foot plate of the stapes. The pressure at the stapes is twenty-two times larger than at the drum. A
similar reduction apparatus is used in man-made recording devices
whenever a lightly damped membrane activated by small forces and
large displacements of the air has to produce larger forces and small
displacements in a more heavily damped liquid system.

There are two muscles in the middle ear, the *tensor tympani*, which
pulls the drum inwards, and the *stapedius*, which pulls the stapes
away from the oval window. These muscles show a reflex contraction
when sound falls on the ear and the increased tautness they produce
provides protection against loud sounds by decreasing the amplitude
of the vibrating systems. Their action is thus analogous to that of the
iris of the eye.

4. The inner ear

The otic sac forms a series of cavities, the membranous labyrinth,
containing receptors for the separate functions performed (Fig. 217).
There are two sacks, the *utricle* and *saccule*, three *semicircular canals*,
set in different planes, and a coiled tube the *cochlea*. All remain in
communication with each other and with the saccus endolymphaticus,
a blind chamber representing the stalk of the original invaginating
otic sac. The sensory passages derived from the otic vesicle contain a
fluid, the *endolymph*. They are surrounded by a series of spaces in the
mesodermal tissues that separate the labyrinth from the bone. The
membranous labyrinth is therefore only in contact with the periosteum of the bone at a few places (Fig. 218). For the most part it is
surrounded by quite large irregular cavities, corresponding to the
subarachnoid spaces. These cavities are crossed by trabeculae connected with the periosteum and filled with a fluid, the *perilymph*,
which corresponds to the cerebrospinal fluid.

Altogether there are six sensory areas in the labyrinth. Three of
these, the *cristae ampullares*, occupy swellings one at one end of each
of the three semicircular canals. The organs of static or tonic balance
are the two *maculae*, one each in the utricle and the saccule. Finally,
the auditory organ is a long ridge running up one side of a coiled tube,
the *cochlea*.

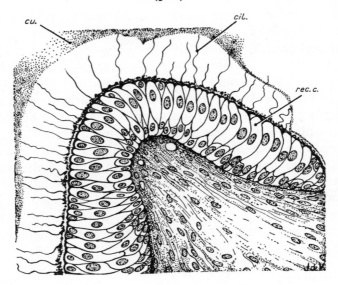

FIG. 216 A. Crista of the ampulla of a semicircular canal of a white rat.
(*For Key see* Fig. 216 B.)

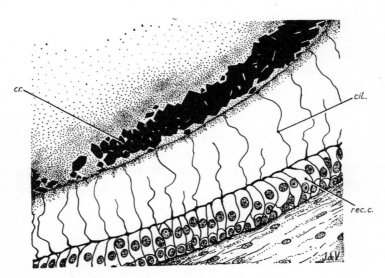

FIG. 216 B. Macula of the sacculus of the rat.

cil. ciliary hairs; *cr.* crystals; *cu.* cupula; *h.c.* hair cells; *pil.* outer pillar; *rec.c.* receptor cells;
ret. reticular membrane around outer ends of hair cells.

(After Engstrom, *Acta Oto-laryngol.* **40,** 1951.)

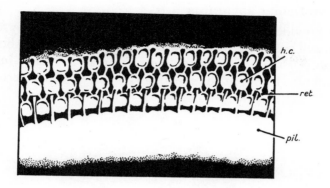

FIG. 216 C. Hair cells from the cochlea of a rat seen in surface view.
(*For Key see* Fig. 216 B)

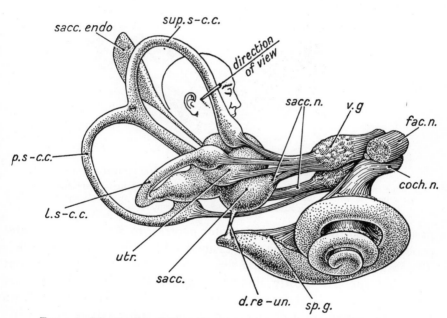

FIG. 217. Distribution of the auditory nerve to the membranous labyrinth.

coch.n. cochlear nerve; *d.re-un.* ductus reuniens; *fac.n.* facial nerve; *l.s-c.c.* lateral semicircular canal; *p.s.-c.c.* posterior semicircular canal; *sacc.* saccule; *sacc.n.* saccular nerve; *sacc. endo.* saccus endolymphaticus; *sp.g.* spiral (cochlear) ganglion; *sup.s-c.c.* superior semicircular canal; *utr.* utricle; *v.g.* vestibular ganglion.
(After Hardy, M., 1934, *Anat. Rec.* **59**, 403.)

5. The vestibular apparatus

This provides an important part of the information by which the balance and posture of the body is maintained (p. 413). About 19,000 nerve-fibres supply its receptor organs in man and carry impulses to the vestibular nuclei in the medulla (Fig. 173). From here impulses

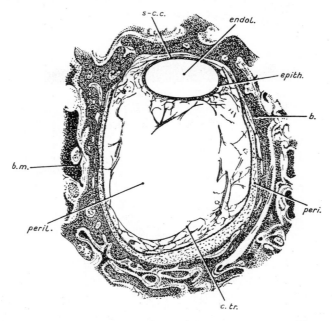

FIG. 218. Transverse section of adult human lateral semicircular canal.

b. bone of bony labyrinth; *b.m.* bone marrow; *c.tr.* connective tissue trabeculae; *epith.* epithelium of semicircular canal; *endol.* endolymphatic space; *peri.* periosteum; *peril.* perilymphatic space; *s.-c.c.* semicircular canal.

pass to spinal motor and oculomotor centres, to the cerebellum and probably also to autonomic centres and to the cerebral cortex (p. 404). The influence of the vestibular receptors is thus very widespread but probably operates mostly along high-probability channels, fixed by heredity. The relatively small number of vestibular nerve-fibres allows the transmission only of small amounts of information, producing effects forecastable for all members of the species.

6. The semicircular canals

The three semicircular canals are tubes forming almost complete circles and set at right angles to each other (Fig. 217). They spring from a larger central sac, part of whose wall is evaginated to form the utricle. Each tube carries an ampulla at one end, and in this lies the sensory crista, a ridge of cells, some supporting and others, the hair-cells, having long processes (stereocilia), which are partly embedded in a gelatinous mass the *cupula*. The cupula projects into the ampulla and thus acts like a swinging door, hinged on the cilia and moving because of endolymph pressures. The finest processes of the vestibular nerve-fibres ramify among the bases of the hair-cells. The system is very sensitive; it is calculated that in fish (where the movements of the cupula can be watched directly) a change of pressure of 0·05 mm. water is sufficient to produce movement of the cupula. Another way of testing the sensitivity is to record the minimum head movement that gives rise to compensating movements of the eyes. In rabbits movement has been found to follow angular accelerations of as little as 0·09 degrees/sec. per second. Sensory nerve-fibres of the eighth (auditory) nerve ramify around the bases of the hair-cells and the movement of the fluid in the tube controls the impulses set up in these, by its action upon the cupula and thus on to hair-cells. These impulses travel to the vestibular nuclei (Fig. 173) and set in action righting movements of the back, limbs, and eye muscles, which compensate for the rotation of the head. Records of nerve impulses in the vestibular nerve of fishes (rays) have shown that there is a continuous discharge from the cristae, increasing when rotation of a canal is in one direction but decreasing when it is in the other (see Lowenstein, 1950).

7. Utricle and saccule

The utricle communicates with the saccule by a narrow duct, from which springs a long tube the ductus endolymphaticus, representing the original canal connecting the otic vesicle with the surface during development. The maculae of the utricle and saccule consist of patches of sensory epithelium, containing, like the ampullary cristae, supporting cells and hair-cells. The hairs are not actively motile and are embedded in a gelatinous membrane in which there are also many tiny crystals of calcium carbonate, the *otoliths* or ear dust (Fig. 216). The membranes are thus weighted and since the two maculae are placed vertically and at right angles to each other the hair-cells are pulled upon in a characteristic manner for each position of the head. The receptor organs of the maculae therefore provide steady streams of impulses, varied in pattern for each position and providing the in-formation by which the motor nerve centres maintain the muscles in an appropriate state. The maculae are thus organs for tonic, the cristae for phasic, maintenance of posture. There is also some evidence that the saccule is an auditory receptor for vibrations of low frequency.

8. The cochlea

The auditory receptor of man lies in a tube leading from the saccule and coiled in a spiral with three turns, the *ductus cochlearis* or scala media (Fig. 219). This narrow tube, containing a viscous fluid, the *endolymph*, is enclosed in a much wider tube of *perilymph*, the whole

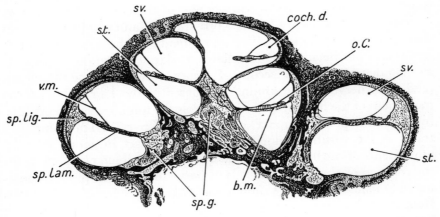

FIG. 219. Section of human cochlea.

b.m. basilar membrane; *coch.d.* cochlear duct; *o.C.* organ of Corti; *sp.g.* spiral ganglion; *sp.lam.* spiral lamina; *sp.lig.* spiral ligament; *s.t.* scala tympani; *s.v.* scala vestibuli; *v.m.* vestibular membrane. (After Schaffer.)

making the coils of the cochlea. The cochlear duct does not lie at the centre of the perilymph space but is attached to one side and rests on a partition, the spiral lamina, that divides the whole perilymphatic space into two, a lower scala tympani and upper scala vestibuli.

The vibrations of the stapes, the innermost of the three ossicles, are not transmitted direct to the cochlear duct but to the perilymphatic fluid at the base of the scala vestibuli. Here the outer wall of the labyrinth comes into contact with a hole in the bony wall, the *fenestra ovalis*, into which the end of the stapes fits. The fluid in the vestibular scala is thus set into vibration. The whole cochlea is enclosed in bone, except at the lower end of the scala tympani, where there is a second hole in the petrous temporal bone, the *fenestra rotunda*. Every inward movement of the membrane covering the oval window must therefore be followed by an outward movement of the round one and the fluid system between these two is so arranged that its vibrations set in motion the *spiral lamina*, the membrane on which the sensory hair-cells of the cochlea are placed. The scala vestibuli communicates at the tip of the coil with the scala tympani by a minute pore, the helicotrema, but this is too small to allow movements of the frequency of auditory vibrations to be transmitted through the fluid. Accordingly every time the pressure rises in the scala vestibuli the membranes

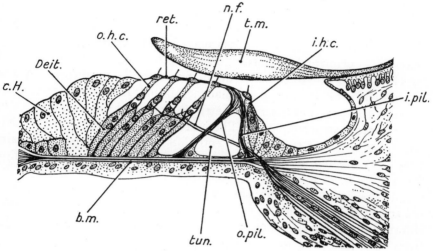

FIG. 220. Cochlear duct and organ of Corti of a dog.

b.m. basilar membrane; *c.H.* cells of Hensen; *Deit.*, cells of Deiters; *i.h.c.* and *o.h.c.* inner and outer hair cells; *i.pil.* inner pillar; *n.f.* nerve-fibres; *o.pil.* outer pillar; *ret.* reticular membrane; *tun.* tunnel of Corti; *t.m.* tectorial membrane.

separating this cavity from the scala tympani are moved, including the spiral lamina, which forms the base of the cochlear duct.

The lamina is of complicated structure and includes the *basilar membrane*, a strip of tissue about 3 cm. long, containing a number of *auditory strings* or basilar fibres, placed transversely to the axis of the cochlea (Fig. 220). On these rests the sensory ridge, forming part of the lining of the inner cochlear duct itself. This sensory ridge, the *organ of Corti*, consists of supporting cells and sensory hair-cells. The outer processes of the hair-cells are embedded in an overhanging gelatinous *tectorial membrane*, which rests lightly upon them. This membrane has a structure of fine fibres. Its properties must be of importance in determining its pattern of vibration to sound-waves. It is said to be of higher specific gravity than the endolymph. The dendrites of sensory nerve-fibres ramify around the bases of the hair-cells and are connected with the cells of the cochlear ganglion of the eighth nerve, which lie in the centre of the spiral. As the basilar membrane is moved by vibration the hair-cells are thus bent and stretched, one or both of which movements sets up a train of events resulting in propagation of nerve impulses.

9. Frequency analysis by the ear

The cochlea, with its 31,000 nerve-fibres and associated centres, constitutes a system that enables the organism to give different reactions to tones over a range from as low as 20 cycle/sec. up to 20,000 (see Galambos, 1954). There has been much debate about how the analysis is performed. According to the resonance theory put forward by Helmholtz in 1863 the frequency analysis is performed by the mechanical properties of the basilar membrane. In this view the membrane is composed of a series of strings, arranged like piano wires in order of resonance frequency. These are supposed to resonate according to the incident sound-wave and thus to excite appropriate hair-cells by pressing them against the tectorial membrane, or pulling them away from it.

The basilar membrane shows some features that support this theory. It is a sheet about 32 mm. long and its histological structure shows about 24,000 distinct transverse fibres. These increase in length from 60 μ near the base to 500 μ at the tip of the spiral. At the apical end there are about 470 strings per octave and the intervals of pitch that can be discriminated allow about $2\frac{1}{2}$ strings for each interval. However, it is by no means certain that the basilar membrane consists of strings under tension. It can be examined directly by removing the inner ear after death and drilling holes in the bone; its responses to the application of local pressure seem to be those of a gelatinous sheet. When fine cuts are made in it the edges do not gape as they would in a membrane under tension (Békésy and Rosenblith, 1951).

The movement of the membrane in response to sound-waves can be seen by sprinkling fine silver particles on it and observing with a microscope. Below 25 c.p.s. the upper end of the basilar membrane vibrates but there is no change of position of maximum movement with frequency. Between 25 and 300 the position shifts gradually down the cochlea and between 300 and 2,000 cycles there is a more rapid shift. At higher frequencies observation is difficult because the movements of the membrane are small.

It seems probable therefore that mechanical frequency analysis such as is required by the Helmholtz theory plays at least a part in the discrimination of tones. It remains uncertain how fine discrimination is achieved. The frequency of discharge of nerve-fibres may follow that of incident sound-waves to give discrimination over the lower frequencies. Above 1,000/sec., which is the maximum that can be carried by any single nerve-fibre, action potential waves corresponding to the frequency of incident sound may still appear. This synchronization at higher frequencies is presumably produced by individual nerve-fibres taking turns in alternate sound-waves. There is still much to be learned about how a complex sound-wave is propagated along the cochlea and coded into a pattern of nerve impulses that can be analysed by the brain.

Small differences in sound patterns are faithfully transmitted over considerable distances and are therefore used by many animal species as the clues for social and sexual behaviour. Fishes and birds use the auditory system in this way and the recognition of speech patterns provides the main basis for the detailed human communication system. Little is known of the means by which the fine differences are discriminated either by the peripheral or central apparatus (p. 448). The number of nerve-fibres in the cochlear nerve is not high, considering the wide range of distinct actions they allow.

10. Echolocation by bats

Special use is made of the auditory system by bats, which avoid objects by a system similar to the echo sounding used at sea. The squeaks of the bat are a series of pulses of a frequency of about 50,000/sec. sent out in bursts at a repetition rate of about 50/sec. The echoes of these pulses provide auditory clues by which the bat flies, avoiding even fine wires. It has been known since the experiments of Spallanzani in 1793 that blinded bats avoid obstacles in flight as well as do normal animals. After plugging the ears this is no longer possible and there is good evidence that the bat finds its way by the system of 'echolocation'. Threads as small as 1 mm. in diameter can be located by this means and the bats can also discriminate between smooth and rough surfaces and objects of different sizes. The echo sense is effective only up to a distance of about 50 cm.

XXVIII

CHEMO-RECEPTORS

1. Chemical changes near and far

IT is of great importance for organisms to be able to identify the chemical nature of substances that they meet around them, distinguishing the valuable from the dangerous. Chemical cues are particularly useful for higher animals that have elaborate systems for computing associations and for making predictions; food, enemies, companions, and many other factors are associated with characteristic chemical conditions. It is significant that the cerebral cortex, the most elaborate and successful of all computers and predictors, arose from the part of the brain concerned with the discrimination of smells. Chemo-receptors are found in many animals and it is interesting that the substances to which they are sensitive are usually organic compounds such as are likely to be produced by other organisms. Elements and inorganic compounds are less often identified.

The chemo-receptors of mammals are the organs of taste and smell, between which there is a sharp distinction anatomically and functionally. The sense of smell is in the main a distance chemo-receptor, whereas that of taste only comes into operation when substances are in close contact with the body, often only after they are in the mouth. Corresponding to this difference in distribution is a wide difference in biological functions, the sense of smell serves to detect clues that guide the animal to its food or mate. The sense of taste only enables it to discriminate between 'desirable' and 'undesirable' food. This explains why the smell system is connected to the elaborate forebrain computor and produces responses based upon memory, whereas the afferent impulses in taste-fibres enter the medulla oblongata and are mainly connected directly with relatively simple motor systems.

Correspondingly there is also a great difference in thresholds. Quinine can be tasted at a molar concentration of 4×10^{-7}, sugar only at 2×10^{-2}, but organic sulphur compounds, such as amyl thio-ether, can be smelled in solutions as dilute as 5.8×10^{-9} molar. It is said that musk can be smelled when there is as little as 0.00004 mg./litre of air (Pfaffmann, 1951).

The taste receptors allow for the collection of only a small amount of information, enabling us to distinguish the four qualities sweet, salt, acid, and bitter, whereas by smell an animal or man can recognize a great many substances, especially organic compounds. The 'tastes' of food are their smells as produced by the effect of small quantities reaching the olfactory epithelium from the mouth. Responses to the true taste receptors are produced with a high degree of probability over relatively simple pathways, containing few fibres. The cortical centres for taste, if present at all, are small. Responses to smell on the other hand, involving discrimination of many distinct situations, are mainly learned. The number of olfactory receptors is very high and the central pathways are complicated.

2. Taste

Distinct organs for smell and taste can be recognized in insects; throughout the vertebrate series the two capacities are always localized in separate regions. In man the receptors for taste are the taste-buds, born on special papillae on the tongue and certain other parts of the mouth. These taste-buds consist of groups of specialized epithelial cells (Baradi and Bourne, 1953), among which ramify the endings of afferent fibres that run into the central nervous system via the dorsal roots of the seventh and ninth cranial nerves to reach centres in the medulla oblongata (Patton, 1950). There are probably different types of receptor for each of the four taste qualities and each taste-bud mediates either one only of the four or a mixture of two or more. The four sorts of receptor are not uniformly distributed over the tongue, so that with care it can be discovered that the regions differ in sensitivity, for example, the tip and sides are especially sensitive to salt. In teleostean fishes the taste-buds are not limited to the mouth, but extend all the way down the body, innervated by special branches of the vagus nerve.

3. Smell

The receptive surface for the distance chemo-receptor, smell, is the olfactory epithelium of the nose. The receptors are primary sensory cells, that is to say cells lying in the epithelium whose axonic processes pass as the olfactory nerve-fibres through the cribriform plate of the ethmoid bone to the olfactory bulb (Fig. 183). Neurosensory cells of this type are not found in any other part of the body of any vertebrate above *Amphioxus*. The receptor cells have a spindle-shaped body whose cytoplasm contains basophilic Nissl bodies (Fig. 221). The peripheral end is a long thin olfactory rod, bearing a number of fine hairs at the outer end. The hairs are not motile. The axons are exceedingly fine, some of them as small as 0·1 μ in diameter. There is a total of about 100 million of them in the rabbit, this large number being no doubt the basis of the capacity to discriminate between numerous distinct smells (Gasser, 1956).

Mixed with the olfactory receptor cells are a number of supporting

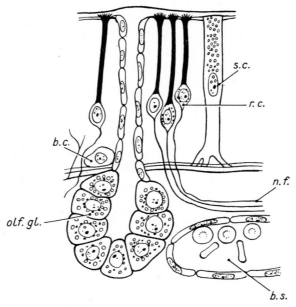

FIG. 221. Section of olfactory epithelium from the rabbit showing an olfactory gland (*olf.gl.*), receptor cells (*r.c.*) sending their axons into the olfactory nerve in a bundle (*n.f.*), a supporting cell (*s.c.*), a basal cell (*b.c.*) and a blood sinus (*b.s.*). (From Allison, A. C., *Biol. Rev.* **28**, 195–244, 1953.)

cells. The epithelium is also sensitive to touch. There are many *olfactory glands* in the form of simple tubes, opening all over the olfactory epithelium (Fig. 221). They secrete a yellow substance, which surrounds the outer ends of the olfactory rods. These glands and their secretion are strictly limited to the olfactory surface and they may play an important part in the receptor process. In albino animals the pigment is lacking and the sense of smell is impaired or absent. Albino pigs and sheep are liable to eat poisonous plants that are avoided by normal animals and for this reason albinos are not kept by farmers in areas where these plants occur.

The olfactory cells are all histologically identical; yet animals and men are capable of distinguishing by smell between a wide range of substances. There is no complete theory that will account for this capacity. There cannot be as many types of peripheral receptor as there are qualities of smell and it is difficult to see how a single set of

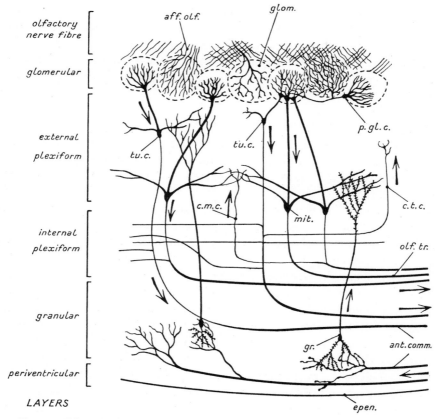

FIG. 222. Diagram showing the main pathways for impulses within the olfactory bulb.

aff.olf. afferent olfactory fibres; *ant.comm.* anterior limb of the anterior commissure; *c.m.c.* collateral fibre of mitral cell; *c.t.c.* collateral fibre of tufted cell; *epen.* ependymal lining of olfactory ventricle; *glom.* glomerulus; *gr.* granular cell; *mit.* mitral cell; *olf.tr.* olfactory tract; *p.gl.c.* periglomerular cell; *tu.c.* tufted cell.

receptors could be variously stimulated by different substances so as to produce the different impulse frequencies necessary to allow the discrimination. The difference from taste clearly lies in the multiplicity of qualities that can be recognized. Presumably the basis of this capacity is the fact that the olfactory receptor cells and their nerve-fibres are exceedingly numerous. They run as bundles of minute non-medullated fibres to end in the olfactory bulb. Before entering the glomeruli of the latter the fibres interweave in a complicated manner, so that each glomerulus receives fibres from different areas, though not from very distant parts of the receptor surface. The olfactory fibres make synapse in the glomeruli (Fig. 222), each of which is connected with the dendrites of a single mitral cell or tufted cell (p. 430). These cells have accessory dendrites that interweave in a plexiform layer. There are also periglomerular cells with short axons among the glomeruli. There are thus indications in the olfactory system of the plexiform and overlapping arrangement that is found elsewhere in systems capable of distinguishing between many distinct combinations.

4. Interaction in the olfactory pathways

There are widespread possibilities for interaction between the influences coming from distinct olfactory cells (Allison, 1953, 1 and 2). In the rabbit each glomerulus receives impulses from no less than 26,000 olfactory receptors and sends them to 24 mitral cells and 28 tufted cells. The former then send axons to the olfactory cortical system, the prepyramidal cortex (p. 430). The tufted cells send impulses to centres in the amygdala and related regions at the base of the forebrain, serving probably for rather simple reactions.

It is not certain whether the basis for olfactory discrimination lies in the olfactory bulb or in the secondary or tertiary centres, or in all of these together. It has been suggested that different parts of the olfactory epithelium may have different thresholds but there is little detailed information about this. Probably there are receptors with different thresholds scattered throughout the surface and each glomerulus receives the output from a number of these. Different combinations then set up different output patterns in the mitral cells and these become associated in the cortex with concurrent patterns of activity signalled by other receptors.

Electrodes inserted in the olfactory bulb of the rabbit record series of nerve impulses when smells are added to the air-stream. The impulses are of various types and all smells produce all the types if applied in high concentrations. Smaller concentrations of smells have differential effects, producing impulse discharges in different sets of fibres. There are corresponding differences in latency and threshold with different types of smell. There is therefore evidence that there are several types of olfactory receptor and these are not uniformly distributed over the olfactory epithelium, though there are regions where they are intermingled (Adrian, 1951).

The means by which the olfactory system performs the 'analysis' of smell remains uncertain. The cells of the olfactory bulb give rhythmic discharges, which can be recorded in the absence of olfactory stimulation. Impulses arriving in the olfactory nerve-fibres interact with these rhythmic discharges, both having access to the mitral cell pathways (p. 430). When a smell is first applied the olfactory signals reduce the rhythmic discharges that are transmitted through to the olfactory tract but 'before long the continuous discharge builds up again and swamps the olfactory effect' (Adrian, 1951).

The olfactory tract ends partly in the pyriform lobe of the cortex and studies in the hedgehog (where this lobe is large and readily accessible) show waves of electrical activity at each inspiration. This is probably the result of the effect on the olfactory system of the substances inevitably carried in a stream even of 'pure' air. When smelly substances are added the regular cortical waves no longer appear and their place is taken by small irregular waves. The presence of these small waves suggests that a particular pattern of activity is being set up and is the basis of the discrimination (Adrian, 1942).

5. The classification of smells

The problem would be simplified if we could distinguish a finite number of qualities whose combination makes up the range of smells, as in the senses of taste or colour vision. Unfortunately no such classification of smells has been made successfully, in spite of several attempts. The most ambitious theory is that of Henning (1926), who claims that all smells can be reduced to six primary types, with gradations between them. He called the types flowery, fruity, foul, spicy, burnt, and resinous. Henning allowed a number of people to smell various substances and asked them to place these in order of similarity. He claimed that his subjects placed the substances in linear orders, such that if the six primary scents be represented as lying on the corners of a prism then other scents occupy positions either along the edges, that is to say the scents that are compounded of two of the primary qualities, or on the surfaces, if compounded of three or four, or inside the prism when all six primary scents were involved. This system would seem flexible enough to incorporate almost any experimental results, but subsequent observers have only partly confirmed the linear series of smells represented along the sides of the prism.

A weakness of this type of treatment is that it gives no suggestion of the chemical basis for resemblances and hence of the underlying physiological mechanism. Zwaardemaker has attempted to overcome this difficulty by discovering the organic radicles that are 'osmophores'. Thus the nitrile groups give a pleasant smell to any substance containing them, and are hence termed 'euosmophores', whereas the unpleasant mercaptans are 'kakosmophores'.

No satisfactory theory has been put forward to explain why certain substances are smelled but not others. An intriguing fact, however, is that many smelly substances have the peculiar optical property of absorbing infra-red radiation and producing a Raman shift, that is to say, changing the frequency of light reflected from them. These properties depend on oscillations within the molecules at high frequencies (10^{13}–10^{14} cycles/sec.). Moreover, both properties are so highly specific that they are used by chemists for identifying particular molecules. It may be that these oscillations in the molecules are responsible for the activation of the receptors for smell.

XXIX

ENDOCRINE ORGANS. THE THYROID, PARATHYROID, AND THYMUS

1. Methods for the study of hormones

ONE of the great advances made in biology during the twentieth century has been in knowledge of the regulation of the life of the body by substances produced in endocrine glands and released into the blood. The relation of this system of chemical signalling to other means of maintaining the integrity of the body will be considered after the various endocrine organs and their effects have been described. Then we shall be in a position to consider the class of *hormones*, specific chemical signalling substances, produced in one region and acting elsewhere (p. 572).

It is necessary first, however, to say something about the methods by which the ductless glands have been studied. Recognition that a particular organ has an endocrine nature has come in various ways, sometimes from clinical observation of the results of abnormality, often from experiments with animals. Full demonstration of the existence of a gland of internal secretion can only follow a detailed experimental study. If it is alleged that an organ produces a specific substance acting at a distance it must be shown firstly that removal of the organ is followed by absence of the distant effect. Secondly, extracts of the organ introduced into the blood-stream must be shown to be able to produce these effects and to compensate for the removal. Thirdly, it should be shown that the active substance is produced in effective concentrations during normal life, and the control of its release described. Fourthly, if possible, the substance should be isolated in the pure state and chemically identified. Finally, it is very convincing if excessive or reduced secretion, produced either by disease or by stimulation or suppression of the action of the gland, can be shown to have the expected effects.

In practice achievement of a full understanding of the action of the endocrine glands has been a gradual matter, depending largely on careful study of the methods of preparation of extracts. Extracts from many tissues contain substances that have powerful actions upon other tissues and it cannot be alleged that an organ functions as an endocrine gland, that is to say produces chemical signals, simply because extracts prepared from it have certain effects. For example, histamine, which is found in aqueous extracts of most tissues, has a powerful vasodilatator action. A fall in blood-pressure following injection of a tissue extract is therefore likely to be due to the presence of histamine and not to a principle specific to that tissue. A rise in blood-pressure is more significant. Any results produced by extracts have to be considered in relation to the methods used in preparing them. The fact that a particular substance can be extracted from a gland does not prove that this material is normally released by that gland into the blood-stream.

There has been great progress in the isolation and recognition of specific hormones and many of them, but not all, have been chemically identified. They belong to many different classes of substance. The hormones of the pituitary gland are probably proteins, those of the gonads and adrenal cortex are steroids (p. 546), while the active principles of the thyroid and adrenal medulla are smaller organic molecules. This diversity warns us that the hormones cannot be recognized as a class having any common chemical characteristic. If the word hormone is to have a clear meaning it must be shown that the substances included under it, though chemically unlike, act as signals in the body, by controlled release and transport to a distance.

Much confusion has arisen from the giving of fancy names to substances alleged to be contained in tissue extracts. All names added to scientific nomenclature should be attached to clearly defined and recognizable entities. The only completely exact procedure is to obtain the chemically pure substance before naming it. Only then can the substance strictly be said to be born as an individual scientific entity. If an earlier christening is insisted upon the name should be applied to an extract prepared in a way that is carefully described. Unfortunately endocrinologists have been no less anxious than other systematists to achieve immortality by additions to the nomenclature, and the variety of names used for extracts of the glands has produced much confusion. It is not very instructive to learn that the adrenal cortex contains 'cortin', especially when it is found that more than twenty chemically distinct steroid substances are included in the extract. Yet it may sometimes be helpful to adopt the convention that such a name shall be applied to extracts prepared in a particular way from certain parts of a gland. The standardization of nomenclature and the adoption of agreed methods of assay has occupied a large part of the time of endocrinologists.

2. The thyroid gland

The thyroid, like so many other endocrine organs, is a region where certain metabolic processes that go on throughout the body take place with particular intensity. In this case the process is the uptake of iodine by the cells and its combination to make substances that stimulate respiration. Possibly this uptake originally took place directly from the exterior. The thyroid is derived from the endostylar feeding groove of the pharynx of the earliest chordates, an organ by which mucus is produced for the entanglement of minute organisms. In the lampreys (cyclostomes) the change in function takes place during ontogeny. The larval lamprey lives in the mud and has an open endostylar sac, which secretes mucus; at metamorphosis this sac turns into a series of typical thyroid vesicles (Young, 1950, p. 110).

In higher vertebrates the thyroid gland separates from the floor of the pharynx during development; it takes its raw material from the blood and gives its product back to the blood again. This transformation of a region performing a general function in relation with the outside world into a special endocrine organ may first have been dictated by a change of habits (Lynn and Wachowski, 1951). The result has been to allow detailed control of a particular aspect of life by centering that type of activity in one organ. The earliest Craniates, feeding on micro-organisms, possessed a large pharynx and perhaps collected their iodine there. When they came to take in large pieces of food the iodine had to enter the blood-stream lower down the alimentary canal, and perhaps it was present only in small amounts. The deficit may actually have played a part in the stimulation of the cells of the pharynx that were previously concerned with its uptake to develop into an active thyroid. The endostyle is a mucus-secreting gland but it is concerned with iodine metabolism, for *Amphioxus* or larval lampreys placed in water containing radioactive iodine show a concentration of this substance in the endostyle.

Whatever may have been the origin of the thyroid the secretion of the gland has become of such importance that in mammals its presence in too great or too small amounts influences the functioning of every part of the body. The cells of the mammalian thyroid are arranged in characteristic vesicles. They give the appearance of secretory alveoli but are actually closed sacs (Fig. 223). Each vesicle is lined by cuboidal epithelium, whose cells are the active secreting agents of the gland (see Braunsteiner *et al*, 1953). The vesicles contain a material known to histologists as the 'colloid'. This substance consists of the effective product of the gland and is a reservoir from which the material can be passed back through the cells into the blood-stream. Between the vesicles lie blood and lymph capillaries and nerves, the latter controlling the blood-flow but not actually providing secreto-motor fibres to the cells. The thyroid has an exceptionally rich blood-supply.

The evidence that the thyroid functions as a gland of internal

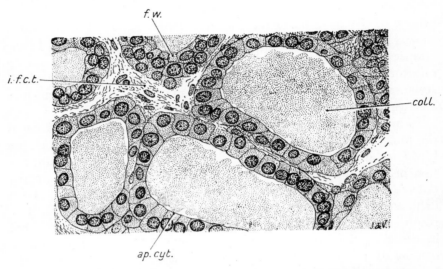

FIG. 223. Adult human thyroid gland, showing cubical epithelium and moderate distension of the follicles with colloid.

ap.cyt. apical cytoplasm of cubical epithelial cell; *coll.* colloid; *f.w.* follicle wall; *i.f.c.t.* interfollicular connective tissue. (From a photograph by Mr. K. C. Richardson.)

secretion is complete along all the five classic lines: (1) Symptoms follow its removal. (2) They can be prevented by treatment with extracts. (3) It has been proved that the gland emits an active substance into the blood-stream. (4) The active principle has been isolated, identified, and synthesized. (5) Diseased conditions involving both reduced and excessive secretion are known.

Historically our knowledge of the gland has grown gradually and recognition of the more superficial symptoms of thyroid dysfunction preceded understanding of its general role in the control of metabolism. There lingers still a tendency to describe its activities in terms of certain more obvious symptoms of its removal, for instance, retardation of growth. It is now possible, however, to specify thyroid activity more exactly (see Gross and Pitt-Rivers, 1953). The gland produces an iodine-containing substance that acts throughout the body by promoting the activity of the oxidizing systems, in particular those that involve cytochrome.

The iodine is stored in the gland in combination with a protein (thyroglobulin). The hormone that is released into the blood is probably the tyrosine derivative tri-iodothyronine:

$$OH \langle \rangle \overset{I}{-}O-\overset{I}{\underset{I}{\langle \rangle}}CH_2.CH(NH_2).COOH$$

Thyroxine, a similar substance with four iodine atoms in the molecule, may also be present. These substances are powerful stimulants of the action of respiratory enzymes. Injected into the body they cause a marked rise in the basal metabolic rate. There can be no doubt that this is the chief part that the thyroid plays in life; presumably by virtue of some special property of the iodine atom.

The thyroid tissue has thus become a specialized region for producing metabolic stimulants. The gland contains 20 per cent. of all the iodine in the body and attracts this element when it enters the blood.

3. Control of thyroid secretion

There is a close relationship between the demands of the tissues and the activity of the thyroid itself. The effect of partial removal or underactivity of the gland may be to stimulate growth and activity of the remaining thyroid tissue. It is therefore difficult to say whether an enlarged condition of the gland (*goitre*) is an index of reduced or excessive activity. The sulphur-containing substances thiourea and thiouracil have the effect of preventing synthesis of the hormone. Following their administration the gland becomes enlarged, although at the same time symptoms of hypothyroidism develop. Goitres can also be produced by treatment with cyanides and other substances that depress the respiratory systems of the cells, the thyroid responding by increased output.

The amount of hormone secreted by the gland is therefore related in some way to the 'demand' for it by the tissues and we get a glimpse of the complicated sets of relationships by which the activity of the body promotes the production of substances that themselves make further activity possible (Maqsood, 1952). Thyroid secretion is also controlled by more specific factors; the nervous system may exercise a regulatory influence through control of the blood-supply, and the anterior lobe of the pituitary produces a thyrotropic hormone (p. 556), which stimulates discharge of the colloid vesicles and produces symptoms of increased thyroid functioning. Being influenced by so many factors the gland fluctuates considerably in size and such changes can often be observed in man, for instance, during puberty, menstruation, or pregnancy.

4. Hypothyroidism

The thyroid hormone is necessary for the normal metabolism of most if not all cells of the body and it is not surprising that any defect in the gland produces profound and widespread effects. Complete removal is not fatal, but produces retarded growth in young animals and in the adult a lowered metabolic rate, apathy, thickening and other changes in the skin, and many other effects on the nervous system, gonads, pituitary, adrenals, and other organs. Administration of thyroid extract or of thyroxine can compensate for these defects.

Symptoms indicating serious reduction in thyroid activity in man are known as *cretinism* when they occur during development and as *myxoedema* in the adult. A cretin shows slow growth, with many abnormalities, for instance pot-belly, gross intellectual deficiency, and retarded sexual development. The influence of the thyroid in controlling growth and differentiation is seen in the fact that it is responsible for producing metamorphosis in amphibian tadpoles, acting by promoting the growth of some cells, the atrophy of others. The gland is also necessary for the periodic moulting of reptiles, birds, and some mammals, probably it influences all processes of continual replacement of cells, such as proceed in the skin, the adrenal cortex, and the blood vascular system.

The name myxoedema refers to a characteristic thickening of the subcutaneous tissues of the skin, but this is not a true fluid oedema. In any case the name is inadequate to describe the complete changes in appearance and personality that are produced by thyroid deficiency. The characteristic feature of the condition is the reduction of the basal metabolic rate, which may fall to 60 per cent. of the normal, associated with lowered cell respiration throughout the body and serious impairment of many activities. Treatment with extracts of the gland, or with thyroxine, produces marked improvement, first an increase of basal metabolic rate and then a reversal of the changes in the nervous system, skin, and elsewhere throughout the body.

5. Goitre

It would perhaps be expected that the symptoms of myxoedema should be associated with shrinkage or small size of the thyroid, actually the reverse may be the case, the gland is often enlarged. A further complication is that the symptoms of thyroid deficiency and enlargement of the gland may follow from a lack of iodine in the diet. It has long been known that goitre and cretinism are common in continental and mountainous districts remote from the sea. Such 'endemic' goitre occurs in Switzerland, in Derbyshire, and in the middle west of America. Iodine is abundant in sea-water and the presumption is that in these continental districts men and animals fail to get the small amounts that become available closer to the sea. The use of dried sea-weed and sponges was a Hippocratic remedy for goitre.

It is not entirely clear how the circulation of iodine proceeds in nature and there may well be complicating factors that make the iodine unavailable, for instance, the presence of fluorine or other ions. Moreover, there are undoubtedly hereditary forms of hypothyroidism and the dietary factor cannot too easily be assumed to be wholly responsible for the large number of goitres in any area. The two factors may, of course, go together, a low level of inherited activity only becoming apparent when associated with low iodine intake. Treatment with thyroid preparations may be equally helpful in either case; it has been shown by large-scale experiments in the United States and Switzerland that addition of iodine to drinking-water, or provision of iodized chocolate or salt, can reduce endemic cretinism and goitre.

6. Hyperthyroidism

A true condition of excessive action of the thyroid occurs with the symptoms that would be expected, high metabolic rate, fast pulse, warm skin, raised nervous excitability, and various disorders of metabolism. Such symptoms may appear either because of hereditary enlargement of the gland or from the development of a tumour of its cells (thyroid adenoma). These conditions of hyperthyroidism are not always easy to distinguish from their opposites. In the forms known as exophthalmic goitre the eyes protrude, probably because of the deposition of fat in the orbits. A further paradox of thyroid behaviour is that administration of iodine may temporarily relieve the symptoms of hyperthyroidism! Understanding of the iodine balance of the body is indeed still far from complete.

Study of the thyroid thus shows clearly how difficult it is to describe the factors that control the activity of any part of a living organism. Conventional biological analysis attempts to recognize a 'body' provided by 'heredity' and acted upon by its 'environment'. If this scheme were adequate we could forecast the result of alteration in any part of the system; hereditary overdevelopment of the thyroid would produce one result, deficiency of iodine (change in the 'environment') another, and removal of part of the gland a third. Such predictions are falsified by the interactions of the parts of the body, and the tendency to self-regulation of the whole. Deficiency of iodine may be followed by increase in the size of the gland and a goitre may be a sign either of excessive or of reduced 'hereditary' activity. We need a new method of thought, which instead of throwing emphasis on the fixed material body shall describe the activities of each life and the factors that control the steady states that they maintain.

7. The parathyroids

The pharyngeal wall, besides providing the thyroid cells specialized to regulate the metabolic rate, provides cells that perform the important function of regulating the calcium exchanges of the body. The parathyroid glands (see Bartter, 1954) are four minute masses of tissue arising from the endoderm of the third and fourth branchial pouches, close to the thymus (p. 734). They are usually partly embedded in the thyroid gland and are liable to be removed with it. They are necessary for the maintenance of life and it is therefore easy to see how early experimenters were led to suppose that thyroid removal is fatal in some animals. The glands weigh altogether only about 0·1 to 0·2 gm. in man. They consist of closely packed cells, only exceptionally arranged as vesicles. Numerous vascular sinusoids lie between the cells.

After removal of the parathyroids the animal or man within a few hours develops abnormal muscular contractions and convulsions, leading to death by spasm of the laryngeal and respiratory muscles. This tetanus results from a changed excitability in the muscle-fibres and nerve-centres and is now known to be only one sign of the fall of calcium that is the result of lack of the parathyroid secretion. Normally in man there is 10–12 mg. of calcium and 4–5 mg. of phosphorus per 100 ml. blood. Following parathyroidectomy the calcium may fall to 6 mg. or lower and the inorganic phosphorus rise to 9 mg. Relief of the symptoms can be obtained by injection of calcium salts or of an acid extract of the gland, known as *parathormone*, or from its discoverer, Collip's hormone. The chemical nature of the hormone has not been discovered and it has not been prepared in a pure state or crystallized. The most active preparations are of protein nature.

The function of the secretion of the parathyroids is thus to control the amount of calcium circulating in the blood. In performing this function the glands co-operate with the vitamin D introduced with the food or synthesized by the action of sunlight in the skin, this vitamin being necessary for the deposition of calcium in the bones. Injection of large amounts of the hormone produces solution of calcium from the bones and a high calcium level in the blood (as much as 20 mg./100 ml.), which may be followed by calcification of soft parts, for instance of the walls of the arteries.

The parathyroids, like the thyroid, are influenced by the demands made for their products by the tissues. If the diet is deficient in calcium the glands become enlarged and they also increase during lactation, when much calcium is being mobilized for transfer to the milk.

The amount of calcium in the interstitial fluids affects the surface properties of every cell and it is obvious that the stabilization of this ion is of the first importance for a balanced life. In fish-like animals this is probably achieved at the same time as regulation of the total salt content of the blood, by the special chloride-secreting cells in the gills, which are able to pass salt inwards or outwards as required by the state of the surrounding water (Young, 1950, p. 197). Presumably the parathyroids of land vertebrates have developed from these cells; they continue to perform a function of the gills that was still needed after aquatic respiration ceased and the only site of outflow of salts became the kidney. Control of the salt exchanges of the latter continued to be influenced by a hormone produced by cells of the branchial region, which had originally been responsible for the direct secretion of the salts but later controls calcium metabolism elsewhere, for example in bone.

8. The thymus

The thymus is an enigmatic organ lying dorsal to the sternum around the great vessels. It contains much lymphoid tissue and perhaps also has an endocrine nature. It arises by outgrowth of the ectodermal and endodermal epithelia of the third branchial cleft and pouch to form a solid mass of cells. Many lymphoid cells enter this mass and proceed to give dense aggregates of 'thymocytes', which are probably identical with small lymphocytes (Fig. 224). Many of these cells move away into the blood-stream and the cortical region of the thymus, in which this tissue mostly appears, is probably best considered as an organ for producing lymphocytes.

The medulla is occupied by many reticular cells, derived from the original folded pharyngeal epithelium. It also contains the characteristic *corpuscles of Hassall*, concentric arrangements of cells of ectodermal origin, those at the centre showing signs of degeneration and perhaps undergoing a process similar to keratinization.

The thymus is relatively large during the embryonic period and in early life and it is usually supposed that in man it undergoes continual reduction ('involution') after puberty. Yet the thymus is quite conspicuous in many adult mammals (for example the rabbit) and study

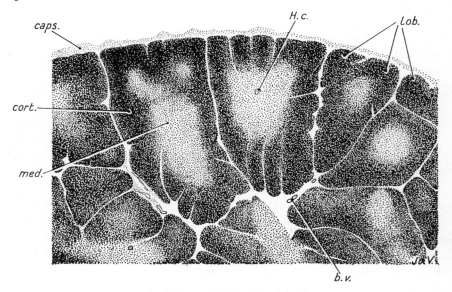

FIG. 224. Thymus gland of new-born human.

b.v. blood-vessel; *caps.* connective tissue capsule; *cort.* cortex; *H.c.* Hassal's corpuscle; *med.* medulla; *lob.* lobules of lymphoid tissue. (From a photograph by Mr. K. C. Richardson.)

of suitable cases shows that quite large thymus glands may be found in people of all ages. The reason that it is usually small after death is that it becomes reduced in size when the body reacts to conditions of severe stress, such as those inflicted by disease (p. 548). This process of thymic atrophy may be promoted by activity of the gonads and adrenal and is accentuated if these are excessively stimulated by pituitary hormones. Conversely castration or adrenalectomy delays or perhaps reverses the atrophy of the thymus. The thymus is thus concerned in some way with the activity of resisting infection and in the reaction of the various endocrine organs during that process.

These changes in the thymus during stress presumably depend upon its content of lymphocytes. The significance of the reticular cells and the corpuscles of Hassall remain quite obscure. They may be concerned in the curious relation that is found between the thymus and muscular contraction. In the disease known as *myasthenia gravis* there is a weakness of action of the striped muscles, due to some defect at the neuromuscular junction. The condition is sometimes associated with enlargement of the thymus; removal of part or all of this gland may ameliorate or cure the disease (Keynes, 1953). This is so even if the gland is not grossly enlarged, but as already explained it is not easy to define the normal size of the thymus.

Further evidence of secretory activity by the thymus is the fact that extracts of the glands removed from myasthenic patients prevent the effect of nerve impulses in producing contraction of the muscles of the rat's diaphragm. It seems that the property of the thymic secretion is to alter the balance between the production or activity of acetyl choline and the enzyme cholinesterase that destroys it, in favour of the latter, so that nerve impulses are not able to produce contraction (Wilson, 1952; Keynes, 1953). Further information will be needed before the full significance of this aspect of thymic functioning is understood. It may perhaps be related to the part played by another pharyngeal derivative, the parathyroid, in the control of calcium and phosphorus metabolism.

XXX

THE ADRENAL GLANDS

1. Chemical signals ensuring response to stress

THE adrenal bodies of mammals (sometimes called suprarenals) are a pair of organs of orange-yellow colour, lying near the kidneys. They contain two distinct types of cell, the cortical, arising from the coelomic epithelium, and the medullary, which develops with the sympathetic ganglion-cells from the neural crest. The significance of the association of the two types of tissue is still not clear.

The two tissues both serve to send signals that elicit in various parts of the body reactions that are appropriate to conditions of stress. Adrenaline, secreted by the medulla, produces immediate preparations for attack or defence, by changes in the distribution of the blood, in the level of blood-sugar, and in other ways (p. 543). The secretions of the adrenal cortex are concerned with long-term preparations to resist adverse conditions and infection, making it possible for the various organs to undertake the slower regulatory adjustments by which they assist in maintaining homeostasis. An animal without its adrenal cortex is therefore apt to fail when any of its tissues are called upon to adapt themselves to changed conditions. This organ is therefore of central importance in the processes that ensure that the various tissues remain adequate to meet the conditions of the environment.

2. Evolution of the adrenal glands

As with several other endocrine organs we can trace the phylogenetic history from the condition in which the adrenals consisted of cells scattered widely through the body. Even in mammals there remains a considerable amount of adrenal tissue that is not incorporated within the gland. In *Amphioxus* no tissue of definitely adrenal nature has been identified and in lampreys and hag-fishes (cyclostomes) there are no compact adrenal bodies but some cells found scattered along the cardinal veins have been claimed as cortical and medullary tissue. It is probable that in these early types of vertebrate the individual tissues throughout the body make their own responses to conditions of stress, without the assistance of secretions by a centralized adrenal system.

In elasmobranch fishes there are two separate sets of tissue, the *interrenal glands*, representing the adrenal cortex, and the *suprarenals* the medulla. Both tissues are found spread over many body segments, the suprarenals being a long series of pairs, extending from the level of the heart to the hind end of the coelom (Young, 1950, p. 160). In bony fishes the two parts are also separated, but in all tetrapods they are combined to form a single organ, the interrenal tissue (cortex) more or less enclosing the suprarenal tissue (medulla). In urodeles the organ is spread out over many segments, but in tetrapods it develops mainly in a few segments, although small groups of cells of both sorts occur elsewhere. In mammals the sympathetic ganglia contain medullary tissue and there are masses of cortical cells in various parts of the abdomen. Centralization of the adrenal cells into one organ has therefore proceeded gradually throughout vertebrate history and is not complete even in mammals. The hormones evidently operate locally, as well as for the body as a whole under central control.

3. The adrenal medulla

The adrenal medulla occupies the centre of the gland, forming an irregular parenchyma of cells secreting substances that assist the sympathetic system in making the body ready for attack or defence. The cells contain powerful reducing substances and show chemical reactions that are rare elsewhere in the body, from which they get the name of *chromophil cells*. The tissue has a characteristic open structure on account of the large vascular sinusoids between the cells (Fig. 225, p. 540).

The adrenal medulla is richly innervated and the nerve-fibres make contact with the gland-cells themselves and not merely with the blood-vessels (Fig. 226, p. 541). The nerve-fibres reach the glands from the splanchnic nerves (p. 387) and since they carry a myelin sheath it was suggested by Elliott that they are preganglionic fibres (p. 385). This has been proved to be correct by the demonstration that the fibres in the gland degenerate after the ventral roots of the hinder thoracic and upper lumbar region have been severed (Fig. 227, p. 541).

Like other preganglionic nerve-fibres those of the adrenal produce their effect by the liberation of acetyl choline close to the surfaces of the adrenal medullary cells (p. 398). No other visceral tissue is innervated in this way, without the interposition of a postganglionic autonomic nerve-cell, and it is clear that the chromophil cells of the adrenal themselves represent the postganglionic neurons. The interest

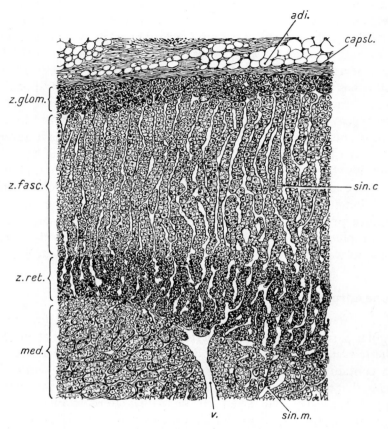

FIG. 225. Adrenal gland of a monkey (*Macacus*) showing zones of the cortex.

adi. adipose tissue; *capsl.* capsule; *med.* medulla; *sin.c.* sinusoids of the cortex; *sin.m.* sinusoids of the medulla; *v.* vein; *z.fasc.* zona fasciculata; *z.glom.* zona glomerulosa; *z.ret.* zona reticularis.

(Drawn from a photograph supplied by Mr. K. C. Richardson.)

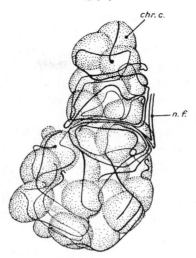

FIG. 226. Diagram of the innervation of the adrenal medulla of a guinea-pig showing the nerve-fibres (*n.f.*) ramifying around the chromophil cells (*chr.c.*). (After Willard, D. M., *Quart. J. micr. Sci.* **78**, 1936.)

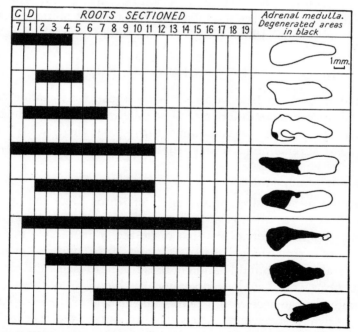

FIG. 227. Diagram showing degeneration in the adrenal medulla following section of spinal roots in the cat. The black rectangles show the nerves cut at operation. The figures to the right show the area of degeneration that results. (Young, J. Z., *J. Anat., Lond.* **73**, 1939.)

of this relation is greatly increased by the discovery that the sympathetic nerve-fibres as well as the adrenal-cells act by the production of adrenaline, or a similar substance (p. 399). The hormone manufactured in the gland is poured into the blood-stream and acts at a distance, that produced at the ends of sympathetic nerve-fibres is liberated where the nerve-fibres run close to the smooth muscle-cells or gland-cells that they control.

It was shown by Oliver and Schafer in 1894 that the adrenal (like the pituitary) contains a substance that on injection produces rise of blood-pressure. The adrenal substance was identified in 1901 and synthesized soon after. Like thyroxine, *adrenaline* (= epinephrine) is a derivative of tyrosine, but in this case a relatively simple one, its composition being *l*-3.4-dihydroxy, α phenyl, β methyl amino ethanol:

$$\text{OH}\langle\rangle\text{—CH(OH)CH}_2.\text{NH(CH}_3).$$

Salts of adrenaline are readily soluble in water but are quickly oxidized in alkaline solution to a pink substance. Large amounts of a reducing substance, probably ascorbic acid (vitamin C), are present in the gland.

Besides adrenaline the medulla also contains the homologous non-methylated ethanol amino base, *nor*-adrenaline:

$$\text{OH}\langle\rangle\text{—CH(OH).CH}_2.\text{NH}_2.$$

The actions of this substance are similar to those of adrenaline, though there are quantitative differences. The adrenaline-like substance produced at sympathetic nerve endings throughout the body (p. 398) is mainly *nor*-adrenaline (v. Euler, 1951).

4. Actions of adrenaline

Injection of adrenaline produces effects throughout the body that mimic those of stimulation of the sympathetic nerves (p. 392); bringing into play the mechanisms that make the animal ready to fight or run. There is constriction of the arterioles of the skin and of most of the visceral organs, but dilatation of those of the muscles and especially of the heart, producing a diversion of blood into these organs. Adrenaline has an accelerating action on the beat of the isolated heart if the vagi have been cut; when they are intact the rise of blood-pressure that follows the adrenaline injection may act upon the receptors of the carotid sinus to produce a reflex fall of heart-rate. An adrenaline concentration of 0·002 mg./kg. is sufficient to raise the blood-pressure when injected into a decerebrate cat and this probably represents about the amount released per minute by the animal under experimental conditions (see below). Adrenaline inhibits the contraction of the smooth musculature of most of the viscera, including that of the stomach and urinary bladder, but it excites contraction of the gall-bladder, ureter, and sphincters of the gut. Its action is thus in general to stop visceral activities, although it causes contraction of the uterine muscle, especially during pregnancy.

Several of its actions promote the efficiency of oxygen transport and of the supply of fuel to muscle. It produces relaxation of the muscles of the bronchioles of the lungs (advantage is taken of this in the use of adrenaline for the relief of asthma) and contraction of the spleen, causing an increase in the number of circulating red corpuscles. Acting upon the liver, adrenaline causes mobilization of sugar and thus has effects opposite to those of insulin (p. 565), producing hyperglycaemia and even glycosuria. The clotting time of the blood is decreased. Other particular actions of adrenaline produce further assistance in defence, varying with the animal species. Thus by causing contraction of the dilatator muscle of the iris the pupil is opened wide. Action on the muscles of the hairs produces 'bristling' of the fur in cats; salivation and lachrimation occur in some species and sweating in many ungulates, though not in man.

This is an imposing list of actions; adrenaline, a substance produced normally in the body, is evidently a very potent drug. Related substances such as ephedrine, tyramine, and benzedrine are mostly somewhat less powerful in action than adrenaline itself but are used instead of it as coagulants, for the relief of asthma, to constrict inflamed vascular membranes in the nose, or for their general 'tonic' and stimulating effects. Being more stable than adrenaline, they can be taken by the mouth.

5. Amount of adrenaline secreted

It would be of great interest to know the conditions and rate of secretion of adrenaline in the intact body and various techniques have been devised for estimating this. Cannon and his colleagues used cats whose hearts had been denervated by severing the vagi and sympathetic nerves. They found that the heart accelerated when such animals were excited or hurt. For instance, when a dog was placed in front of a cat the increase occurred within 10 seconds and reached as much as 40 beats a minute. If the adrenal glands were then removed these increases were no longer seen and this provides a convincing demonstration of the 'emergency' function of the gland. Electrical stimulation of the great splanchnic nerves produced acceleration of the heart-rate of intact cats.

Direct assay of the amount of adrenaline produced has been performed by using the vena cava, into which the adrenal veins discharge, as a collecting pocket. The amounts recorded by this technique are small when the animal is at rest (about 0·002 mg./kg./min.) but they increase nearly ten times during splanchnic stimulation. It has been suggested that the adrenaline has a tonic rather than an emergency action and some workers have even denied that it plays any part at all in the normal life of the body. This would be strange indeed for such an active substance. There is little doubt that adrenaline is secreted to provide a specific set of signals that rapidly reach all parts of the body when an animal or man is frightened or angry and also during violent exercise, pain, and perhaps in other conditions such as cold, anaesthesia, or asphyxia. We must, however, avoid such over-simplifications as the statement that 'the emotion of fear is due to the secretion of adrenaline'; our new knowledge of these matters is interesting, but not yet sufficient to encompass a complex human emotion. The controversy emphasizes the importance of detailed quantitative knowledge about endocrine organs. After the general outlines of the function of an organ have been discovered by experiment much quantitative investigation is required before we are able to acquire satisfactory understanding and control of its actions during normal life.

6. Structure of the adrenal cortex

The outer portion of the adrenal gland is more extensive than the medulla and even more important for life. An animal can survive cautery of the two medullas but complete removal of both adrenal glands leads to death within 15 days, except under special conditions. The greater part of the cortex consists of radially arranged cords of cells, the *zona fasciculata* (Fig. 225). These are continually added to from the outside by small groups of cells just beneath the capsule of the gland, the *zona glomerulosa*. Next to the medulla is the *zona reticularis*, in which the cords are irregular and the cells are mostly degenerating.

The adrenal cortical cells are filled with fatty droplets, including neutral fats, steroids, and phosphatides. There are few of these droplets in the cells of the glomerulosa, many in the fasciculata and fewer again in the reticularis. Throughout life cells are probably continually moving inward, passing through cycles of development, function, and degeneration.

The activity of the adrenal cortex is not under the direct control of

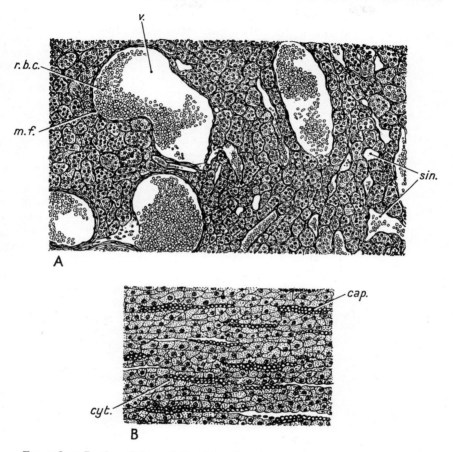

FIG. 228. A, Portion of the medulla of the adrenal gland of a baboon; B, portion of zona fasciculata of the cortex of the adrenal gland of a rabbit.

cyt. cytoplasm of cortical cells vacuolated by removal of lipoids; *cap.* capillary of the cortex; *m.f.* smooth muscle-fibres, mostly longitudinal; *r.b.c.* red blood corpuscles; *sin.* sinusoids; *v.* vein. (Drawn from photographs kindly supplied by Mr. K. C. Richardson.)

any nerve-fibres. Regulation of secretion is by the slower method of chemical signals sent from the pituitary gland, and by the 'demand' of the target tissues, which affects the level of adrenal hormones in the blood. This type of control is typical of the slower processes of 'adaptation', in contrast to the quicker control mediated by the nervous system.

7. Cortical steroids

The demonstration of the endocrine function of the adrenal cortex began with the discovery that extracts ('cortin') are able to prevent death following adrenal removal. The active principles of the cortex are steroid substances, probably synthesized from cholesterol, which

Cyclo-penteno-perhydro-phenanthrene
THE STEROID RING STRUCTURE

CORTICOSTERONE   17 *hydroxycorticosterone*

11 *dehydro* 17 *hydroxycorticosterone*
CORTISONE

18 *aldehydocorticosterone*
ALDOSTERONE

occurs in large concentration in the gland. Twenty-nine different crystalline steroid substances have been extracted but many of these may be intermediates in the course of hormone production. It is uncertain whether the adrenal cortex emits into the blood one or several different steroids. The substances corticosterone, 17-hydroxycorticosterone, and aldosterone are almost certainly normal products. Those who believe that the gland produces a variety of specific hormones speak of control of carbohydrate metabolism by glucocorticoids, of salt exchanges by mineralocorticoids and of development of the male characters by testocorticoids. These steroid substances resemble the sex hormones (pp. 668, 686), indeed progesterone and androgens also occur in considerable amounts in the adrenal. It is significant that the adrenal cortex develops from the mesoderm of the coelomic epithelium, close to the gonads.

8. Effects of corticosteroids in the body

We are far from a complete understanding of the significance of the steroids for the metabolism of cells in general but it may be that the activities of the adrenal cortex represent a specialization of steroid exchanges that occur in all cells throughout the body. The cortical hormones influence many tissues and it is uncertain what common factor, if any, is involved (see Sayers, 1950; Verzar, 1952). The effect of these substances is to assist the mechanisms by which each type of cell mobilizes energy for the performance of its characteristic type of work. There are indications that the adrenal steroids influence the permeability of the surfaces of cells and perhaps also of mitochondria and of other surfaces within cells at which enzymic actions proceed (p. 22). Among other effects the cortical steroids influence carbohydrate metabolism and water and salt exchanges, which are among the most fundamental of all cell activities. Adrenal deficiency leads to change in concentration of carbohydrates and salts in the blood, and especially to a fall in blood sodium. The intracellular potassium is raised as the sodium of the intercellular fluids falls. Further effects follow these changes, especially loss of water.

It may be that the fundamental effect of the corticosteroids is on the energy-producing systems of the cells. Control of these would, of course, influence many other metabolic activities, including protein metabolism, fat production, and salt exchanges. There are indications that all the adrenal and gonadal steroids act in this way on the fundamental metabolic activities of the cells. The actions of the different steroids differ in the details of their effects and are thus able to serve as signals that produce specific influences on the tissues.

After removal of both adrenals there is loss of appetite, vomiting, muscular weakness, lowering of blood-pressure and of temperature. Lesions appear in the linings of the gut and the actions of the renal tubules are affected. Death follows within 2 weeks after removal of the adrenals in most animals, but survival is prolonged during pregnancy, perhaps on account of the presence of progesterone from the corpus luteum. Injection of progesterone will prolong life after adrenalectomy, but complete protection is obtained by injection of cortical extract or cortisone, especially if accompanied by a diet low in potassium but rich in sodium. Doses of large quantities of sodium ions are of considerable benefit in maintaining life after adrenalectomy.

9. Reaction of the adrenal to stress

After an animal or man has undergone stress, say by trauma, there are changes in glucose tolerance and nitrogen excretion and other signs of alteration of the fundamental processes of energy interchange and protein metabolism by the cells. The adrenal cortical secretions play a part in these adjustments. For example, adaptation of the blood-sugar and liver glycogen to low atmospheric pressure does not occur after adrenalectomy. The adrenal cortex is very sensitive to the demand for its secretions by the tissues. If one or more of these target organs uses increased amounts there follows a hypertrophy of the adrenal cortex. Response by this gland therefore plays a large part in the processes by which the organism adapts itself to particular conditions.

Both parts of the adrenal are thus involved in the actions in which the body reacts to situations that are liable to produce serious disturbance of its activities. Selye and others have recently emphasized the wide variety of changes that are involved in this *general adaptation syndrome* in response to stress. Stress may be set up in various ways, for example, by cold, fatigue, infections, or toxic agents. In response to any of these the body shows a common syndrome, which includes discharge of adrenal hormones, hypertrophy of the adrenal cortex, involution of the thymus and lymphoid apparatus (p. 536) and disturbances of the gastrointestinal tract, kidneys, reproductive organs, and others. This syndrome includes both immediate defence reactions that are produced mainly through the sympathetic-adrenal medullary system and slower adaptive reactions, which, as Selye puts it, 'comprise the "*learning*" of defence against future exposure to stress' (Selye, 1950).

The control of the adaptation syndrome is complicated. The pituitary body plays a central part through secretion of its adrenocorticotropic hormone (ACTH) following stress. The adrenal cortex responds to this substance during the immediate, or *alarm reaction*, stage by an output of steroid hormones and other substances. This is seen histologically within a few minutes of stressing (say, by exercise or haemorrhage) as a loss of lipid granules and cholesterol from the cells and a reduction of the normal high ascorbic acid content of the gland. There follows a stage in which the body shows increased powers of resistance to stress and during this period the adrenal cortex increases in width and there is an increase in the lipid granules, and in cholesterol and ascorbic acid. At the same time there is an increase in the number of mitotic figures in the cortex, especially in the outer layers (zona glomerulosa). Stress of a continuous type, such as is produced by fasting, low temperature or pregnancy, produces a gradual increase in the amount of ACTH secreted and in the size of the adrenal gland. Following removal of the adrenals animals show a

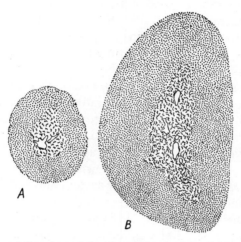

Fɪɢ. 229. Diagrams of sections of the adrenal glands of A, a domesticated rat and B, a wild rat, showing the effects of environmental conditions on the size of the adrenal glands. (After Richter, C. P., *Ciba Foundation Colloquia on Endocrinology*, iii. 1952.)

greatly reduced capacity to resist the damaging effects of various environmental conditions, such as cold, burning, anoxia, or infection.

The cortical steroids probably exert their protective effects in different ways under various conditions. It has been suggested that the gland serves to neutralize toxic products of shock, such as histamine, but that has never been proved. Injections of ACTH or cortisone lead to stimulation of the activity of the lymphoid tissue and to the breaking up of great numbers of lymphocytes. If these cells constitute a reserve of the serum globulins responsible for anti-body production (p. 268) we should see here the explanation of the activity of the gland in resisting infection.

Injections of ACTH and cortisone have a marked influence upon a series of conditions such as rheumatoid arthritis, which may collectively be called *collagen diseases*. It is not clear how these responses are related to other aspects of the adaptation syndrome, or indeed whether there is any such connexion. The influence may be directly upon the fibroblasts and other mesenchymal tissues or upon some aspect of the antigen-antibody relationship.

An interesting example of the effect of different environmental conditions is seen in the adrenals of rats of wild and laboratory stocks described by Richter (Fig. 229). The male rats whose adrenals are shown both weighed 390 gm. but the adrenal weighed 93 mg. in the one and only 18 mg. in the other. Correspondingly it was found that the domesticated rats showed a much lower resistance to various poisons than did the wild strain. On a deficient diet the laboratory animals had fits and died within 5–15 days, whereas the wild ones showed few fits and never succumbed. The behaviour of the two strains is also markedly different, the wild animals being fierce and aggressive. In captivity they are always ready to escape and they feed and breed poorly; animals of the laboratory stock rarely try to escape and they breed well. After adrenalectomy the laboratory rats were readily kept alive by suitable provision of salt solutions, whereas the wild ones always died under this therapy and often did not survive even with large doses of desoxycorticosterone.

Thus the condition of the adrenal system and indeed of the whole defence mechanism corresponds to the environmental conditions under which the animals live. It is not certain how much of the difference is due to hereditary influences and how much to memories established during the lifetime of the individual. Norway rats have become domesticated for laboratory use only during the last 100 years at most. Yet it may be that selection of genes has produced large changes even during this relatively short time. Richter observes that selection would operate especially severely at times of mating and lactation. Wild rats are so fierce and 'suspicious' that only the tamest of them will mate in captivity. Similarly the mothers are so 'apprehensive' that at the least disturbance they kill the entire litter. Laboratory conditions could rapidly provide selection for the tamer types. Richter reports that attempts to tame young wild rats are only partly successful. They remain nervous and ready to bite or escape and their adrenals are large. Yet, it may be that a large part of the difference depends upon the amount of stressing received during the lifetime and hence on the different conditions of the adrenals and other organs.

10. The adrenal glands and sexual development

The adrenal cortex sends signals that assist in the control of sexual differentiation and the maintenance of the oestrous cycle in the female. After removal of the ovaries cyclical changes may continue in the uterus and vagina, but they cease if the adrenals are removed and the animal is maintained on a uniform dose of cortical extract (Zuckerman *et al*, 1938). This suggests that rhythmic changes in the adrenal may be an essential part of the basic timing mechanism of the oestrous cycle.

Abnormal activity of the adrenal cortex is associated with abnormalities of sexual development and functioning. These are usually in the direction of masculinity, producing precocious development in boys and masculinization of girls. The overactivity, which may be due to a tumour, leads to production of unusual amounts of androgenic steroids. The fact that such changes can so greatly alter the time of onset of sexual maturity makes plausible the suggestion that mutation and selection may have operated through the adrenal to produce new races. If, as has been suggested, man has developed by the neoteny of a race of apes, the necessary genetic changes may have affected the functioning of the adrenal cortical tissue, perhaps related to a change in the action of the pituitary gland.

XXXI

THE PITUITARY GLAND

1. The master gland

THE pituitary body (hypophysis cerebri), like the other ductless glands, is derived from tissues that previously performed other functions. Its activities are a special development of a fundamental part of the control system of all cells, namely, that which regulates metabolism and growth. The effects of the pituitary hormones influence the processes of synthesis of the very substance of the cells, including the metabolism of proteins, carbohydrates, and fats. The substances produced by the gland are themselves proteins and some of them act upon the enzyme systems of cells throughout the body that affect synthesis and growth. Many other activities are also influenced by the pituitary and thus proper co-ordination of these with the metabolic and growth processes is ensured.

On account of the multiplicity of its effects the pituitary is therefore accurately described as a master gland; it is the central computor of the chemical co-ordinating system, acting upon the other endocrines and in turn acted upon by them, so that it provides a focal point at which much of the bodily activity is adjusted.

The gland weighs only about 0·5 gm. in man and lies in the sella turcica of the sphenoid bone, close to the optic chiasma and attached by the infundibular stalk to the floor of the diencephalon. In the regulation of many processes it works with the overlying nervous centres of the hypothalamus, which constitute the central neural mechanism for the control of the internal activities of the body.

2. Phylogenetic history of the pituitary

The gland develops from two distinct rudiments, an inpushing of the buccal ectoderm, known as *Rathke's pouch* (hypophysis in the narrow sense), and a downgrowth from the brain, the *infundibulum*. The buccal portion perhaps corresponds to Muller's organ in *Amphioxus*, which is a patch of thickened ciliated and glandular ectoderm, probably concerned with feeding. In the sea squirts (Tunicates) there is a ciliated pouch, the *subneural gland*, lying in a similar position. Carlisle has shown that this pouch is a receptor organ, serving to control feeding. It also detects the presence of eggs or sperms in the water current and causes liberation of sperms, or ovulation, by production of a chemical substance that stimulates the nearby ganglion. The substance may be related to the gonadotropin of higher chordates and injection of mammalian chorionic gonadotropin to a sea squirt is followed by liberation of gametes.

The two parts of the pituitary are found constantly throughout the

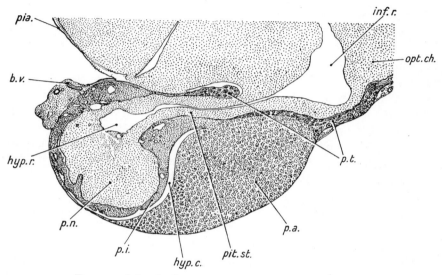

FIG. 230. A longitudinal section of the hypophysis of a cat.

b.v. blood-vessel; *hyp.c.* hypophysial cavity; *hyp.r.* hypophysial recess; *inf.r.* infundibular recess; *opt.ch.* optic chiasma; *p.a.* pars anterior (distalis); *p.i.* pars intermedia; *pia.* pia mater; *pit.st.* pituitary stalk; *p.n.* pars nervosa (posterior lobe); *p.t.* pars tuberalis.
(From a photograph by Mr. K. C. Richardson.)

Craniata but with some differences of position. The cavity of Rathke's pocket remains large and open to the exterior in lampreys and in the fish *Polypterus*, but becomes much reduced in many vertebrates and in adult man consists only of a few separated spaces. The cavity of the infundibular stalk likewise varies from a large space in cyclostomes to none at all in man.

3. Parts of the pituitary

The major parts of the adult pituitary (Fig. 230) are the *pars anterior* (= distalis), formed by folding of the epithelium of the front face of Rathke's pouch, the *pars intermedia*, developed from its hinder face, *pars tuberalis* from its upper portion, and *pars nervosa* from the infundibulum. From the position of the rudiments it follows that, in mammals, the pars intermedia lies against the pars nervosa and the pars tuberalis surrounds the infundibular stalk and thus lies close to the tuber cinereum of the brain. It has been common in the past to distinguish between anterior and posterior lobes of the pituitary, with a dividing line at the pituitary cleft (remains of the cavity of Rathke's pouch), but it is not certain that the parts of the posterior section act as one unit.

These four parts can be recognized in nearly all vertebrates (Green, 1951), but their relative positions in the adult may vary, for instance, in elasmobranchs the pars 'anterior' is behind the others and in anurans the tuberalis forms a separate region. Experimenters have taken advantage of such special conditions for the independent removal of the parts. The parts are not developed to the same extent in all vertebrates, for instances, there is said to be no intermedia in birds, whales, sea cows, or armadilloes. Again, the pars nervosa is a single-layered epithelium in lampreys but a relatively massive solid organ in man. Much may be learned from such differences; it is to be expected that an organ so closely bound up with the growth and life of the animals would change as the life changes.

The blood-supply of the pituitary comes partly by hypophysial arteries but also from a portal system of vessels running along the infundibular stalk. Capillaries within the neural tissue of the hypothalamus unite to form these portal vessels, which open into sinusoids of the pars distalis and thus constitute a second capillary bed. From the sinusoids collecting veins lead to the venous sinuses around the pituitary body.

4. Pars anterior

The pars anterior is so distinct in function that it may be considered as a separate unit. It consists of masses of cells of three types, chromophobes (= chief, principal, or reserve cells), acidophils (α cells), and basophils (β cells), whose names explain their characteristics. About half of all the cells are chromophobes and of the chromophils there are usually three times more α than β cells, but the latter increase after castration. The pars anterior is very vascular and there are large sinusoids among the cells.

The secretions of the anterior pituitary probably affect every cell in the body. At least eleven 'functions' have been claimed for the gland and six separate anterior pituitary hormones with distinct actions have been recognized. It is not easy to reduce this bewildering variety of effects to order. The substances extractable are proteins or portions of proteins, several of them have been isolated in apparently pure form. It is not certain that such a large number of wholly distinct substances is actually secreted during life. It may be that the methods used for extraction separate off portions from a large protein complex, each fraction having a particular action. Such 'purified' extracts have been called 'hormone fragments'.

The actions of the anterior pituitary may be classified into two main groups, concerned respectively with (1) the promotion of growth and the regulation of metabolism ('metabolic hormones'), (2) the control of the functions of the gonads and adrenals ('gonadotropic and adrenocorticotropic hormones'). There is some evidence that correspondingly two main hormone types are produced, the first from the α and the second from the β cells, but there are effects of the gland that do not fall clearly into either category. Pituitary secretions influence so many aspects of cell metabolism that classification is very difficult.

5. Regulation of growth and metabolism

It has long been known that there is a connexion between the pituitary gland and growth. In the condition known as *gigantism* or *acromegaly*, where the bones are abnormal, the pituitary fossa is found to be enlarged. Conversely, if the pituitary gland is deficient or is damaged growth is seriously impaired and the individual becomes a dwarf. The proof of the existence of a growth-promoting factor was given by Evans and Long in 1921. They made injections of saline pituitary extracts intraperitoneally into young rats, which proceeded to grow to twice the size of control animals. Further studies have confirmed that the acidophil cells secrete a substance whose injection causes increased retention of nitrogen and rapid growth. Dwarf races of mice lack α cells in the pituitary and conversely such cells are numerous in giants. Evidently this substance in some way promotes the processes of protein synthesis throughout the body. The growth hormone is a simple protein, whose molecular weight is claimed to be 46,800.

There are various other 'metabolic' effects of extracts of the anterior pituitary. Under suitable conditions they may produce (1) Control of production of body fat and its deposition in the liver ('ketogenic' effects). (2) Mobilization of sugar from the liver, acting in the opposite sense to insulin in producing hyperglycemia ('glycotropic' effects) (p. 565) Diabetogenic effects, causing destruction of the islets of

Langerhans. (4) Pancreatotropic effects, increasing the amount of islet tissue. It is probable that all of these effects are produced by similar substances, perhaps by a single 'growth' hormone (Young, 1953).

Probably associated with the α cells are some further important specific influences on other organs. The thyrotropic action of pituitary extracts causes discharge of the colloid vesicles and appearance of mitosis in the thyroid epithelium. Following removal of the pituitary there is atrophy of the thyroid and reduction of basal metabolic rate and of nitrogen excretion. Tadpoles fail to undergo metamorphosis after this operation. A puzzling finding is that injection of pituitary extracts may cause metamorphosis of tadpoles from which the thyroid has been removed.

The promotion of milk secretion is another activity of the pituitary that is probably performed by the α cells, the hormone being known as *prolactin*. Besides its effect on the mammary gland this substance also promotes secretion of 'milk' by the crop-gland of pigeons, which indeed provides the standard method for assay of prolactin. This is a curious parallel response by tissues of birds and mammals, whose derivation must surely be completely independent even though their biological values are similar. Perhaps the clue to the connexion may be found in the similarity of the metabolic processes that are concerned in the secretion.

6. Influence of the pituitary on the gonads

The regulation of the development and functioning of the gonads depends on a gonadotropic substance, or series of them, formed by the β cells. Following removal of the pituitary glands the gonads fail to develop in young animals and atrophy in adults. During pregnancy and following castration the number of β cells increases. This reciprocal interaction between endocrines and the organs that they stimulate is a constantly recurring theme.

Two types of effect are produced on the gonads by the pituitary and these are apparently due to distinct hormones, which can be separated. The *follicle-stimulating hormone* (FSH) causes growth of the ovarian follicles during the early phase of the oestrous cycle (p. 680) and also stimulates spermatogenesis in the testis (Van Oordt *et al*, 1952). The *luteinizing hormone* (LH) causes development of the tissue of the corpus luteum after discharge of the ovum at ovulation. It also stimulates the interstitial cells of the testis and ovary and is therefore sometimes called the interstitial-cell-stimulating hormone (ICSH).

Substances similar in action to these pituitary gonadotropic hormones are excreted in the urine of some species during pregnancy. Their effect on the ovary is used as the basis of the Ascheim-Zondek test for pregnancy. These *prolans* isolated from the urine are produced by the placenta.

The gonadotropic pituitary hormones are both glycoproteins. LH has been isolated and has molecular weight of the order of 100,000. Fluctuations in the relative amounts of FSH and LH produced are probably intimately concerned in the maintenance of the oestrous and menstrual cycles (p. 685).

7. Influence of the pituitary on the adrenals

Some of the most marked effects of the anterior pituitary are produced through its influence upon the adrenal cortex. The adrenocorticotropic hormone (ACTH) is probably produced by the β cells and there may be something in common between its action on the steroid-secreting adrenal cells and the actions of the gonadotropic hormones, which control steroid secretion by the gonads. The fact that both the adrenal cortex and the gonads develop from the mesoderm of the coelomic epithelium may be significant in this connexion. After removal of the pituitary the adrenal cortex undergoes atrophy and after injection of ACTH it becomes greatly enlarged. ACTH has been isolated and is a simple protein of molecular weight 4,600.

Injection of small amounts of ACTH produces rapid discharge of adrenal cortical hormones, with all their marked effects on the connective and other tissues throughout the body (p. 549). It is probable that it is by this means that the compensating mechanisms produced by stress are released (p. 548). Trauma or sudden demand for action first initiates release of adrenaline. Either by the action of this on the pituitary, or by some other pathway, ACTH is liberated and through its influence the adrenal produces the substances that assist the tissues to give the proper reactions that adapt them to meet the new conditions.

8. Control of the anterior pituitary

There are some reports of sympathetic nerve-fibres in the pars anterior but their cells of origin and their function are uncertain. They may possibly regulate the blood-supply. Fibres of the hypothalamo-hypophyseal tract (p. 559) do not reach to the pars anterior. It is therefore probable that the secretion of this part of the gland is not directly regulated by nervous means. Several facts suggest that the hypothalamus controls the anterior pituitary by the transport in the blood of a substance that is produced in the nervous tissue. By embedding a suitable induction coil within the head of a rabbit it is possible to provide stimulation, by remote control, over a period of time of tissues close to electrodes attached to the secondary coil. Using this method Harris (1948, 1955) found that with electrodes embedded in the hypothalamus stimulation produces ovulation in the rabbit, but that this response did not follow when the electrodes were in the pars anterior of the pituitary. It is known that the ovulation is produced by the circulation to the ovary of a secretion of the anterior lobe (p. 690) and the conclusion is that the hypothalamus induces this secretion by hormonal means. An appropriate vascular pathway is present in the abundant vessels of the infundibular stalk (p. 554); the very vascular tissue of the pars tuberalis, which is applied to the floor of the hypothalamus may have the special function of mediating this transport. It may be, however, that substances secreted by the hypothalamus can reach the pituitary by other pathways, it is not certain that the integrity of the hypophysial stalk is essential for the transport.

The main factors controlling the actions of the anterior lobe of the pituitary are probably provided by the tissues upon which it acts. The activity of the adrenal cortex and gonads, for example, profoundly influence the pituitary. These are outstanding examples of mutual interactions that occur between the pituitary and many other cell types throughout the body. The target organs for pituitary hormones can influence the pituitary by substances that they themselves secrete into the blood-stream or by the effect that their utilization of pituitary hormones has upon the levels of those hormones in the blood, which alters the 'demand' made upon the pituitary. In these ways a complex interlocking control system is set up, which ensures that the metabolic actions throughout the body are appropriate to the demands made by the tissues and thus ultimately by the environment. Methods for describing this control system exactly should help in understanding how continual correspondence between the action of the organism and the environment is ensured.

9. Summary of the anterior pituitary actions

The actions of the anterior pituitary therefore fall into two main classes, the growth-promoting and the sex- and adrenal-regulating, but several 'hormones' with distinct effects are found in each group. The substances that affect growth include the 'growth', 'thyrotropic', and perhaps 'lactogenic' hormones, whereas the gonad-regulating group includes 'follicle-stimulating', 'luteinizing', and 'adrenocortico-tropic' fractions. Our knowledge of pituitary activity has shown remarkable advances recently, considering the small size of the gland and the protein nature of its products, which make work on the subject very difficult. There is every reason to hope that further work will throw still more light on how the activities of these cells stimulate and are stimulated by those of other parts of the body. The varied complexes of symptoms that accompany pituitary disease suggest that the gland regulates the life of the various parts of the body by some delicate balance of activities within its own cells. This balance is itself influenced by secretions from other organs and an elaborate chemical control system is thus established.

10. The posterior pituitary

The posterior lobe of the pituitary includes the partes nervosa, intermedia and tuberalis but it is not certain how far each of these contributes to the functions of the gland. The nervosa, derived from the floor of the brain, consists in man and most mammals of a solid mass of fusiform cells with long branched processes, the *pituicytes*. They are probably derived from the ependyma and are comparable with neuroglia cells rather than with neurons.

The pars intermedia consists of a thin band of basophil cells, lying between the anterior and the nervosa and mingling in the form of a number of cords with the tissue of the latter so that the two are difficult to separate. The pars tuberalis consists of masses of cells similar to those of the intermedia. The nerve-supply of the posterior lobe is mainly provided by the hypophysial tract, a bundle of fibres that arise from cells of the supra-optic and paraventricular nuclei of the hypothalamus, pass down the infundibular stalk and spread out to end in contact with the cell processes of the pituicytes (Figs. 231 and 232) and perhaps also with the cells of the intermedia. This peculiar bundle of nerve-fibres must be considered as a central tract rather than a peripheral nerve and it probably controls the output of secretion from the posterior portion of the gland. Indeed it is claimed that at least one of the active principles of the posterior lobe is produced within the cell bodies of the hypothalamic nerve-cells and carried down their axons to the pituitary (Bargmann and Scharrer, 1951). The neurons that give rise to the fibres of the hypophysial tract contain abundant granules (Fig. 233), and these can also be seen within the axons and in the posterior lobe. If the tract is severed the material

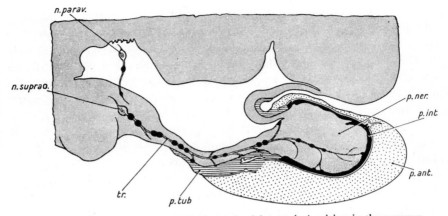

FIG. 231. Diagram of course of the hypophysial tract (*tr.*) arising in the paraventricular (*n.parav.*) and supra-optic nuclei (*n.suprao.*) and passing to the pars nervosa (*p.ner.*).

p.ant. pars anterior; *p.int.* intermedia; *p.tub.* tuberalis. (After Bargmann.)

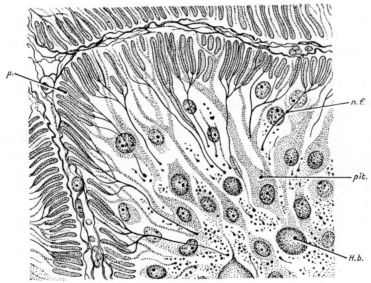

FIG. 232. Histological organization of the pars nervosa as seen in the opossum. Nerve-fibres of the hypophysial tract (*n.f.*) make contact with the pituicytes (*pit.*) whose outer processes make palisades (*p.*) perhaps coated with some neurosecretorv substance. *H.b.* Herring bodies.

(After Bodian, *Bull. Johns Hopkins Hosp.* **89**, 1951.)

accumulates at the cut central ends of the fibres (Fig. 233). Material is normally transported along nerve-fibres for trophic purposes (p. 333); the process found in this particular tract is a special case of use of this transport for a form of chemical signalling that has been called *neurosecretion*. The transport and release of these active stimulating substances may be especially suited to the maintenance of a given

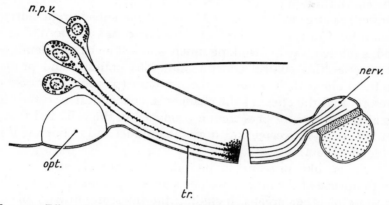

FIG. 233. Effect of sectioning of the hypophysial tract. Granules accumulate at the central ends of the cut fibres.

nerv. pars nervosa; *n.p.v.*, paraventricular nucleus; *tr.*, hypophysial tract; *opt.*, optic nerve. (After Bargmann, *Amer. Scientist* **39**, 1951.)

level of activity for a long period of time. The passage of nerve impulses, each lasting only for a short time, may be less efficient for this purpose.

11. Hormones of the posterior pituitary

Extracts of the posterior lobe have several physiological effects. The extract known as *pituitrin* has been shown to contain three fractions with distinct effects, *pitressin*, *pitocin*, and *intermedin*. Pitressin causes constriction of all blood-vessels except those of the kidney, the latter are consequently then passively dilated by the rise in blood-pressure. The effect of pitressin on the blood-pressure is therefore less specific than that of adrenaline; there is little evidence to show what part it plays in the control of blood-pressure in life. Besides its action on arteries it produces constriction of the capillaries of frogs and perhaps also of mammals.

A more important action of pitressin, or a substance like it produced by the pituitary, is the antidiuretic effect. Pituitary extracts promote reabsorption of water from the kidney tubules and when the posterior pituitary is not functioning properly the condition of *diabetes insipidus* results, enormous quantities of water being passed while the subject suffers from intense thirst. Injections of pitressin quickly alleviate the condition, stopping the outflow of water.

The flow of urine is normally regulated by the response of the cells of the supra-optic nucleus of the hypothalamus, acting as detectors of the concentration of salts in the blood (p. 420). If the blood is concentrated, as after much sweating, more of the anti-diuretic hormone is produced. Conversely, secretion of the hormone is reduced when the blood is diluted, say by drinking much water. The hypothalamic cells that exercise this control contain numerous granules and probably pass them along their axons to the pituitary (p. 560). It is possible, therefore, that the effect of the changes in concentration in the blood is to alter the amount of secretion produced in the cells and that the pituitary serves to receive and store the product and to liberate it into the blood-stream.

Pitocin is, like pitressin, a peptide substance. It stimulates the smooth muscle of the uterus in some stages of pregnancy and perhaps also those of other organs, including the intestine, urinary bladder, and the alveoli and ducts of the mammary glands. It does not affect the bronchioles of the lungs. The uterus, when near term, is exceedingly sensitive to pitocin, contracting in a solution of 1 in 25 million; the name pitocin ('sharp-pituitary substance') refers to this powerful action. There has been some doubt about the part played by the substance in normal parturition, in some animals birth can certainly take place after the pituitary has been removed. The increasing sensitivity of the uterine muscle as labour approaches can hardly be altogether accidental and in some animals delivery is slow if the hypophysial tract has been severed. Pitocin is used by obstetricians to assist the later stages of labour.

Intermedin (the 'B substance') causing the expansion of melanophores in fishes and amphibia can be extracted from the mammalian pituitary and separated from pitressin and pitocin. Its significance in mammals is not known and there is no clear evidence for the suggestion that it assists in light and dark adaptation in the retina.

There is still much doubt about the physiological significance and mode of action of the posterior lobe and its parts. All three 'hormones' can be extracted from all parts of the gland. At one time it was believed that they are elaborated in the intermedia and tuberalis and passed to the nervosa. This theory was developed to explain the fact that the nervosa contains great amounts of active material but has no typical gland-cells. 'Colloid' material passes along the stalk, but probably from hypothalamus to pituitary rather than in the reverse direction. It may be that the pituicytes serve to store this material or to co-ordinate its release with that of other substances.

The pituitary and hypothalamus thus often affect the same functions, both are regulators of the internal workings and metabolism of the body. Moreover, they probably influence each other reciprocally. The anti-diuretic effect, for instance, is produced very strongly when pituitary extracts are applied direct to the tissue of the hypothalamus. Thus by balancing the actions of parts of the body against each other, a combination of chemical and nervous signals is sent out by which steady continuity of life is maintained.

XXXII

THE PANCREATIC ISLETS AND THE CONTROL
OF CARBOHYDRATE METABOLISM

1. Diabetes

IT was discovered at the end of the nineteenth century that removal of the pancreas from a dog or cat produces a characteristic set of symptoms involving disturbance of the carbohydrate metabolism. The amount of sugar (glucose) present in the blood, normally about 0·1 per cent., rises after the operation to 0·2 and even 0·4 per cent. (hyperglycaemia), and sugar appears in the urine. Meanwhile sugar is produced in great amounts, mainly from protein, and there are also characteristic disturbances of fat metabolism. The animal shows muscular weakness, wasting, and other abnormalities and usually dies within 3 weeks. This set of symptoms resembles that seen in the human condition known as *diabetes mellitus*, in which sugar is found in the urine.

2. The pancreatic islets

The pancreas, besides the secretory acini that produce its digestive enzymes, also contains groups of cells that have a rich blood-supply but no secretory ducts to the exterior, the *islets of Langerhans*. As early as 1909 it was suggested that these cells produce a substance, later called *insulin,* that is responsible for preventing the conditions seen after removal of the pancreas. In 1922 Banting and Best provided satisfactory evidence that extracts of the pancreas are able to alleviate the symptoms of diabetes. The final proof that the islet cells produce the hormone has been complicated by the fact that they are mixed with the enzyme-secreting acinar tissue, and by the presence of at least three types of cell within the islets. The β cells are the most numerous and contain granules soluble in acid alcohol. The granules of the α cells are not soluble in alcohol, the γ cells have no granules. It is now considered that the β cells are the source of the hormone insulin, for the following reasons:

(1) In bony fishes the islets and enzyme-producing tissues can be separated and the former are found to contain insulin but not the

latter. (2) Ligation of the pancreatic duct in a mammal is soon followed by degeneration of the acinar tissue but the islets remain for a while and during this period the insulin content of the pancreas remains high. (3) If part of the pancreas is removed the β cells of the remainder undergo changes that can be interpreted as hypertrophy, especially if the animal is kept on a high carbohydrate diet. These changes do not, however, occur if injections of insulin are given. (4) When there is a tumour that increases the number of the β cells abnormally large amounts of insulin appear, moreover, growths of the islet tissue in abnormal parts of the body by metastasis of the tumour produce insulin. (5) Conversely if the β cells (but not the α cells) are destroyed by injection of certain anterior pituitary extracts or of the substance alloxan then the insulin content of the gland is found to fall proportionately.

3. Insulin and blood-sugar

The active product of the islets has now been isolated and crystallized in the form of combinations that it makes with zinc or other metals. It is a protein, of molecular weight about 6,000. As judged by its influence on the blood-sugar the substance is similar in the pancreas of various mammals and fishes, but there are chemical differences between insulins. The effect of injection of insulin is to produce rapid and complete reversal of the hyperglycaemia and other symptoms of pancreatic removal. The blood-sugar level falls and glucose disappears from the urine. Protein breakdown is reduced, abnormalities of fat metabolism are corrected and glycogen begins to be laid down in the liver. These results suggest that insulin has an effect on the oxidation of sugar by the tissues and on the utilization of glucose in the liver for conversion to glycogen (see Stadie, 1954). Like so many other hormones, therefore, insulin affects one of the fundamental metabolic processes that occur in every cell throughout the body; in this case the oxidation of carbohydrates by which energy is provided for doing work.

Various sugars can be utilized by the body but before being oxidized they are converted to glucose and we may therefore consider only the metabolism of this substance. Glucose is a mixture of two isomers in which the α-form predominates. The amount of sugar in the blood of man is kept at between 0·08 and 0·16 per cent. This sugar serves to provide fuel for combustion by the muscles and other tissues to provide energy. The breakdown of the glucose, like many other of the metabolic operations of carbohydrates, involves phosphorylation. The glucose is converted by a series of enzymes, first to hexose phosphate, then to triose phosphate, which in turn is converted to pyruvic acid, and this, if there is abundant oxygen available through the cytochrome and other oxidase systems, breaks down to carbon dioxide and water.

Alternatively, under anaerobic conditions, the pyruvic acid forms lactic acid; in either case the effect is that when glucose is present in large amounts the series of reversible enzyme reactions proceeds in the direction of breakdown of glucose, with liberation of energy. The whole process is accelerated by insulin and takes place less readily in its absence, but the exact points of the cycle at which the insulin acts have not been determined.

The carbohydrate of the blood is kept constant by ingestion from the alimentary canal and by formation of glucose in the liver, either from the carbohydrate reserve (glycogen) or if necessary by production of glucose from other sources, such as protein. Following ingestion of carbohydrate the blood glucose may rise above 0·2 per cent. but the excess is rapidly removed from the circulation by conversion to glycogen in the liver and muscles. Glycogen, like starch, is a polysaccharide, formed from a number of glucose units $(C_6 H_{10} O_5)_{11}$. It is formed from glucose after phosphorylation to give a hexose phosphate, from which by further conversions the polymer is produced. The reaction is reversible and the influence of insulin is probably to push it in the direction of increased glycogen production. Adrenaline has the reverse effect and its liberation during muscular activity therefore assists in maintaining stable conditions by ensuring mobilization of glucose from the liver. An example of this action is the apocryphal case of the diabetic who, having taken an overdose of insulin, suffered from hypoglycaemia and was arrested as a drunk. His anger at the injustice of the treatment given him by the police was accompanied by adrenaline production sufficient to mobilize sugar, which effected a cure that astonished the police surgeon.

The human liver contains about 100–200 gm. of glycogen, which would provide for less than a day's supply if the body were left without food. Provision of glucose to the tissues is essential for the maintenance of life, the nerve-cells in particular are soon damaged in its absence. The results of hypoglycaemia (reduced blood-sugar) are first of all a hyperexcitability and desire for food and then in extreme stages convulsions and coma, due to impairment of the actions of the nerve-cells. If glucose provided by ingestion and mobilization from glycogen is inadequate the level of blood-sugar is maintained by formation of sugar (gluconeogenesis), mainly from proteins, in the liver. It is probable that fat can also be converted to sugar.

4. The production and utilization of carbohydrate

A supply of fuel to the tissues is of the first importance to any animal and especially to a warm-blooded one. It is not strange, there-fore, to find that the quantity of glucose in the blood is subject to the influence of the actions of a number of other parts of the body. The amount of insulin secreted by the pancreas is a factor of first impor-tance. This substance is essential to the proper utilization of glucose in the liver, but it is not known exactly how it influences the enzyme systems of the liver-cells. Increase of sugar in the blood produces in-creased secretion of insulin by the pancreas, probably mainly by a direct effect on the cells, perhaps assisted by a nervous reflex control operating through the vagus. There is a supply of autonomic nerve-fibres to the blood-vessels of the pancreas and perhaps there are also nerves controlling the cells themselves.

It is not known what defect initiates the processes that lead to deficiency of insulin and so to the disease diabetes mellitus in man. There may be a hereditary deficiency in the amount of pancreatic islet tissue, or perhaps a failure to respond adequately to a rise of blood-sugar by increased formation of the hormone. The pancreas may appear normal histologically in a diabetic person. It is possible that the condition is due to an increased utilization, destruction, or in-hibition of the insulin by hormones or the proteinases or other com-ponents of the tissues.

The effect of the insufficiency of insulin is that the tissues are unable to obtain energy for their work, although abundant glucose circulates in the blood. The operation of cells throughout the body is thus impaired. Injection of insulin has dramatic results, the glucose becomes available to the tissues and there is an immediate fall in the blood-sugar level. By periodic injections the insulin deficiency can be made good for an indefinite period. Of course the disease is not thereby 'cured', although it has been claimed that the treatment im-proves the action of the remaining islet tissue by reducing the 'strain' upon it. Since the need for insulin is one of the stimuli to its liberation by the pancreas this argument clearly cannot be pushed too far.

5. The control of blood-sugar

The functioning of the pancreas and the level of the blood-sugar are greatly affected by other endocrine organs. Injection of anterior pituitary extracts was shown by Young and Richardson to cause first stimulation and then degeneration of the islets of Langerhans, thus producing diabetes (Young, 1945). Pituitary extracts also have an effect directly antagonistic to that of the pancreas in depressing carbohydrate oxidation in the muscles. The anterior pituitary has a still further action on carbohydrate metabolism through the adrenal cortex (Chapter XXX). The adrenal cortical hormones stimulate the process of sugar production in the liver, and the pituitary through its adrenocorticotropin therefore assists in the processes that lead to glycogen storage. Removal of the anterior pituitary often has the effect of alleviating the symptoms of diabetes produced experimentally in dogs by removal of the pancreas, and allows the animals to survive for a considerable time. Conversely, anterior pituitary injections aggravate the diabetes. In the cases of diabetes mellitus in man that are not accompanied by obvious abnormalities of the cells of the islets of Langerhans it is probable that overaction of the anterior pituitary gland is responsible, producing either excessive amounts of a substance directly antagonistic to insulin or an overaction of the adrenal cortex.

Claude Bernard long ago showed that damage to certain parts of the medulla oblongata, by the insertion of a needle, produces irregularities of carbohydrate metabolism, his so-called 'diabetic puncture'. We have little further information about this 'centre' or its method of action, presumably it is through the vagus. The hypothalamus probably acts as a still higher centre influencing carbohydrate metabolism.

The rate of glucose metabolism, like so many other activities of the body, is thus subject to the influence of many factors and it is difficult to say with certainty that it is 'controlled' by any single organ. The amount of sugar ingested and the demands made for fuel by the activities of the body directly influence the blood-sugar level. If these factors operated alone there would be fluctuations in the amount of glucose available for the tissues, whereas a constant supply is needed for their proper working, especially for the brain and the heart. Two means are available to ensure this: (1) a store of carbohydrate in the liver, in the form of glycogen, which can be readily converted into glucose, and (2) an enzyme system that is able to produce sugar from protein sources if needed. To ensure that these systems are called into action at the right times and to the right extent there is an elaborate hormonal and nervous control.

Rapid mobilization of reserves is largely produced by secretion of adrenaline. Increased utilization of excess carbohydrate depends on increased secretion of insulin. Adrenal cortical and perhaps thyroid hormones stimulate the process of gluconeogenesis, by which the extra sugar is formed when necessary, and these glands operate under control of the anterior pituitary, which also has direct effects by producing a substance antagonistic to insulin. Regulation of the pituitary itself is a complicated affair, probably dependent partly on actions of the central nervous system and partly on the reciprocally stimulating effects of the pituitary on the other endocrines and the influence of the level of blood-sugar and other metabolites on these organs. A characteristic feature throughout this, as so many other systems in the body, is the tendency of the action of a set of cells to be increased when the demand for its product rises.

6. Evolution of blood-sugar control

This elaborate balance of activities regulating the blood-sugar level is probably a recent mammalian acquisition, but we have too little information about the conditions in lower vertebrates to be able to trace its history in detail. As in other endocrine systems we find a key position occupied by a substance that is produced in a gland of internal secretion, the pancreas, which, within the chordate series, has become differentiated from a tissue that was earlier concerned with ingestion from the outside world. It is interesting that in lampreys the islet cells still form part of the intestinal wall. The cells lining the intestine have thus become regulators of carbohydrate metabolism by their actions at the source. The balance of sugar between these cells and the blood probably originally depended on the demands made by other tissues. A fall in blood-sugar would stimulate within the intestinal cells the processes of sugar absorption and production, which are presumably common to all tissues.

In this way we can imagine that the process of producing the substance that is able to stimulate carbohydrate metabolism became especially active in these intestinal cells. Those animals with sets of genes ensuring that this activity was especially pronounced would be particularly successful and the intestinal cells would come to have their effect not only by actively producing sugar for the blood but by liberating insulin into the blood to stimulate appropriate processes elsewhere in the body. By some such method a substance related to a particular metabolic process came to be produced at a single central site, the pancreas, by a specialization of activities that are common to tissues throughout the body.

The adrenal cortex plays an equally prominent part in the control of carbohydrate metabolism, acting upon the intracellular metabolic activities throughout the body. Thus many influences affect the blood-sugar level, some mainly at the points of entry and production of carbohydrates, others controlling their use. The interaction of this elaborate set of factors to control the blood-sugar level in a mammal presumably serves to maintain a constancy that would not be possible with a simpler system. The demand for sugar by the tissues sets in action a series of processes that not only release carbohydrate from reserves but stimulate its production and probably activate the animal to search for fresh supplies. No detailed analysis of this elaborate homeostatic system is yet available but it serves as an excellent example of the way in which the living organization maintains its constancy.

XXXIII

INTERNAL SECRETIONS AND HOMEOSTASIS

1. History of the hormone concept

HAVING surveyed the various endocrine organs we may now proceed to say something more about the 'hormone concept'. The idea that action is produced at a distance by the transport of chemical substances came rather late to biology, perhaps because such chemical signalling is remote from the classical scheme of causation that was applied to living things by the seventeenth-century physicists. Incidentally, the development of other chemical ideas has suffered in the same way; it is a curiosity of the growth of science that descriptions of the motions of the planets became quite precise at a time when ideas about the composition and combining powers of terrestrial matter remained very imperfect. Similarly—physics was applied to biology long before chemistry was and the integration of the activities of the various parts of the body was ascribed to the working of the nerves, by the conduction along them of the vital spirits.

Yet the specific effects that certain organs exercise upon distant parts of the body has been known since antiquity, for instance, that castration of men produces eunuchs, with changes in the body form, hair, and reproductive organs. In 1849 Berthold showed by the transplantation of the testes of cockerels to various parts of the body that they are glands, producing effects by pouring substances into the blood-stream.

Knowledge of chemical correlation developed little further until the end of the nineteenth century, in spite of some attention to the subject by Claude Bernard, in connexion with his concept of the maintenance of the stability of the milieu intérieure. Clinical observers proceeded in advance of physiologists, correlating symptoms seen in patients with abnormalities of the thyroid, adrenal, and pituitary glands. Then Oliver and Schafer showed in 1894 that the adrenal and pituitary bodies contain substances that raise the blood-pressure, and adrenaline was isolated and chemically identified in 1901. Even after this advance progress was still slow; the greater part of our knowledge about hormones has been acquired since 1920. Before that date little was known of the functions of the thyroid and sex glands, less of the pituitary and pancreatic islets, and nothing at all of the parathyroids or adrenal cortex.

The name hormone was first used by Starling in 1905 to describe the substance secretin (p. 246) that he and Bayliss had discovered in 1902. In 1914 Starling defined a hormone as 'any substance normally produced in the cells of some part of the body and carried by the blood-stream to distant parts which it affects for the good of the body as a whole'. This definition includes not only specific excitants, such as adrenaline or secretin, but also substances like carbonic acid, which is produced by the tissues during their respiration and acts upon the respiratory centre of the medulla (p. 306). Indeed, with this definition it is difficult to exclude many other substances, for example, the amino-acids that are poured into the blood-stream by the cells of the intestine and produce definite effects in the liver.

The study of hormones is clearly closely bound up with investigation of how the cells of the body of a metazoan animal influence each other for their common good. Indeed the specific hormones, produced by special cells, are only performing in an exaggerated manner actions that are common to all cells. Yet it is not convenient to use the term hormone so widely as to include all stimulants (Huxley, 1935). The word is now usually reserved for the specific excitants, the term autacoid suggested by Schafer for this purpose not having gained general acceptance. The word parahormone is available for the non-specific excitants such as carbonic acid, but it is not in common use.

The essence of a hormone, in the exact sense, is that it constitutes a specific chemical signal. We have seen that the concept of signalling implies a system with a set of instructions to act in a certain manner (p. 22). The signals ensure correct action because they are sent out in a controlled pattern or code, transmitted to a distance and 'decoded' by receivers by the selection of some of the possible actions of the latter. The glands of internal secretion are able to act in this way because the hereditary instructions of the genes ensure that release of their products is so controlled that it occurs under appropriate conditions. The signals are decoded by certain tissues that are sensitive to them and are hence known as target organs.

For full understanding of the working of such a system we need quantitative information about the controlled release of the hormone, about the amounts of it that circulate in the blood and about the effects that it produces in various tissues.

2. Vascular hormones and tissue hormones

Even with this definition the distinction between hormones and other stimulants remains difficult, especially since in recent years it has become increasingly clear that much signalling in the body is achieved by the transport of chemical substances for short as well as for long distances, and not necessarily through the blood-stream. Thus the classic experiments of Loewi (1921) showed that nerves exert their effects upon muscles by the liberation of specific excitatory substances. The hearts of two frogs were perfused in such a way that the Ringer's fluid passing in and out of them became mixed. Stimulation of the vagus nerve to one of the hearts then produced slowing of both. There is now little doubt that such specific chemical excitors ('*neurohumors*', Parker, 1932) are released not only by the nerves to smooth muscle but also by those of skeletal muscle and perhaps at interneuronal junctions throughout the nervous system (p. 347). One of the substances involved is the ester *acetyl choline*. This is produced by the 'cholinergic' nerve-fibres, which include preganglionic autonomic fibres, postganglionic parasympathetic and some sympathetic fibres, and the nerve endings in striated muscle.

Are we to call such substances that are liberated in the tissues hormones? Adrenaline provides an especially interesting case since it is produced by the cells of the adrenal medulla and a similar substance ('sympathin', *nor*-adrenaline) is liberated at nerve endings of sympathetic postganglionic nerve-fibres (p. 399). Moreover, whereas acetyl choline is destroyed by the enzyme *cholinesterase* before it can escape into the circulation adrenaline that is produced by sympathetic stimulation may enter the blood and produce distant effects. This is shown by the following experiment. The nerves of a tissue with sympathetic innervation, say the dilatator muscle of the pupil, are cut and after a few days the muscle then becomes highly sensitive to adrenaline. If now the sympathetic nerve that serves some distant tissue is stimulated electrically the pupil will dilate, activated by the 'sympathin' that is released in the tissue and escapes into the blood-stream. Are we then to call adrenaline produced by the adrenal gland a hormone but not to give it this name when it is produced in other tissues?

Many other instances of the transport of stimulating substances for long or short distances through the tissues are known. The evocating action of invaginated chordamesoderm on the overlying ectoderm (p. 620) might be called hormonal, but there is not complete evidence that it depends upon the transport of a substance. Similarly, in the development of the gonad the medulla and cortex mutually inhibit each other (p. 743). When two newt tadpoles of unlike sex are grafted together (parabiosis) the 'medullarin' produced by the gonad of the male diffuses into the twin and suppresses the proper development of the *nearer but not the further ovary* (see Witschi, 1939). This case therefore closely resembles that of the bovine free-martin (p. 744), except that in the tadpoles the hormones diffuse through the tissues and not in the blood-stream. In other species of amphibia the effect is blood-borne, so that in parabiosis *both* ovaries are influenced.

These facts make a strong case for recognizing besides the classical *vascular hormones* also a class of *tissue hormones* and we might even speak of *intracellular hormones* if it is true that specific substances are produced in the nucleus and carried to other parts of the cell to control differentiation and daily metabolic activities (Young, 1934, 1956). The value of such discussion of terms is that it focuses attention on the way the homeostasis of the body is ensured, the products of cells or parts of cells being carried to a distance and serving as specific signals that control metabolism elsewhere.

3. Relation of endocrines to cell metabolism

Even if we consider only the more familiar blood-borne hormones we are recalled at many points to their relation to the ordinary metabolism of the tissues. The earlier investigations of each hormone often seemed to indicate that it exerts only one specific action upon some other part or tissue of the body, for instance, adrenaline on blood-pressure, 'pituitrin' on the uterus, or sex hormones on the secondary sex characters. Further study has shown that in nearly every case the substance secreted influences not only certain distant cells but some special aspect of the functioning of many cells throughout the body. Thus the growth-promoting hormone of the anterior pituitary not only 'stimulates growth of the long bones', as earlier accounts suggested, but modifies protein synthesis throughout the body (p. 555).

Similarly, the thyroid secretion stimulates the respiration of many tissues, and the parathyroid hormone controls the exchanges of calcium and phosphorus. The adrenal cortical steroids and those of the gonads affect cell metabolism throughout the body, while insulin, adrenaline, and the pituitary substances have varied actions on carbohydrate metabolism. The difference between these effects and those produced by the non-specific 'parahormones', such as amino-acids secreted by the intestinal cells, is that the amount of 'true' hormone secreted is regulated by nervous and other means. The hormone thus serves as a specific signal, part of the internal control system. The parahormone fluctuates under external influence. The essence of a 'signal' is that it is part of a 'code' for transmitting information within a given system and in this it differs from an outside 'influence' subject to random fluctuations (p. 13).

There is evidence from the phylogenetic history of the endocrine organs that in the earlier stages of vertebrate evolution there were no definite endocrine glands or systems of specific chemical signals. No ductless glands have been recognized in *Amphioxus*. No aggregations of cells comparable to the adrenal cortex or medulla have been found in lampreys. In the larval lamprey there are no separate islets of Langerhans and no thyroid; there are no parathyroid bodies in any fish. It may be that all the specific endocrine organs have arisen by control in certain cells of a type of metabolism that was at first more general throughout the tissues. Thus the thyroid cells show special development of the mechanism for regulating respiratory enzymes, the parathyroids that for control of calcium metabolism and the adrenal cortex for interchanges of sodium and potassium. In the pituitary we see specialization of the system for control of growth and metabolism, which must be present in all cells throughout the body. The cells of these organs have thus become endocrine glands by control of the release into the blood-stream of substances that act all over the body or on some special organ. In this way some feature of cell metabolism that was at first at the mercy of fluctuations in the environment, or of the influences of all the cells upon each other, came to be more exactly regulated. This form of chemical signalling may well have advantages over the transmission of nerve impulses for the continuous control of the level of metabolic activity in a large number of cells (see p. 26).

4. Evolution of the endocrine system

It is a striking fact that the ductless glands have nearly all been produced by a metamorphosis of function during evolution, so that a set of cells that was under the direct influence of the outside world became cut off from it. In several instances an organ dealing with some raw material has become separated from its external source of supply and then converted into an endocrine gland. Thus the thyroid gland is derived from the endostyle, which at an earlier stage took up iodine directly from food or water and passed it to the tissues (p. 529). The parathyroids are probably derived from the cells of the gills of fishes

that are concerned with salt transfer (p. 535). The organs corresponding to the pituitary in earlier chordates are concerned with the uptake
of food (Müller's organ of *Amphioxus*) or with receptor functions (subneural gland of tunicates, p. 552). The pancreatic islet tissue is in
lampreys actually dispersed in the intestinal wall (p. 569).

We are fortunate in having in the tunicates, *Amphioxus*, and the
lampreys survivors of the early stages of so many of these endocrine
systems and the picture that they show is too general to be accidental.
It seems that in the later vertebrates there has been a change in the
use of these tissues. For instance, the cells of the parathyroid region,
instead of dealing locally with salts presented to them by the environment and by the blood, come to secrete regulating substance into the
blood. Similarly for the thyroid, pancreas, and perhaps other glands.
The transformation involves the conversion of an organ whose products are subject to the fluctuations of the environment into one that
releases controlled amounts to stimulate cells elsewhere. We can speak
of this as the evolution of a signalling system, indicating that the
gland becomes specialized to emit hormones and certain tissues become specialized to react to them, so that information is transmitted
in a code.

The picture of the actual transformation of cell functions remains,
unhappily, more vague. We have, however, some further hint in the
fact that the endocrine glands, like other cells, are responsive to the
need for their products. Poisoning of the respiratory enzymes of
the cells with cyanide leads to hypertrophy of the thyroid (p. 531);
castration is followed by increase in the production of gonadotropic
hormone by the pituitary (p. 556), increase of blood-sugar leads to
increased secretion of insulin (p. 567), and so on. Admittedly these
reactions to demand are themselves little understood but they certainly occur and they suggest that, following a change in habits, the
products that accumulate because of lack of some substance, say
iodinated amino-acids, may become the morphogenetic stimulus that
produces a hypertrophy of the cells that previously provided the
material. This may eventually lead to the production of a new endocrine organ. Evidently here, as elsewhere, we cannot separate studies
of evolution from those of development, nor of development from
physiology and biochemistry. Our task is to try to have in mind as
much as possible of all the past web of interactions that has made
existing vertebrates what they are.

5. Evolution of homeostatic control

In any organism an elaborate balance is continually struck between various metabolic activities and with the environment, the end result being that the action of the whole system maintains itself. Presumably in the simpler metazoans, including the early chordates such as *Amphioxus*, every cell performs all the necessary functions for itself and co-ordination is at a low level. There is little provision for maintaining a steady level of concentration of essential substances in the body. Violent oscillations would be expected in such a system and as a corollary there is no capacity to maintain the delicate balance of activities that is necessary to make use of a complicated organ such as the cerebral cortex. In particular, storage of the effects of past experience is obviously likely to be poor in a system that is subject to violent fluctuations.

Stability in all living organizations is ensured by the double dependence of the tissues (p. 22). They react to the information received through their hereditary mechanism and to the information that is provided by the events occurring around them. In lower organisms this two-way communication goes on within each tissue, fluctuations are liable to result and no very elaborate ('improbable' or 'higher') organization can result. The organism remains relatively similar to its environment and fluctuates with it.

Evolutionary change has consisted largely in the development of specialized systems of control by a code of signals and with feed-back, allowing more steady adjustment of the various phases of life. In such higher animals each individual differs more widely from the environment than primitive organisms do, but the whole organization provides an elaborately coded representation of the changes that are likely to occur in the surroundings. By means of this representation anticipatory actions are taken, which enable the animal to remain constant in spite of wide external fluctuations.

Evolution of the endocrine organs of vertebrates provides beautiful examples of this development. For instance, the increasingly elaborate organization of the organs that affect carbohydrate metabolism has produced a steadier blood-sugar level (p. 569). The details of the way in which the glands achieve such homeostasis in the body is a very attractive field for research, especially of a quantitative and mathematical nature. For instance, it seems likely that something could be done to express the mutual interactions of rate of ingestion of sugar, rate of insulin secretion, level of liver glycogen and blood glucose, rates of secretion of the anterior pituitary, adrenal cortex and medulla, and thyroid glands, as well as the level of muscular activity. All these processes and levels influence each other and the blood-sugar, and it is possible to imagine a set of equations to express these relations by considering the transmission of the information that determines the life of the animal. Unfortunately we still lack knowledge about the amounts of hormone in the blood and their control and rate of change, which is needed before any such expressions can be made exact.

The pituitary gland evidently provides a focus which, influencing the organs and influenced by them, allows a balance to be struck. It may well be that control or 'feed-back' systems are involved here, as in the nervous system. Many endocrine organs become enlarged when 'demand' for their product is increased. There is also some evidence that excess of a hormone in the blood may stimulate the production of an antihormone. For instance, after repeated injection of thyrotropic pituitary extracts rats become refractory to them. Several of the endocrines are known to be involved in the elaboration of specific substances as a defence against infection and the connexions between the endocrine and lymphatic systems are seen in the similar effects on the thymus of adrenal cortical injections and infective fevers (p. 536).

In order to understand the metabolic life of the body we must not make sharp distinctions between different phases, anabolism, catabolism, respiration, excretion, and so on. The workings of the various types of enzyme system remain closely linked, even when they proceed mainly in specialized organs. The maintenance of the life of the organism depends on the balancing of these actions against environmental changes. The endocrine glands, as regulators of the balance, perhaps more than other systems determine the course of the whole life. This is conspicuous in the effects, for instance, of thyroid withdrawal— which reduces the level of activity of cells throughout the body and transforms the 'character' of the individual. The existence of such effects has led to speculative attempts at classification of human and animal types, active persons as hyperthyroid, sluggish as hypothyroid, large and bony ones as acromegalic, and so on.

Following this reasoning change in the relative rates of development of the various endocrines has been held responsible for many evolutionary developments—for example, those involving neoteny, such as are expressed by saying that 'Man is a foetal ape'. There is not enough evidence at present about the actual amounts of hormones circulating in the blood to allow much detail in such analysis but it probably contains a germ of truth. The secretions of the glands are no doubt of outstanding importance in determining the characteristics of each type of life, as are also many other factors, for instance, the proteolytic enzyme make-up or the arrangement of the cerebral cortex. The differences between species of mammals or races of men as sets of polyphasic systems cannot yet be expressed by any simple set of factors, but it is a satisfactory sign of the progress of biology that the task can be envisaged and that attempts to deal with it have begun.

XXXIV

THE COURSE OF DEVELOPMENT

1. Long-term homeostasis and the significance of embryogenesis

THE capacity of the adult organism to receive information from the environment ensures that it shall make correct responses under a variety of circumstances; in other words its organization guarantees homeostasis within a certain range of environmental change. In order to allow the race to remain stable in spite of wide changes in the environment, greater alterations in the organization are necessary and these are made slowly by the process that we ordinarily refer to as evolution. Evolutionary change is produced by adjusting the hereditary make-up of the race by mutation, recombination of genes, and natural selection. These processes provide an inherited information store that allows the organisms to make responses that are correct forecasts and thus to survive in the environmental situations that they meet.

The mechanism of hereditary variation by mutation and recombination assures this adjustment of the race through the centuries. Essentially this is achieved by changing the genetic system slightly and then trying out the new combinations of genes. A variety of combinations is thus presented to the environment and is tested by natural selection —since more are produced than can survive. For this process to be possible it is clearly necessary that new individuals shall be built by embryological development each time that a new hereditary combination has been formed. The processes of embryogenesis can thus be regarded as the means by which individuals differing slightly from each other are produced, so that the race may remain stable in spite of changes in the environment. Developmental processes, like those of the adult, are thus concerned with ensuring survival by the making of forecasts about the future.

The fertilized ovum is therefore a system whose function is to exploit the new inherited instructions that are provided by the fusion of the gametes. These instructions control the metabolic sequences in various parts of the developing organism in such a way as to ensure development of an adult that is capable of self-maintenance by appropriate response to environmental change. In man the original single 'undifferentiated' cell, the fertilized ovum, weighing less than a milligram, becomes converted into an adult that contains about 10^{12} cells, of at least 100 different types, and weighs many kilograms. The processes by which this change is produced may be classified as

1. Growth.
2. Cell division.

3. Cell movement.
4. Cell differentiation.

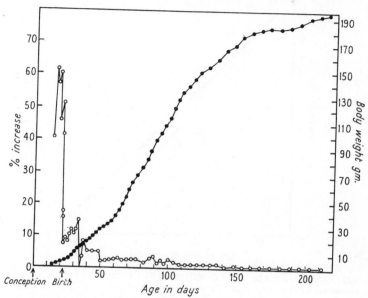

FIG. 234. Growth of the albino rat. The solid circles show the actual weight of single animals. The open circles show the percentage increase per day (Minot's curve). (From Brody after Needham.)

2. Growth

The power to add to the amount of matter organized within the system is characteristic of all living organisms. The definition of growth is not easy, however. Are we to include addition of water, of fats and of proteins as all equally signs of growth? This definition is a matter of arbitrary decision; more important is the study of the rate at which addition of each of the components proceeds. After fertilization some metabolic activities of the egg increase (p. 599), and an outburst of cell division occurs. It is the special 'function' of the fertilized ovum to try out the new genotype by making a large new mass of living matter. The first rapid rate of growth is not maintained; it gradually dies away until the 'adult' mass is achieved. In spite of considerable study it is still not certain how the initial increase and subsequent gradual decrease in growth rate are controlled. Minot first pointed out that the rate of growth declines fastest in the early stages of life (Fig. 234). This may be expressed in the aphorism that we grow old fastest when we are youngest. Medawar was able to show that cells of the heart of the embryo chick decline in power of growth with age,

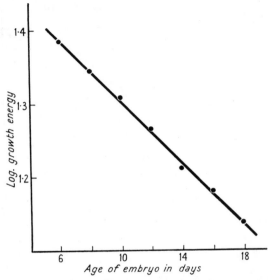

Fig. 235. Decline with age of the growth energy of the heart. Each point shows the amount of an inhibitor needed to prevent growth of pieces of chick's heart cultivated *in vitro*. (Medawar, P. B., *Proc. Roy. Soc.* B. **129**, 1940.)

this power being measured by finding the amount of an inhibitory substance that was needed to suppress growth (Fig. 235).

In young mammals the intake of matter as food, oxygen, &c., is greater than the output, so that the whole increases in bulk. The rate of this increase is regulated by unknown factors in the system and it gradually declines until by the time the adult stage has been reached a balance is set up. There is, however, an important sense in which growth has even then not ceased. Throughout the body there is a continued turnover of materials so that no part long remains the same, even in the bones (p. 100). In some tissues cells are continually being removed and replaced by fresh ones.

3. Cell division

The rate of cell division is high soon after fertilization and thereafter declines. The elaborate shape and organization of a metazoan body is made possible by limitation of the growth and division of cells. The decline in the rate of cell division with age takes place at different rates and at different times in the various parts of the body. These local differences play a large part in determining the shape of the embryo. In many tissues a definite number of cells is formed during development and these must then last for the whole of the rest of the life of the individual. An extreme case is seen in the nervous system, whose number of cells becomes fixed soon after birth. In some fishes

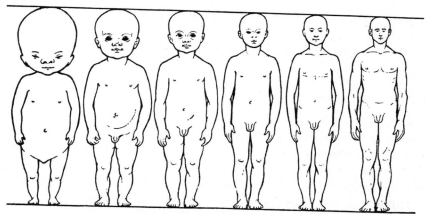

FIG. 236. Outline shape of human beings seen in frontal elevation. (After Jackson from Medawar, *Growth and Form*, 1945.)

and amphibians there is a single pair of large nerve-cells, the Mauthner cells, connected with the vestibular system, which can be identified throughout the whole life of an individual; they are never replaced (Fig. 156).

In other tissues the power of cell division continues throughout life, for example, in the blood-forming tissues and the skin. It is so regulated that the amount of cell replacement equals that of cell removal, but the feed-back mechanism by which this control is ensured is not understood. Death of cells is a common feature of many tissues, especially during development; it is one of the factors that ensure the production of organs of the appropriate size and shape (Glucksmann, 1951).

4. Rates of growth and cell division. Relative growth

The rate of growth and of cell division is not the same throughout the body. The final form of the organs is achieved largely as a result of the fact that some parts grow faster than others. The rate at which any part grows is not necessarily constant throughout development. Thus in man the head enlarges relatively faster than the body during early uterine life. Later the reverse is the case (Fig. 236). Yet relative growth-rates may remain constant over considerable periods (Fig. 237). If an organ increases faster or slower than the body as a whole its growth is said to be allometric. The rate of growth of an organ and the body as a whole can sometimes be expressed in the form

$$y = bx^k$$

where x is the magnitude of the organ at total body size y, and b and k are constants. If k is greater than 1 the organ will become relatively larger in larger animals (see Huxley, 1932, and Reeve and Huxley, 1945).

5. Cell movement

The form of the developing embryo is greatly influenced by active migratory movements of the cells. This factor is especially important during the early stages of development. For example, in the frog, cells of the outer layer of the blastula move in over the dorsal lip of the blastopore (p. 607). The formation of the neural folds is another example of an act of morphogenesis that is produced by movement of cells as well as by change of cell shape (p. 609).

Such movements are produced by changes within the cells that are presumably fundamentally like those producing amoeboid movement or muscular contraction, and they must involve expenditure of energy. There is now some information about how these movements are initiated and controlled (see Holtfreter, 1948; Willier *et al.*, 1955).

6. Cell differentiation

The efficient responses of the mammalian organism to its environment are achieved by the presence of cells with a wide variety of functions. The unfolding of an organism with so many different parts under the control of the relatively simple set of instructions contained in the egg is one of the most amazing of all natural phenomena. Perhaps we can understand it best by considering that the egg and *all cells alike exercise to some extent all of the cellular activities*. They all take in materials, respire, synthesize, excrete, contract, conduct, and respond to environmental change. In each specialized tissue of the adult, however, one or more of these activities is exaggerated. The process of *differentiation* consists in the gradual emphasizing during development of one or more of the fundamental morphological features

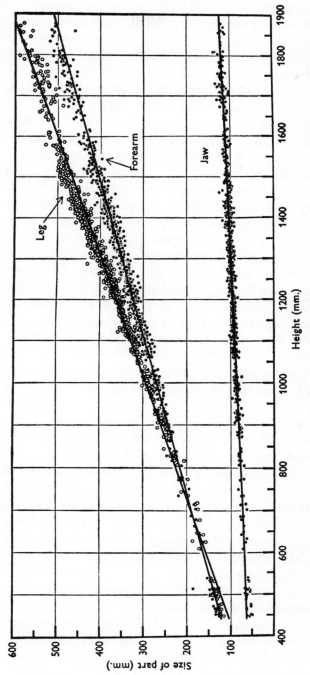

Fig. 237. Plots of the size of leg, arm, and jaw of 795 male human beings from the London area. The relation of the size of each to the height of the individual is approximately linear and the lines shown are the regression lines calculated from the data. The leg grows faster than the arm and both much faster than the jaw.

(From Sholl., *J. Anat. Lond.* **83**, 1949, by permission of the Cambridge University Press.)

or living activities in each type of cell (Weiss, 1953; Gustafson, 1954). This is made possible by the fact that not all parts of the developing organism are in exactly the same condition. Even within the ovum the various parts of the protoplasm have different environments and therefore the metabolism proceeds in different ways. One end becomes the animal pole and the other the vegetative pole and each part of the cytoplasm has a characteristic structure (p. 590).

The whole course of development thus depends on the power of each tissue to react with its environment. This is, of course, the universal secret of the survival of all living matter and once again we see that development is not different from the rest of living processes. The capacity to react in appropriate ways is conferred by the specific sets of molecules provided by heredity, in particular in the nucleus. Studies of embryology therefore consist in showing how the various tissues react, according to their position relative to each other and to the environment, each differentiating to form a distinct part of the adult organism. During development, as in adult life, the metabolism of the cells thus shows double dependence (p. 22). It is influenced by information proceeding from the material of the nuclei (see Brachet, 1952) and by that provided by the changes occurring outside the cell. The form that the cell achieves depends upon its reactions to the flow of information along this two-way communication channel.

In *descriptive embryology* the various stages of development are recorded but it is clear that this cannot tell us much about the processes that control the differentiation. In order to know about these it is necessary to follow the changes by which development proceeds from stage to stage. Such a *cinematic* view of development can obviously only be achieved by observation of the process of change as it proceeds, rather than by study of individual stages. In order to follow changes going on within opaque embryos indirect methods have been employed, some of them most ingenious, for example, watching the movements executed by coloured marks placed upon the developing embryo (p. 612). *Experimental embryology* includes such observational techniques but also attempts to study the sequence of processes by interfering with the course of development so as to show how, during differentiation, the various tissues depend upon each other. Thus after planting a developing eye-cup into the abdominal region the ectoderm of the latter may be induced to form a lens, which it otherwise would not do (p. 623). From this we learn that the differentiation of tissue to form a lens depends upon the proximity of an eye-cup. Conversely, a piece of limb-bud made to grow in isolation from any other part of the body can become a complete humerus (p. 76); the material has the power of self differentiation. In such ways we can study how the cells of the embryo come to acquire their particular modes of growth and functioning. There is no sharp break between the metabolic processes of the egg and those of the various types of cell in the adult. The inherited organization enables the parts so to react to the environment that, considering all members of the species together, survival is ensured.

XXXV

THE OVUM AND ITS FERTILIZATION

1. The origin of oocytes

THE egg (ovum) is in a sense one of the most highly specialized cells of the body. Its 'function' is so to react after fertilization that it proceeds to the formation of an embryo and then an adult. In spite of much study there is still controversy about the processes by which these specialized egg-cells are produced. Weismann proved that in some animals (round worms, *Ascaris*) the cells that give rise to the germ track are set aside during the early stages of cleavage. In vertebrates 'primary oocytes' have been described, arising from the endoderm of the early embryo and later finding their way to the gonad (p. 743). The development of the ovum in the mammalian ovary is described on p. 680.

The characteristic feature of the ovum is the capacity for a variety of parts to appear within it in response to environmental differences. It is therefore of interest to see at what stage the developing oocyte first shows signs that it is not a radially symmetrical structure. The development first of an axis and then of a plane of symmetry shows the early stages of the long process of differentiation that will end in an adult, with an approximately bilateral symmetry. Little is known of the development of axes in mammals, but some of the critical stages can be seen in animals with large yolky eggs, such as the frog. In the study of embryology as of other parts of biology we can best reach an understanding of the processes at work by considering not only one species or class but also the variants that are found in different animals.

2. The acquisition of axes

A cell of the ovary is recognizable as a definitive oocyte when it enlarges and in many species begins to accumulate the materials known as *yolk*, in the forms of granules of various shape and composition. The cytoplasmic inclusions (Golgi bodies and mitochondria) play a part in the formation of the yolk, perhaps enabling enzymic synthesis to proceed by the provision of intracellular compartments within which reaction products become segregated. The materials for the growth of the oocyte and for the deposition of yolk are partly derived from the follicle cells that surround it (Fig. 238B). In birds

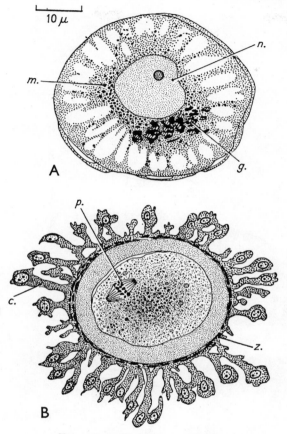

FIG. 238. A, Young human oocyte.
g. Golgi bodies, forming yolk nucleus; *m*. mitochondria; *n*. nucleus.
(Ackroyd, *Zeitschr. f. Zellforsch.* **27**, 1937.)
B, Ovum from mature follicle of guinea-pig.
c. corona radiata; *p*. first polar spindle; *z*. zona radiata. (After Rubaschkin.)

(probably also in reptiles) portions of the Golgi substance of these follicle cells can be seen actually entering the oocyte.

During the earlier stages of oogenesis the Golgi substances in the oocyte are usually concentrated around the centrosome to form a structure known as the *yolk nucleus* (Fig. 238A). This yolk nucleus lies from the start eccentrically on one side of the nucleus, and the oocyte is therefore radially symmetrical about an axis rather than about a point. Soon the yolk nucleus enlarges and breaks up into pieces,

which spread through the cytoplasm and lay down the spherules of
yolk (Fig. 238B). It is difficult to be sure that the axis due to the

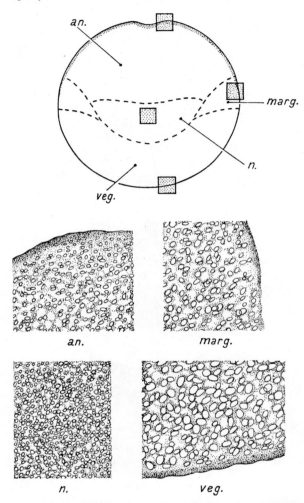

FIG. 239. Regional differences in the unfertilized egg of the toad *Xenopus*.

an. animal pole filled with a mixture of many mitochondria, a dense network of basophil granules containing ribonucleic acid, and small yolk granules; *marg.* marginal zone containing a different proportion of yolk granules and basophil material; *n.* central region containing mitochondria, basophil granules, and small yolk granules; *veg.* vegetative pole containing very large yolk granules that overlap one another, mitochondria and basophil granules.
(After Pasteels, *Bull. Soc. Zool. France* **76**, Fig. 6, **1951**.)

original eccentricity of the yolk nucleus is maintained into the later
stages. In most ova another sign of the existence of an axis now
appears, namely, the movement of the nucleus towards one pole. The

side towards which the nucleus lies, in an area of yolk-free proto-plasm, is called the *animal pole*, the opposite, yolk-containing end is the *vegetative pole* (Fig. 239). An axis is thus established and this is carried through into the embryo and adult, the animal pole being on the future dorsal side of the body. The presence of such an axis in the ovum is a sign that different parts now begin to have distinct properties. At first the differences may be slight, but they are sufficient to ensure that enzymatic processes go on at different rates and so the parts of the developing embryo gradually become differentiated.

The possession of axes thus enables the embryo to develop into a heterogeneous adult rather than into a radially symmetrical lump, and it is therefore of the greatest interest to know how these first axial differentiations are produced in the oocyte. It has been alleged that in vertebrates the animal pole is that directed towards the ovarian arterioles, which thus receives better nourishment and becomes the dominant head end of the embryo. It is not certain that this is always so but it may be by this means that differences in metabolism are set up and produce differences in the activities of the cytoplasm of different parts of the ovum.

The unfertilized ovum is thus not by any means a homogeneous system. Many of its contents differ along the animal-vegetative axis. In amphibian eggs there are abundant large yolk granules in the vegetative half, fewer and smaller ones near the animal pole (Fig. 239). Associated with these granules are large mitochondria. Among them, chiefly in the animal pole half, is a network of granules of baso-phil material, which is mainly ribonucleoprotein in nature but also contains other substances essential for growth metabolism, such as respiratory enzymes, proteins containing sulphydryl groups, and phosphatides. There is reason to suppose that the outer cortex of the ovum also contains specially differentiated regions and this is shown visibly by the fact that in the animal pole the cortex is pigmented. Indeed there are concentric gradients between inside and outside in-volving many kinds of chemical substances. Some of these gradients arise simply because of the tendency of surface active substances to concentrate towards the outside. Subsequently, as a result of reactions between these substances and external factors, concentric patterns of concentration of different substances arise. There will be critical levels of pH, oxygen tension and many other features, allowing different processes to occur at each level. If the resulting compounds have determinative properties the original quantitative differences can thus provide the basis for tissue differentiation.

The ovum is therefore an elaborately organized system in which there are quantitative differences between the parts. It has been suggested by some workers that these differences are distributed along two gradients, one of these may be called the yolk gradient, proceeding from animal to vegetative pole, the other is a gradient in the cortex

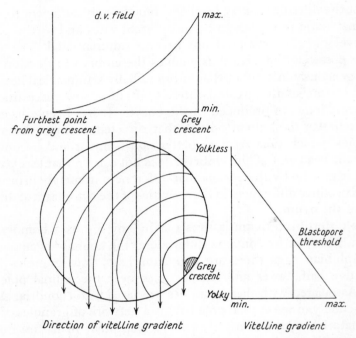

FIG. 240. Diagram of dorso-ventral and vitelline gradients in the amphibian egg. The former proceeds from the grey crescent, the latter from the animal to vegetative pole. The curves show the approximate presumed course of the gradients, but there is no accurate means of measuring these.
(After Needham.)

proceeding from the future dorsal to ventral side (Fig. 240). If some such system exists then it would serve to specify the future fate of each part of the ovum. There is indeed some evidence that the various regions of the developing embyro arise according to their position relative to such gradients. Yet the gradients are certainly not rigidly determined before fertilization. Our knowledge is still not sufficient to say exactly which features are significant and the gradient system may be much more complicated. The evidence does, however, show that quantitative differences have already developed between different parts of the unfertilized ovum and that these represent the first stages in the long journey towards the production of an adult with cells of many types, in each of which one or more functions is exaggerated.

3. Various types of egg

The amount of yolk contained in the ovum varies enormously. The eggs of sea squirts, *Amphioxus* and mammals (other than monotremes), are small (0·1–0·2 mm. diameter in man), contain very little yolk, and are said to be *oligolecithal*. Those of lampreys, the persistent earlier (ganoid) types of bony fish, of lung fishes, and of amphibia are larger (1–2 mm. *Rana*), heavily yolked, and hence *mesolecithal*. In sharks, modern bony fishes, reptiles, birds, and monotremes the eggs contain relatively more yolk and are large (85 mm. diameter in the ostrich); they are said to be *megalecithal* or *telolecithal*.

The amount of yolk is directly related to the type of development, the megalecithal eggs being found in general in those groups in which the greatest complexity of organization has been developed. It has been pointed out by Milnes-Marshal (see Needham, 1931) that the presence of much yolk is correlated not with a long development but with one in which the embryo reaches a high degree of completeness before hatching. In embryos with little yolk the earlier stages are passed through more rapidly than in yolky eggs and a larva that can feed for itself is rapidly produced. In mammals special mechanisms have been developed to make it possible for development to proceed for a long time under the care of the mother and hence for the adult to attain a high degree of complexity of organization.

Other things being equal it is found that the eggs of freshwater animals are larger than those of their marine relatives, those of the trout, for instance, are larger than those of marine teleosts such as the cod or herring. This difference may be partly a measure of the difficulty that the young larva has in establishing itself in freshwaters, which are often rapidly moving. It may also be due to the necessity to provide the energy necessary for the maintenance of osmotic equilibrium in freshwater, involving a pumping of water out of the cells against the osmotic gradient.

The composition of the egg of vertebrates must be such as to provide all of the materials necessary for early development, except oxygen and water. The ovum therefore contains proteins, carbohydrates and fats, also salts, vitamins, and, of course, a complex enzyme system for dealing with these substances. The relative amounts of protein and fat vary in different groups. In the hen's ovum proteins represent almost 40 per cent. and fats 60 per cent. of the dry weight of the egg proper (excluding the albumen), whereas in lower vertebrates the proportion of fat is less, only 14 per cent. in the frog's ovum, where the proteins make up 60 per cent (Romanoff and Romanoff, 1949).

The unfertilized ovum, like other living entities, is a system in a steady state, not in equilibrium, and there are many signs of its meta-bolic activities. To give one curious instance, the unfertilized trout's egg performs rhythmical movements of precession (but not spinning) within its chorion, at a frequency of about $3\frac{1}{2}$ minutes (Fig. 241). The

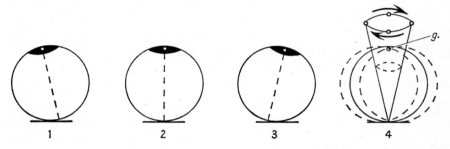

FIG. 241. Movements of the egg of the trout.

1–3. Successive appearances as seen from the side; 4. superimposed diagrams of the suc-cessive positions, showing the elliptical path traced by a globule at *g*. The whole cycle takes about $3\frac{1}{2}$ minutes.
(After Rothschild, *J. exp. Biol.* **24**, 1947.)

significance of these movements is not known but they are affected by cyanide and other agents that are likely to influence respiratory systems and presumably they depend on metabolic fluctuations that change the distribution of materials in the egg. Movement may thus be detectable very early in development, even in a cell that we do not ordinarily think of as motile.

4. The nucleus of the ovum

During the period of growth and deposition of yolk in the ovarian ovum the nucleus becomes a large sac, often called the *germinal vesicle*. The chromosomes cannot be recognized as such for during this stage the nucleus is generally in the resting phase of the first meiotic division. The maturation of the nucleus by the completion of meiosis and the reduction of the number of chromosomes usually takes place at the end of the growth period, either just before or just after fertilization. The germinal vesicle now bursts, allowing a con-siderable amount of nuclear material to mix with the cytoplasm; the significance of this mingling is not known. The maturation results in the formation of two polar bodies (sometimes three by division of the first), which lie close to the animal pole.

5. Egg membranes

In theory it is possible to distinguish three types of membrane around an ovum. The *primary* or *vitelline membrane* is formed by the activity of the surface of the ovum itself, the *secondary membrane* by the follicle cells that surround it and the *tertiary membranes* by the secretory activity of the ducts down which it passes. In practice it is difficult to distinguish between primary and secondary membranes and the structure known as the vitelline membrane in the frog is probably of double origin. The cortex of the egg of fishes and amphibians forms a *surface coat*, which is important in directing all movements during gastrulation. The vitelline membrane lies outside it. The primary membrane in mammals is often called the *zona pellucida* and it may show striations, presumed to be channels for the passage of nourishment, in which case it is called the *zona radiata* (Fig. 238). Primary and secondary membranes, since they are formed before fertilization, are often provided with holes (*micropyles*) for the entry of sperms.

Tertiary membranes may be of various sorts. Protein solutions are common, for instance, the jelly around frog's eggs and the albumen (white) of the hen's egg. The former consists of a mucoprotein, which apparently does not provide a suitable medium for the growth of bacteria and hence serves to keep the ova sterile until the time of hatching.

The *shells* around the eggs of sharks (mermaid's purses), reptiles, birds, and monotremes are also tertiary egg membranes. They are formed, like the outer layers of the skin, of sulphur-containing proteins of the keratin type, impregnated in the case of the hard shells with salts of calcium, mostly the carbonate. The pigment of the shell of birds is derived from the bile pigments. No horny shell is present around the eggs of most mammals, but it is still present in the marsupials *Dasyurus* (wombat) and *Phascolarctos* (koala).

6. Fertilization and the appearance of a plane of symmetry

The means by which the meeting of the ovum and sperm are ensured are discussed on p. 695. When the sperms reach the ovum they swarm around it and one or more enters. In oligo- and mesolecithal eggs monospermy is usual but several sperms usually enter the megalecithal eggs (polyspermy) and the supernumerary ones form

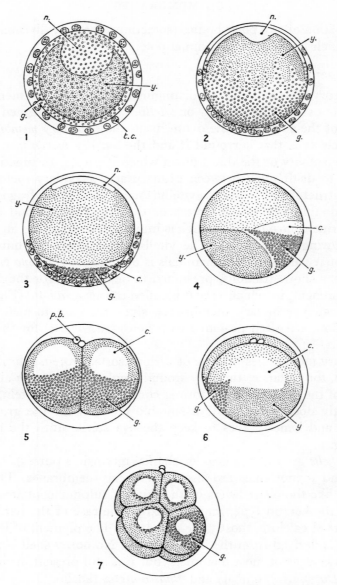

FIG. 242. Movements within the egg of *Styela* after fertilization.

1. Unfertilized egg showing nucleus (*n*.), central mass of grey yolk (*y*) and peripheral layer with yellow granules (*g*). Around the egg are a number of test cells (*t.c.*); 2. shortly after fertilization. The nuclear membrane has disappeared and the material of the nucleus has spread out at the pole. The pigmented material (*g*) is streaming towards the opposite pole; 3. further stage of concentration of the yellow granules with a layer of clear protoplasm (*c*) above them; 4. side view. The yellow material and the clear layer now form crescents at the future hind end; 5. the first two blastomeres seen from the posterior pole; 6. the same seen from the side; 7. 8-cell stage. The pigment is mostly at the hind end but there is some around the nuclei; *p.b.* polar body.

(After Conklin, *J. Acad. Nat. Sci. Philad.* **13**, 1905.)

accessory nuclei, the merocytes, which may help in breaking up the yolk for utilization by the embryo.

The changes that take place in the ovum at fertilization differ in details in various vertebrates but they probably always follow a common plan. After they have occurred the ovum shows a plan of organization that can be recognized in all chordates. It is therefore convenient to describe the process of fertilization first as it occurs in one of the earliest types of chordate, the tunicate (sea squirt) *Styela*, subject of the classic work of Conklin (1905). The ripe ovum of this animal contains sparsely distributed yellow pigment and a germinal vesicle near the animal pole (Fig. 242). The sperm penetrates along any meridian of the vegetative half of the ovum and its entry is followed by a series of conspicuous flowing movements of the cytoplasm. The cap of nuclear material produced by the bursting of the germinal vesicle, and the yellow pigment, flow down from the animal to the vegetative pole and collect around the point of sperm entry. The sperm head then begins to move upward through the cytoplasm until it rests just below the equator and the female pronucleus moves down towards it. The yellow pigment moves with the sperm head and comes to form a crescent around the ovum as shown in Fig. 242. The position of this crescent and of the nuclei now marks the future hind end of the embryo, which is therefore no longer radially symmetrical about an axis but bilaterally symmetrical about a plane. The plane of symmetry has therefore been made manifest by the fertilization. It must not from this be concluded that the entry of the sperm determines the main plane of the embryo. Because the sperm nucleus reaches the equator not by the shortest path but often by a long and devious one Conklin concluded that it is passing to an already predetermined spot, in fact that the unfertilized ovum already possesses a plane of symmetry, which is made visible by the events that follow fertilization.

During the first cleavage a further differentiated area of cytoplasm, the *grey crescent*, appears, opposite to the yellow crescent. By this time, therefore, the egg of *Styela* shows four clearly differentiated cytoplasmic regions, a clear animal pole, the yellow and grey crescents, and the yolky vegetative pole. Signs of an essentially similar organization are seen in many other chordates. We have little information about the chemical differences between these areas.

7. Fertilization of the frog's egg and origin of the grey crescent

In amphibia there is also reason to suppose that the ovum already possesses a plane of symmetry, which becomes manifest at fertilization (see Ancel and Vintemberger, 1948). The animal pole of these animals is covered with a cap of pigment (melanin), in the form of granules in the cortical layers (Fig. 243). In *Rana* the sperm enters somewhere in the animal half of the egg and there follow various flowing movements. The change by which the bilateral symmetry becomes explicit consists of a migration of material of the cortex of the egg towards the point of sperm entry in the animal pole. The result is that the mantle of black pigment now seems to extend less far downwards on the side opposite the point of sperm entry, giving an effect that is known as the *grey crescent*.

This grey crescent lies just above the site at which the future dorsal lip of the blastopore (the organizer region) will develop and substances localized here probably control the whole sequence of later differentiation. The future median plane of the embryo divides the grey crescent into equal halves. The dorsal lip develops just below the level at which the yolky material meets the animal hemisphere. If eggs are held upside down the yolk falls through the cytoplasm and comes into contact with the cortical layer at two or more points, at each of which a blastoporal lip develops. The requirement for the setting up of such a lip is presumably a certain combination of activities represented perhaps by the yolky vegetative pole material, the mitochondria and ribonucleoproteins of the animal pole, and some constituent of the cortex. The appropriate combination ensures the setting into action of the sequence of activities that produces the initiation of gastrulation and all the phenomena of 'organization' that are associated with the dorsal lip of the blastopore (see p. 603).

The position of the grey crescent marks the posterior end of the future embryo, which is therefore now symmetrical about a plane running through the animal pole and the middle of the grey crescent. It was long supposed that the position of this grey crescent was actually determined by the entry of the sperm and it was claimed that when two sperms were induced to enter the ovum the grey crescent was formed in the resultant plane between them. Bataillon showed that the ovum of the frog can be made to develop parthenogenetically by pricking with a dirty needle. This acts by carrying a particle of blood or dust into the egg, where it acts as does a sperm in starting off development. Brachet found that there was no relationship between the grey crescent that forms in these parthenogenetic eggs and the point of puncture. Therefore there must be either some already existing planes of symmetry in the ovum or an unknown mechanism for producing a new plane. That the former is correct has been shown by Tung who found that there is a preferential meridian of fertilization along which sperms normally enter (see Dalcq, 1935). Nevertheless this plane is not absolutely fixed before fertilization and it can be varied by appropriate procedures such as centrifugation or localized insemination.

8. The changes occurring at fertilization

Many other events take place immediately after fertilization. Often there are changes in the membranes around the ovum, for instance, the vitelline membrane may lift off from the surface. There are also sometimes visible alterations in the structure of the cortex of the ovum itself (see Swann, 1952; Mitchison, 1952). The metabolic changes are even more striking. There is often a rapid change in the oxygen consumption and carbon dioxide output of the egg after fertilization. There may be an increase in permeability to water and electrolytes, changes in viscosity and in many other properties.

It is clear that the unfertilized ovum is a highly specialized cell, which is, so to speak, set ready to go when appropriately activated. We still have little idea of the nature of the events that follow sperm entry and produce so many visible and chemical changes in the ovum. The enormous number of studies of the gametes up to the time of their fusion has still not sufficed to give us more than a glimpse of the nature of the organization of processes by virtue of which the zygote goes on to develop into an adult vertebrate. Little is known of the times at which the ova acquire their axes, even less of the manner of their acquiring them. Tunicate and amphibian eggs certainly have an axis and probably also a plane of symmetry before fertilization and the physico-chemical basis of this axiation is beginning to be known. There are marked streaming movements in the ovum after fertilization, but we are ignorant of their significance. When we remember that these are superficial questions compared to the really fundamental ones about the organization of materials and processes in the nucleus and cytoplasm of the gametes and zygote we obtain only too vivid a picture of the immaturity of biology. Perhaps the fact that we can see lines along which embryology may grow up shows that its adolescence is approaching; great new changes may be possible in the near future if attention is sufficiently concentrated on finding ways by which the sequence of processes in development can be accurately and adequately described.

XXXVI

THE PRODUCTION OF AN EMBRYO. CLEAVAGE AND GASTRULATION

1. Cleavage

THE process of cleavage by which the ovum becomes divided into blastomeres is greatly influenced by the amount of yolk present. In the oligolecithal eggs, such as those of tunicates, *Amphioxus* and placental mammals, the blastomeres are all approximately equal in size and the cleavage is said to be *total* or *holoblastic* and *equal* (Fig. 242). Where much yolk is present the formation of cleavage furrows in the vegetative half of the egg becomes delayed, so that larger blastomeres are formed at this than at the animal pole; cleavage is then said to be total but *unequal*. In the megalecithal eggs the great amount of yolk completely prevents the cleavage of the vegetative half of the egg; after the divisions of the nucleus, furrows are formed stretching down into the yolk and eventually these furrows round off to form a cap of cells, the *blastoderm* or *blastodisc*, resting on the uncleaved yolk and separated from it by a mass of liquefied yolk, the subgerminal cavity. Such cleavage is called *partial* or *meroblastic*.

The directions of the planes of cleavage partly follow two sets of rules. Hertwig's rules state (1) that mitotic spindles always orientate themselves along the greatest protoplasmic axis of a cell, and (2) that cleavage furrows form at right angles to the spindle axis. Sachs' rules are (1) that at division equal cells are formed, and (2) that each cleavage furrow bisects the previous one at right angles. The inert yolk occupies the greater part of the volume of the vegetative pole (see Fankhauser, 1952) and therefore the spindle, following Hertwig's first rule, lies parallel to the equator of the ovum. The first cleavage furrow therefore passes through the animal pole. In tunicates this furrow also divides the embryo into symmetrical right and left halves; in the amphibia this is so in many eggs, the furrow then dividing the grey crescent into equal parts (Fig. 243).

The second mitotic spindle also lies parallel to the equator and following Sachs' second rule it is at right angles to the first. In oligo- and mesolecithal eggs the third furrow is at right angles to the first two; being nearer to the animal than to the vegetative pole it separates four small micromeres from four macromeres. At the points of junction of the cells at the centre of these embryos a small space (the *blastocoel*) filled with fluid early appears and after only a few divisions the embryo has the form of a hollow ball, the *blastula*. The superficial

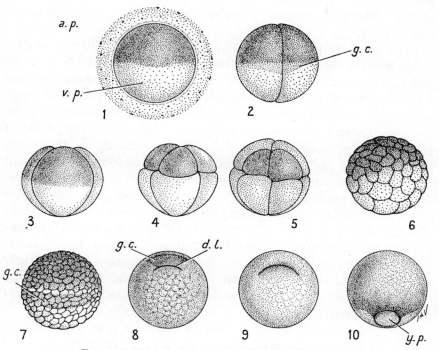

FIG. 243. Stages in development of the toad (*Xenopus*).

1. Fertilized egg; 2. 2-cell stage; 3. 4-cells; 4. 8-cells; 5. 16-cells; 6 and 7. blastula; 8–10. gastrulation. *a.p.* animal pole; *d.l.* dorsal lip of blastopore; *g.c.* position of grey crescent, which does not show clearly in the embryos; *v.p.* vegetative pole; *y.p.* yolk plug.

layer of cells may be ciliated and rotates the embryo within the egg case.

2. Differentiation and embryogenesis

It has already been emphasized that the process of formation of an embryo from an ovum is the device, repeated in each ontogeny, by which the Metazoa achieve the characteristic specialization of tissues. The essence of development is therefore the production of many different sets of cells arranged in relations appropriate for their later functioning. In studying embryogenesis we have to follow (*a*) the changes by which the various parts develop into different types of cell, and (b) the processes by which the embryo and its parts are moulded into their final shapes. Moreover, the science of the study of the mechanics of development aspires to describe not simply a sequence of stages but also the manner in which the events during any one period of development lead to those of the next period. It attempts to give a continuous, integrated analysis, which might be called causal embryology.

Even before fertilization the ovum contains various parts: the presence of axes shows that some portions of the cytoplasm must be different from others (p. 590). After fertilization in amphibia we can recognize animal and vegetative poles and in some species an equatorial grey crescent, which marks the future posterior end of the embryo. There is every reason to suppose that during the period of cleavage the process by which the various parts acquire differences goes on rapidly (p. 617) but these differentiations do not at first result in the appearance of any visible organs. They are quantitative differences, which gradually become more acute, causing the metabolism of the parts to diverge so that they acquire tendencies to develop into different final structures. The course of the appearance of these tendencies can be studied by suitable experiments, which show that the various regions gradually acquire the power to develop independently into their final definitive condition. Parts of the embryo acquire tendencies to grow into particular tissues long before they show structural differentiation.

As this process of differentiation of the cells goes on there are visible changes of shape leading to the formation of the embryo. During this period the *various areas move towards the positions that they will occupy in the adult*. The blastula is a hollow ball, the adult a complicated creature, with many layers and blocks of tissue. The movements of *gastrulation* by which the one begins to be converted into the other now begin.

The first stage of this process was for many years considered as consisting in the conversion of a one-layered blastula into a two-layered sack, the *gastrula*. It is now realized that the movements in question cannot be described simply as forming a second layer; they are not concerned only with producing a gut, but with the putting into place of other rudiments, for instance those of the notochord and the muscles. As Pasteels (1937) puts it 'gastrulation is a kinetic process and can only be described in a kinetic manner as *the migration and putting in place in the embryonic body of the various territories which were at first spread out on the surface of the blastula*'. In the development of many of the earlier types of vertebrate these movements lead among other things to the production of an inner tube, the *archenteron*.

The course of the movements of gastrulation has been fully analysed by the technique of Vogt (1925 and 1929), in which coloured marks are placed on the outside of the blastula by the application of non-toxic dyes such as Nile blue, Bismark brown, or neutral red. The subsequent movements of these marks can then be followed for many days, since the dye remains localized in the cells to which it was first applied (Fig 248).

3. Gastrulation in amphibia

The most thorough analysis has been made in amphibia and we will first describe the changes of shape that take place in the frog's egg, a convenient object for elementary laboratory study. The egg of the newt is more convenient for experimental work, because it is less yolky and more easily separated from its membranes.

The blastula soon ceases to be a single-layered sphere. Cleavages take place in a tangential plane, dividing inner from the outer parts of the original tall surface cells. This process is known as *cortical ingression* (Ballard, 1955). The first external sign of gastrulation is the appearance below the boundary between the pigmented animal pole cells and the lighter cells of the yolk, immediately below the middle of the grey crescent, of a small darkly pigmented lip. This represents the future postero-dorsal side of the embryo and is known as the *dorsal lip of the blastopore* (Fig. 243). It is produced by a slight sinking of some of the vegetative pole cells and the stretching over them of the neighbouring animal pole cells. These processes extend laterally, so that the lip occupies more and more of the circumference of the egg and at the same time advances over the yolk (Fig. 243). It forms a wider and wider crescent and eventually makes a circle, the *blasto-pore*. This circle proceeds to narrow until the pigmented cells cover the whole embryo except for a small yellow *yolk plug* at the vegetative pole.

Study of sections shows that during the course of these movements the vegetative portion of the embryo has come to form an inner layer, the *endoderm*, lining a new cavity, the *archenteron*. At first this cavity is only a groove beneath the dorsal lip (Fig. 244) but later it becomes large, the blastocoel being meanwhile reduced to a crack. Ultimately the archenteron becomes the gut of the tadpole. During the process of formation of the archenteron a further development is also proceeding, the putting into place of the tissue of the future notochord, and of the *mesoderm*, which produces most of the muscles, skeletal tissues, blood system, urinary and genital systems, and some glands. This chordamesodermal material becomes rolled in over the blastoporal lips, the chordal material ultimately forming a rod above the archenteron, and the mesoderm a sheet of tissue between the endoderm and the outer layer of cells, which are known from this time on as the ectoderm (Fig. 245).

The names given to the various parts of the embryo at this stage (ectoderm, &c.) should be used to refer each to a mass of cells occupying a particular position in the embryo. Considerable confusion has resulted from attempts to define these *germ layers* in terms of the tissues to which they give rise. The ectoderm, for example, the outer layer of the embryo after gastrulation, gives rise to a variety of tissues including the nervous system, skin, and part of the skeleton. But other parts of the skeleton are formed from the middle layer of the embryo, the mesoderm. These 'layers' must therefore be defined primarily by their position in the embryo and not by their later history. This problem is the basis of the controversy that has arisen over the 'germ layer theory'. The terms ectoblast, entoblast, and mesoblast are often used instead of those ending in -derm. There is no purpose in discussing the nomenclature in detail here; it will not be found confusing if the names such as ectoblast or ectoderm are used simply as a means of referring to particular masses of tissue of the embryo.

4. The neurula

During the later stages of the above changes the nervous system begins to appear. The dorsal side of the embryo becomes flattened to form the *neural plate* (*medullary plate*), which then rolls up from the sides to form the *neural tube*, the rudiment of the brain and spinal cord. Thus the material of the nervous system (*neural ectoderm*) is separated from the rest of the ectoderm of the outer layer, which proceeds to form the outer skin of the embryo. The three main parts of the brain, fore-, mid-, and hind-brain, can be recognized in the medullary plate almost from its first appearance, as can the rudiments of the eyes, forming by evagination from the brain. The embryo at this stage is called a *neurula* (Fig. 246).

By the time that the neural folds are fully formed the blastopore has become further reduced to a narrow slit, elongated in the main plane of the body. In the frog the slit becomes covered over by the hind part of the neural folds, creating a passage, the *neurenteric canal*, leading

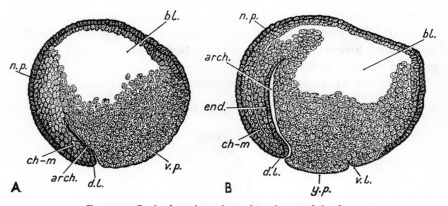

FIG. 244. Sagittal sections through embryos of the frog.

A, early and B, late in gastrulation. *arch.* archenteron; *bl.* blastocoel; *ch-m.*, chordameso-derm; *d.l.* dorsal lip of blastopore; *end.* endoderm; *n.p.* presumptive neural plate; *v.l.* ventral lip of blastopore; *v.p.* vegetative pole; *y.p.* yolk plug.

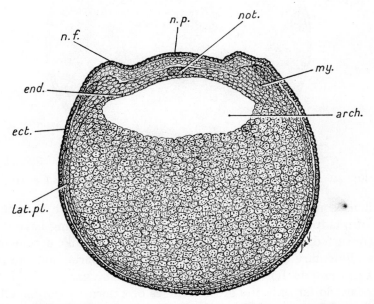

FIG. 245. Transverse section of early neurula stage of the frog.

arch. archenteron; *coel.* coelom; *derm.* dermatome; *ect.* non-neural ectoderm; *end.* endo-derm; *lat. pl.* lateral plate mesoderm; *my.* myotome; *n.f.* neural fold; *n.p.* neural plate; *not.* noto-chord; *n.t.* neural tube.

from the archenteron to the neural canal. The neurenteric canal is not formed in urodeles and its presence in anurans depends on the time and method of formation of the neural folds. No far-reaching morphological conclusion can be drawn from this communication between gut and nervous system.

During the whole period of gastrulation and neurulation the embryo

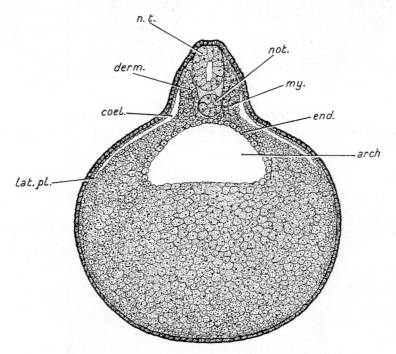

Fig. 246. Transverse section of young frog neurula. Lettering as Fig. 245.

lengthens considerably and the later neurula begins to assume the form of a tadpole. The changes we have been describing have therefore converted a hollow ball of cells into a tadpole-like organism, in which alimentary canal, nervous system and its parts, and the rudiments of the notochord, muscles, and other structures are beginning to appear. So far only the gross changes of external form have been described. By means of Vogt's method of applying coloured marks it has been possible to follow the detailed tissue movements by which these shapes are produced. The recognition that these stages of embryogenesis take place by a series of movements of masses of cells has produced a revolution in embryological science during the years since Vogt's technique was first developed in the decade 1920–30.

5. The morphogenetic movements of gastrulation

The processes may be analysed into five *morphogenetic movements*, responsible for the changes of shape during gastrulation and neurulation. These movements are found in all vertebrates, though they are modified when the egg contains much yolk. First there is *invagination*, the movement by which part of the original external surface comes to lie internally. At its simplest this movement is seen in the sinking in

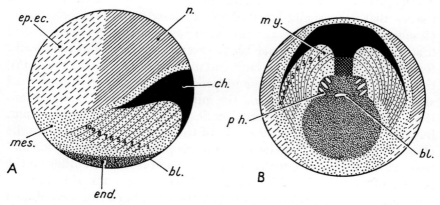

FIG. 247. Map showing the fate of the areas on the outside of the early gastrula of the newt *Triturus* seen A, from the side, B, from the vegetative pole.

bl. blastopore; *ch.* chorda; *end.* endoderm; *ep.ec.* epidermal ectoderm; *n.* neurectoderm; *mes.* mesoderm; *my.* position of myotomes; *ph.* pharyngeal pouches. (Partly after Vogt.)

of the yolky vegetative pole cells below the dorsal lip of the blastopore to form the archenteron. The movements by which the cells lining the archenteron extend forwards and obliterate the blastocoele are also those of invagination. More complex movements included under the same heading produce the rolling in that takes place at the lips of the blastopore.

Marks placed on the outside of the embryo above and to the sides of the dorsal lip soon disappear and can later be found inside by dissection or by sectioning the larva. By means of numerous such experiments it is possible to make a complete map of the fate of the various portions of the outer surface of the embryo that invaginate over the lips of the blastopore (Fig. 247).

The region around the original blastoporal pit becomes the lining of the front part of the gut and is known as the *pharyngeal endoderm*, i.e. the part that comes to lie in front of the notochord. The areas that will form the gills can be recognized within it. The material lying in a fan-shaped area immediately above and to the sides of the dorsal lip will give rise to the notochord. In newts it rolls over the lip of the blastopore in such a way that it makes part of the roof of the archenteron. It then separates off to make the notochord. In the frog the chordal material never makes part of the archenteric roof but forms a distinct rod as it passes over the blastopore lip.

A large crescentic area to the right and left of the dorsal lip becomes rolled in over the lateral and ventral lips of the blastopore and ultimately gives rise to the muscles and to most of those skeletal and other tissues that are usually referred to as mesodermal (see below). So closely are the endoderm and mesoderm associated in the frog that at first they form a single inner layer, several cells thick but not clearly formed of two parts. Then later the mesoderm separates (Fig. 246), the split beginning dorsally and proceeding until the mesodermal sheet is separated off all round the gut and proceeds to develop into the muscles and other structures as described below. It is important, however, to recognize that the cells of the mesoderm only come to lie close to those of the endoderm during the process of invagination and that previously the two were clearly separated from each other on the surface of the blastula. Indeed in urodeles, on account of the somewhat different time relations, the two tissues never form a combined sheet as they do in anurans. It is not correct to say that invagination produces an inner layer (or 'hypoblast') and that this then splits into endoderm and mesoderm; these two are only associated for a time during gastrulation, being separated from each other both at earlier and later stages. In other animals, for instance, the tunicates, the endoderm and mesoderm are even more widely separated, from the blastula stage onwards (p. 633). Invagination in the frog, then, is the invasion of the blastocoel by the lower materials of the egg, first of endoderm then of chordamesoderm. It is an active process produced by movement or change of shape of the masses of cells concerned.

6. Extension

It is convenient next to describe extension, the second of the morphogenetic movements by which gastrulation is produced. It consists of a stretching of tissues, which produces spreading of the blastoporal lips over the yolk. This results in the closure of the blastopore and the process continues after gastrulation has ended, producing elongation of the embryo and the formation of the tail-bud. Vogt has emphasized that this process is an active 'self-stretching' of the tissues of the embryo, presumably produced by change in shape of the cells.

It is a movement distinct from the rolling in at the lips, though it often accompanies this latter.

7. Convergence

During gastrulation all of the layers of the embryo partake in a movement of dorsal convergence. The first sign of this is the movement of future mesodermal tissue backwards towards the lips of the blastopore. Similar processes continue until much later as the convergence by which the neural folds are raised by the movement of material towards the middle line. Coloured marks placed on the sides of the early gastrula above the equator can be seen to pass dorsally, and ultimately to become incorporated in the neural folds (Fig. 248).

A similar movement of dorsal convergence takes place in the sheet of mesoderm and results in the piling up dorsally of a thickened mass, which then becomes divided up into blocks to form the *somites*, from which the musculature of the trunk and limbs is developed. A movement of convergence also occurs in the endoderm and serves to complete the formation of the gut roof after the separation from it of the notochord. This is shown most clearly in urodeles, where the notochordal material, although it is quite distinct from the endoderm, occupies the roof of the archenteron in the period immediately after gastrulation. When this chordal material separates away to develop into the rod-like notochord it leaves the upper edges of the endoderm free and the archenteron is roofless. The movement of dorsal convergence then rapidly closes the gap, the edges of the endoderm moving up, essentially as do the neural folds, until they meet in the mid-dorsal line. In anurans the process is similar but takes place precociously so that the notochordal material never actually forms part of the gut roof but separates away as soon as it is rolled in.

8. Epiboly and ventral divergence

In the movement of *epiboly* the epiblast of the roof of the blastula thins out so that the marginal zone is pushed outwards and downwards. This movement was previously thought to be the main factor concerned in closure of the blastopore and was conceived of as an 'overgrowth' of the animal pole cells over those of the vegetative pole. The thinning out of the ectodermal cells that actually takes place does in fact produce a movement of this sort, and thus may be called epiboly, provided it is recognized that it is not an overgrowth in the sense of being produced by cell division at a margin, and also that it is not a major factor in closure of the blastopore.

Epiboly may be defined as the extension of the ectoderm by which the material rolled in at the blastoporal lips becomes covered up, but this spreading divergence is a process that extends farther and lasts longer than the epiboly as conceived by the older workers. The thinning of the ectoderm goes on after the blastopore has closed, in fact during and after the formation of the neural folds by convergence. Indeed it is complementary to convergence and the extension of the lateral and ventral ectoderm helps to push up the neural folds. The process of divergence goes on over the whole lateral and ventral surfaces and marking experiments show that material is continually passing outwards and dorsally away from the mid-ventral line. This part of the movement is sometimes called *ventral divergence* to distinguish it from the epiboly, which is divergence in the more lateral and dorsal regions. Similarly, processes of divergence can be recognized in the mesoderm, complementary to the dorsal convergence in this layer. There is no detailed information about the cell-processes that produce these movements, presumably they involve a change of shape of the cells such that their surface area is increased. A contraction in the radial direction across each cell would produce this effect.

9. Discussion of early morphogenetic movements

We have now considered the visible changes by which a hollow ball, the blastula, is converted into an embryo of tadpole shape in which the materials for the gut, muscles, notochord, and nervous system are all in place and are beginning to differentiate. This conversion is brought about by a series of movements of tissue that can be resolved into five components, though it is not yet clear how far these are independent of each other. It should be emphasized once again that these movements of the cells are not produced mainly by cell division. In teleostean fishes Pasteels (1936) showed that the division rate is nearly equal in all parts of the embryo during the period in which morphogenetic movements are taking place. In other vertebrates there may be differences in mitotic rates in different regions but there is little to suggest that they cause movements (Bellairs, 1955). The morphogenetic movements are produced by changes in cell shape or by the active individual movements of cells, controlled by forces which we are beginning to understand. Isolated pieces taken from the surface of one blastula and implanted into another continue to show movements characteristic of their origin. Thus pieces of future chordamesoderm sink in and pieces of neural ectoderm spread out even when they are placed in situations on other larvae where these movements are quite inappropriate. Considerable movement can even be seen in pieces of blastula cultivated in solutions *in vitro*. Moreover, by treatment of amphibian embryos with alkali, it is possible to make all the cells separate from each other. They can then be mixed up in various ways and yet nevertheless continue their development. Reaggregation occurs, the cells of each type collecting together and proceeding to make movements similar, so far as possible, to their normal ones. Thus after mixture of disaggregated cells of the epidermis and medullary plate an organism is formed in which the outside is wholly composed of epidermal cells and the centre is occupied by neural cells arranged to form a tube (Townes and Holtfreter, 1955). The movements of the two types of cell in this experiment are characteristic of the two types of movement that are seen in such aggregates. Some cells move *outwards*, as do the epidermal cells, and spread peripherally, others, for example the neural plate cells or mesoderm cells move *inwards*. The normal patterns of development are produced by such specific tendencies for cells of the same type to adhere and move together. A further controlling influence is an outer syncytial coat of intercellular material, present over the outside of amphibian embryos and serving as a substrate that unites the cells into interdependent units (Holtfreter, 1948).

These facts emphasize that morphogenesis is produced by specific active movements made by the cells of the embryo itself. Indeed a moment's reflection will show that during development the new creature must build itself in this way. There is at present much study of the mechanism of these movements, their energy requirements, and the instructions that control them. They are the 'functions' of the embryonic cells, just as contraction is the function of the adult muscle-cell. Energy is needed during development not only for the performance of morphogenetic movements but also for the synthesis of large energy-rich molecules such as the proteins and phospholipids. However, there is not necessarily any great energy expenditure involved in the production of specific molecules during differentiation, which may be a matter of selection of specific proteins from generalized precursor molecules.

During amphibian gastrulation the main source of energy is at first glycogen, then lipids. Protein is probably also used as a source of fuel and some ammonia and urea are produced by the frog's egg. The steps by which carbohydrate is metabolized are similar to those that take place in muscle. The dorsal lip has a higher rate of respiration than the ventral but the difference is due to the amounts of yolk rather than to specific differences in type of metabolism (Barth and Barth, 1954).

10. Summary of morphogenetic movements

The marks of Fig. 248 show approximately the courses taken by pieces originally lying at the spots marked 1 to 15 on the outside of the

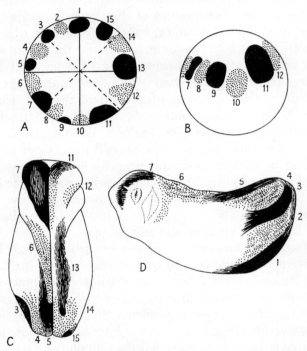

FIG. 248. Movement of marks of Nile blue (dots) and neutral red (lines) placed upon a blastula of the frog *Bombinator*.

A, Seen from animal pole; B, lateral view; C, late neurula; D, young tadpole. (After Dalcq.)

blastula. They elongate by the process of *stretching* or *extension*. By the process of *invagination*, either by inpushing or by rolling over the lips of the blastopore, portions of the originally outer wall come to lie internally. By these two processes an archenteron is created, the blastopore is closed, and the tissues that will form the endoderm, notochord and mesoderm are put in place. By the movement of *dorsal convergence* the tissues are then pulled (or pull themselves) dorsally, so that the ectoderm piles up to form the neural folds, the mesoderm to form the somites, and the endoderm in some species to complete the gut roof after the separation of the notochord.

By thinning out the walls of the animal pole (*epiboly*) the animal pole cells move down over those of the vegetative pole. Later this movement continues as a thinning out of the ectoderm and mesoderm and their *ventral divergence* from the mid-ventral line, by which the convergence of the dorsal materials is assisted.

Different parts of a given tissue on the outside of the blastula may reach their definitive positions by different routes. For example, most of the tissue that will form mesoderm invaginates over the lips of the blastopore. Yet in urodeles some of it never invaginates but forms part of the neural plate, which thus gives rise to the muscles of the tail.

It will be recognized that this analysis of morphogenetic movements, due originally to Vogt, still leaves much to be done before we can give a really concise description of early development. What we should like to be able to say is that as a result of physico-chemical changes X, Y, Z cells of the region R of the blastula swell (or stretch or divide or whatever it may be) and so pull or push their neighbours that a movement in direction RS takes place. One may hope that it may ultimately be possible to unravel the course of ontogeny so that it makes use of the exact terms of the physical sciences. When we can speak of forces or attractions produced by physico-chemical changes, for example, dehydrations or molecular folding, we shall have a science of embryology more powerful and easier to understand than the present one, which has to use its own special terms. Moreover, only when we can do this will it be possible to understand properly the question of the relationship of the pattern of the nucleoproteins in the nucleus of the zygote to the activities of the embryo and adult, and this is one of the central problems of biology.

Vogt and his successors have shown for the first time the true directions of the movements that take place during this period. Previous work by observation from the outside and the study of sections could provide an account only of the *results* of the morphogenetic movements: Vogt has been able to describe these movements themselves. He has described the cinematics of development. Nearly all of the analysis, valuable as it is, has so far been visual; embryology is now beginning to win greater understanding and control of these processes by proceeding to use physical and chemical methods.

XXXVII

THE SEQUENCE OF DIFFERENTIATION

1. The course of differentiation

W E are now in a position to make a general review of the processes of development. It is evident that the oocyte before it begins to grow must be considered as a system capable of responding to asymmetrical stimulation by the development of differentiation within itself. For example, in response to the supply of raw materials (or of some key material) each part of the ovum, being related differently to that supply, acquires a characteristic differentiation of potency. Some such system of response by differentiation must exist in the ovum but it is one of the greatest weaknesses of embryology that we have no clear knowledge of the details of either the stimuli or the responses.

Child in his theory of *axial gradients* supposes that the greater 'metabolic' activity at one pole of the egg makes this become the apical or dominant region of a gradient extending throughout the cytoplasm, so that each level will develop different potencies according to its distance from the apex of the gradient (see Child, 1915 and 1941). This theory is open to some criticism (see Huxley and de Beer, 1934; Willier *et al.*, 1955) but it serves to draw attention to the fundamental phenomenon of differentiation, which it is a primary purpose of embryology to describe. Some approach to the study of such gradients is possible by examination of the gradations of structure and by experiments to show powers of differentiation within the ovum.

2. Differentiation within the egg

A frog's egg before fertilization already shows considerable evidence of the presence of specialized regions; it possesses a rather definite internal structure (p. 590). Nevertheless, not only can an ovum be made to produce two embryos but two can be combined to make one! If the two first blastomeres of an amphibian are separated each will often give rise to a complete embryo. Each is said to be *totipotent*. This is perhaps to be expected since the first cleavage furrow often divides the egg in what will be the future medial plane; each blastomere therefore contains a portion of the grey crescent and all other parts of the ovum. In some experiments of this sort, especially in newts, one of the first two blastomeres fails to develop after isolation, presumably because the cleavage plane did not divide the grey crescent.

If the embryo at the early two-cell stage is turned upside down the yolk granules stream through to the animal pole and there is a gross disturbance of the visible internal organization. Nevertheless *two* perfect embryos are often produced. Evidently the 'structure' of the inside of the ovum cannot be very precise if it is capable after much mixing of materials of producing two complete embryos. Similarly, if two embryos at the two-cell stage are placed together in the appropriate directions a single embryo of abnormally large size results. These are examples of the power of *regulation*, which is characteristic of many developing organisms. Systems thus capable of providing a perfect whole in spite of additions or subtractions are said to be *harmonious equipotential systems*. This capacity of regulation is evidently a special aspect of homeostasis.

Mixture of the internal parts of the ovum or early embryo does not affect its power and it thus appears to be essentially homogeneous; yet it is the characteristic function of eggs to produce heterogeneous embryos. This paradox lies close to the central problem of embryology, which is to understand how the relatively simple egg builds the complex adult. To Driesch and others the paradox seemed to necessitate the postulation of some spiritual agent or *entelechy*, lying outside the material system. This is a typical case of the use of 'person language' to prescribe a situation that is not fully understood (p. 5). The description of development is difficult because there are no tools or machines of comparable complexity with which a developing embryo may be compared. This is no reason for despair, we can begin to give a description in terms of the fundamental scientific entities, for example, the heterogeneous composition of the ovum can be partly described chemically. In order to give a useful account of the complicated organization that emerges as development proceeds we shall need to use the analogy of machines that proceed to make forecasts under the control of the instructions they have received (p. 19).

3. Differentiation in the blastula

The tissues do not remain totipotent indefinitely. The time comes when portions separated from the whole vertebrate embryo are found to have lost the power of regulation to make a whole, or to put it conversely they become so differentiated that they can produce only a certain part. There is little information as to the features of the cells

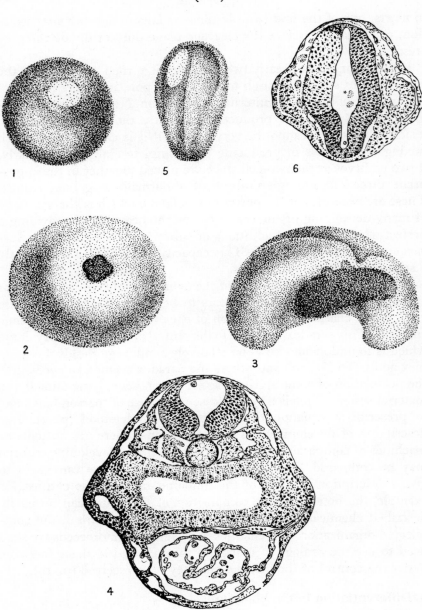

FIG. 249. Effect of grafting before chemo-differentiation. A piece of presumptive medullary plate from a dark embryo of *Triton taeniatus* (1) is exchanged with a piece of presumptive epidermis of the light *T. cristatus* (2). Each piece develops according to its new position so that later a dark patch is seen on the skin in the one case (3 and 4) and a light patch in the nervous system in the other (5 and 6).
(After Spemann, *Arch. Ent-mech.* **48**, 1921.)

that give this power of *self-differentiation*. Presumably the basic equipment of molecules and supra-molecular aggregates such as mitochondria becomes appropriately varied to produce a system characteristic of each type of cell. Ultimately these differences appear as the characteristic cytological features such as secretion granules, Nissl substance in nerve-cells or pigment granules. But the developing cells acquire different potencies long before they show cytological differentiation. The cells of the blastula of an amphibian have not yet fully acquired this power of self-differentiation. This can be shown by grafting pieces of the outer layer of the pigmented blastula of the newt *Triton taeniatus* into some foreign portion of the unpigmented *T. cristatus* (Spemann, 1924). The grafted piece will be found to mould itself to its new position (Fig. 249). Pieces of prospective ectoderm can be shown in this way to be able to co-operate in forming part of the mesoderm or even endoderm. Pieces of prospective mesoderm or endoderm are somewhat less adaptable: their cells tend to pursue their characteristic activities wherever they are placed (p. 619).

There are therefore some indications that the tendencies towards later powers are appearing in the cells of the blastula. For instance, some cell characteristics (pigment, nuclear size, developmental rate) are clearly present and are maintained after transplantation, or even after cultivation *in vitro*. This differentiation of the districts proceeds only slowly during cleavage, so that not only can a single one of the early blastomeres give rise to a whole embryo but even a half blastula is able to regulate and to produce a whole embryo, if the cut is made so as to include part of the derivatives of the grey crescent.

In the blastula and young gastrula careful experiments have been made by many workers to discover the potentialities of the different regions that are shown by the work of Vogt to be fated to develop into the various parts of the embryo. By culture of isolated pieces of the blastula, either *in vitro* or grafted beneath the cornea of the eye of an older larva, it has been shown that some self-differentiation can take place. If the portion of the young gastrula that will give rise to nervous tissue is cultivated strictly alone it gives rise only to undifferentiated epithelium though if a little mesenchyme is added various differentiations may occur.

Holtfreter found that portions of the presumptive endoderm taken from the early gastrula stage and cultivated *in vitro* developed into epithelia recognizably similar to that of one of the regions of the gut. Portions of the future chordamesoderm, however, from wherever on the blastula they are taken, always develop into a tissue that is a

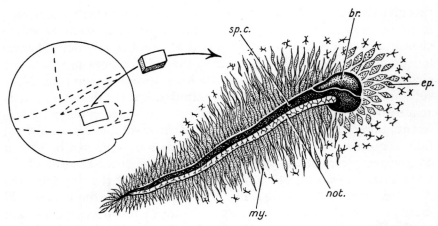

FIG. 250. Explantation before chemo-differentiation. An explant from the prospective somite material on the outside of an early gastrula differentiates to form an axial system with a brain-like enlargement (*br.*) capped by epidermis (*ep.*). The main axis contains notochord (*not.*), spinal cord (*sp.c.*) and myoblasts (*my.*).
(After Holtfreter, *Growth Symposium*, **10**, 1951.)

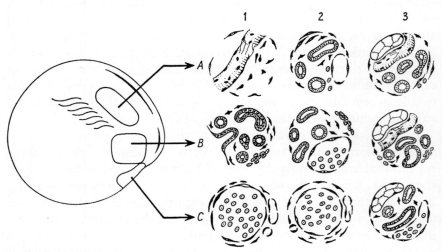

FIG. 251. Effect of environment on differentiation of parts of the blastula surface in amphibia.

Row A represents presumptive somite mesoderm, row B presumptive pronephros, and row C presumptive blood, sited as shown in an embryo.

Column 1 shows their fates, when the tissues are undisturbed, to be muscle, pronephros, and blood. Column 2 shows their fates, when isolated from the embryo and allowed to develop in a ball of ectoderm, to be pronephros, blood, blood. Column 3 shows their fates when isolated together with notochordal tissue and allowed to develop in a ball of ectoderm to be muscle, muscle, and pronephros. (After Yamada, 1940, *Folia Anatomica Japonica*, **19**.)

mixture of notochordal and mesodermal cells, even if the piece taken would normally have given rise only to notochord. The potencies of this region, therefore, have not yet been fully separated. Pieces of this chordasomite district often regulate after transplantation to form a complete axis with notochord, somites, and often also neural tissue and sense organs (Fig. 250).

In the young neurula there is a gradation in the powers of differentiation of this region. The future notochord represents the highest region, then the future myotomes, then the regions that will give rise to the pronephros, and finally the ventral mesodermal region. After cultivation *in vitro* each region tends to give rise to a tissue lower in the sequence than that which it would normally have produced (Fig. 251). Presumptive notochord usually differentiates into chordal tissue, but presumptive somites give rise to pronephros, presumptive pronephros to blood-vessels, which are normally derived from the ventral mesoderm. However, Yamada claimed that addition to the culture of a small amount of material from the highest part of the gradient, the presumptive notochord, caused the cultures to develop according to their presumptive fates or even into tissues higher in the sequence. The results could be interpreted however as showing the presence of several overlapping fields of partial determination, each greater than the presumptive region of the organ concerned, the directions of differentiations being readily influenced by the conditions of culture (Muchmore, 1951).

Evidently the surface of the young neurula is made up of cells that are partly determined to develop in various directions but are not yet entirely fixed in their fate. This state of partial differentiation may prove to be of great interest for the analysis of the nature of the processes concerned.

The time of chemo-differentiation varies greatly in the development of different species. In the amphibia it occurs rather late and the ovum and early embryo are thus capable of considerable regulation. Hence such eggs are called *regulation eggs* as distinct from *mosaic eggs*, in which determination occurs early. In mosaic eggs, for instance in the ascidian *Styela* (p. 635), removal of a part of the early embryo or even of the fertilized ovum, may give rise to a defect in the resulting larva.

4. The organizer. Primary induction

If a piece of the chordamesoderm that is passing or has just passed over the dorsal lip of the blastopore is planted into the flank of another gastrula it will develop there into a complete set of somites and a notochord (Fig. 252) (Pasteels, 1951). It is therefore now tending to become *chemo-differentiated* or *determined* to produce certain structures. *More-*

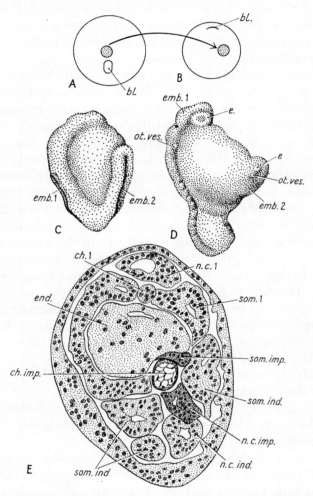

FIG. 252. Induction by grafted organizer of *Bombinator* to a gastrula of *Triton*.

A, Donor gastrula; B, host; C, neurula, and D, young embryos developed from B. E, transverse section in trunk region.

bl. blastopore; *emb. 1* and *2*, primary and secondary embryos; *ch.1, n.c.1*, and *som.1*, notochord, nerve cord, and somite of primary embryo; *ch.imp., n.c.imp., som.imp.*, organs differentiated from the implanted tissue; *n.c.ind.* and *som.ind.*, induced organs; *e.* eye; *end.* endoderm; *ot.ves.* otic vesicle. (After Geinitz in Dalcq, 1935.)

over, it has also acquired powers of inducing the differentiation of other structures. The ectodermal tissue above the graft in such an experiment will roll up to form a neural tube, often complete with brain, eye-cups and otic vesicle. The implant of chordamesoderm is said to

have *induced* or *evoked* the formation of a neural tube. The two phenomena together, formation of somites and notochord from the graft and
evocation of a neuraxis above it are referred to as the *organizer phenomenon* (see Spemann, 1938).

The dorsal lip of one species can produce its effects when planted
into larvae of another species, tissues of urodeles may produce them
when planted into anurans. On account of the differences in cell size
between the species it is possible to be sure that the effect of the graft
is to organize the tissue of the host, not merely to grow at its expense.

The production of an almost complete new individual in this way
is indeed so striking as to suggest that the material grafted must contain the organizing centre of the whole embryo. This invaginated
tissue is, however, only showing to a striking extent the power to
evoke chemo-differentiation, a power that arises continuously in the
tissues as development proceeds. Isolated portions of the material of
the outside of the blastula have, as we have seen, only limited powers.
Material that has passed over the blastopore lip becomes chemo-
differentiated; thereafter if placed under suitable conditions it will
itself differentiate without further assistance into its characteristic
tissues and can also evoke responses in other tissues.

It is evident that some profound change takes place in the cells as
they pass over the lip. It will be remembered that the lip is not a growing point spinning out the tissues behind it, but is a region over which
the cells are rolled (p. 608). There is, therefore, no constant mass of
tissue that can be called 'the dorsal lip material', the material of the
lip is constantly changing. As the tissues pass this lip region and roll
under they acquire the power to differentiate into notochord and
somites and to evoke the formation of a nerve-cord. The dorsal
blastoporal region, which when on the outside of the blastula possesses
regulative capacities, becomes capable at the time it passes over the
blastopore lips of inducing various structures when it comes into contact with suitably competent epiblastic material.

The nature of this evocating action remains uncertain, but it may
be chemical. Pieces of newt gastrula ectoderm cultured alone form
sheets or balls of cells, with no further differentiation. If cultured in a
medium that contains or *has contained* a mesodermal explant, however, the cells differentiate into chromatophores, nerve-cells and
-fibres, or myoblasts (see Niu and Twitty, 1953). The 'conditioned'
medium contains substances that absorb ultra-violet light at 265 mμ
and 245 mμ and may be nucleic acids.

The different parts of this district have distinct inductive capacities

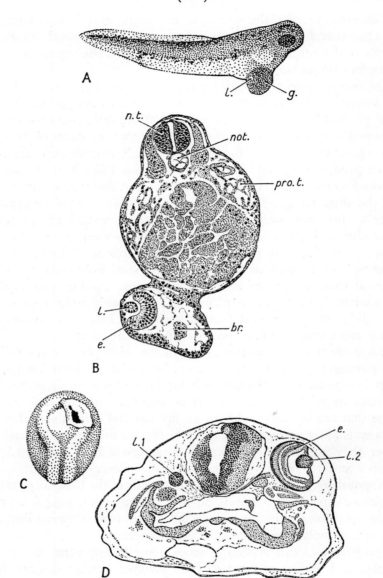

FIG. 253. Lens induction.

A and B, Larva of *Triton* into which at mid-gastrula stage a piece of presumptive brain and eye was grafted from another larva. The graft (*g*) differentiates into a portion of brain (*br.*) and eye-cup (*e*) and the latter induces the formation of a lens (*l*) from the overlying ectoderm. C and D, Extirpation of presumptive eye rudiment from early neurula of *R. esculenta*. The lens (l_1) develops in spite of the absence of the eye, but is smaller than the normal lens (l_2).
n.t. neural tube; *not.* notochord; *pro.t.* pronephros.
(After Mangold.)

and a complete secondary embryo is produced only by a graft that includes the whole chordamesoderm. The material that invaginates first is capable after isolation with indifferent ectoderm of inducing only the front end of an embryo, with brain, sense organs, mouth, and visceral arches. Explants from the more lateral regions induce only the spinal cord and mesenchyme typical of a portion of the trunk or tail.

These distinct powers can also be seen by grafting of portions of the archenteron roof after invagination. The extreme anterior tip has little or no inductive power. The portion representing prechordal plate and front end of the notochord and somites influences the overlying tissues to produce forebrain, eyes, and other anterior cephalic structures. The middle section induces hindbrain and ear vesicles and the hind portion only spinal cord, pronephros, and the mesodermal tissues of trunk and tail (see Nieuwkoop *et al*, 1952).

5. Secondary and tertiary induction

Once the ectoderm has become determined under the influence of the primary inductors it becomes itself the inducing agent of a series of *secondary inductions*. Different portions of the neural plate are able to induce the formation of nasal pits, ear vesicles, lens, gills, teeth, and even dorsal fin, by tissues that would not normally give rise to these structures.

The evidence that a particular tissue may produce a specific differentiation in another is beyond question, yet the phenomenon is not a simple one and its physico-chemical basis is not well understood. It must not be supposed that each portion of the embryo that acts as an evocator possesses a unique physical or chemical characteristic capable of influencing other tissues. In many cases more than one factor operates to produce induction. Thus an ear vesicle is induced from ectoderm either by prospective hindbrain or by cephalic mesoderm but the fully differentiated labyrinth only appears if both these influences are present.

The development of the lens of the eye shows further features of induction. In *Bufo, Triton,* or *Rana temporaria* if the eye-cup is removed no lens forms. Conversely, a suitable portion of the front part of the neural plate of one of these species, if grafted under the skin of the trunk, will produce there a complete eye-cup and evoke the formation of a lens from the overlying ectoderm, which, of course, would normally have produced no such structure (Fig. 253 A and B). In other amphibians, however, the lens develops even if the eye-cup is removed (*R. esculenta*, Fig. 253 C and D). Presumably in these species the determining influence is given out very early by the eye rudiment, while it is still part of the neural plate. This is confirmed by grafting tissues from other parts of the body to the eye region. In *R. temporaria* epidermis taken from any region, even in the late tail-bud stage, will form a lens but in *R. esculenta* this is possible only at earlier stages and by the late tail bud stage only epidermis from the lens region can make a lens. The quantitative character of these differences is shown by the fact that if *R. esculenta* embryos are kept warm the determination of the lens follows the same course as in *R. temporaria*.

It is characteristic of inductions that they are not species specific. For example, epidermis of *Bufo* grafted over an eye-cup of *R. esculenta* will make a lens, even if the experiment is done at the late stage when *esculenta* epidermis itself has lost this power.

6. Nature of the primary evocator

In spite of a long series of researches the physical and chemical nature of inductive processes is still not clear and the matter is complicated by the facts that (1) tissues not normally inductive can be made to become so, and (2) inductions can be produced by non-specific agents such as adult liver and even by inorganic bodies and foreign chemical substances.

For example, although the cells of the outside of the blastula do not normally have evocating powers yet if they are killed by boiling they then acquire this power. Holtfreter (1934) was able to show this by covering the boiled piece of tissue with a portion of indifferent epiblast to act as a detector. Moreover, extracts and pieces from a wide variety of animal tissues have been shown to have evocating powers, though plant derivatives do not in general possess them. For some time it was thought that the appearance of organizing power was somehow linked with the metabolism of glycogen, because this substance is present in the cells before but not after they have been rolled in at the dorsal lip. Further study showed that the evocator substance is soluble in such solvents as ether but not in water and hence cannot be glycogen itself. Needham, Waddington, and Needham (1934) believed the evocator to be a sterol derivative and they obtained inductions by implantation of various synthetic phenanthrenes. Brachet claims that there are abundant granules containing nucleic acid in the material invaginated over the dorsal lip of the blastopore. These disappear from the cells after invagination and at that time similar granules appear in the overlying medullary plate. It would be most important to show that the signalling action of evocation is produced by discrete particles. So many substances produce the effect, however, that we cannot at present say which, if any, is responsible in the normal embryo. So far no unambiguous information has been obtained as to how the evocator produces its effects and it would perhaps be worth while to study more minutely such processes as the rolling up of the neural tube, with a view to finding out more about the relation between the evocator and the cellular changes that it produces.

The inducing effect of the cells varies according to whether they were rolled in early or late over the dorsal lip (p. 623), but there is no further information about the difference between the material of the various parts of the archenteric roof, which might provide clues to the question that interests us here, namely, the division of the embryo into fields determined to develop in various directions. All that can be said is that at the time of the appearance of the dorsal lip the cells in certain positions begin so to metabolize as to produce substances or conditions that cause other cells to roll up to make a neural tube or differentiate in other ways. The next stage in analysis is presumably to identify the differences that are associated with these specific inductive capacities.

All differentiation depends on the effects of the environment or of neighbouring cells upon each other. We can imagine that in the earliest Metazoa some cells (for example, those at the front end) were stimulated to different metabolism by their asymmetrical relationship to the environment and that these by their different metabolism then produced change in the shapes and metabolism of their neighbours. The organisms would then become progressively more complicated by change in the genotype and hence in the mode of response of the metabolism of the cells to the stimuli impinging on them from their environment or from their neighbours. We can catch a glimpse here of stages of the process by which the uniform metabolism throughout the egg gradually becomes modified in different directions in various parts. We can see how these differences of metabolism might produce substances that in turn affect the neighbouring cells, producing changes in cell-division rates or physical states, by which the shapes of the various organs are determined. The further development of this theme will depend on a combined study by embryologists and cellular physiologists.

7. The sequence of induction as a selection of instructions

During development the ovum, which began as a single system of equipotential material, becomes divided into a series of districts, each with certain powers of self-differentiation, each capable of regulation within itself, and each able to evoke further differentiations. We obtain thus an idea of the course of development as a hierarchical series of evocations. The material of the early ovum has the power of responding to some asymmetrical environmental condition so as to produce a simple system of parts. These move in a particular manner during cleavage and gastrulation and as they move they acquire further differences and further powers. In this way a system with many parts is built up out of one that was itself simple but endowed with the power to give rise to difference internally in response to environmental stimulus. There is every hope that it should be possible in future to discover more of the nature of these stimuli and responses that lead to differentiation.

It must not be forgotten that the nature of the responding tissue plays a large part in the result. The jaws of anurans have horny, those of urodeles calcareous teeth; if anuran skin is planted to the head of a urodele the teeth that develop will be horny and vice versa. There is even evidence that evocators exist that are unable to produce any response in tissues of their own species. Newts possess an outgrowth below the eye called the 'balancer' but this is absent from axolotls. Newt skin grafted to the head of an axolotl will produce a balancer, showing that the host produces the evocation stimulus but that its own tissues are unable to respond to it. As would be expected axolotl skin grafted to a newt's head forms no balancer. This evidence that inductors are not species specific emphasizes again the importance of the reacting material, suggesting that the particular characteristics produced are not dependent upon the stimulus derived from the inductor.

This problem of the complexity of the response shown by the tissues is also emphasized by cases in which induction is produced by fragments of organs of adult animals. Thus a portion of mouse kidney implanted into a newt gastrula may produce a brain, flanked by nasal placodes, eyes and ear vesicles (Fig. 254). A piece of newt liver placed in a skin of ectoderm from a gastrula induces a complete tail. Induction can even be obtained by 'damaging' a piece of ectoderm by toxic solutions, without submitting it to any specific morphogenetic stimulus (Fig. 254c).

All these experiments emphasize that discovery of the phenomenon of induction has not solved the problem of identifying and describing the sequence of changes by which a complicated embryo is produced. The inductors often do not themselves organize the differentiation in the responding tissues, they merely release powers that are latent in the latter. We shall only understand more about this situation, when we learn how to describe the set of instructions that is conveyed by heredity. A given inductor acts as a signal, selecting certain among these to constitute the instructions to be followed within a particular

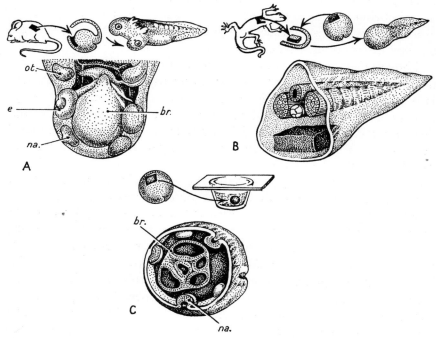

Fig. 254. A, After implantation of a piece of mouse kidney into a newt gastrula a brain (*br.*) flanked by nasal placodes (*na.*), eyes (*e.*), and ear vesicles (*ot.*) is induced; B, a piece of newt liver implanted into a jacket of gastrula ectoderm gives rise to a tail; C, an isolated piece of gastrula ectoderm exposed to a toxic solution differentiates into a brain vesicle (*br.*) and several nasal placodes (*na.*).
(After Holtfreter and Chuang.)

mass of tissue, so that it shall develop into, say, ear vesicle or lens of the eye.

8. Induction after gastrulation

The inductive powers still remain strong after chemo-differentiation and are of two sorts, those of *heterogenetic* and *homogenetic induction*. The former consists of further induction essentially of the type produced by the dorsal lip itself and the classic example is the lens of the eye. There are many known cases of such heterogenetic induction or, to put it more generally, of the modification of the metabolism of one part by its neighbours in such a way that the former differentiates into some other tissue.

Homiogenetic or assimilatory induction is the power possessed by many parts of the organism to cause cells with which they come into contact to become like themselves. Muscle-cells from the late neurula when planted into the blastocoel of a younger larva will cause the neighbouring tissues to develop into myotomes. Conversely, pieces of indifferent ectoderm grafted into the neural plate of a late neurula develop into nervous tissue.

Thus the whole young tadpole may be considered as divided into a number of different regions or districts (for uses of the term 'field' see Huxley and de Beer, 1934; Willier *et al*, 1955) each having a characteristic type of metabolism and structure, which ensures their further development along certain lines. The cells of each district are moreover able to impose on indifferent cells placed near them a type of metabolism like their own.

During this period, as throughout the whole of development, there must be an intricate co-ordination of the processes that are going on in different parts of the embryo. Regulative processes in relation to the environment are, however, less necessary in the embryo than in the adult, because the supplies of food and the mechanisms for protection and defence provided by the parent are still available. The tissues of the developing organism therefore receive little information from the environment. The direction of their operations depends upon the hereditary constitution and upon the 'stimuli' that they receive from neighbouring tissues in the body. The system of evocators can be regarded as providing a set of signals supplying the information by means of which the appropriate response is selected in each tissue. At present we can only see dimly how this communication system operates to control the whole course of development.

9. Functional differentiation

As development approaches completion the effects of the environment become more and more marked and the organism gradually begins to take actions that ensure its homeostasis. The receptors provided by heredity begin to come into action, signalling about conditions around and within the body; the hereditary nervous connexions ensure the making of appropriate responses. This is the beginning of the period of *functional differentiation*.

Many of the organs only acquire their definitive form under the influence of the stress imposed upon them as they are used by the body against the resistance of the environment. A classic example is the detailed architecture of the bones, which comes to be appropriate to the stresses that are imposed (p. 99). Functional conditions and requirements influence in this way the detailed structures of muscles (p. 123), glands (p. 531), nerves (p. 338), and indeed probably of every part of the body. Thus each tissue acquires its own individual 'memory' of the conditions that have been met with and this is additional to the general memory of the species, received by heredity. The combination of the two provides a creature equipped with organs that adequately represent the conditions of the environment in which it finds itself and are able to take actions that ensure homeostasis.

10. Morphogenesis in the adult

The onset of the period of functional differentiation does not mean the end of the operation of hereditary factors. These continue to exercise a major controlling influence throughout the whole lifetime. It is they indeed that provide the capacity to react to external change that is the basis for the formation of individual memories by the tissues. The control of the continual turnover of materials within the organism is presumably ultimately a function of the nuclear and other hereditary materials, though we know little of how they operate. In this sense morphogenesis continues throughout adult life. In some tissues, for example, the blood and skin, cells are continually destroyed and replaced. The morphogenetic influences that control the differentiation of the new cells are presumably similar in a general way to those of the developing embryo. Considering the importance of the changes that proceed in, say, the bone marrow or the liver it is astonishing how little is known of the morphogenetic factors that control them.

11. Repair and regeneration

The processes of healing and repair constitute a special case of the exercise of morphogenetic powers in the adult. They show dramatic instances of the power of the body to regulate and maintain the organization in spite of changes imposed upon it by the surroundings. The fact that replacement of what has been removed is possible in many tissues shows that the differentiation into districts with distinct developmental powers persists into adult life. Knowledge about the properties of these districts would be of great interest to pathologists as well as to embryologists, whose studies overlap in this as in so many other fields.

A particularly favourable situation for the study of these fields of differentiation is the regeneration of limbs by urodele amphibians. A newt is able to regenerate a lost limb or tail, even when adult. The regeneration takes place by the formation of a small bud of dividing cells, whose origin is uncertain. If in amputating the limb the area removed is too great then no regeneration takes place. Presumably some tissue having limb-type metabolism has to be left so that by homogenetic induction it can control the development of the new bud.

The fact that in mammals regeneration of whole limbs is not possible does not mean that there is no morphogenetic control in the adult. On the contrary, proper and detailed control of replacement is essential for the maintenance of life. In each part of the body the morphogenetic powers are specialized, the Malpighian layer of the skin produces cornified cells, the red bone marrow blood-cells, and so on. Moreover, replacement after damage is much more extensive than is often supposed. A complete liver is regenerated in a mammal even if more than half of it has been removed. Bones become reunited after fracture and remodelled to meet strains efficiently (p. 97). Nerves that have been severed are able to recover their functions (p. 333). Many of the morphogenetic systems that are set up during embryogenesis thus continue to operate throughout life.

12. The sequence of differentiation

Our analysis has thus shown that the course of differentiation is not quite so mysterious as it at first seemed. There is all too little information about the nature of the changes at each stage but in principle we can understand the sequence of events by which a differentiated organism is formed from the less heterogeneous system that was capable of wide regulation and could develop normally after disturbance of its parts. The secret of the whole sequence is the power to respond differentially to asymmetrical stimulation. By virtue of perhaps quite small quantitative differences in the surroundings heterogeneity can be produced in a previously homogeneous system. The asymmetrical relation of the ovum to the ovary is probably a fundamental condition, setting up quantitative differences of metabolism, which result in the yolk gradient from animal to vegetative pole. The second axis of the egg of amphibians is manifest in the grey crescent differentiation, determined after fertilization. These determinations are not strongly fixed, so that development is possible even if the structures and substances that they produce are disturbed.

The later stages of differentiation depend on selection of particular activities in response to specific stimulation. The previously homogeneous material of the dorsal ectoderm becomes heterogeneous when stimulated by distinct signals from the underlying chordamesoderm, parts of it form brain vesicle, other parts eye cup, and still others neural tube.

The essentials for orderly development are an appropriate external environment and appropriately responding cells. Each tissue develops its characteristics by the selection for emphasis of some among the metabolic activities that are made possible by heredity. The inductors are specific signals able to exercise this selection, in other words to pass information to the communication systems of the cells. Natural selection has ensured that the cells shall react differentially to the various evoking signals, some of which come from neighbouring tissues, others from the environment. The final result may be modified by change in the environment (what Weiss, 1939 calls the circumstantials) or by change of the responding tissues under the influence, ultimately, of their genetic make-up.

We obtain in this way a reasonably clear general picture of the means by which organisms have developed through the centuries, an ontogeny differing from the previous one when either environmental circumstances or hereditary instructions were different. The ovum is provided with a certain power to divide and the products of this division then undergo various movements and differentiations, which produce a new creature. We can now understand at least vaguely how the properties of this finished animal are related to the simple properties of the more nearly homogeneous protoplasm of the ovum. The essential properties that the egg must have are on the one hand the power to divide and to produce cells that undertake morphogenetic movements and on the other to respond differentially to external stimuli in such a way that homogeneity gives place to heterogeneity. These are great and mysterious powers and the analysis of them will tax the ingenuity of embryologists for many a generation before a proper general theory of development appears.

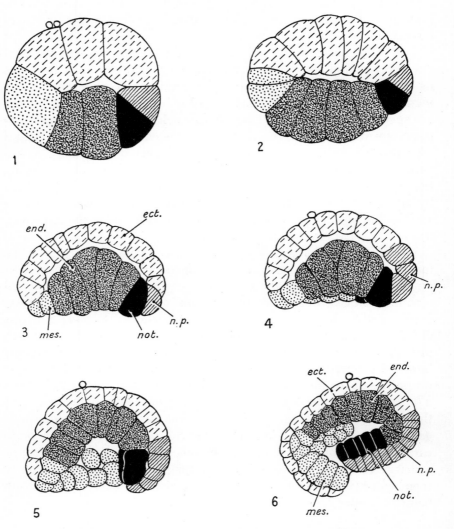

FIG. 255. Diagrams of the gastrulation of sea-squirt, *Styela*.

1. Stage with 24 cells, cut in median plane; 2. 64-cell stage; 3. 110 cells; 4, 5, and 6. schematic representations of later stages of gastrulation. Dashes show general ectoderm (*ect.*), close dots endoderm (*end.*), continuous lines, neural plate (*n.p.*), black, notochord (*not.*), sparse dots mesoderm (*mes.*), whose cells contain yellow granules. (After Conklin.)

XXXVIII

A COMPARATIVE SURVEY OF GASTRULATION IN VERTEBRATES

1. The common plan of vertebrate development

GREAT progress has been made in recent years with the comparison of the methods of gastrulation in different vertebrates. We can now see that the process is essentially similar in all forms, the various types of development being produced by acceleration of some movements and delay or suppression of others. This study is a most important one for the general biologist because it is one of the few cases in which we have information as to how variations in the processes of development produce different forms of adult. Such studies are essential if we are to understand the mechanism by which the hereditary factors control the adult, and how change in these factors has resulted in the appearance of the series of animal types during evolutionary history.

In order to examine the nature of the plan of development of chordates and its variations we shall first describe gastrulation in tunicates and *Amphioxus*, where there is relatively little yolk and movements of the cells can be easily observed. Then we shall see how gastrulation is accomplished in vertebrates that are provided with a large amount of yolk, the processes being clearly modifications of those found in less yolky ancestors. Finally, in the mammals, although the egg is no longer yolky, gastrulation proceeds in a manner that shows signs of reptilian ancestry. By following the morphogenetic movements in these various types of vertebrate we can obtain an insight into the nature of the fundamental processes of development.

2. Gastrulation in tunicates

The blastula of the sea-squirt *Styela*, thoroughly studied by Conklin (1905), has animal pole cells rather larger than those of the vegetative pole and a crescent of yellow pigment in the cells of the portion that will become the hind end of the animal (p. 597). The first sign of gastrulation is a movement of the vegetative-pole cells upwards, tending to obliterate the blastocoel and producing a concavity (Fig. 255). This is clearly a movement of invagination, comparable to that of the cells of the vegetative pole in the frog.

Soon afterwards the cells of an arc at the front end of the embryo begin to push down towards the vegetative pole. They form a lip, which begins to roll over the inpushed vegetative cells, and the cells of the inner layer thus formed differentiate into the notochord. At the same time from the posterior end the cells filled with yellow pigment begin to move forwards, making a row on each side of the pit that is formed by the invagination. These cells proceed to become the

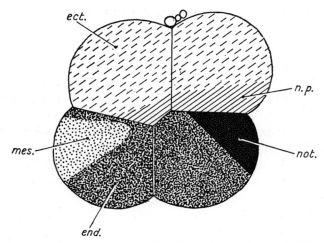

FIG. 256. Fate map of eight-cell stage of tunicate. Conventions as in Fig. 255. The yellow granules occupy the area of the mesoderm. (After Vandebroek from Dalcq, 1938.)

muscles and connective tissues. The pit (the blastopore) thus closes to a narrow opening, largely by the activity of the anterior (dorsal) lip, partly by the lateral lips. The embryo then elongates and the dorsal surface flattens and rolls up to form the neural tube.

It is easy to compare these movements with those found in amphibia. The overgrowth of the dorsal lip is presumably a movement of extension, probably assisted, as in amphibia, by an epiboly or thinning out of the animal pole cells behind it. Convergence takes place to produce the nervous system and other dorsal masses.

Certain differences from amphibia must be noticed. The notochordal material is rolled in independently of the mesoderm and a map of the position of the rudiments of the various tissues on the outside of the blastula shows that there are considerable differences in position (Fig. 256).

During and after gastrulation the larva increases in length and 10 hours after fertilization it is ready to hatch from the egg as a fully formed individual, capable of living an independent life, the ascidian tadpole, which swims for a while at the surface of the sea before settling down and undergoing metamorphosis into the adult sea-squirt (Young, 1950, p. 65). During a few hours, therefore, a remarkably complex creature has been built up from the fertilized egg (Berrill, 1955).

3. Experiments on differentiation in tunicates

The particular interest of the development of tunicates is that it is possible to study closely the time at which these differentiations appear. The method of analysis has been to isolate fragments of the ovum or embryo, or else to displace the parts relative to each other, with the object of determining whether, at any given stage, a part will develop in a normal manner independently of the whole. For instance, in normal development some of the yellow cells give rise to mesoderm, others to mesenchyme. At the four-cell stage the two posterior blastomeres contain the yellow granules (Fig. 242) and if these blastomeres are destroyed then a larva without muscles or mesenchyme develops (Conklin, 1905). Conversely the hinder two blastomeres cultivated alone produce a mass consisting of little else but muscles, which may become well differentiated and contractile.

Clearly the course of development of tunicates includes a series of cell divisions and cell movements by which the various regions capable of developing into different parts are segregated. How early can these separate regions be recognized? It will be remembered that the first cleavage plane lies in the sagittal plane of the future embryo and several workers have shown that after separation of the first two blastomeres (p. 597) each of them develops into a half embryo. Dalcq (1932) has pushed the analysis further by cutting up the unfertilized ovum and then fertilizing the fragments. He was surprised to find that any half of an egg can gastrulate and produce a tadpole, which seems to show that the ovum at this stage is not yet divided up into parts whose fates are determined. Further study showed that although the two fragments produced by longitudinal divisions of the ovum may both develop into tadpoles, this is never so when cuts are made parallel to the equator, after this only one of the halves forms a perfect tadpole. In a few favourable cases, with cuts close to the equator, Dalcq was able to obtain a larva from each portion and to show that the one deriving from the animal hemisphere lacked muscle-cells, while that from the vegetative hemisphere lacked nerve-cord.

It therefore seems that in the unfertilized ovum of *Styela* there are regions predisposed to develop into certain structures. These can be seen in the map of the eight-cell stage (Fig. 256). Clearly the areas for chorda and mesoderm resemble those of the crescents that are seen by study of the pigmentation of the normal embryos. As Dalcq says: 'Who would have imagined that when Conklin described the famous pigmented crescents of *Styela* and *Ciona*, Nature then revealed to him the essential features of the germinal organization in chordates?'

Similar conclusions can be drawn from experiments in which the position of materials within the egg is altered by centrifugation. The resulting larvae are grossly distorted and the tissues are all in the wrong places, for example, notochord and endoderm on the outside and neural tissue within. This is the result we should expect if the various parts of the egg are already chemo-differentiated and able to undergo self-differentiation. Such experiments, however, also give a warning against referring the capacity for differentiation in a particular way to one observable constituent of the cell. The yellow granules can easily be shifted to other parts of the egg *but they do not cause development of muscles in that part*. It is not therefore the presence of yellow granules that determines that a particular portion of the egg shall become muscle-cells but the yellow pigment is, in normal development, found in the region of the egg that is so determined.

4. Gastrulation in Amphioxus

Gastrulation in *Amphioxus* shows clearly the way in which the cells pass to their destinations under the influence of morphogenetic movements (Conklin, 1932). The blastula is flattened on account of the elongated columnar shape of the cells of the vegetative pole (Fig. 257). These proceed to move into the blastocoel by a process of invagination, produced partly by change in shape of these tall future endoderm cells, partly by the activity of the neighbouring cells. A crescent of cells, the future notochord, lying along the mid-dorsal edge of the blastopore, rolls in to form the middle part of the roof of the archenteron. The cells that will form the mesoderm lie as a crescent around the ventral margin of the blastopore. They roll in over its edges and pass up dorsally to a position on either side of the notochordal material, forming part of the roof of the archenteron.

Meanwhile the cells of the outer layer spread out by a process of epiboly, which assists the invagination of the endoderm, notochord, and mesoderm and also produces an extension or elongation of the embryo along the antero-posterior axis.

The three sorts of tissue making up the wall of the archenteron then become separated by a process of convergence. The material of the mid-dorsal wall rolls up and separates off to form the notochord. The mesodermal material moves further upwards; furrows separate it from the endoderm and finally it forms a series of hollow sacs, the mesodermal somites (Young, 1950, p. 42). The wall of the archenteron

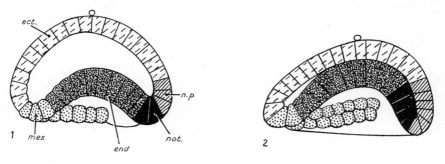

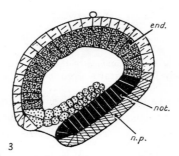

FIG. 257. Diagrams of gastrulation in *Amphioxus*. Conventions as in Fig. 255. (After Conklin.)

then completes itself by a process of convergence of the margins of the endoderm, moving up to meet in the mid-dorsal line. Meanwhile, convergence in the outer layer produces the rolling up of the neural tube.

Thus, in *Amphioxus*, the various movements of gastrulation can be seen at work with little complication by yolk. Unfortunately we can only guess at the cell changes by which they are produced.

5. Gastrulation in fishes

The various groups of fishes have been evolving independently for hundreds of millions of years and there are considerable differences in their modes of development. Nevertheless, it is possible to see in all of them a common pattern similar to that of protochordates and amphibians. The differences are mainly related to the proportion of yolk present. In the cyclostomes (lampreys) this is moderate and gastrulation proceeds in a manner remarkably similar to that of amphibians. In sharks and bony fishes there is a great deal of yolk and cleavage results in the formation of a group of cells, the *blastodisc*, lying on the uncleaved yolk (Fig. 258). The segmentation cavity below the blastodisc may be compared approximately with the blastocoel. The

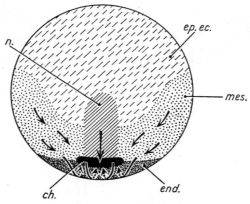

FIG. 258. Fate of areas on the surface of the blastodisc of a teleostean fish. The tissues move as shown by the arrows. Conventions as Fig. 247. (After Pasteels.)

blastodisc extends gradually over the yolk in all directions. At its future posterior edge gastrulation begins by the raising up of the hinder edge to form the lip of the blastopore, which then extends laterally. Material passes in over this lip to form the mesoderm and perhaps endoderm, essentially as in gastrulae with less yolk. A map of the presumptive areas on the outside of the blastula shows that in these fishes they are in the same relative position as in amphibians (Fig. 258), but have been pushed upwards during evolution by the development of the great amount of yolk.

The later stages of gastrulation also show the familiar morphogenetic processes, but they are modified somewhat differently in the various groups of fishes. The blastodisc extends only slowly over the yolk but ultimately reaches right round it, completing the lips of the blastopore and forming a yolk plug. This process is partly one of epiboly, thinning out of the tissue already formed, and partly an active pushing of the margin forward over the yolk (Trinkaus, 1951).

Meanwhile there is convergence towards the centre of the blastodisc to form the neural folds and somites, and the embryo becomes lifted off the yolk. Elongation occurs by a process of extension and in the course of this the lips of the blastopore may become drawn out to form a pair of folds in the antero-posterior axis, recalling the primitive streak of amniotes (p. 648).

The formation of the embryo of the megalecithal fishes therefore takes place by movements essentially similar to those found in eggs with less yolk. The chief differences are in timing. Convergence occurs early, raising up the margin of the blastopore lips. The endoderm may be partly formed by invagination over the lips but some of it is probably formed precociously. A mass of tissue is found lying beneath the blastodisc before invagination has occurred. The source of this tissue is not clear, it is interesting because similar precocious endoderm formation is found in birds (p. 645). Epiboly and extension are processes that continue for a long time in fishes, the former being largely responsible for the enclosure of the yolk (see Willier, 1955).

6. Development of reptiles

The account given by Pasteels (1937) for the turtle *Clemmys leprosa* may be taken as typical of reptiles, although some of his interpretations differ from those of other workers. Fertilization is, of course, internal and the very yolky ovum is covered as it passes down the oviduct first with a layer of albumen (white) and then with a shell. Cleavage begins while the egg is in the oviduct and is meroblastic, producing a small blastodisc, which then rapidly expands in all directions over the yolk, becoming itself very thin and reduced almost to a single layer of cells of uniform thickness throughout. The segmentation cavity below is a narrow crack and there are a few large cells of uncertain origin and nature between the outer layer and the yolk (Fig. 259A).

The segmentation cavity then becomes more clearly marked at the centre of the blastodisc, giving a clear *area pellucida*, surrounded by a less transparent *area opaca* or germ wall, where the blastodisc rests on the yolk. Outside the germ wall the blastodisc continues to extend over the yolk. The embryonic bud now appears as a whitish spot, lying evcentrically in the area pellucida. At the hind end of this whitish area invagination begins, either at an elongated trench or at two distinct pits more or less separated from each other (Fig. 262). Sections show that the surface of the blastodisc is thicker at the region of these pits than elsewhere and that cells are passing inwards and then both forwards and backwards into the blastocoel, to form a mass of endoderm (Fig. 259B). Some of this material spreads out forwards below the embryonic shield; much passes laterally and

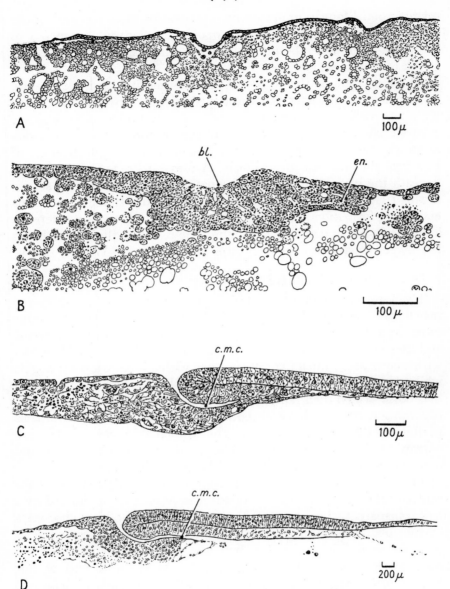

FIG. 259. Stages in development of the tortoise (*Clemmys*).

A, Portion of the embryonic area at a stage when it is hardly more than one cell thick;
B, parasagittal section showing beginning of formation of blastopore (*bl.*), the primary
endoderm (*en.*) streams forwards; C, sagittal section showing beginning of formation of
chordamesoblastic canal (*c.m.c.*); D, the canal at a later stage when it is open internally.
(After J. Pasteels, *Arch. d. biol.* **48,** 1936.)

becomes extra-embryonic endoderm, while a large portion remains just behind the region of invagination as a solid mass, the blastoporal plate, also sometimes known as the primitive plate. Unfortunately since these events all occur before laying, which takes place at about

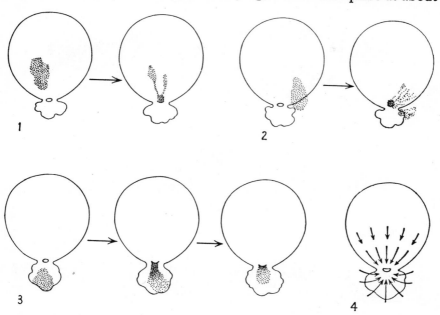

FIG. 260. Movement of blue-coloured marks placed on the outside of the blastoderm of the tortoise. In experiment 1 a mark placed in front and to one side of the blasto-pore has been drawn out 18 hrs. later into streams converging on the blastopore lip. In experiment 2 a mark lying lateral to the blastopore is partly drawn into it. Experiment 3, material behind the blastopore is drawn forwards. The diagram (4) shows the direction of streaming movements deduced from these experiments. (After Pasteels.)

the stage now reached, it has not been possible to confirm the course of events by intra-vital staining.

The two pits, if originally separate, now join in the middle line and a deeper depression appears, with a well-marked dorsal blastoporal lip. Invagination proceeds (and can be followed by stains) to produce a definite tube the *chordamesoblastic canal*, also known as the archenteric, blastoporal, or notochordal canal (Figs. 259, 260, 261). The endoderm below this canal has now become arranged as a definite though thin layer, but the gut has still to be formed. The walls of the chordameso-blastic canal probably contain no endoderm and do not give rise to the gut. The canal does not long remain intact. The material of its lateral and ventral walls, i.e. that which has migrated over the ventral lip of the blastopore, scatters away rapidly laterally and posteriorly, to form extra-embryonic mesoderm, and in this way the floor of the chordamesoblastic canal as Pasteels put it 'empties itself of its own

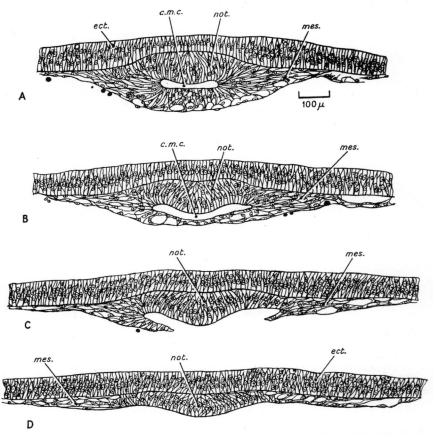

Fig. 261. Tortoise (*Clemmys*). Four cross-sections through the chordamesoblastic canal (*c.m.c.*) from behind (A) forwards.

ect. ectoderm; *mes.* mesoderm migrating laterally; *not.* notochord. (After Pasteels.)

substance'. The thin underlying layer of endoderm is ruptured at the same time and the chordamesoblastic canal thus comes to open directly into the blastocoel, first anteriorly and then completely, leaving only a narrow passage leading from the exterior to the blastocoel.

The notochord is thus left in place and the material invaginated over the dorsal lip is put in position as the embryonic mesoderm and that from the walls and floor of the canal as the extra-embryonic mesoderm. But there is no embryonic endoderm, the layer that was formed earlier having disappeared. The roof of the gut is now formed afresh from endodermal folds growing in from the side, exactly as in Urodeles (p. 609) but the origin of the material that forms the folds is not certainly known. Probably it is the lateral edges of the original endodermal layer.

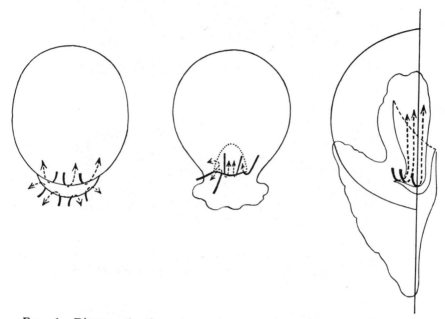

Fig. 262. Diagram of cell movements during gastrulation of *Clemmys*. The full lines show movements on the surface, the dotted lines at a deeper level. (After Pasteels, J., *Biol. Rev.* **15,** 1940.)

The layers having now all appeared the embryo becomes outlined in the familiar way. A neural (medullary) plate appears and rolls up, finally covering the external opening of the remains of the chorda-mesoblastic canal and converting it into a neurenteric canal. An amnion appears anteriorly in the manner that will be described later for the chick, and grows back over the surface of the embryo.

It will be already clear that the gastrulation of these reptiles is produced by movements essentially similar to those of Anamnia but differing in time sequence. *Epiboly* takes place very early and strongly, thinning out the blastodisc before any of the other movements have begun. *Invagination* differs from that of the Amphibia in that the endoderm invaginates before and separately from the chordameso-derm. *Extension* instead of taking place at the same time as the other

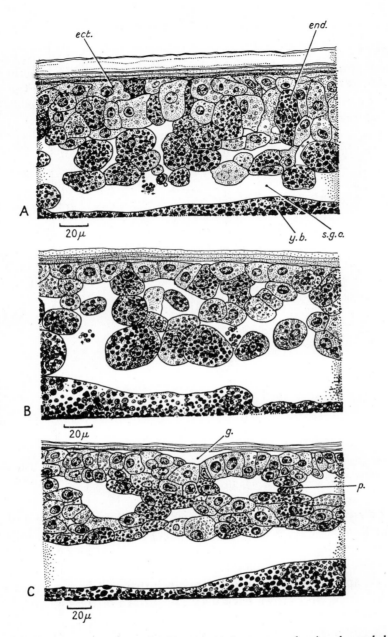

FIG. 263. Sections through the blastodisc of the sparrow showing the probable
method of formation of the endoderm.

A, The blastodisc, consisting of prospective ectoderm (*ect.*) and endoderm (*end.*) cells, is
separated from the yolk bed (*y.b.*) by the sub-germinal cavity (*s.g.c.*); B, the prospective
endoderm cells migrate inwards leaving the prospective ectoderm cells, which form a
superficial layer; C, prospective endoderm cells migrating inwards form pillars (*p.*). The
grooves (*g.*) over the pillars indicate active migration and divide the superficial layer into
segments. (After Flynn, T. T., and Hill, J. P., *Trans. Zool. Soc.*, **26,** 1947.)

processes begins later. *Convergence* takes place throughout in a typical manner and the scattering of the mesoderm on the floor of the chorda-mesoblastic canal may be compared with the *ventral divergence* found in amphibia. Some idea of these movements is given in Fig. 262.

7. Development of birds

The enormous quantity of yolk necessary for the maintenance of the metabolism of a warm-blooded organism for the long period of development, without outside provision, makes the ova of birds the largest of all cells. Fertilization takes place in the upper end of the oviduct and further provision of raw materials in the form of the protein solutions of the white is made by the glands as the egg rolls down the oviduct.

By the time that the shell has been added and the egg laid, cleavage, which is of course meroblastic, has proceeded to the formation of a blastodisc overlying a subgerminal cavity (blastocoel). In many birds the blastodisc is then already two-layered, the endoderm being produced before the egg is laid. There has been much discussion as to how this inner layer develops (see Waddington, 1952). Earlier reports suggested that it was by invagination at the hind end of the blastodisc, but this is not now believed to take place. There is some evidence that cells sink in individually all over the disc, the process of *polyinvagination* (Fig. 263). Others believe that the lower layer simply splits away from the inner side of the original sheet (*delamination*). The sparrow is very suitable for investigation of this subject since the germ-layers are formed after the egg has been laid (see Flynn and Hill, 1947). The earliest blastodisc contains two types of cell (Fig. 263) and the endoderm is formed by the inward migration of those that are filled with yolk-spheres, while the smaller cells form an outer epithelial layer, the epiblast. The establishment of the germ-layers is therefore 'the outcome of two combined and essentially active processes, segregation and delamination'.

After laying the blastodisc develops only very slowly unless it is kept warm (incubated). The further account will be of the development of the chick at the standard temperature of 37·5–39·5° C. Even with careful attempts at standardization the time of the first detectable movements varies by from 5 to 12 hours. The blastodisc at this time consists of a central *area pellucida*, below which is the blastocoel, resting by a germ wall on the yolk to form an *area opaca*. The germ wall extends continually over the yolk in all directions during the whole of the early part of development.

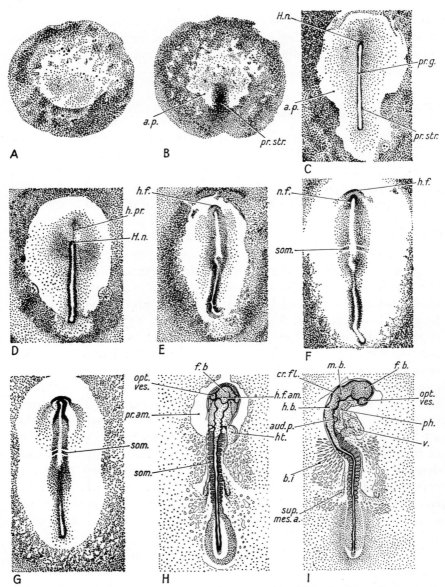

FIG. 264. Stages in the development of the chick with approximate times.

A, Pre-streak. B, Intermediate streak (12 hours). The primitive streak (*pr.str.*) is broad and extends forwards from the posterior border of the area pellucida (*a.p.*). C, Definitive streak (18 hours). The primitive streak has reached its maximal length. Hensen's node (*H.n.*) and the primitive groove (*pr.g.*) are present. D, Head process (20 hours). The head process (*h.pr.*) or notochord extends forwards from the anterior edge of Hensen's node. E, Head fold (24 hours). The anterior end of the embryo is marked by the head fold (*h.f.*). F, One somite (25 hours).

(*For continuation see opposite*)

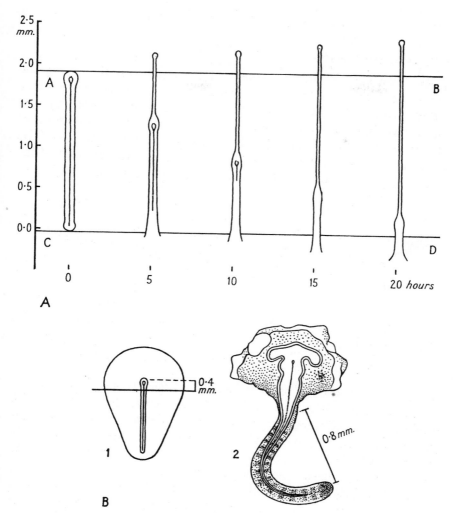

FIG. 265. A, Regression of the primitive streak and elongation of the notochord of the chick. Taking the lines AB and CD for reference the streak shortens but the notochord elongates by a greater amount. B, Experiment to show elongation of primitive streak material. An embryo was cut into two pieces 0.4 mm. posterior to the node as shown in 1 and the anterior piece explanted. 20 hours later the anterior piece had elongated and differentiated as shown in 2.
(After Spratt, N. T., *J. exp. Zool.* **104**, 1947.)

Continuation of underline to Fig. 264.

The first somite (*som.*) to appear forms the second of the adult series. Neural folds (*n.f.*) are visible in the head region. G, Three somites (27 hours). The neural folds have nearly met in the midbrain region. H, Fifteen somites (45 hours). The head is beginning to rotate on its left side. *f.b.* forebrain; *h.f.am.* head fold of amnion; *ht.* heart; *opt.ves.* optic vesicle; *pr.am.* pro-amnion. I, Twenty somites (50 hours). Rotation of the head has proceeded and the cranial flexure (*cr.fl.*) is apparent. *aud.p.* auditory pit; *b.i.* blood islands; *h.b.* hind brain; *m.b.* midbrain; *ph.* pharynx; *sup. mes.a.* omphalomesenteric artery (superior mesenteric artery; *v.* ventricle. (Partly after Lillie.)

8. The primitive streak

The first sign of the appearance of the embryo is that along the centre of the area pellucida there appears a thickening, the *primitive streak*, which takes the form of a groove terminating anteriorly in a slight swelling, the node of Hensen (Fig. 264). The continuation of the primitive groove into the node is known as the primitive pit. The primitive streak is fully formed by about the nineteenth hour of incubation in the chick and shortly afterwards the embryo itself begins

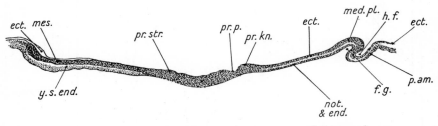

FIG. 266. Median sagittal section of a chick embryo of about 24 hours.

ect. ectoderm; *f.g.* fore-gut; *h.f.* head fold; *med.pl.* medullary plate; *mes.* mesoderm; *not. & end.* notochord and endoderm; *p.am.* pro-amnion; *pr.kn.* primitive knot; *pr.p.* primitive pit; *pr.str.* primitive streak; *y.s. end.* yolk-sac endoderm. (After Lillie.)

to appear as the head process in front of the streak (Fig. 264) and develops neural folds and somites. Subsequently, for a considerable period (up to the third day) the primitive streak remains at the hind end of the embryo, and gradually moves back and shortens as the embryo differentiates in front of it. Careful observation of embryos explanted on to plasma clots has allowed the rates of these movements to be studied by marking of the embryo and of the clot on which it is growing (Spratt, 1947). During 20 hours of growth *in vitro* the primitive streak decreases from about 1·9 mm. (its maximum length) to less than 0·5 mm. Meanwhile the embryo proper increases from 0·2 mm. to 1·8 mm. There is therefore a slight overall increase, with an absolute forward movement of the front end of the embryo and a marked backward movement of the node of Hensen (Fig. 265). The small remainder of the node after its regression becomes the end-bud, whose activity is responsible for further growth in length of the embryo.

There has been much controversy as to the nature of the primitive streak and its relation to the various phases of the development of other vertebrates and especially to the blastopore. Structurally the primitive streak consists of a solid mass of tissue, indented by the primitive groove. In the midline it continues anteriorly into the neural folds and into a rod of tissue, the head process, whose front part becomes the prechordal mesoderm and hinder part the notochord (Fig. 266). Laterally the deeper layers of the streak are continuous with the mesoderm. The undifferentiated appearance of its cells, together with the fact that the embryo appears as if budded off from the primitive streak, led many to suppose that the streak consists of 'undifferentiated tissue', which produces the embryo and extra-embryonic layers by proliferation.

The modern view is that the streak does not consist of any special undifferentiated tissue, nor does it proliferate. There are not more mitotic figures in the streak than elsewhere in the embryo (Derrick, 1937) and marks applied to portions of the streak are not later found in all of the layers derived from it but usually in one only. Marking experiments show that material of the streak is not constant from moment to moment, but that it is a region at which invagination takes place, at least during the earlier stages. As the primitive streak develops material invaginates and emigrates laterally and posteriorly to form extra-embryonic mesoderm. The first part of the streak to form thus corresponds to the ventro-lateral lips of a blastopore. Then, more anterior material becomes incorporated in the streak and streams forwards and laterally to form the mesoderm and notochord. The front end of the streak thus corresponds to the dorsal margin of a blastopore. Meanwhile the more lateral parts of the area pellucida move backwards and towards the middle line (Fig. 267). The effect of these movements has been compared to a polonaise dance figure.

Material reaching the streak from the sides can be shown to sink in and then to move outwards and anteriorly between the epiblast and endoderm and to become the mesoderm. Later, the material of the streak streams backwards in the midline during the period when the node retreats and leaves the embryonic axis in front of it.

The exact comparison of these movements with those of other vertebrates is difficult but it is clear that the primitive streak can be considered as a blastopore, not indeed in the sense of a pore leading to the archenteron, but in the strict etymological sense of the 'orifice of entry of the cells which invaginate' (Pasteels, 1937).

In spite of the great modifications we can still recognize the same general plan of development in a bird as in a reptile, which in turn is derivable from that of an anamniote. There is a marked difference in the method of formation of the endoderm, which in birds occurs not at the margin but at the centre of the blastodisc. Endoderm formation is in fact dissociated from growth over the yolk (epiboly). The 'blastopore' is at no time in contact with the posterior margin of the blasto-disc, whose edge is composed only of extra-embryonic ectoderm.

The blastodisc just before formation of the primitive streak there-

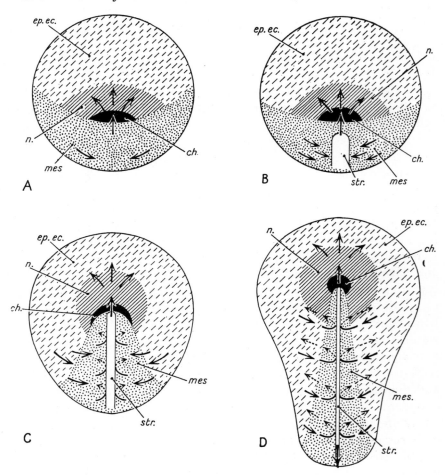

FIG. 267. Stages in gastrulation in the chick.

Conventions as in Fig. 247. *str.* primitive streak. Arrows show direction of movement of material, solid on the surface, dotted beneath the surface.
(Partly after C. H. Waddington, *The Epigenetics of Birds*, 1952.)

fore contains on its surface only the structures shown in Fig. 267. The presumptive ectoderm is relatively more extensive than in the anamnia and nearly surrounds the other prospective tissues. The streak itself is produced by the backward polonaise movements that are perhaps new and not comparable to the morphogenetic move-ments of other forms, accompanied by convergence and invagination of the mesoderm in a manner recognizably similar to that of chelonians. The rudiments thus take up the position shown in the figure. The prechordal mesoderm is invaginated very early and becomes separated from the somitic mesoderm by the backward movement of the chordal material. The material of the somites, after being arranged transversely across the embryo before invagination, is then strung out so that they lie behind one another. Chorda, somitic mesoderm, and ventro-lateral mesoderm are passed in by invagination at appropriate levels along the primitive streak and then by the movement of extension (retreat of the node of Hensen), the cord and somites are put in place in the embryo. The movements of extension and invagination are thus more distinctly separated in birds than they are in reptiles, whereas in amphibia they are combined. The material of the nervous system partakes of the same general movements as the chordamesoderm and comes to lie above the latter in the primitive streak. Later it moves into place in the embryo during the movement of extension, its lateral portions joining by convergence to form a tube, as in all other vertebrates.

The movements of the endoderm during the period are not altogether clear. It remains present as a continuous layer below the primitive streak throughout development and is probably not added to by material from the streak, though some authors maintain that such additions are made. There is no breaking down of the archenteric roof such as occurs in reptiles and indeed this would not be expected since there is no divergence of the floor of a chordamesoblastic canal. The archenteron therefore remains closed dorsally and never opens to the exterior by a blastopore.

Nevertheless a neurenteric canal is found in some birds and the interpretation of this that is given by Pasteels is most interesting. The canal forms late in development, that is to say when the node of Hensen has partially retreated, by which time all of the notochordal and somitic material is in place in the embryo. The posterior part of the primitive streak consists of ventro-lateral mesoderm and therefore corresponds to the sides and floor of the chordamesoblastic canal of reptiles and like that tissue scatters laterally by divergence. Here then the endoderm comes for the first time under the influence of this movement and ruptures to form a neurenteric canal.

Little is known of the forces that produce the morphogenetic movements of birds (see Waddington, 1952). The invagination of the cells through the primitive streak may be a result of changes in their shape. On the other hand, some of the movements on the outside of the blastoderm seem to be made by whole sheets of cells rather than by alterations in the shape of individuals. It must be emphasized again that at present we can only describe the morphogenetic movements crudely, but by further study along lines that are already evident it should be possible to discover the forces that pull and push the tissues of the embryo to produce the movements. We might then be able to compare the forces at work in the development of the various vertebrates and to show how their modes of action are determined by the genetic composition of the ova.

9. The sequence of differentiation in birds

Numerous experiments have shown that the same processes of gradual determination of competence occur in birds as in amphibia. Pieces of blastoderm of chicks of various ages can be cultured on the chorio-allantoic membranes of other chicks or on plasma clots. Pieces taken immediately after laying differentiate only into epithelia. At the primitive streak stage pieces from various parts of the blastoderm are able to differentiate into nervous system, eye, heart, cartilage, muscles, pharynx, and other tissues. At this stage chemo-differentiation is rapidly occurring and this perhaps corresponds to the similar process in the early gastrula of the frog.

The blastoderm appears to consist of a number of fields, each able to produce a characteristic structure and to act as a harmonious equipotential system, that is to say to regulate to produce a complete whole organ from a fragment. Not all regions become determined at the same time. At the middle primitive streak stage the epiblast outside the streak does not usually give rise to mesoderm if isolated. Within the mesoderm localization is still fluid and isolated portions may give rise to tissues other than their normal fate.

There are also marked phenomena of induction. Perhaps the most striking of these is the induction of the formation of the primitive streak itself. Waddington showed that after removal of the entire primitive streak a new one may be regenerated and a perfect embryo formed. If the primary epiblast is separated from the endoderm and rotated through 90° the streaming movements responsible for the formation of the primitive streak are so altered that the streak may fail to form in its original position, or form incompletely, or form both there and in the 'correct' position corresponding to its new relation to the endoderm, thus leading to the formation of double monsters. Obviously there is some influence exercised by the endoderm on the streaming movements of the epiblast.

Once the primitive streak has been formed it serves as an evocator in a manner similar to the chordamesodermal tissue of amphibians. A portion of the primitive streak placed beneath the ectoderm of another egg continues its own differentiation into notochord and somites and evokes the formation of a neural tube in the overlying ectoderm. This occurs even if this ectoderm belongs to an extra-embryonic region, and the effect is not species specific, the primitive streak of a chick being able to induce in a duck blastoderm and vice versa. The tissues produced vary according to the 'competence' of the induced material. In birds as in amphibians evocating agents are many and non-specific and little progress has been made with analysis of the physico-chemical nature of the phenomenon.

10. Gastrulation in mammals

In the prototherian mammals *Ornithorhynchus* (platypus) and *Tachyglossus* (spiny anteater) the ova are very yolky, cleavage is meroblastic, and gastrulation in the blastoderm takes place by formation of a primitive streak. The primary germ layers are formed as they are in birds. Two distinct types of cell are present in the unilaminar blastoderm and they then proceed to separate into outer ectodermal and inner endodermal layers. The prospective endodermal cells possess amoeboid properties and migrate actively to form the inner layer (Flynn and Hill).

In marsupials the ova contain much less yolk than in monotremes but more than in placentals. Cleavage is total and a hollow *blastocyst* is produced. Hill showed that in marsupials the region of the blastocyst that will produce the embryo is unilaminar but contains two types of cell, which behave like those of monotremes or birds. The inner cell mass (embryonic discs) early comes to possess two layers, by a process of invagination of some of the cells into the blastocoel. This endoderm formation probably usually occurs all over the area of the embryonic disc but in the opossum it is said to be localized towards the hinder end. In placental mammals (eutheria) cleavage is total and equal, forming a blastocyst (p. 695). The inner cell mass becomes the formative area of the embryo, the remainder of the blastocyst (*trophoblast*) serving to mediate the early relationship between embryo and uterine wall (p. 696). There is some evidence that in placentals the germ layers are formed by a separation of two types of cell. In the armadillo the two types can be recognized in the embryonic knot and the endoderm is formed by migration of more deeply staining cells from among the ectodermal cells.

Although the ova of marsupials and placentals contain little yolk gastrulation occurs by means of a primitive streak, a relic of the time when the eggs contained great quantities of yolk. The details of the movements during gastrulation are not well known; experiments are obviously very difficult. The streak appears to be essentially similar to that of birds (Fig. 284), ending anteriorly in a depression, the node of Hensen, which is pierced by a 'notochordal canal' in some mammals, including man (see p. 700 and Fig. 285). There is every reason to think that material of the outer layer moves up to the lips of the primitive streak as in birds, and thence inwards and then forwards and outwards to form notochord and mesoderm.

11. Summary of the movements of gastrulation

Gastrulation therefore takes place in a manner that is recognizably similar in all vertebrates, whether they have much or little yolk. The cells into which the zygote divides early become differentiated into districts possessing distinct powers. Primitively those at the vegetative pole move into the blastocoel (invagination) and differentiate into parts of the gut, while the animal pole cells thin out (epiboly). The cells of a crescent acquire special characteristics such that after passing over the lips of the blastopore they differentiate into notochord or mesoderm, and also induce the overlying epiblast cells to form the parts of the neural tube.

The chief modification of this pattern is in very yolky eggs, where only the animal pole end of the zygote undergoes cleavage and the endoderm comes to be formed by precocious separation of an inner layer of cells from the blastoderm.

The similarity of the method of early development of all vertebrates shows the underlying plan upon which all members of the group are built. As we come to know more about the biochemical differences between the many types of cell that make up a vertebrate we shall be able to understand more fully the nature of the plan of instructions transmitted by heredity, and the way in which various parts of the instructions come into play in different parts of the embryo to control the movements and differentiations that produce the various tissues. Much has been discovered about the processes in recent years but we cannot yet form a clear picture of the method of control and operation of this astonishing self-transforming machine.

XXXIX

EXTRA-EMBRYONIC MEMBRANES

1. Problems of development on land

IN higher vertebrates not all the cells derived from division of the zygote nucleus go to make up the actual embryo. A considerable part of the material produced forms the *extra-embryonic tissues*, concerned with provision of food, oxygen, and other materials necessary for development. These extra-embryonic membranes are, of course, additional to the primary, secondary, and tertiary egg membranes that have already been described (p. 595). They are among the most remarkable of the special characteristics that have enabled reptiles, birds, and mammals to enter and colonize 'difficult' environments.

The *amnion* was presumably the first of them, providing a pond within which the embryo could develop, thus avoiding the hazards of return to the water for breeding. It then became necessary for the amniotes to develop procedures that would allow of a long period of development within a 'closed box' or *cleidoic egg* (Needham, 1931). The great quantity of yolk could not be included within the embryo, but was absorbed by a *yolk sac*, lying outside the body, attached by a stalk. Excretory products were retained in a much enlarged bladder, the *allantois*, which also extended outside the body of the developing embryo and ultimately became so large that it made contact with the chorion lying against the shell and was able to serve as an organ for respiratory exchange (Fig. 268).

These special extra-embryonic tissues, amnion, yolk sac, and allantois, have all been formed by modifications of the fundamental morphogenetic processes that were at work in the ancestors of the amniotes. Eutherian mammals do not rear their embryos in a closed box but provide them instead with means of intake and output by exchange with the wall of the uterus, yet the same extra-embryonic structures are still used, with modifications to suit the new conditions.

2. Metabolism of cleidoic eggs

Development of an embryo largely closed off from the outside world imposes severe conditions, which are met by special metabolic and other adaptations. The whole process of development is often rapid, presumably in order to limit the time spent in the cleidoic state. A developing bird reaches a given weight two to three times as quickly as a comparable embryo mammal.

The production of incombustible nitrogenous waste-products is

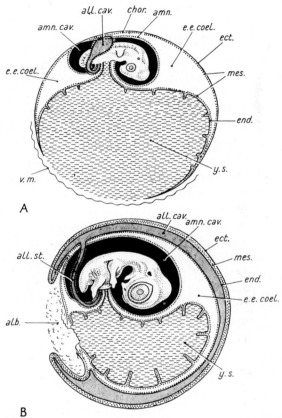

Fig. 268. Diagrams showing the relations between extra-embryonic membranes and the chick embryo at A, the fourth day and B, the ninth day after incubation.

alb. albumen; *all.cav.* allantoic cavity; *all.st.* allantoic stalk; *amn.* amnion; *amn. cav.* amniotic cavity; *chor.* chorion; *ect.* ectoderm; *e.e.coel.* extra-embryonic coelom; *end.* endoderm; *mes.* mesoderm; *v.m.* vitelline membrane; *y.s.* yolk sac.

greatly reduced in cleidoic eggs, by reducing the amount of protein that is consumed as fuel. Only 4 per cent. of the initial protein store of the chick's egg is used as fuel, 90 per cent. of the energy is supplied by fat, the burning of which has the further advantage that it yields a supply of metabolic water.

Perhaps the most striking metabolic adaptation for development on land is evolution of the power of excreting uric acid (see Needham,

1950). The end-product of nitrogen catabolism in the tissues of vertebrates is usually ammonia and this may be excreted unchanged, but, being toxic, it is usually converted to urea, which is excreted by the kidney in fishes and amphibians. Urea is highly soluble in water and in high concentration it also is toxic, and therefore unsuitable for storage in a closed box egg. In reptiles and birds it is converted in the liver to uric acid, which is only slightly soluble and is stored in solid form in the precociously expanded embryonic bladder—the allantois (p. 661). Uric acid remains the end-product of nitrogen metabolism throughout life in many reptiles and birds, and incidentally also in insects and terrestrial molluscs, which solve the problem in the same way.

In mammals the excretory products of the embryo do not accumulate but are passed through the placenta to the maternal circulation and the end-product of nitrogen metabolism is the soluble urea. It is uncertain whether the ancestors of the mammals ever possessed cleidoic eggs. The chelonians (tortoises and turtles), the surviving reptiles perhaps closest to the mammalian stock, excrete urea as well as uric acid. The egg-laying *Tachyglossus* excretes urea, but the shell is not calcareous and the egg develops within a marsupial pouch. Unfortunately there are no data about the nitrogen metabolism of the platypus, which has a calcareous shell. Mammals with the less-developed types of placenta have a large allantois (p. 706). During their long history of evolution in the Mesozoic the mammals must presumably have solved the problem of laying eggs that developed on land, but there is little evidence that they were ever fully cleidoic, with excretion of uric acid.

3. The amnion

While the blastoderm of the chick is undergoing the processes of gastrulation described in the previous chapter it also continues to extend outwards over the yolk. The mechanism of this expansion includes division and movement of the cells of the advancing edge, the *germ wall*, and a thinning out (epiboly) of the cells already formed. All the layers participate in this extending sheet of tissue. Below the ectoderm lie two layers of mesoderm, somatic and splanchnic, which are separated by an extra-embryonic coelom. Next to the yolk lies extra-embryonic endoderm, continuous with that of the embryo.

The amnion is formed by a folding of the two outermost layers, the ectoderm and somatic mesoderm (Fig. 269). This fold occurs first in front of the embryo; then posterior and lateral folds arise and all meet over the back, enclosing the embryo in a sac, the amnion, lined with ectoderm and filled with a watery amniotic fluid. The uprising

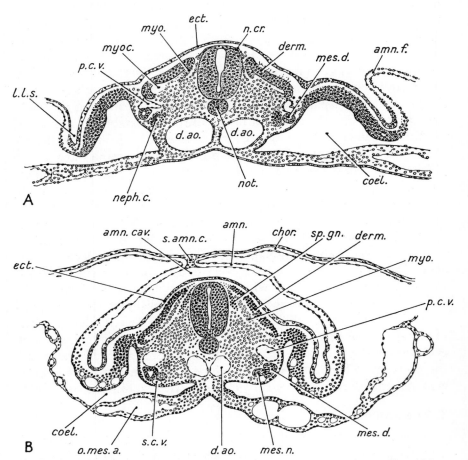

FIG. 269. Transverse sections through A, the 20th somite of a 29 somite chick embryo and B, the 23rd somite of a 35 somite chick embryo showing formation of the amnion.

amn. amnion; *amn.cav.* amniotic cavity; *amn.f.* amniotic fold; *chor.* chorion; *coel.* coelom; *d.ao.* dorsal aorta; *derm*, dermatome; *ect.* ectoderm; *l.l.s.* lateral limiting sulcus; *mes.d.* mesonephric duct; *mes.n.* mesonephros; *myo.* myotome; *myoc.* myocoel; *n.cr.* neural crest; *neph.c.* nephrogenic cord; *not.* notochord; *o.mes.a.* omphalomesenteric artery; *p.c.v.* posterior cardinal vein; *s.amn.c.* seroamniotic connexion; *s.c.v.* sub-cardinal vein; *sp.gn.* spinal ganglion.

(After Lillie, figs. 114 and 116.)

folds are of course double, the inner and outer layers each consisting of ectoderm and somatic mesoderm, separated by an extension of the extra-embryonic coelom. The outer two layers are called the *chorion*, the inner are the *true amnion*.

It has been suggested that the amniotic folds result from a modification of the processes by which the blastoderm extends over the yolk. As the margin of overgrowth approaches the equator there is a tendency for the material already formed to crumple into folds and it may have been in this way that the amnion was at first produced. With little modification of existing morphogenetic processes a complete chamber could thus arise. No doubt further special growth processes have later become included.

In mammals the amnion sometimes forms in the same way by the upgrowth of folds (in the rabbit) but in other species it appears as a cavity in the inner cell mass, above the developing embryo (human, Fig. 283). It is not possible to see exactly what modifications of the original processes of epiboly and growth have been involved in this change.

The amnion is a very thin membrane, serving as a protective layer and for secretion of the contained fluid. Its mesoderm may develop muscle-fibres, which are interesting in that they are not controlled by nerves. The amnion is not usually vascularized. The chorion, on the other hand, being in communication with the outside world (or with the maternal uterus) becomes a most important organ of interchange. Its rich blood-supply is derived from the allantois (see p. 661). The amnion ruptures at hatching or birth, and the flow of amniotic fluid is often the first sign of parturition.

4. The yolk sac

The endoderm and splanchnic mesoderm cover almost the whole surface of the yolk even in the largest eggs of birds. The cavity of the yolk sac is continuous with the mid-gut of the embryo and the aperture gradually narrows to form the yolk stalk. The yolk is absorbed only to a small or negligible extent by the enzymes of the yolk sac; in the main it is taken up by the blood-vessels. These are among the earliest of all blood-vessels, appearing as *blood islands*, at first not connected with the vascular system of the embryo, but later joining with this through the vitelline arteries, branches of the dorsal aorta representing a precocious anterior mesenteric artery. Blood is returned from the yolk sac in the paired vitelline (omphalomesenteric) veins, which appear very early and open into the sinus venosus; they later fuse to form a single ductus venosus, around which the liver develops (Fig. 270). The vitelline veins then come to open into the hepatic portal vessels.

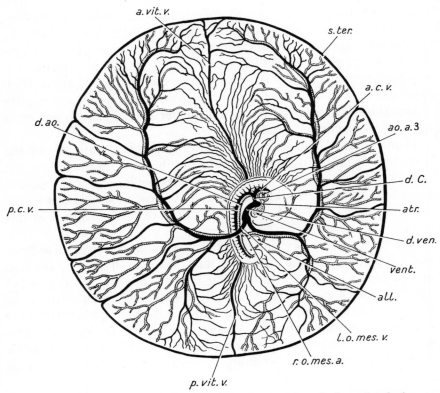

FIG. 270. Blood-vessels of embryo and yolk sac after about 85 hours incubation.

a.c.v. anterior cardinal vein; *all.* allantois, *ao.a.3.* third aortic arch; *atr.* atrium; *a.vit.v.* anterior vitelline vein; *d.ao.* dorsal aorta: *d.C.* duct of Cuvier; *d.ven.* ductus venosus; *l.o.mes.v.* left omphalomesenteric vein; *p.c.v.* posterior cardinal vein; *p.vit.v.* posterior vitelline vein *r.o.mes.a.* right omphalomesenteric artery; *s.ter.* sinus terminalis; *vent.* ventricle. (After Lillie, fig. 120.)

The yolk sac is absorbed into the gut at hatching in the chick. In mammals the yolk sac is empty and serves mainly for the formation of blood. Its lower surface disappears in some mammals, leaving the cavity open to the uterine lumen, from which it may take up secretions ('uterine milk' or histotrophe (p. 705)). The yolk sac may be later taken into the embryo and its wall forms part of the lining of the intestine.

5. The allantois

For the storage of the waste nitrogenous products during embryonic life a cloacal diverticulum becomes much enlarged in the cleidoic amniotes, forming a characteristic embryonic organ, the allantois.

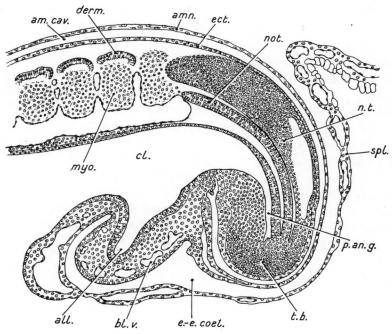

FIG. 271. Sagittal section through the tail region of a chick embryo of about 35 somites showing the allantois.

all. allantois; *amn.* amnion; *amn.cav.* amniotic cavity; *bl.v.* blood-vessel; *cl.* cloaca; *derm.* dermatome; *ect.* ectoderm; *e-e.coel.* extra-embryonic coelom; *myo.* myotome; *not.* noto-chord; *n.t.* neural tube; *p.an.g.* post-anal gut; *spl.* extra-embryonic splanchnopleure; *t.b.* tail bud.

This develops as an outgrowth of the endoderm of the hind gut, covered with splanchnic mesoderm (Fig. 271). Becoming too large for the body of the developing embryo it extends into the extra-embryonic coelom and finally comes to lie between the amnion and chorion. Its connexion with the embryo, the *allantoic stalk*, becomes narrow as development proceeds and is finally combined with the yolk stalk in a single outer covering to form the *body stalk*. At hatching this stalk becomes ruptured and the allantois and its waste materials are left behind.

The allantois of the chick has other important functions besides that of storing waste excretory products. By virtue of its position close to the chorion it serves to bring blood from the circulation within the embryo into close communication with the outside world, where it is able to make respiratory exchanges. The allantoic blood-vessels are, of course, essentially those of the cloaca, but they develop precociously. The *allantoic arteries* arise from the dorsal aorta. The left alone persists. The veins at first open to the sinus venosus, later in development of the chick only the left persists as the *umbilical vein*, opening to the ductus venosus. The allantois is thus provided with an abundant circulation by which oxygenated blood is returned direct to the heart.

In a mammal there is less need for an allantois that can store excretory products, because these can be returned to the maternal circulation through the placenta. Nevertheless in many mammals the allantois is still a large sac filled with fluid (e.g. in the pig) and therefore has excretory functions. Its main function in a mammal is to bring blood to the chorion, making the *allantochorion*, which is the chief agent of exchange with the mother. The mesoderm and blood-vessels of the allantois develop precociously and the lumen may be so reduced as to be hardly apparent, for example, in man (Fig. 283). The circulation through the allantoic vessels serves in a mammal not only for respiratory exchange and the removal of excretory products but also to bring food and water to the embryo, whose whole life is therefore dependent upon these tissues that are formed by modification of the morphogenetic processes that produce the bladder.

XL

THE REPRODUCTIVE TRACT OF MAMMALS

1. Reproduction and long-period homeostasis

THE reproductive system is the part of the body concerned with maintenance of the organization of the race rather than with that of any single creature. Yet it is a mistake to try to separate these two types of control too sharply. The organization that is preserved by homeostasis is not the property of any one 'individual', but of the whole race. The persistence of living things is due to the fact that they have control mechanisms operating with different time-scales. Ordinary physiological activities serve to make rapid adjustments, reproductive activities allow for more gradual ones (p. 26).

Each separate creature plays its part in maintaining the race for a while, but much of its activity is directed to ensuring that others shall continue after its death. This is achieved by the production of numerous and varied offspring and the placing of these in situations where their equipment is likely to allow them to survive. The homeostatic functions of reproduction therefore depend upon efficient action, (1) of the mechanisms of mating, ensuring variety among offspring, (2) of the mechanisms for caring for the young while it develops and for enabling it to start its life under suitable conditions. The production of gametes is thus only a part of reproductive activity. Many of the actions of a mammal are directed towards increasing the chance that the young shall survive; social, family, and individual life are so closely related that they are hardly distinguishable.

The function of the reproductive system being to maintain the stability of the race over very long periods, no system of rapid feedback of signals can ensure that its functions are efficiently performed. The control of the reproductive functions is mostly by the hereditary instructions—they are, as we say, innate or instinctive. To ensure that reproduction occurs at times of the year when the young are likely to survive, the slowly operating chemical signalling of the endocrine system is used (Chapter XLI). Control through the nervous system is important, however, for the performance of reproductive actions in relation to other members of the species and in all mammals there are communication signs by which individuals recognize others of the

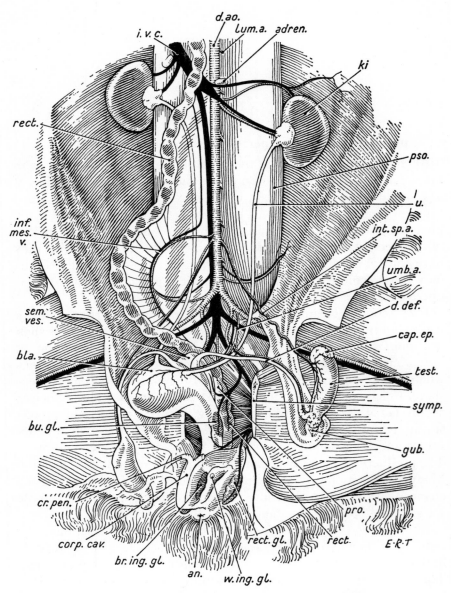

FIG. 272. The urinogenital system of the male rabbit.

adren. adrenal; *an.* anus; *bla.* bladder; *br.ing.gl.* brown inguinal gland; *bu.gl.* bulbo-urethral gland; *cap.ep.* caput epididymus; *corp.cav.* corpus cavernosum; *cr.pen.* crura penis; *d.ao.* dorsal aorta; *d.def.* ductus deferens; *gub.* gubernaculum; *inf.mes.v.* inferior mesenteric vein; *int.sp.a.* internal spermatic artery; *i.v.c.* inferior vena cava; *ki.* kidney; *lum.a.* lumbar artery; *pro.* prostate gland; *pso.* psoas major; *rect.* rectum; *rect.gl.* rectal gland; *sem.ves.* seminal vesicle; *symp.* pubic symphysis; *test.* testis; *u.* ureter; *umb.a.* umbilical artery; *w.ing.gl.* white inguinal gland.

same or opposite sex and elicit the appropriate mating reactions from them.

The reproductive system is therefore elaborately organized and includes not only the ovary and testis that produce the gametes but also the ducts by which these are carried to the exterior. Further, there are *secondary sexual characters* providing signals ensuring that the sexes meet and pair, and mammary glands and special behaviour mechanisms for the care of the young. The whole reproductive system is co-ordinated by an elaborate chemical communication system, centred upon the pituitary gland.

2. The reproductive tracts

The cells that will form the gonads are set aside very early in development (p. 743). They come to lie in organs that develop in the mesoderm and in all vertebrates the gonads have a close relationship to the coelom. In lampreys both the eggs and the sperm are shed into the coelom and pass to the exterior through coelomic funnels (Young, 1950, p. 90). The female reproductive system is still arranged essentially on this plan in mammals but in both sexes the system of ducts has become complicated to allow fertilization and development within the body.

The arrangements by which this is ensured are further developments of those that allow the meeting of eggs and sperm in fishes and other vertebrates whose eggs are laid in the water. The sperms must act in considerable concentration and they can swim only for a short time, therefore special nuptial ceremonies for bringing the sexes together are found in many fishes, and there may be elaborate copulatory organs and internal fertilization. Such mechanisms became further developed in the early terrestrial reptiles.

If the eggs are fertilized internally it is a short step to retain them within the mother, perhaps at first mainly as a means of protection against desiccation. Yet the viviparous habit characteristic of mammals probably did not develop directly from the changes that finally emancipated the vertebrates from the water. There was an intermediate stage in which eggs with shells were laid and the monotreme mammals, platypus and echidna, still remain in this stage. In the marsupial and placental mammals, however, the whole system of genital ducts in both sexes is highly developed for internal fertilization and viviparous development. The ducts are maintained in their proper functional state by the action of sex hormones produced by the gonads under the control of the pituitary gland and the adrenal cortex

(Chapter XLI). These hormones also regulate the manifestation of the secondary sexual characters by which the sexes are attracted to each other and stimulated to the activities of mating.

3. The testis and scrotum

The *testis* of mammals (Fig. 272) is peculiar in that in nearly all

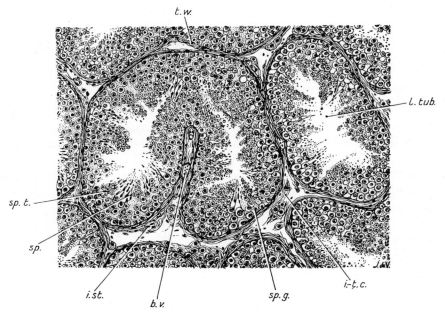

FIG. 273. Low power view of human testis.

b.v. blood-vessel; *i.st.* interstitial tissue; *i.-t.c.* inter-tubular connective tissue; *l.tub.* lumen of tubule; *sp.* spermatozoa; *sp.g.* spermatogonia; *sp.t.* spermatid; *t.w.* tubule wall (basement membrane and connective tissue).
(From a photograph by Mr. K. C. Richardson.)

species it descends from the body cavity into a special portion of the coelom, the *scrotal sac*, apparently because spermatogenesis is not able to proceed at the high temperature of the body cavity. It is not known why this should be necessary, since in birds and a few mammals (elephants) the testes are retained in the body cavity and therefore have a high temperature.

The scrotum is a pouch of the abdominal cavity and in the rabbit the communicating passage is wide and the testis can readily be pushed up into the abdomen. In man the communication is by means of the narrow *spermatic cord*, containing the spermatic artery and vein and the vas deferens. The lining of the sac is continuous with that of the abdominal coelom and its muscle is continuous with those of the abdominal wall. The testis is attached to the base of the scrotum by a cord, the *gubernaculum*. Fixation by this cord is at least partly responsible for the descent of the testis during development (p. 747).

The testis itself (Fig. 273) consists of a number of exceedingly long, coiled *seminiferous tubules*, whose walls produce the spermatozoa. In each tubule there is an outer layer of *spermatogonia*, with nuclei of moderate size, which by dividing produce the *primary spermatocytes* and further spermatogonia. The spermatocytes have large nuclei and pass through the *meiotic divisions* to form secondary spermatocytes with more compact nuclei. These then become the *spermatids*, which by the process of *spermiogenesis* differentiate into spermatozoa. Throughout spermiogenesis the spermatids are attached to nutritive *Sertoli cells*, whose nuclei have large nucleoli, suggesting that they conduct active protein synthesis and transfer the products to the developing spermatozoa.

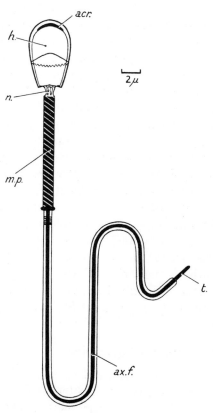

FIG. 274. Diagram of spermatozoon of ram. *acr.* acrosome; *ax.f.* axial filament; *h.* head; *m.p.* middle piece; *n.* neck; *t.* tail. (Modified after Randall and Friedlaender, 1950.)

4. Spermatozoa

Each spermatozoon has a complicated internal organization, which has recently been revealed by electron microscopy (see Randall and Friedlander, 1950; Bradfield, 1955) (Fig. 274). The spermatozoa of different mammals differ markedly in details but all show a head, neck, middle piece, and tail or flagellum. In ram sperm the head is of flattened oval shape ($8\cdot2 \times 4\cdot25 \times 0\cdot5\ \mu$) and is formed largely from the nucleus of the spermatid. It shows a marked birefringence, probably because of orientated deoxyribose nucleotides. Covering the head is a cap composed of a complicated set of fibrillar sheaths, the galea and acrosome, perhaps formed from Golgi material.

The neck and middle piece also show complex structure. The centriole is a granule in the neck, from which originates an axial fibre that runs throughout the middle piece and tail. In the middle piece the fibre is surrounded by a helical structure, the mitochondrial sheath, which may be concerned in the energy-giving exchanges of the sperm. At the hind end of the middle piece is a ring centriole.

Throughout the major portion of the tail (40μ) the axial filament is provided with a sheath and the total diameter is about $0{\cdot}5 \mu$, but the terminal section (3μ) is bare. Nearly all flagella and cilia contain a ring of nine fibrils and two smaller ones at the centre. The tails of mammalian spermatozoa are unusual in that there are two concentric rings each of nine fibrils, and two central fibrils. The relation of this structure to the movement of the sperm is not clear. During swimming S-shape waves pass along the flagellum in such a way as to move water backwards and hence propel the sperm forwards, at a rate of 150–200μ/sec. The energy for the movement is provided in mammals by fructose, which is taken in from the seminal fluid and degraded anaerobically by the enzymes of a carbohydrate cycle similar to that in other tissues, producing lactic acid (see Rothschild, 1952).

The mature sperms are presumably of two types, with X and Y chromosomes, responsible for determination of females and males respectively, but no means of identifying or separating these has been discovered and it is not known if they are present in equal numbers or have the same activity. The sperms are not active while within the testis and only become so for a brief time after mixing with the secretion of the accessory glands (p. 669).

5. Male sex hormones

The production of spermatozoa is continuous in the testis of man after puberty but is affected by nutritional and other environmental conditions. In species with a restricted mating season the spermatogenesis occurs only at that time. The activity of the testis is controlled by secretion of the anterior lobe of the pituitary (p. 690). Besides producing spermatozoa the testis is also the seat of formation of the male sex hormones, *testosterone* and other similar androgenic steroids (see Ciba Handbook No. 4, 1950), whose effect is to produce and maintain the secondary sex characters, by which males are recognized, the female is stimulated to copulation, and the social and family organization is maintained (p. 672). These hormones are produced by the *interstitial cells*, groups of which lie between the tubules (Fig. 273).

testosterone

6. Male genital ducts

The products of the testis are carried away by a system of tubes derived from the mesonephric (Wolffian) ducts (p. 741). The seminiferous tubules open into a system of spaces, the *rete testis*, from which a number of *vasa efferentia* lead to the long, much coiled *epididymis*, which carries the sperms to the *vas deferens*. The cells lining the vasa efferentia are ciliated but those of the epididymis and the vas are columnar, with partial superposition of layers (hence 'pseudo-stratified') and some of them are glandular. The total length of the epididymis reaches 45 cm. in man and this long tube serves as a means of storing sperms.

The vas deferens has a thick muscular wall, giving it a characteristic firm consistency. It enters the abdomen from the scrotal sack and curves medially to open into the urethra. Before reaching this the vas passes through a system of glands and sacs whose secretions, together with the products of the testis and epididymis, make up the *semen* (Fig. 272). The *vesicula seminalis* is a long folded pouch opening at the expanded lower end (ampulla) of the vas. Its cavity is much divided and its wall, like that of the accompanying *vesicular gland*, is secretory. The *prostate* is a large mass of glandular tissue lying around the upper part of the urethra, into which it pours its secretion by numerous ducts. *Cowper's glands* (bulbo-urethral) are a pair opening into the urethra lower down. The secretion of all these glands is mixed with the products of the testis during ejaculation and serves to activate and nourish the sperms as well as to neutralize the acidity of the urethra and vagina and perhaps to perform other functions such as the enzymatic solution of the cumulus cells around the egg (p. 695).

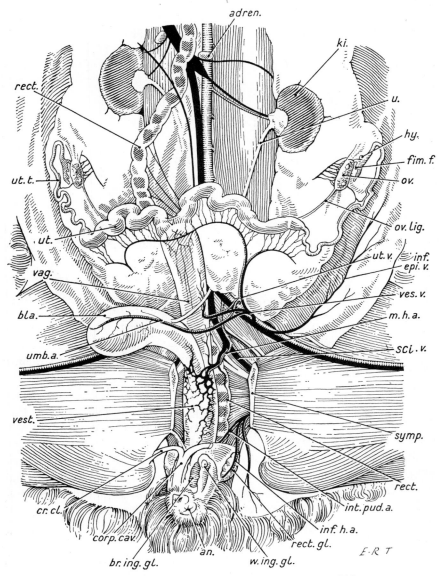

FIG. 275. The urinogenital system of the female rabbit.

adren. adrenal; *an.* anus; *bla.* bladder; *br.ing.gl.* brown inguinal gland; *corp.cav.* corpus cavernosum; *cr.cl.* crura clitoridis; *inf.epi.v.* inferior epigastric vein; *fim.f.* fimbriated funnel; *hy.* hydatid; *inf.h.a.* inferior haemorrhoidal artery; *int.pud.a.* internal pudendal artery; *ki.* kidney; *m.h.a.* middle haemorrhoidal artery; *ov.* ovary; *ov.lig.* ovarian ligament; *rect.* rectum; *rect.gl.* rectal gland; *sci. v.* sciatic vein; *symp.* pubic symphysis; *u.* ureter; *umb.a.* umbilical artery; *ut.* uterus; *ut.t.* uterine tube; *ut.v.* uterine vein; *vag.* vagina; *vest.* vestibule; *ves.v.* vesical vein; *w.ing.gl.* white inguinal gland.

7. The penis

One of the biological problems of life on land is to ensure fertilization in the absence of an external watery medium in which sperm and eggs can be mixed. In early stages of tetrapod life this was brought about by the close apposition of the genital regions, which in fishes are indeed often brought together, and are swollen at the time of breeding by the dilatation of their blood-vessels. In reptiles and mammals the method has been perfected by development of a tube, the *penis*, formed in evolution from the wall of the cloaca. The penis becomes rigid by filling of the blood-vessels of the *erectile tissue*, which has developed from the original vascular network.

The penis thus consists of a tube containing the terminal portion of the urethra and three large vascular columns, the *corpora cavernosa*, one on each side and a median *corpus spongiosum*, below. These columns are attached proximally to the ischium and pubis. Erection is produced by relaxation of the walls of the arteries that lead to these spaces, so that the cylinders become filled with blood under pressure. The tip of the penis (glans) is covered with sensitive skin containing the *genital corpuscles*, probably modified organs of touch, which when stimulated by contact send impulses through the spinal cord to produce the male orgasm involving reflex contraction of the musculature of the vas deferens and urethra and ejaculation of the semen. Fertilization is accomplished high up in the uterine tubes (p. 693).

8. Female reproductive tract

The mammalian female genital tract (Fig. 275) is built on the plan of other vertebrates, namely a pair of tubes (Mullerian ducts) leading from the coelom to the exterior (p. 741). The special mammalian features are the development (1) of part of the tubes as one or a pair of uteri, regions specialized for nourishing the young, and (2) of the terminal part as a vagina for copulation.

The *ovaries* are a pair of solid structures whose surface, the *germinal epithelium* (Fig. 276) perhaps produces a succession of ripening eggs, each enclosed in a follicle (see p. 680). Close to the ovary is the *fimbriated funnel*, whose folded, ciliated lips receive the eggs when shed. The first part of the female tract is the *Fallopian tube* (*uterine tube*), of narrow diameter, whose walls are ciliated, glandular, and muscular. Fertilization occurs in the upper end of this tube (p. 693) and the ova are carried along it by ciliary and muscular action. In many mammals, for instance the rabbit, the tract remains paired and there are thus two uterine horns; in the human the lower parts are fused to make a single *uterus*. This is the part of the tract that can react to the presence of an embryo in such a way as to allow placentation to occur (p. 702). Its walls are glandular and muscular and its blood-vessels have special characteristics. These features enable the uterus to react to the presence of a foetus in forming the *placenta*, by which the foetus is nourished (p. 711). The whole uterus lies in a fold of peritoneum, the mesometrium or *broad ligament*.

The lower end of the single or paired uteri narrows to form a canal, the *cervix*, which communicates with the lowest portion of the Mullerian duct, the *vagina*. This is a tube lined by a variable, often squamous epithelium (p. 683), whose wall contains muscular and erectile tissue. Its exterior opening is protected by two pairs of folds of skin, the *labia majora* and *labia minora*, enclosing a vestibule into which open the *bulbo-urethral* or *Bartholin's glands*, comparable to the Cowper's glands of the male, serving to lubricate the opening to the vagina. At the ventral side of the vestibule lies the *clitoris*, consisting, like the penis, of paired corpora cavernosa of erectile tissue, with a highly sensitive tip.

9. Secondary sex characters and mating

The coming together and mating of males and females is ensured by an elaborate system of signals, receptors, and effector mechanisms whose importance is shown by the large part they play in controlling the appearance and habits of animals and man. The initial bringing together of the sexes is largely a matter of olfactory signals in many mammals (see p. 42) but visual signals also play a large part, especially in primates, including man. The *secondary sexual characters*, differences between the two sexes in parts of the body other than those directly concerned with reproduction, serve mainly to provide signs for recognition and attraction (Fig. 8).

The *sex drives* that impel mating behaviour depend on the internal condition of the individual, produced by action of the endocrine system (especially the hormones of the gonads) on the nervous system. In those mammals that have a breeding season the nervous system of both sexes becomes sensitized at certain times by the endocrine secretions, so that it responds to stimulation by the secondary sexual characters of the opposite sex.

In man the sex drives fluctuate less markedly with the seasons, but they become modified and lessened after removal of the influence of

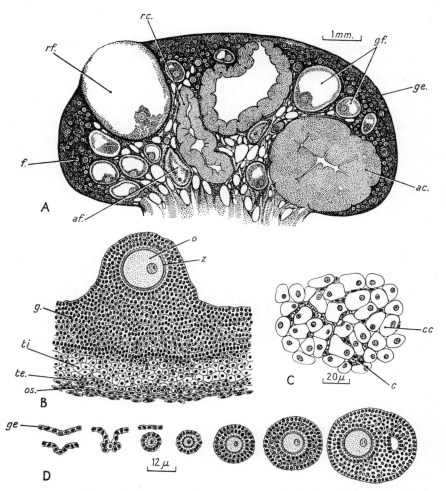

FIG. 276. A, Schematic drawing of the mature ovary of a monkey (*Macaca*); B, cells of the wall of a ripe follicle; C, cells of the corpus luteum; D, suggested stages in the development of a follicle from the germinal epithelium, but it is doubtful whether ova are formed by sinking in the manner shown.

ac. active corpus luteum; *af.* atretic follicle; *c.* capillaries; *cc.* cells of corpus luteum; *f.* follicles; *g.* granulosa cells; *ge.* cells of germinal epithelium; *gf.* growing follicle; *o.* ovum; *os.* ovarian stroma; *rc.* regressing corpus luteum; *rf.* ripe follicle; *te.* theca externa; *ti.* theca interna; *z.* zona pellucida. (Partly after George W. Corner.)

the gonads. We understand little of these interactions of glands and brain and in man the great elaboration of the nervous system makes sexual behaviour varied and difficult to forecast. Much of the work of psychologists has been directed to analysis of the various ways in which the sex drives operate, especially when they are frustrated by the restrictions imposed by social organization.

The completion of copulation requires co-operation between the male and female, which is ensured by the responses to the sexual signals and the sensory equipment of the penis and vagina. Under proper reciprocal stimulation there is erection of the penis, lubrication of the vestibule and vagina by secretion of Bartholin's glands, and finally in the orgasm of both sexes the ejaculate of the male is received into the upper end of the vagina and passes through the cervix into the uterus and uterine tubes.

10. The control of reproduction

The effectiveness of reproduction is judged only by the persistence of the race and therefore no system of signals within the body can ensure that it is adequately controlled. The afferent and efferent impulses involved in orgasm serve to ensure that the eggs and sperm are brought together, but this is only the beginning of the process of reproduction and there can be no feed-back control within the body to guarantee its completion. The further nervous and endocrine systems involved in reproduction operate mainly under hereditary and not under cortical control. The reproductive tracts receive nerve-fibres from the autonomic nervous system and these play a part in regulating the movements of the uterus, vas deferens, and other organs. The parts of reproductive behaviour that involve reaction by the whole individual are of course under the control of the brain, but responses are in the main to hereditarily determined olfactory, auditory, and visual signs. The elaborate computing system of the cortex is only indirectly involved, although in primates and especially in man it comes to play a large part in reproductive as in all other behaviour.

Memories acquired by the tissues during the lifetime of the individual clearly cannot provide useful forecasts about the effectiveness of the reproductive systems. We cannot say that the ovary, testis, or uterus carry memory stores in the sense that we can identify these in the femur or the muscles. The reproductive organs change with use, but the changes are not under the influence of any immediate selective factors that make them more effective as forecasters of efficient reproductive behaviour. The higher nervous centres enter into mating behaviour and there is evidence of changes with learning in the copulatory behaviour of carnivores and primates. This is even more conspicuous in the mechanism for the care of the young and particularly in man, where the information learnt by the individual as to how to teach subsequent generations is one of the most striking characteristics.

In spite of this control by acquired memories it remains true that the hereditary instructions play an outstanding part in the control of reproduction even in man. The stability of the race through thousands of years is ensured by the operations of the gonads and reproductive tracts under the influence of spinal reflex centres and endocrine mechanisms, which develop and function with relatively little intervention by the highest parts of the nervous system. Even the signals for sexual recognition and stimulation are probably largely inherited, though subject to modification by learning, especially in man.

XLI

THE OESTROUS CYCLE OF MAMMALS

1. Preparation of the uterus

THE protection, nourishment, and care of the young within the uterus is ensured in placental mammals by the close integration of ovulation and fertilization with events that prepare the uterus to receive the embryo. The necessary changes in the female constitute the *oestrous cycle*, culminating in ovulation, which in many species is timed to occur close to a period at which the female will receive the male, thus ensuring fertilization. There is a surprising variety in the means by which this timing is achieved in various mammals, notably in the relationship between ovulation and copulation and hence in the time of survival of the sperms and probably also of the ova.

In the mouse, where we have full information on this point, ova remain fully 'active' only for about 6 hours after ovulation and sperms are not found motile in the oviduct later than 12 hours after copulation (p. 693). On the other hand in bats copulation occurs in the autumn, but fertilization not until the following spring. It is obvious that in this field conclusions must not lightly be carried over from one species to another; exact statements can be made only about phenomena known to take place by careful observation of each type of animal. Unfortunately, since mammalian development is internal, accurate data can only be obtained by the slaughter of a large number of animals, which cannot easily be undertaken in the large domestic mammals. In man the operations of obstetricians provide a partial substitute, but we are still without detailed information about some of the most important aspects of human reproduction, such as the length of life of the eggs and sperm.

Yet the present state of our knowledge of these matters contrasts favourably with the ignorance of a short time ago. Considering the vital importance of the subject, especially in man, it is astonishing that even 20 years ago there was no reliable information about the time of ovulation of women, indeed the erroneous view that this usually occurs during or soon after the menstrual flow was very common. Ingenious and patient investigations have now given a satisfactory general idea of the nature of the female sexual cycle in mammals, and also much information about their hormonal control (see Marshall, 1952). The effects of this information, together with the further knowledge of details that will no doubt accumulate to supplement it, will be of great importance in determining reproductive practices and moral codes in the future.

In spite of the variety in the sexual cycles of various female mammals we can recognize a pattern common to all. Several influences control the female sex cycle, one or another predominating in each species, but probably all act to some extent in every female mammal. Thus in the doe rabbit ovulation only occurs after copulation, whereas in women it usually occurs as a result of endocrine factors on or about the fourteenth day after the beginning of the previous menstrual flow, irrespective of mating. But we may not from these facts conclude that endocrine cycles have no influence on the ovary of the rabbit or that copulation is always without influence on that of a woman.

2. The oestrous cycle

In mammals, as in other vertebrates, the secondary sexual characters and condition of the genital ducts are regulated by secretion from the ovary and this is influenced by pituitary secretions, which are in turn themselves influenced by the ovarian hormones. The female reproductive system, therefore, does not remain at a steady level of activity but undergoes cyclical changes (see Krohn and Zuckerman, 1953 and Bullough, 1951). The period of oestrus or heat is the time of sexual activity of the female, occurring either rhythmically throughout the year or at one or more seasons. At the time of oestrus the eggs are shed from the ovary and the females desire and will receive the males. The word oestrus is derived from the Greek name for the gadfly or warble fly, whose sting drives cattle crazy. Its use in the present sense was already suggested by ancient pastoral mythology. The goddess Hera, having discovered that her husband Zeus had lain with another goddess, Io, sent a gadfly to sting her rival, who was driven into many strange places by the torment of this 'oestrus'.

At the time of oestrus the desire and attractions of the females, reacting with those of the males, may produce very violent behaviour in individuals and in herds of mammals. Human social organization is possible because men and women instead of these sweeping changes of desire, experience attractions that are more persistent if somewhat less insistent. Man and old-world monkeys are peculiar in this respect; in most mammals mating only occurs at the times when oestrus overtakes the female. Thus the cat and bitch come on heat two or three

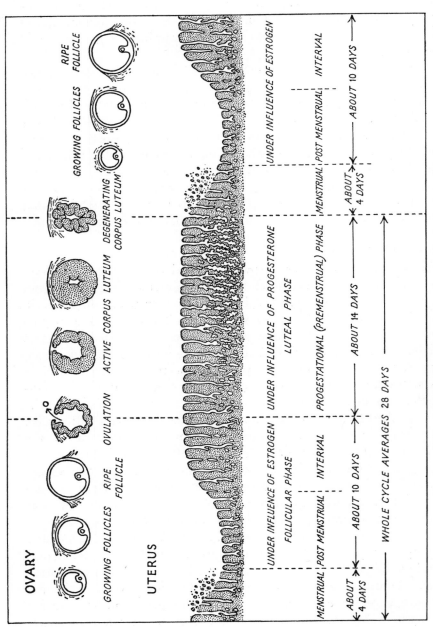

FIG. 277. Diagram showing the sequence of events in the menstrual cycle. (After George W. Corner.)

times a year and these periods of oestrus are separated by long periods of *anoestrus*, in which the reproductive system is quiescent and the female will not mate. In other mammals the oestrous periods follow each other in regular cycles, either throughout the whole year (man) or during a certain breeding season (many rodents). Animals of the type with single periods of heat are said to be *monoestrous*, those with a succession of cycles are *polyoestrous*. The condition is not rigidly fixed for any one species and the surroundings and nutrition alter the sexual cycles markedly. Conditions of domestication seem to increase the number of periods of oestrus, thus wild sheep and goats only have a single mating season, in the autumn, and but a single oestrous period in that season. Domesticated sheep and goats may show several oestrous periods in the autumn and winter, also an extra breeding season in the spring or even, in the case of Australian merino sheep, a regular series of cycles throughout the year (see Asdell, 1946).

In spite of these variations we can give the following general statement about the breeding seasons of the various mammalian orders. Marsupials breed once or twice a year and are monoestrous or polyoestrous. Insectivora, the most primitive placentals, are polyoestrous, thus in the shrew, cycles a few days in length succeed each other throughout a long breeding season, in the course of which several litters may be born. The same condition is found in rodents and primates, groups that remain close to the insectivoran stock. Thus the rat shows cycles 4–5 days long. Old-world monkeys, like man, have cycles of about 28 days, with a special condition of menstrual bleeding, discussed below. In some bats copulation occurs in the autumn but fertilization is delayed until the spring. In armadilloes, some carnivores and roe deer there is delayed implantation, the blastocyst lying dormant in the uterus.

Perissodactyla are mainly polyoestrous. The mare in domestication experiences a series of cycles throughout the spring and early summer, each lasting 19–23 days. In the wild state the season is probably shorter but includes several cycles. Artiodactyla are frequently monoestrous in the wild state, and it is in these animals, especially those living in herds, that the 'rutting season' produces the greatest disturbance in the lives of both sexes. The males experience a season of rut, corresponding to the oestrus of the females, and animals such as the bison congregate into great herds of fighting and copulating individuals.

Carnivora are also monoestrous in the wild state, but the fact that they, like the artiodactyls, become polyoestrous in captivity suggests that the primitive state for mammals is one in which at the appropriate time of year several successive periods of oestrus occur. We have therefore to look for the basic changes that produce this rhythmicity.

3. Proestrus. The follicular phase

The various types of cycle do not differ fundamentally and we can

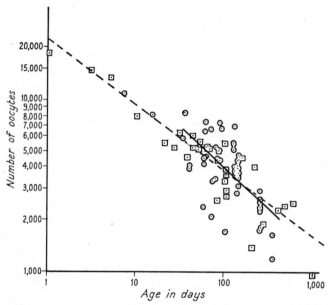

FIG. 278. Change in numbers of oocytes with age in the rat. The circles and continuous regression line are from a series of rats measured in Birmingham, the squares and dotted line from a series counted by Arai in America.
(From Mandl and Zuckerman, *J. Endocrinol.* **7**, 1951.)

recognize a series of events common to all mammals (Fig. 277). In monoestrous species there is a period of *anoestrus* during which the female reproductive organs are quiescent. Then follows a gradual ripening of follicles in the ovary, quickening under the influence of external stimuli such as light, acting as we shall see through the pituitary gland. Thus anoestrus passes into *proestrus*, in which the ova in the follicles of the ovary ripen rapidly. This is the period of 'coming into heat', which precedes the true oestrus.

4. The ripening of ovarian follicles

The follicles consist of a central ovum surrounded by follicle cells (Fig. 276). There has been much discussion whether during each cycle new ova are formed from the germinal epithelium. Allen (1923) and others have suggested that there is 'a cyclical proliferation of the germinal epithelium giving rise to a new addition of young ova to the cortex of the adult ovary at each normal oestrous period'. This would

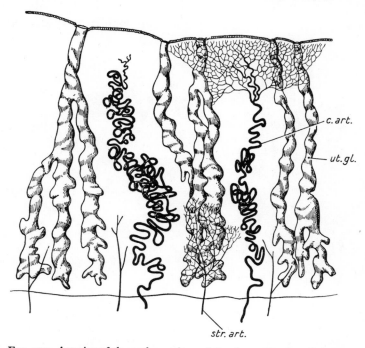

FIG. 279. Arteries of the endometrium of the rhesus monkey (*Macaca*).
c.art. coiled artery; *str.art.* straight artery; *ut.gl.* uterine gland.
(Partly after Daron, G. H., *Amer. J. Anat.* **58**, 1936.)

explain the fact that ovaries contain large numbers of follicles undergoing the process of degeneration (*atresia*). However, it is now thought probable that no new formation of oocytes takes place in the adult (see Zuckerman, 1951). Counts of the total number of oocytes of all sizes show a gradual decline throughout the life period (Fig. 278) and this accounts for the atretic follicles (see Mandl and Zuckerman, 1951). If one ovary is removed the other undergoes a compensatory hypertrophy but there is no increase in the total number of oocytes that it contains. The rate at which oocytes are destroyed is, however, reduced after removal of one ovary. Evidently some control mechanism is present to regulate the rate of loss according to the amount of ovarian tissue remaining in the body.

The surrounding follicle cells have a supporting and nourishing function and also produce the oestrogenic hormones. The wall of the follicle grows faster than the ovum, so that the latter occupies only a relatively small part of the ripe follicle, surrounded by a mass of *granulosa cells* (the *cumulus*). These cells secrete the liquor folliculi, which fills and gradually distends the follicle. Outside them is a layer of special cells, the *theca interna*, rich in fatty compounds,

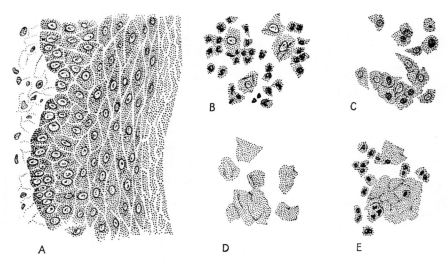

FIG. 280. The vaginal cycle in the white rat.

A, Part of the vaginal wall at the time of ovulation (oestrus). The cells of the inner surface, at the right, are cornified and without nuclei; B, C, D, and E show cells shed from the inner surface of the vaginal wall; B, at dioestrus in the vaginal cavity there are epithelial cells (pale nuclei) and leucocytes (dark nuclei); C, just before oestrus the epithelial cells swell; D, corni-fied cells as in A after being shed; E, after oestrus, leucocytes return and cornified cells disintegrate. (After Long, J. A., and Evans, H. M.)

well supplied with blood, and probably responsible for producing the oestrogenic hormones, which are therefore present in increasing amounts as the follicle ripens. Under their influence various changes occur in the genital ducts and in the secondary sexual characters. Oestrogens thus prepare the female for copulation by thickening the wall of the vagina and they also begin the preparation of the uterus to receive the embryo.

5. Changes in the uterus and vagina

The lining layers of the uterus become thickened during proestrus. These layers include the inner layer or *endometrium*, provided with abundant glands, which increase during proestrus (Fig. 279), and the outer *myometrium*, whose muscle-fibres also increase in size and perhaps also in number. The uterus gradually becomes better supplied with blood during this period and towards the end of it will be found to be swollen and hyperaemic, with much secretion in its lumen.

During this period there are also changes in the cells of the *vagina*, especially of rodents. In anoestrous or castrated animals the vaginal epithelium consists only of one or two layers; the only cells to be found in the contents of the organ are leucocytes, which can pass readily through the thin wall. Under the influence of oestrogens, however, the vaginal epithelium becomes much thickened and keratinized and some of the superficial cells are shed into the lumen and can be recognized if a 'smear' preparation is made (Fig. 280).

6. Oestrus

Proestrus is succeeded by the climax of the cycle, oestrus proper. During this time ovulation usually occurs, either spontaneously or in some species (rabbit, cat, ferret) only if there is copulation. The distended Graafian follicle bursts, washing out the enclosed ovum, still surrounded by some of the cumulus cells. The ovum is thus shed close to the opening of the oviduct, whose fimbriated funnel is provided with cilia. The eggs pass down the oviduct partly by ciliary, partly by peristaltic action. It is during this period of oestrus that the female of many species is receptive to mating. The vaginal wall is now thick and often highly cornified and a smear preparation of the vaginal contents shows cornified epithelial cells that have been shed, but no leucocytes.

Marked changes of electrical potential, as recorded between the abdominal wall and the vagina take place at the moment of ovulation. This sign has served to confirm that ovulation occurs in women near the fourteenth day after the beginning of the previous menstrual flow. At this time pains ('Mittelschmerz') are sometimes felt, some women experience characteristic sensations and claim that they know the time of ovulation; it is also sometimes alleged that desire is then increased. A change in body temperature also occurs at the middle of the human menstrual cycle. There is a drop on about the fourteenth day, followed by a rise, so that the temperature is generally higher during the second half of the cycle than the first.

There is considerable variation in these matters and clearly the climax of oestrus is less marked in women than in most mammals. In some monkeys the time of ovulation is indicated by sharp changes in the coloration of the face and buttocks and in other secondary sexual characters. In the baboon these changes were early used in demonstrating that ovulation occurs at the middle of the menstrual cycle (Zuckerman, 1932). In other mammals various phenomena of receptivity are seen at the height of oestrus, the vaginal lips become tumid and special secretions are formed that attract the males, for instance to a bitch on heat. In some animals there is slight bleeding from the vagina either just before or at the height of oestrus. It was natural to compare this with menstrual bleeding, leading to the erroneous view that ovulation occurs soon after menstruation. Bleeding in the middle of the month sometimes occurs in women and would correspond to this oestrous bleeding of animals.

The facts thus suggest that in women the follicles begin to ripen after the menstrual flow. This period may therefore be characterized as the follicular phase of the cycle. The oestrogens produced by the developing follicle cause proliferation of the wall of the uterus and cornification of cells of the vagina. This part of the cycle culminates in ovulation, usually on about the fourteenth day after the beginning of the previous menstrual flow.

7. The corpus luteum, pseudo-pregnancy

The events following oestrus vary considerably according to the type of mammal and as to whether ovulation, fertilization, and placentation have occurred. The ruptured ovarian follicle rapidly becomes filled with gland-cells derived from the granulosa cells, forming the *corpus luteum* (Fig. 276) and producing the steroid hormone *progesterone*. This gland exerts profound effects throughout the body but it only maintains its full development if implantation has occurred. However, in some species the luteum begins to form even if there has been no conception and the days that follow may be characterized as a progestational period (*dioestrus*) (see Harrison, 1948).

In women the uterine lining continues to grow after ovulation, under the influence of the progestational hormones of the corpus luteum, even in the absence of fertilization. The changes in the uterine wall during this progestational period consist of a great further development of the glands, which become much coiled and begin to secrete. The arteries near to the surface of the endometrium acquire a peculiar coiled structure (Fig. 279). Their function is to provide a rich blood-supply just under the endometrial surface at the time the developing ovum is ready to implant. At the height of the progestational period the endometrium acquires a marked sensitivity to mechanical stimuli, which induce in it changes similar to those of early placentation (p. 704) and known as a '*decidual reaction*'.

If fertilization has not occurred the progestational period lasts for about 14 days in women. At the end of this time the corpus luteum regresses and the thickened endometrium breaks down, producing the menstrual flow. The coiled arteries constrict, so that the endometrial surface becomes ischaemic; they then dilate individually for short periods, leading to the loss of blood. Some tissue also sloughs off and the endometrium becomes much thinner. The changes of menstruation are therefore due to contraction of the coiled arteries, but some slight menstrual flow occurs in New World monkeys, which have no coiled arteries. Evidently this type of blood-supply is a specialization superimposed on an older mechanism.

The factors that produce development of the corpus luteum in the absence of conception vary in different mammals. In some species (rabbit) sterile copulation may be followed by *pseudopregnancy*. If there is no mating, however, the corpus luteum exercises little or no influence and there is a gradual regression of the uterine thickening (*metoestrus*), without sloughing of tissue or bleeding. There is, however, some bleeding at this time in the bitch and cow. In all cases metoestrus leads to a return to the condition with fewer glands and smaller muscles and smaller blood-supply to the uterus. The vaginal wall at this time also shows degenerating epithelial cells and leucocytes. In animals with interrupted breeding periods the metoestrus is followed by anoestrus, but in those with a regular rhythm the uterus, after a longer or shorter period, again begins to develop.

8. The menstrual cycle

The regular menstrual rhythm of a woman is therefore a series of oestrous periods (Fig. 277). Following the flow, proestrus, the follicular phase of the cycle, prepares the body for ovulation, which occurs about 14 days after the beginning of the previous flow. The remaining 14 days of the cycle are a luteal (progestational) phase in which the uterine growth continues, making preparation for the foetus and ending only if the latter fails to arrive.

This interpretation of the menstrual cycle as a combination of follicular and luteal phases has been challenged on the ground that in monkeys and perhaps also in the adolescent human, menstrual cycles without ovulation may occur. The fact that a cycle of uterine development and bleeding can be accomplished without formation of a corpus luteum emphasizes the similarity of the functions of the undischarged and the ruptured follicles, to which we shall refer later (p. 689).

9. Control of the oestrous cycle

The various phases of the oestrous cycle are accompanied by changes in many parts of the body, especially in the endocrine glands. It is not easy to see which, if any, of these changes constitutes the master mechanism that regulates the rhythm. The cycle may in fact be the result of the interaction of the various factors, without any master timing mechanism.

Recent investigation has shown that a considerable number of substances is involved, including the protein-like hormones produced in the pituitary and placenta, and various steroid substances formed in the ovary, adrenal cortex, placenta, and probably at other sites. The normal rates of production of these substances are still largely unknown but much has been learned by extraction, purification, and injection of them.

10. Oestrogenic hormones of the ovary

The ovary itself is a major source of the substances now known as oestrogenic hormones, previously loosely called female sex hormones. The nomenclature is much confused by the numerous names that have been introduced to describe various extracted substances, but fortunately now that many of the more important ones have been isolated, crystallized, and even synthesized it is possible to give agreed chemical names to these and to reject the earlier names. Two of the active substances obtained from the ovary are *oestrone* and *oestradiol*.

oestrone   oestradiol   stilbestrol

There are also many other naturally occurring and synthetic substances that have oestrogenic activity. *Stilbestrol* is one of these; it is not destroyed by digestion and therefore can be taken by mouth.

Though the formula of stilbestrol as thus written has some resemblance to that of the naturally occurring oestrogens the substance is not chemically very similar. Dodds compares its action with that of a skeleton key and the similarity is certainly suggestive, but the mode of action of synthetic oestrogens remains uncertain.

In mammals the oestrogenic hormones certainly play a major part in the control of the secondary sexual characters. Following removal of the ovaries there is a loss of the sexual instinct of the female, and indeed a loss of activity in general, as measured in rats in a revolving cage. The operation is also followed by reduction in size of the uterus and vagina, reduction of the glands of the uterus, reduction in the mammary glands, and changes in many of the soft parts and skeleton. Of special interest is the fact that removal of the ovary produces changes in the anterior lobe of the pituitary, which is one of the main influences controlling the ovary (see below). Injection of ovarian extracts or oestrogens is able to reverse all of these changes. The uterus becomes hyperaemic and distended with secretion, following multiplication of the gland-cells by mitosis, while the vaginal epithelium becomes thickened and cornified.

There can therefore be little doubt that the changes characteristic of the proestrous phase of the oestrous cycle are produced by the oestrogens secreted by the ovary. It is probable that the main source of such substances is the cells of the theca interna of the ripening follicle, which, as we have seen are large cells, containing fatty substances and with a rich blood-supply. The oestrogenic substances are present in considerable amounts in the liquor folliculi. Small amounts of oestrogens are probably produced elsewhere in the ovary but the theca interna is the main source and the phase of the cycle in which it is active is therefore appropriately referred to as the follicular phase. The oestrogens produced are probably mainly oestrone and oestradiol.

Oestrogens also have many other effects throughout the body, maintaining the secondary sex characters peculiar to the female. In some species certain characters become specially accentuated at the height of oestrus, serving as signals to attract the males. Thus the colouring of the buttocks, genitalia, and face of some female monkeys reaches its full development just before ovulation, of which indeed it provides an excellent sign (p. 683).

The secretion of oestrogens is also responsible for the later stages of development of the genital ducts before puberty. The vagina of the rat remains a solid cord of cells until maturity, which occurs at two months after birth. It can be made to open at one month or earlier by injection of oestrone. The constancy of this reaction throughout vertebrates is remarkable, oestrone also causes opening of the genital ducts of immature lampreys (Young, 1950, p. 93).

11. Hormones of the corpus luteum

Following release of the egg from its follicle the cells of the granulosa develop into luteal cells and produce the related steroid *progesterone*, whose effects are partly like those of the oestrogens, partly

progesterone

distinct. If fertilization has occurred and an embryo is present in the
uterus the corpus luteum continues to develop and its secretions effect
the changes in the female uterus and metabolism that are necessary
for the support of the foetus. The change-over of function at ovulation is probably not sudden and indeed small amounts of progesterone
are secreted in the later days of the follicular phase of the cycle.
Oestrogens continue to be produced in the progestational phase, from
persisting cells of the theca interna.

Progesterone has a powerful action upon the uterus, causing further
growth of both endometrium and myometrium, especially if the organ
has already been stimulated by oestrogens. There is a strong influence
on the uterine glands, muscles, and blood-vessels. Other effects
throughout the body prepare the female for pregnancy by various
changes in metabolism.

The corpus luteum is therefore the 'pregnancy gland' and is essential for the earlier stages of pregancy though it may be removed later
in women (but not in rat or cow) without leading to abortion. The relaxation of the ligaments of the pubic symphysis before birth depends
in some species at least (guinea-pig) on a substance produced by the
ovary, but this 'relaxin' is probably not identical with progesterone.

The action of progesterone in some doses may be opposite to that
of the oestrogens in preventing the maturation of further ovarian
follicles. Conversely oestrogens may prevent the actions of progesterone if the two are administered together. Injections of oestrone
will interrupt pregnancy in some species, but the dose that will be
tolerated increases with the time from conception and in later stages
becomes very large. The details of the relationship of oestrogens and

progesterone in the normal life of the mammals remain, in spite of much study, still obscure. The substances are interestingly similar in some effects, opposite in others. Since they may be both produced by the same cells, perhaps even simultaneously, it is not surprising to hear that there are many similarities in their actions. It must not be forgotten that menstrual cycles can be completed without ovulation (p. 685), with or without formation of a corpus luteum, though of course not necessarily without liberation of any progesterone.

12. Artificially induced oestrous cycles

The effect of the two hormones on the endometrium has been studied by the ingenious technique of planting small portions of the uterine epithelium into the anterior chamber of the eye in monkeys (Markee, 1940; Phelps, 1946). The piece becomes supplied with blood from the vessels of the iris and remains as well differentiated uterine tissue for years. Its monthly fluctuations follow those of the uterus and can be studied by direct observation through the cornea. Using this technique as a test it has been found possible to produce by appropriate injection and withdrawal of hormones an almost complete replica of the menstrual cycle in animals from which the ovaries had been removed. When oestrogen only was given daily the fragment implanted in the eye became progressively larger and more vascular and coiled arteries could be seen within it, though they never reached close to the surface. If after 28 days the injections of oestrogen were stopped, then 2 or more days after the last injection bleeding of the fragment began. This shows that menstrual bleeding can occur following a change in the level of oestrogen only.

Changes equivalent to those of ovulatory menstrual cycles were obtained by injecting the castrated monkeys with oestrogen throughout the month, together with progesterone on days 15 to 28. The grafted pieces of endometrium now showed their full development. Coiled arteries grew close to the surface and formed characteristic terminal loops and curls. Both hormones were discontinued on the twenty-eighth day and 1–3 days later (more regularly than after oestrogen only) bleeding from the fragment (and from the vagina) began.

These experiments confirm all the other evidence in showing that the endometrial changes are produced by the effect on the uterus of the hormones secreted by the ripening follicles and the corpus luteum. The development of the endometrium in the later part of the cycle is due to the influence of progesterone added to that of oestrogens, and the final breakdown and flow of blood follows the withdrawal of the hormones and consequent constriction of the coiled arteries, which depend on them. The ischemic endometrial surface then partly breaks away and some blood escapes.

13. Effect of the pituitary on the ovary

Throughout the vertebrates the pituitary shares the control of reproduction with the gonads themselves and in mammals its secretions are of fundamental importance for all reproductive functions. Removal of the hypophysis prevents maturation of the gonads of young mammals and is followed by atrophy of those of an adult; conversely implants of anterior pituitary tissue cause precocious development of the gonads of immature animals.

The effect of injection of aqueous alkaline pituitary extracts into immature female rats is to cause ripening and development of many ovarian follicles, followed by their discharge and conversion to corpora lutea. Further analysis of the extracts has shown that separate fractions can be prepared (p. 528). The *follicle stimulating hormone* (FSH), soluble at any pH between 2·5 and 10, causes ripening and discharge of the follicles, but they are only converted to corpora lutea in the presence of a *luteinizing hormone* (LH), which is not soluble below pH 5·0. This connexion of the gonads with the pituitary is common to all vertebrates. Injections of mammalian anterior pituitary extracts have produced changes in the gonads of lampreys (Young and Bellerby, 1935) and ovulation in amphibians, whose eggs may thus be obtained out of season.

The secretions of the ovary influence those of the pituitary as well as vice versa. Methods of assaying quantities of FSH and LH are now well developed and have led to the discovery that injection of oestrogens decreases the amount of FSH released by the pituitary, while increasing the production of LH. This suggests a mechanism for the maintenance of cyclical oestrous and menstrual activity. Leaving aside for the moment the initiation of the first activity we can see that at the beginning of the follicular phase little oestrogen is being secreted and therefore much FSH. The latter causes maturation of follicles and hence production of oestrogen, which gradually cuts off the FSH and increases LH. Ultimately there is a cut off of progesterone (in the absence of pregnancy) and the cycle is completed.

This hypothesis is useful but it is still far from complete. In particular it must be remembered that the various secretions of the ovary and the products of the pituitary are probably derived from the same or similar cells. It may well be that the changes involved are in the quantities produced by each cell and that with further analysis we shall be able to understand the rhythm more fully. Other factors no doubt play a part in the cycle, in particular the adrenal cortical hormones. After the corpus luteum has been formed it is maintained by the action of oestrogens and the luteotropic hormone of the pituitary (prolactin).

14. Factors that control breeding seasons

The organization of the ovarian and pituitary secretions of mammals therefore ensures a cyclical hypertrophy of various tissues of the uterus and vagina, so timed as to allow fertilization to take place when the uterus is ready to receive the embryo. These cycles may go on regularly and continually throughout the reproductive life of the individual, as in the case of women. There are, however, two influences that intervene most powerfully in this rhythm in most mammals, namely, the seasons and the males. In nearly all animals there are one or more breeding seasons, during which complete cycles are produced. For instance, in Macaque monkeys menstrual cycles continue throughout the year, but for much of the time they occur without ovulation; only in a limited breeding season can conception occur. In many rodents oestrous cycles occur only at certain seasons and, as we have seen, in monoestrous species, such as the wild sheep, there may be only a single heat period in each year.

It is not known what factors in the environment produce these seasonal changes. Nutrition certainly plays a part, both by the total quantity of food taken and the presence of essential vitamins. Inadequate nourishment readily disturbs the menstrual cycles of women, and species that are monoestrous in nature become polyoestrous with the better food-supplies available in domestication.

It has often been suggested that change in the length of day is a factor responsible for producing the onset or regression of breeding, and this is certainly true in some mammals. The light probably acts by influencing the pituitary secretion and a special part of the optic tract carrying such impulses has been identified in the ferret. Seasonal breeding cannot depend only on such influences, however, since under conditions in which there is very little change in length of day, rainfall, or any other known factor, animals may show a sharply marked breeding season. For instance, fruit bats in the New Hebrides all become pregnant once a year, though their island is near the equator and shows a nearly constant rainfall, while they themselves live all day in dark caves with almost constant temperature. There is still much to be learned about the control of breeding seasons.

15. Influence of copulation on the female cycle

The influence of copulation on the female cycle is marked in some species. In the cat and the ferret follicles ripen spontaneously but only rupture if copulation occurs during oestrus. In the rabbit the follicles do not fully mature without copulation, which is therefore followed by ovulation some 10 hours later. Here the details of the process have been explored and it has been shown that stimulation of the nerves of the female genitalia sends nerve impulses via the spinal cord to the brain, where they cause the pituitary to produce follicle-stimulating hormone. It is not clear why this mechanism should be present only in some species; it has been suspected that something similar may occur in other mammals and it is obviously important to know whether it is present in man. Unfortunately we have no clear evidence on the point. It is certain that ovulation usually occurs spontaneously at about the middle of the cycle in a woman, but this does not prove that copulation is without influence in controlling the moment of ovulation near mid-cycle, or even at other parts of the cycle. Evidence from the few young human embryos that have been carefully investigated suggests that conception normally occurs near mid-cycle. Statistics of pregnancies following alleged isolated copulations show the middle of the cycle as the time of maximum fertility. They also suggest, however, that fertilization may exceptionally occur at other times and there is some other independent evidence for this (see Robson, 1947). It is thus probable that in man the normal time of conception is near mid-cycle and that ovulation is not induced by copulation. It is not yet demonstrated, however, that conception is impossible at other times, especially in cycles that are irregular.

XLII

THE DEVELOPMENT OF MAMMALS

1. Early development of the mouse

THE observations of Lewis and Wright (1935) provide more data about the fertilization and early development of the mouse than are available for other mammals. In the strain that they studied the average length of the oestrous cycles was about 9 days, dioestrus lasting 1–11 days, proestrus ½–1½ days, oestrus 1–3 days, and metoestrus 1–5 days. Search for ova in the tubes of animals killed at various periods showed that ovulation will occur spontaneously at some time during oestrus even in the absence of the male. There is, however, a connexion between ovulation and copulation because 'most females killed shortly after copulation at various parts of oestrus have (in the oviduct) freshly ovulated eggs'. It is still not certain whether this concurrence is due to the fact that the female will only accept the male near to the time of ovulation or to a stimulation of ovulation by copulation. The complexity of the stimuli necessary for completed mating is shown by the fact that some of the females would not mate throughout oestrus and yet many of these ovulated spontaneously.

The sperms pass rapidly up the oviduct and some have been found near its upper end 15 minutes after copulation. They probably remain mobile for less than 12 hours and the ova are only able to be fertilized within 6 hours after ovulation. The margin of time available for fertilization is therefore rather narrow, probably it usually occurs within 2 hours after copulation. The maturation divisions of the ovum also occur during the hours immediately after ovulation, the second division following fertilization.

The ovum itself at this stage is about 70 μ in diameter[1] and contains granules of various sorts, including yolk. There is, however, no recognizable animal pole, the nucleus lies near the centre of the ovum. The freshly ovulated ovum is surrounded by a number of follicle cells, *corona* or *cumulus cells*, which leave the ovary with it and serve to cement together all the ova ovulated from one ovary (Fig. 281). Within the corona cells lies a transparent membrane, the *zona pel-*

---

[1] Other mammalian ova are larger, 125 μ in the rabbit, 140 μ in man. There is no simple relationship between the sizes of the ovum and of the adult.

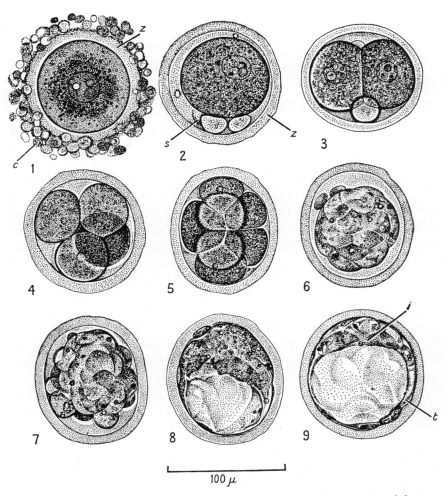

FIG. 281. Stages in early development of the egg of the mouse, recovered from Fallopian tubes and uterus at known times after ovulation and copulation. (After Lewis and Wright, 1935.)

1. Ovarian egg, obtained 7 to 10 hours after copulation in late-oestrus, surrounded by corona cells (c). Note accumulation of dark yolk about nucleus, two nucleoli, clear peripheral zone and fuzzy surface of zona (z). 2. Normal egg, 20 to $20\frac{1}{2}$ hours after copulation. Two polar bodies and sperm (s) in perivitelline space. Zygote nucleus somewhat diagrammatic. 3. 2-cell stage 24 hours after copulation. 4. 4-cell stage $44\frac{1}{2}$ hours after copulation. Nearly spherical cells each in contact with the other three by small contact areas. In this and subsequent figures only the nucleoli are seen. 5. 7 cells, 48 hours after copulation. 6. Morula from uterus, 72 hours after copulation. 7. Young blastocyst from uterus 82 hours after copulation, loosely arranged cells on surface. 8. Blastocyst formed from same specimen as fig. 6, kept for 4 hours *in vitro*. 9. Blastocyst 82 hours after copulation. Inner cell mass (i), trophoblast (t). Vitellus completely fills zona. Note large amount of fluid.

lucida (Fig. 281) inside which the ovum undergoes its development. The sperms have to penetrate the corona cells and their power to do so probably depends on the presence of the enzyme hyaluronidase in the ejaculate. Although one sperm alone enters each egg a considerable amount of semen is needed to make fertilization possible, the probability of effective fertilization by any one sperm is small, and this explains the fact that large numbers of sperms are produced. Even if a sperm collides with an ovum it is not certain that it will achieve fertilization. The sperm probably does not actively bore its way into the ovum but is engulfed by the latter by a complex process, perhaps resembling phagocytosis. After entry the sperm head rotates through 180° and the egg and sperm nuclei then fuse.

The process of fertilization thus provides the next generation with a set of chromosomes derived nearly equally from the two parents. The nucleoproteins of these chromosomes act as the main controlling agent for the subsequent life of the individual. Their characteristics determine the activity of each enzyme system and hence profoundly influence the use that is made of the materials available and the whole course of differentiation and subsequent life. The act of fertilization serves not only to bring the two sets of chromosomes together but also to initiate the complicated changes by which a new individual is produced (p. 599).

Cleavage takes place as the ova pass down the oviducts and by the time the embryo reaches the uterus, about 3 days after copulation, it has reached the early blastula stage and is composed of a hollow ball of cells, known as a *morula*. Cleavage is complete but not quite equal yet even at the morula stage the cells differ so little in size that no clear distinction of animal and vegetative poles is possible.

The total volume of the embryo has so far remained about that of the ovum but during the fourth to sixth days it swells, apparently by the secretion inwards of fluid. At this stage it is known as a *blastocyst*, a hollow sphere whose wall, the *trophoblast*, is thin over most of the circumference but thickened at one point, the *inner cell mass* (Fig. 281). The increase of diameter causes the embryo to press against the zona pellucida, which becomes thin and finally ruptures, liberating the embryo into the uterus.

Among the young embryos collected by Lewis and Wright from uterine tubes of mice many were abnormal in various ways, perhaps due to late fertilization during the period when the ova were in the borderland between potency and impotency. Lewis and Wright comment that 'the chances in man of late fertilization are probably greater than in unhampered animals and perhaps some of the abnormal human conception products are of this origin'. In amphibia delay in fertilization of the eggs produces striking aberrations in the sex ratio of the offspring and it is by no means impossible that deviations of this sort occur in mammals and especially in man, where there is no definitely fixed relation between the times of ovulation and copulation. Lowered fertility and small litter size as a result of late fertilization have been reported in various mammals.

The mouse embryo reaches the blastocyst stage, ready to implant

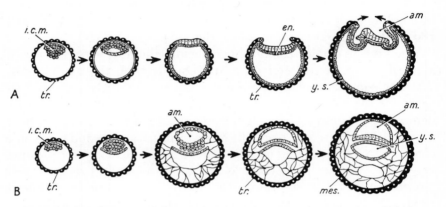

FIG. 282. Development of the amnion (*am.*) in mammals, A, in the rabbit by formation of folds; B, in man by hollowing out the inner cell mass (*i.c.m.*); *en.* endoderm; *mes.* primary mesenchyme; *tr.* trophoblast; *y.s.* yolk sack. (After Boyd and Hamilton in Marshall.)

in the uterus, about 6 or 7 days after fertilization. This time-interval is similar in a wide variety of mammals, irrespective of the length of the uterine tubes. Implantation occurs after about a week in the rabbit and human, as well as in the mouse. In the macaque it occurs a little later (ninth day), in the pig, dog, and cat after about 2 weeks. In deer, however, the blastocyst lies unattached in the uterus for several weeks and in the badger for as long as eight months. The embryos of rodents, primates, and carnivores remain spherical at this stage, but in the artiodactyl ruminants an extraordinarily rapid elongation occurs, the pig's blastocyst being nearly 30 cm. long by the time of implantation.

2. Gastrulation in mammals

Until the blastocyst stage the development of placental mammals consists of a cleavage not differing essentially from that of other vertebrates with little yolk, such as *Amphioxus*. The blastocyst stage itself and the subsequent stages of gastrulation are less easy to compare with those of lower vertebrates; moreover, they vary widely in different mammals. The inner cell mass is the definitive embryonic region, the remainder of the blastocyst wall constitutes the trophoblast or extra-embryonic ectoderm, whose function is to establish intimate relationship with the tissues of the mother.

The inner cell mass gives rise very early to endoderm and often to some precocious mesoderm. The endoderm-cells grow out in all directions from the edges of the embryonic disc formed by the inner cell mass and thus come to line the trophoblast, converting it into a *yolk sac*, though this contains no yolk. In some embryos, presumably of the more primitive mammals and including the insectivora and the rabbit, this endoderm may be in close contact with the trophoblast and the yolk sac is large (Fig. 282). In others scattered 'mesenchymal' cells separate endoderm and trophoblast, so that the yolk sac forms a small separate inner vesicle. This primary mesoderm early arranges itself to form inner and outer mesodermal sheets, with an extra-embryonic coelom between them (Fig. 283).

The relation of these changes to those that occur during the early gastrulation of other forms is obscure (p. 653). Presumably during evolution as the yolk has first increased and then decreased in amount the processes of gastrulation have become so changed that many aspects of them are no longer recognizably similar to those of amphibia. Possibly further work will show traces of the early morphogenetic movements that are seen in non-mammalian groups.

3. Embryonic membranes of mammals

From this stage onwards the mammalian development again shows recognizable similarity to that of reptiles and birds. The *amnion* is formed very early, either by the production of folds covering the embryonic disc (rabbit, Fig. 282), or as a hollowing out of the inner cell mass, without the formation of folds (man, Figs. 282 and 283).

The effect of the variations in early development is to produce embryos that appear at first sight to differ considerably. In those mammals that have departed less from the reptilian condition the appearance at this stage is very like that found in an animal with yolky eggs. The embryo is covered by amniotic folds of ectoderm and somatic mesoderm and rests on a relatively large (though empty) yolk sac. In the more modified types, such as man, at the corresponding stage the embryo itself is less developed and lies as a germinal disc between two sacs, an upper amniotic and a lower yolk sac (Fig. 283).

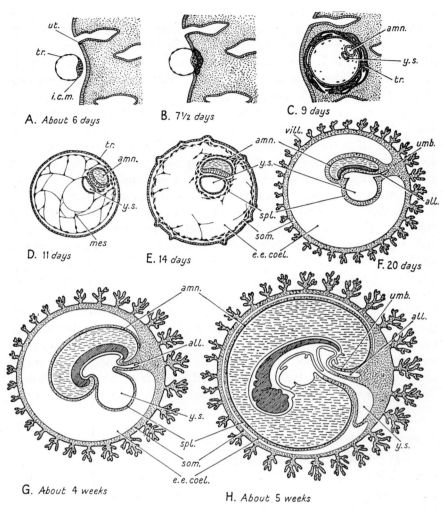

A. *About 6 days*   B. *7½ days*   C. *9 days*

D. *11 days*   E. *14 days*   F. *20 days*

G. *About 4 weeks*   H. *About 5 weeks*

FIG. 283. Early stages of development in man.

amn. amnion; *all.* allantoic diverticulum; *e.e.coel.* extra-embryonic coelom; *i.c.m.* inner cell mass; *mes.* primary mesoderm; *som.* somatopleur; *spl.* splanchnopleur; *tr.* trophoblast; *ut.* uterine epithelium; *umb.* umbilical stalk; *vill.* villi; *y.s.* yolk sac.
(Partly after Corner, Patten, and Arey.)

The latter is small and the main part of the chorionic sac is occupied by mesoderm and extra-embryonic coelom.

The differences are essentially quantitative and are concerned with the precocious development of the mesoderm, which is the means of communication between the outer trophoblast and the embryo itself. In the earlier mammals this communication is provided (as in reptiles and birds) when the *allantois* grows out into the extra-embryonic coelom. In other mammals mesoderm formation anticipates this outgrowth; the allantoic cavity itself then never becomes large and the embryo is connected with the trophoblast by a strand of mesoderm. This strand represents both the meeting points of the chorion and amnion and the outgrowing allantois of earlier forms (Fig. 285) and

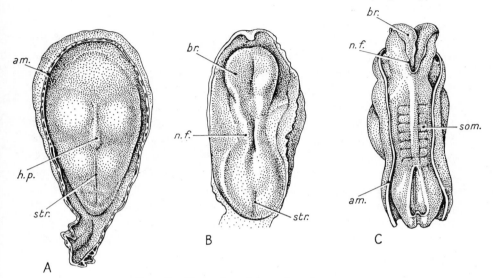

FIG. 284. Formation of the embryo in man.

A, 16 days, surface view of germ disc after removing the roof of the amniotic sac; B, 18 days; C, 20 days. *am.* cut edge of amnion; *br.* developing brain; *h.p.* head process; *n.f.* neural folds; *str.* primitive streak; *som.* somites.

(Partly after George W. Corner from models and specimens in the Carnegie Collection. *Ourselves Unborn.*)

it becomes the umbilical stalk. In both modes of development the amniotic cavity eventually becomes large and the fully formed embryo, attached by its umbilical stalk, floats in a fluid-filled sac. The amniotic wall consists of two layers, as in the chick, an inner true amnion and outer chorion (the original trophoblast), which when vascularized, forms the most important link between embryo and mother.

4. Formation of the embryo

The manner of development of the embryo is one of the most tantalizing parts of mammalian embryology (see Gladstone and Hamilton, 1941; Hertig and Rock, 1941; and Streeter, 1942 and 1945). We can discern enough to be sure that the processes are modified from those found in animals with yolky eggs, but almost no details are available of the actual morphogenetic movements in any mammal. The embryonic area ceases to be round and during the beginning of the third week of intra-uterine life in man (or second week in the rabbit) it can be seen at the bottom of the amniotic sac as an oval shield, consisting of ectoderm above and endoderm below. This shield can be compared with the blastoderm of a chick or reptile embryo and soon comes to show, towards its hind end, a primitive streak, provided with a primitive knot about the middle of the shield (Fig. 284). A head process appears as a thickening of the shield in front of the primitive knot, at about the sixteenth day in man.

These appearances suggest strongly that gastrulation and embryo formation proceed by morphogenetic movements resembling those of a reptilian ancestor (p. 643). We may suppose that material streams towards the middle line and passes in at the primitive streak, then forwards and outwards to form the notochord and mesoderm. The primitive groove is continued forward as a 'notochord canal', representing the 'chordamesoblastic canal' of reptiles. This canal may actually open into the yolk sac (as in man, Fig. 285). Grafts of the embryonic axis of rabbits are able to induce formation of neural tissue from the ectoderm of a chick. We may therefore assume that in mammals there is the same sequence of induction by invaginated material as in other vertebrates.

Mesoderm (sometimes called secondary mesoderm to distinguish it from the earlier formed 'mesenchyme') can be seen in connexion with the sides of the primitive streak, as would be expected if invagination is occurring. Everything suggests movements of this sort and the primitive streak moves backwards (extension) in man, just as in the chick, as the embryo forms in front of it (p. 648). Owing to the conditions of intra-uterine development it has not yet been possible to observe any of these processes directly and we must for the present be content with the study of whole embryos and sections prepared at various stages.

By the eighteenth day in man a distinct embryo with neural folds and somites can be seen in front of the primitive streak. The neural folds begin to close a little later, first at the mid-dorsal level and then progressively forwards and backwards (Fig. 284). Meanwhile head and tail folds appear as in reptiles and birds, constricting off the embryo from the yolk sac by a narrow yolk stalk. The heart forms as in lower vertebrates and the blood-system early becomes connected with a system of blood islands that is established in the yolk sac. A pair of omphaloidean arteries formed in the yolk stalk joins the paired

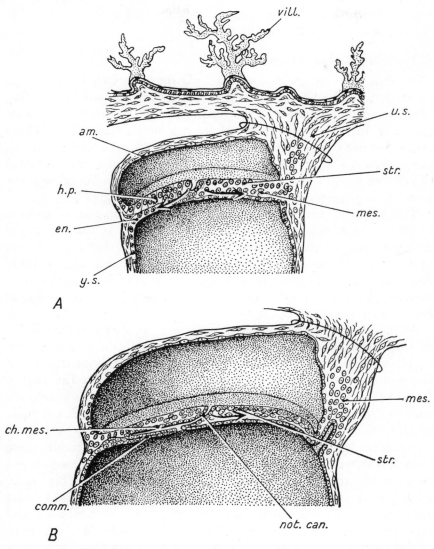

FIG. 285. Semi-diagrammatic views of human embryos cut in the sagittal plane.
A, about 16 days and B, a little later. *am.* amnion; *comm.* communication between notochordal
canal and yolk sac; *ch.mes.* chordamesoderm; *en.* endoderm; *h.p.* head process; *mes.* mesoderm (in B streaming into umbilical stalk); *not.can.* notochordal canal; *str.* primitive streak;
u.s. umbilical stalk; *vill.* villi; *y.s.* yolk sac. (Modified after Hamilton, Boyd, and Mossman.)

dorsal aortae, which arch round the pharynx as the first pair of branchial arches, joining the ventral aorta to the heart. This stage of a definitive embryo with beating heart is reached in the fourth week in man and after 10 days in the rabbit.

5. Implantation of the embryo

We can now return to consider how the embryo establishes the connexions with the mother that are characteristic of mammalian development. Preparation to receive the embryo begins before ovulation with the effect of oestrogens on the uterus (Ch. XLI). These cause increased development of the glands and muscles and an improved blood-supply. Preparation is continued in the progestational phase that follows, the glands becoming further developed and the arteries, in primates, approaching close to the surface (Fig. 279).

The means by which the implantation takes place, and its position in the uterus, varies greatly in different mammals. In the majority it occurs on the side away from the broad ligament that supports the uterus, and is hence said to be *antimesometrial*. In most the germinal disc itself lies on the inner or attached side, that is to say is also antimesometrial, but it may project outwards into the uterine cavity, as for instance in many rodents.

As the blastocyst grows it often lies free in the cavity of the uterus, its trophoblast in contact all over its surface with the endometrium. In other species the blastocyst remains attached only at the site of first contact, leaving a free surface projecting into the uterine cavity. In yet other types, including man, the whole blastocyst sinks into the endometrium and becomes surrounded by maternal tissues, the *interstitial* form of placentation (see Amoroso, 1952).

Whatever the means by which the first attachment is made, there soon develops an organ allowing for interchange between mother and foetus over part or all of the surface of the trophoblast. This organ, the *placenta*, thus consists of the intimately apposed or fused foetal and maternal tissues, which allow the interchange (see Huggett and Hammond, 1952). On the foetal side the extra-embryonic ectoderm of the trophoblast (chorion) is connected with the blood-stream of the embryo either by contact with the wall of the yolk-sac (*vitelline placenta*) or allantois (*allantoic placenta*). In the latter condition the outer covering is often known as the allanto-chorion and this name is used also when, as in man, the blood-vessels come from the precociously developed mesoderm of the allantois, although the cavity of the latter fails to develop. The events of early placentation in man have

recently become more clear, through the finding by Hertig and
Rock (1945) of an embryo about $7\frac{1}{2}$ days old, actually in process of
embedding (Fig. 286). The trophoblast in this specimen is greatly

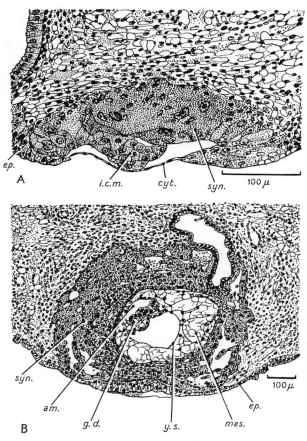

FIG. 286. Early stages of implantation in man.

A, Hertig-Rock embryo $7\frac{1}{2}$ days; B, $11\frac{1}{2}$ days. *am.* amnion; *cyt.* cytotrophoblast; *ep.* uterine
epithelium; *g.d.* germinal disc; *i.c.m.* inner cell mass; *mes.* primary mesoderm; *syn.*
syncytiotrophoblast; *y.s.* yolk sac. (After Hamilton, Boyd, and Mossman.)

thickened on one side and its cells are so active in division that cell-
boundaries are not reformed and a *syncytio-trophoblast* results. This
tissue, rapidly invading the uterine wall, has already destroyed the
maternal epithelium and is proliferating in the endometrium beneath.
The remainder of the surface of the blastocyst still projects into the
uterine cavity and consists of a relatively thin layer of *cytotrophoblast*.

Study of such a single stage does not, of course, show what has happened since the blastocyst entered the uterus, and we can only guess that the implantation has been produced by some action of the cells of the trophoblast on the uterine wall. It is not clear at what stage the mammalian embryo begins to draw nourishment from the mother, but it must be early, since the egg contains remarkably little yolk, less even than in other 'oligolecithal' eggs such as that of *Amphioxus*. Several days pass before the egg arrives in the uterus. Being presumably an actively metabolizing tissue it must soon be in need of supplies. It is probable that these are provided by the mother even before the blastocyst implants.

In man the blastocyst rapidly sinks into the endometrium and becomes surrounded on all sides. Although it is usual to ascribe this implantation to enzymatic invasion by the trophoblast it is possible that the uterine wall at this stage readily undergoes erosion on contact with any foreign object. In higher primates especially, the presence of the coiled arteries close to the endometrial surface gives the latter very peculiar properties; it may be regarded as an unstable system, ready to react. The '*decidual reaction*', a change of the endometrium produced by contact with an embryo, can be made to occur by mechanical stimulation of the progestational uterus by such objects as glass beads or suture threads. In other mammals the action of the trophoblast on the uterine tissues is less violent than in primates, but in all the blastocyst comes into contact with the uterine epithelium over part or the whole of its surface.

The reaction of the uterus to the embryo is therefore an important part of the mechanism of placentation, but the trophoblast itself is very active. This has been shown by planting fertilized mouse ova into the anterior chamber of the eye and watching their development (Runner, 1947). The trophoblast of this implant develops well for as much as three weeks, forming phagocytic trophoblastic giant cells, which penetrate the epithelia of the eye and produce extravasation of blood.

6. The yolk sac

The next phase to be considered is the establishment of special means of connexion between the trophoblast as an organ of interchange with the mother and the developing embryo itself. This seems to have been effected in the earliest mammals by means of the yolk sac, which is still the only organ responsible in most marsupials, and plays a large part during the earlier stages of development in placentals. We have seen how the endoderm early spreads out over the inner side of the trophoblast to make the yolk sac. This double wall forms the non-vascular yolk-sac placenta that occurs in marsupials and in the early stages of many placentals. Later the 'primary mesoderm' extends between the trophoblast and the endoderm. In this mesoderm the first blood-vessels develop; becoming connected with the omphaloidean arteries and veins they are able to carry nourishment back to the embryo. Obviously in mammals it is the outer covering of the yolk sac that is important rather than the inner endodermal layer that digests the yolk in a reptile or bird. Accordingly this outer trophoblastic layer becomes highly developed and folded into villi, while the endodermal sac becomes greatly reduced. In primates the yolk sac does not become applied to the outer wall of the trophoblast at all; when the yolk stalk is formed the sac remains only as a small dilatation at its distal end (Fig. 283). In the mammals that have a less developed placenta the yolk sac is a more important organ. In marsupials it forms the organ of interchange throughout the whole of the rather short intra-uterine life. In rodents the vascularization of the yolk sac proceeds only over about half of its surface and the remaining portion may become eroded away, leaving the yolk-sac cavity open to that of the uterus. The *inner* wall of the yolk sac may then become applied to the maternal endometrium, a condition known as *inverted yolk-sac placentation*. Yolk sacs that have opened in this way may be used directly as digestive organs for the absorption of material from the uterus.

7. Histotrophe and haemotrophe

The material for nourishment of the embryo (*embryotrophe*) is derived from two sources. The *histotrophe* includes secretions of the uterine glands and break-down products of the uterine mucosa and placenta, absorbed through the wall of the yolk sac. The *haemotrophe* is the nourishment supplied through the blood-stream. The secretion of the uterine glands is rich in fatty substances in many animals ('uterine milk'). This histotrophe probably provides an important source of nourishment in ruminants and other animals but is less important in man, where the association of foetal and maternal circulations soon becomes very close.

8. The allantois

The chief connexion between the absorbing surfaces and the embryo is provided not by the yolk sac but by the allantois. In reptiles and birds an outgrowth from the hind gut, covered by splanchnic mesoderm, provides a direct channel for the transport of oxygen to the foetus, besides fulfilling its primary function as a bladder for the storage of excretory products. In the early placental mammals, in addition to these two functions, it also serves to bring nourishment from the mother to the embryo. In most marsupials the allantois is a small sac growing out into the extra-embryonic coelom and forming no special contacts with the trophoblast. It presumably serves as a storage bladder. In the marsupial bandicoot (*Perameles*), however, it joins the chorion over a considerable area, villi being formed inter-digitating with those of the uterus.

This is essentially the arrangement in the placenta of the majority of eutherians. Insectivores, bats, artiodactyls, perissodactyls, and primitive primates, carnivores, cetaceans, and others all possess a medium or large allantoic bladder, filled with fluid, presumably excretory matter that cannot be returned to the mother across the placenta. In the horse and in artiodactyls crystals of calcium urate (*hippomanes*) occur in the fluid. These large allantoic sacs are found in the mammals in which the contact between embryonic trophoblast and maternal tissue is perhaps less close (p. 708). The allantois in these animals is thus in the condition found in reptiles, birds and marsupials, a sac lying in the extra-embryonic coelom, and its splanchnopleuric mesoderm vascularizes the chorion. Its arteries, the umbilical arteries, become the main source of blood for the placenta and its veins (allantoic or umbilical veins) drain into the right atrium.

In primates (except lemurs) and rodents, which have a haemochorial placenta, conditions are much modified by the reduction of the cavity of the allantois. Thus in man the mesoderm corresponding to the splanchnopleur of the allantois forms very early (Figs. 283 and 285). The allantoic cavity appears later as a small diverticulum extending from the hind gut into the strand of tissue that attaches the embryo to the trophoblast. It never becomes enlarged, presumably because the placenta serves from the earliest stages to carry away the excretory products, which it is well suited to do since few layers intervene between maternal and foetal circulations (p. 708). The portion of the allantois within the foetus becomes the bladder, and a cord, the *urachus*, connects this with the umbilicus and may contain a small allantoic cavity.

9. Villi and cotyledons

Correlated with these differences in the yolk sac and allantois are great differences in the mode of formation of villi by the trophoblast

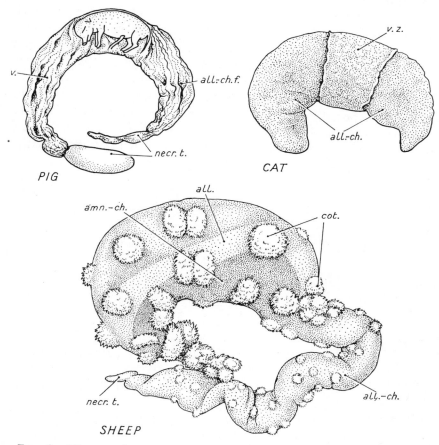

FIG. 287. Diagrams of some mammalian chorionic sacs showing differences in the distribution of villi.

all. allantois; *all.-ch.* allanto-chorion; *all.-ch.f.* allanto-chorionic folds; *amn.-ch.* amnio-chorion; *cot.* villi arranged in cotyledons; *necr.t.* necrotic tips of allanto-chorion; *v.* villi distributed diffusely on allanto-chorion; *v.z.* zone of villi. (After Amoroso in Marshall.)

and the contact of these with the uterine wall. It is not clear what morphogenetic processes are responsible for villus formation. At its simplest it seems to be merely a wrinkling of the surface of the combined chorion and allantois. Thus in the pig the very long blastocyst contracts, forming a number of wrinkles over the surface (Fig. 287).

A similar *diffuse placenta* is found in the horse and other perisso-dactyls. In the carnivores a much more complicated arrangement of villi is formed and they are restricted to a band around the centre of the embryo, hence *zonary placenta*. There are found intermediate conditions between the diffuse and zonary arrangements, and also between the latter and the condition known as *cotyledonary*, in which only certain parts of the placental zone of the allanto-chorion form villi. This is found in many ruminants (sheep and cow) though others may have a combined diffuse and cotyledonary placenta (Mexican deer, *Cervus mexicanus*) or even a purely diffuse one (*Moschus*, the musk deer). The position of the cotyledons is apparently determined by the presence of specially differentiated areas in the wall of the uterus. In the insectivores, bats, rodents, and primates the villi are at first found over the whole trophoblast but sooner or later become restricted to a limited area, producing a *discoidal placenta*.

TABLE I. *Placental types*

Types of placenta	Maternal uterine mucous membrane				Foetal chorion				Examples
	Maternal blood	Maternal endothelium	Maternal mesodermal connective tissue	Maternal epithelium	Foetal epithelium	Foetal mesodermal connective tissue	Foetal endothelium	Foetal blood	
Epithelio-chorial	+	+	+	+	+	+	+	+	Horse, pig, donkey
Syndesmo-chorial	+	+	+	–	+	+	+	+	Cow, sheep, goat
Endothelio-chorial	+	+	–	–	+	+	+	+	Dog, cat
Haemo-chorial	+	–	–	–	+	+	+	+	Primates, some rodents
Haemo-endothelial	+	–	–	–	–	–	+	+	Some rodents and rabbits

10. Types of placental union

More important than the distribution of the villi, which may be quite different in closely related forms, is their actual structure and the opportunities that they provide for interchange between mother and foetus. It has long been realized that the closeness of this connexion varies greatly in different mammalian orders. In some animals, such as the pig and horse, the chorionic villi are readily detached from the maternal tissues at parturition, so that no uterine material is lost. This is the *non-deciduate* condition, to be distinguished from the *deciduate* forms, in which some uterine tissues come away with the foetal membranes.

This is, however, a relatively gross way of classifying the conditions, which include various different arrangements of the foetal and

Foetal

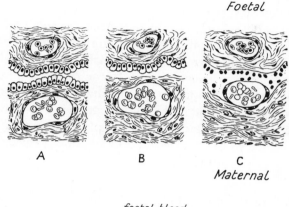

A   B   C

Maternal

foetal blood

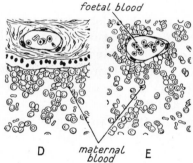

D   *maternal blood*   E

FIG. 288. Diagrams of the various types of placenta showing relations between foetal and maternal tissues.

A, Epithelio-chorial; B, syndesmo-chorial; C, endothelio-chorial; D, haemo-chorial; E, haemo-endothelial. (After Amoroso in Marshall.)

maternal tissues. The villi in all cases are tubular folds of the foetal chorion, having a core of foetal mesoderm, richly supplied with blood-vessels. These villi make branching structures of various forms, invading the maternal tissues in the area in which the placenta is developing. In the diffuse placenta of the sow and mare the epithelium of the villi is in contact with the maternal uterine epithelium and interchange must take place between foetal and maternal blood across all the intervening tissues, that is to say foetal endothelium, connective tissue and epithelium and maternal epithelium, connective tissue, and endothelium (Table I and Fig. 288). Such a type of placenta is known as *epithelio-chorial*. A similar condition is found in the lemurs. In many higher placentals, however, the intervening barrier is reduced by the erosive action of the foetal trophoblast on the uterine tissues. In the ruminants, such as cow and sheep, the maternal epithelium is removed in this way, producing the condition known as *syndesmo-chorial*. In carnivora the erosion goes farther, so that the villi are in contact with the maternal endothelium, hence, *endothelio-chorial*. In insectivores, rodents, bats, and higher primates the maternal endothelium is eroded so that the foetal villi are bathed in a lake of maternal blood, an arrangement known as *haemo-chorial*. In the rabbit and rat the chorionic epithelium itself disappears, producing a still closer relationship (*haemo-endothelial*). Although this classification is a most useful one it must not be applied too rigidly. Parts of a placenta may show different degrees of intimacy of connexion and in any one species the placenta may pass through various stages.

11. Efficiency of the placenta

It would seem from these histological facts that the placenta varies greatly in efficiency as an organ of interchange and there is some evidence that this is the case (see Huggett and Hammond, 1952). The closeness of foetal and maternal circulations is found to be approximately correlated with (1) the size of the molecules that can cross the barrier, (2) the rate of diffusion of ions, (3) the presence of a large allantois, (4) the amount of the histotrophe secreted by the uterine glands, (5) the richness of the colostrum, the secretion of the mammary glands immediately after birth before the flow of milk begins.

Studies with radioactive salts have shown that the rate of passage of sodium chloride across the placenta in milligrams per gram per minute is as follows:

Sow	0·03
Goat	0·41
Cat	0·69
Rat	8·30
Rabbit	6·80

This series agrees approximately with expectation based on the structure of the placentae. Yet it must be noted that the so-called 'less efficient' placentae may result in the production of very well developed and active young, for example we may contrast the foal with the newborn human baby. Attempts to decide the 'efficiency' of placentae of various types leads to much confusion and uncertainty. Nearly all the mammals that produce large and well-developed young have placentae of the allegedly less efficient type, with a large allantois.

12. Evolution of the placenta

It is equally difficult to correlate placental structure with our knowledge of the affinities of the mammalian orders based on other evidence. Common sense would suggest that the diffuse and epithelio-chorial type of placentation is primitive; but it is found among the most specialized mammalian orders. The insectivores, shown both by their anatomy and geological history to be an ancient group, are said to have discoidal haemo-chorial placentation! If our ideas of affinity were based on placentation alone we should include lemurs with 'ungulates', because their placentae are epithelio-chorial, and the conies (Hyracoidea) with the insectivores, primates, and other haemo-chorial types. A classification based on placentation would put the sloths among man's nearest relatives. It may be that such absurdities are the result of imperfect study and classification of placentae, and it is difficult to believe that the haemo-chorial placental type is the primitive one. Probably the earliest eutherians possessed epithelio-chorial placentae.

13. Metabolism of the placenta

In general the placenta allows the passage of substances of small molecular weight such as salts, sugars, urea, amino-acids, simple fats, and some vitamins and hormones, but not the larger molecules of proteins, nor red blood corpuscles or other cells. Small molecules pass more readily than larger ones, and this process resembles ultra-filtration. Changes on one side of the barrier usually lead to corresponding changes on the other but there may be persistent differences on the two sides that are difficult to explain by diffusion theory. Thus in some epithelio-chorial placentae the blood-sugar is higher on the foetal side.

Discrete particles and non-pathogenic bacteria never pass the placental barrier nor, in general, do antigenic proteins. Anti-bodies may do so, however, so that the foetus may acquire a passive immunity from the mother. In the rabbit it has been shown that the antibodies pass from mother to foetus through the lumen of the uterus and the yolk-sac splanchnopleur. It is not known whether this is the route in other species in which the foetus acquires passive immunity before birth. In ungulates there is no such transfer, the young being immunized a few hours after birth by the colostrum (Brambell et al., 1951).

In addition to acting as an organ of transfer the placenta has many other important biochemical properties, for instance it stores much glycogen. Various special types of cell develop in the placenta, presumably in connexion with these metabolic processes. The *decidual cells* are connective tissue-cells of the endometrium that become loaded with glycogen or lipoids. They are usually prominent early in pregnancy but are lacking altogether in some placentae. The giant cells, which may be mono- or multinuclear, develop from the trophoblast, their function is unknown but they may be phagocytic.

The placenta is also the seat of production of a surprising variety of hormones. The substances known as *chorionic gonadotropins*, which resemble pituitary hormones, are present in large quantities and are excreted in the urine during pregnancy, at least in some species. Their presence is the basis of a test for pregnancy in women. During the second month large amounts of a substance able to stimulate ovulation are excreted and the test consists of injecting urine samples into rabbits and later examining the ovaries. A recent modification uses the ovulation of the aquatic toad *Xenopus*. The placenta contains at least as much oestrogenic hormone per gram as does the ovary and probably secretes it into the maternal blood. If the ovaries are removed during pregnancy the secondary sex organs of the mother do not atrophy. Progesterone is also present in the placenta.

The placenta therefore contains a range of hormones even greater than that of the pituitary. Their significance for chemical signalling is not understood but it is reasonable to suppose that they interact with the hormones produced in the permanent ductless glands to ensure proper adjustment of metabolism during pregnancy; the placenta becomes a master gland overriding even the pituitary with a massive and integrated output of chemical signals.

14. Parturition

Parturition at the end of gestation is evidently a more serious matter in those mammals in which there is a close interfusion of foetal and maternal tissue than in the non-deciduate types in which the allantochorion simply comes away from contact with the uterine surface. It is still not clear exactly what stimulus initiates parturition. The posterior pituitary produces a secretion (*pitocin*) that has a powerful effect on the smooth muscle of the uterus, but during the earlier part of pregnancy some agent protects against its action. The effective stimulus to parturition is thus perhaps the withdrawal of this protection, allowing uterine contractions to begin. The progesterone secreted by the corpora lutea (and perhaps later by the placenta) may provide the inhibition. If a rabbit is made to ovulate by injection of pregnancy urine on the 25th day of pregnancy, birth does not occur normally on the 32nd day but is delayed until the 40th, when the induced corpora lutea degenerate. The villi of the human placenta are very rich in acetyl choline, which may play a part in stimulating the uterine musculature. Very complicated processes must be involved in the separation of foetal and maternal tissue, and in the healing of the latter where the placenta is deciduate.

XLIII

SEGMENTATION. DEVELOPMENT OF SKELETON, MUSCLES, AND COELOM

1. Segmental differentiation

AT the close of the period of gastrulation and neurulation a vertebrate embryo has become divided into a mosaic of differentiated fields. As a result of the stimuli from each other and from the environment the cells of different regions have come to show exaggeration of particular aspects of their metabolism, and they proceed to differentiate into many distinct tissues. The processes at work during development from this period onwards are so numerous and intricate that it is difficult to describe them coherently. Yet they show some degree of order because of the segmental plan underlying the organization of all vertebrates. Many of the parts are repeated in a rhythmical manner along the length of the body. This segmental plan is a legacy of the period when locomotion was fish-like, depending upon propagation of a wave of contraction along the body (Young, 1950, p. 127). The segmentation is therefore primarily a feature of the muscular system (the myotomes) though it has come to influence many other features of the body.

Development of the embryo consists of an elaborate set of interactions and during evolution it changes only very slowly. For example, the locomotion of a mammal no longer depends on a segmental series of muscles, yet development still follows a segmental plan. Segmental features can be recognized in the muscular, skeletal, vascular, and nervous systems. There are traces of them in the urino-genital system and in the pharynx. Even the complicated organs of the head are produced by modification of a segment-producing process. Part of the value of the study of comparative anatomy and embryology is that it helps to identify these and other underlying processes and hence to show the factors by which special organs are produced.

Nothing is known of the physiological processes underlying this repetitive or metameric characteristic of development. It may be that some dominant centre is formed at the front end of the body of the embryo and that an influence spreads from this in a rhythmical manner, but this is only one of several possible hypotheses to explain the segmentation. During the early stages differentiation of many organs proceeds in a cephalo-caudal direction; for example, in the somites and in the nervous system. Further investigation of this spreading rhythmical process might help to reveal the method by which the various types of cell and organ are produced.

There is, of course, no certainty that only one single process of segmentation is involved. Some workers believe that the serial repetition of the gill slits is distinct from that of the myotomes, yet the two sets largely correspond. It is more difficult to see a relationship between the segments that arise in the neuraxis ('neuromeres') and those of the mesoderm (see p. 770). Consideration of these difficulties is a valuable exercise in itself if it calls attention to the need for further knowledge about the morphogenetic processes that produce segmentation.

2. Differentiation of the mesoderm

In describing the further differentiation of the embryo it is impossible to follow simultaneously the changes taking place in all the various parts. We may logically begin by describing the further development of the mesodermal tissues and of the segmental structures to which they give rise. The conditions described will be those in the human embryo except where otherwise stated.

The greater part of the mesoderm differentiates from tissue that has been invaginated over the lips of the blastopore or the primitive streak. It comes to lie between the ectoderm and the endoderm, and the more lateral part proceeds to differentiate to form layers applied to the ectoderm on the outside and endoderm within, leaving a cavity, the coelom, between (Fig. 289). The coelom has a complicated shape, changing greatly as development proceeds. The walls are not of the same thickness throughout. In the dorsal region of the embryo they are thick, forming the *paraxial mesoderm*, lying on either side of the spinal cord. By migration of the cells this part of the mesoderm becomes divided into a series of similar blocks, the somites, which are the fundamental basis of the segmentation of the embryo (Fig. 290). Each somite consists, in the early stages, of thick walls of cells and a small cavity, the *myocoel*. As development proceeds the cells of the walls differentiate to form laterally the *dermatome* and medially the *myotome*. The cells of the dermatome spread out beneath the ectoderm to form part of the dermis. The cells of the myotome elongate in the main axis of the body and become the myoblasts, from which the axial muscles differentiate. From the medial parts of the myotomes, cells separate off to form the *sclerotomes* around the neural tube and noto-

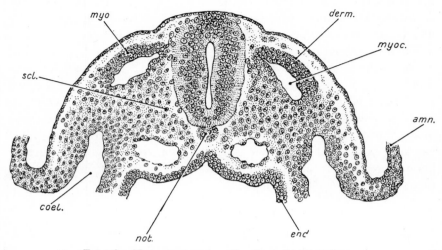

FIG. 289. Transverse section of a 16-somite pig embryo.

amn. amnion; *coel.* coelom; *derm.* dermatome; *end.* endoderm; *myo.* myotome; *myoc.* myocoel; *not.* notochord; *scl.* sclerotome. (After Patten.)

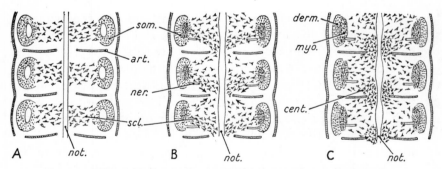

FIG. 290. Diagrams of stages in the differentiation of the somites in man.

A, Origin of sclerotomal cells (*scl.*) from somite (*som.*); B, the sclerotomal cells of neighbouring somites move together; C, they form the rudiment of the centrum (*cent.*). The remainder of the somite differentiates into dermatome and myotome; *art.* intersegmental artery; *derm.* dermatome; *myo.* myotome; *not.* notochord; *ner.* ventral nerve root.

(Modified after Hamilton *et al.*)

chord. This tissue gives rise to the skeletal tissues of the vertebral column and some of those of the skull (p. 723).

The myocoels soon become obliterated and they leave no traces in any adult vertebrate. Below the somites the mesoderm narrows to form a strand, the *intermediate mesoderm*, and this is joined to the *lateral plate mesoderm* of the ventral part of the embryo (Fig. 291).

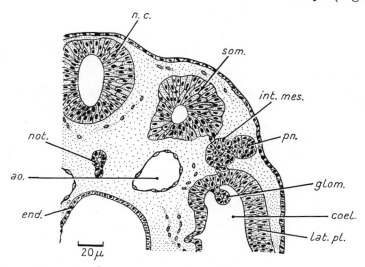

FIG. 291. Section through the 10th somite of a 14-somite human embryo.
ao. lateral dorsal aorta; *coel.* coelom; *end.* endoderm; *glom.* glomerulus; *int.mes.* intermediate mesoderm; *lat.pl.* lateral plate mesoderm; *n.c.* nerve cord; *not.* notochord; *pn.* pronephric duct; *som.* somite. (After Heuser and Hamilton, Boyd, and Mossman.)

The intermediate mesoderm gives rise later to the excretory system and gonads and its cavity becomes obliterated.

The somites extend from the level of the front end of the notochord all the way down the body. There are about forty-four of them in the human embryo (Fig. 292). They appear from in front backwards and a count of the number of somites thus provides a useful measure of the age of an embryo.

The three somites in front of the otic capsule give rise to the extrinsic muscles of the eyeball (see Gilbert, 1952). The first forms the superior, inferior, and medial recti, and the inferior oblique, the second the superior oblique, and the third the lateral rectus. The occipital somites immediately caudal to the otic capsule regress and form no muscles, but those of the hinder head region produce the intrinsic muscles of the tongue (p. 735). The somites of the trunk region give rise to the axial musculature and downward extensions form the muscles of the chest and abdominal walls and of the diaphragm. The thoracic muscles retain their original segmentation. The muscles of the fins of fish-like vertebrates were formed from extensions of the myotomes but in a mammal the limb muscles develop independently (p. 728).

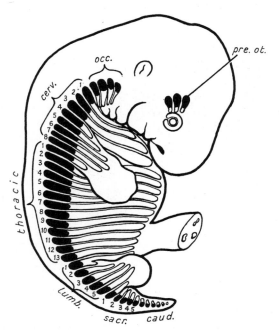

FIG. 292. Diagram of the myotomes of a human embryo. The blackened areas show the extent of the original mesodermal somites.

caud. caudal (regressing); *cerv.* cervical; *lumb.* lumbar; *occ.* occipital; *pre-ot.* pre-otic; *sacr.* sacral. (After Patten.)

The lateral plate mesoderm differentiates to make the mesothelial lining of the coelomic cavities of the adult. It therefore comes to consist of an outer layer, in contact with the ectoderm, the somatic layer, and an inner splanchnic layer covering the alimentary canal and other viscera. The lateral plate mesoderm is not segmented and the coelom at first forms a continuous cavity ending at the pericardium in front. The caudal limit of the coelom, in front of the pericardial cavity, is called the *septum transversum*. As the head fold develops and the embryo elongates the septum transversum comes to lie behind the heart instead of in front of it (Fig. 293). The connexion between the pericardium and the rest of the coelom remains as a pair of long *pericardio-peritoneal canals*. The developing lungs push into these canals, which thus become the *pleural cavities*. The communications between the pleural cavities and the pericardium and peritoneal cavities ultimately become closed.

The organs that lie in the coelom are supported above and below by folds of mesoderm (Fig. 294) and it is from these folds that the

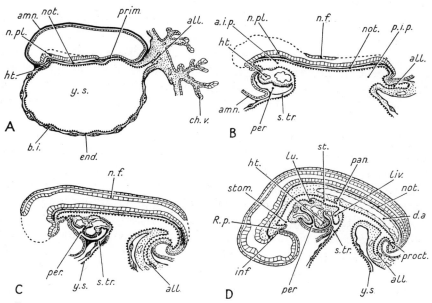

FIG. 293. Diagrams showing stages in the development of the neural tube and septum transversum in man.

a.i.p. anterior intestinal portal; *amn.* amnion; *all.* allantoic diverticulum; *b.i.* blood island; *ch.v.* chorionic villi; *d.a.* dorsal aorta; *end.* endoderm; *ht.* heart; *inf.* infundibulum; *liv.* liver; *lu.* lung; *n.f.* neural fold; *not.* notochord; *n.pl.* neural plate; *pan.* pancreas; *per.* pericardial cavity; *p.i.p.* posterior intestinal portal; *prim.* primitive streak; *proct.* proctodaeum; *R.p.* Rathke's pouch; *st.* stomach, *stom.* stomodaeum; *s.tr.* septum transversum; *y.s.* yolk sac. (Partly after Patten.)

mesenteries of the adult are formed. They serve to attach the organs to the body wall and for the passage of blood-vessels, lymphatics, and nerves. The lateral plate mesoderm of the somatopleur gives rise to little muscle in the trunk region but it has been held to contribute to the musculature of the abdominal wall. The muscles of the gut wall are derived from the splanchnic mesoderm.

The lateral plate mesoderm of the head region produces the musculature of the branchial arches of fishes. Some of this persists in mammals as the muscles of mastication, tensor tympani, facial muscles, muscles of the pharynx and larynx, and parts of the sternomastoid and trapezius. These muscles show their origin in the fact that they are innervated by nerves that can be identified developmentally as dorsal roots (e.g. the spinal accessory nerve). Derivatives of the myotomes are always innervated by ventral roots though afferent fibres may run in them.

3. Mesenchyme

The cells migrating from the medial aspect of the myotome to form the sclerotome are often said to consist of *mesenchyme*. This is a term used somewhat loosely to indicate the packing tissue of non-epithelial character that fills up the spaces between the developing organs. Mesenchyme is formed from the splanchnic and somatic mesoderm as well as from the somites, and in the head it may also arise from ectoderm (p. 733).

The cells of the mesenchyme of the young embryo are star-shaped and their processes make contact to give a loose network. Between the cells lies a jelly-like material, probably a muco-scleroprotein (p. 55). The mesenchymal cells have active powers of migration and the movements they make play a considerable part in determining the form of the organs. They may also become phagocytic. By differentiation the mesenchyme cells give rise to the cells of the skeletal, connective, and blood vascular systems. Some of them also form fat-cells and others the macrophages of the reticulo-endothelial system. They include the wandering macrophages (macrocytes) and fixed macrophages (histiocytes).

4. Development of the axial skeleton

The mesenchyme of the sclerotomes differentiates to form the rudiments of the vertebrae. These first appear as condensations of mesenchyme around the notochord. The main aggregations of cells come to lie opposite the intervals between the myotomes, contributions being made to each group from two segments (Fig. 290). These aggregations make the centra of the vertebral bodies; the intervertebral discs develop from the somewhat less concentrated cells opposite to each myotome. Cartilage soon begins to form in the centra and the rudiment of the notochord is there obliterated. It persists, however, in the intervertebral regions to produce the nucleus pulposus of the discs (p. 137). Meanwhile further condensations of mesenchyme have arisen dorsally and laterally to make the neural arches and transverse processes, which later join the centra.

The vertebrae form first as cartilaginous rudiments, which are later

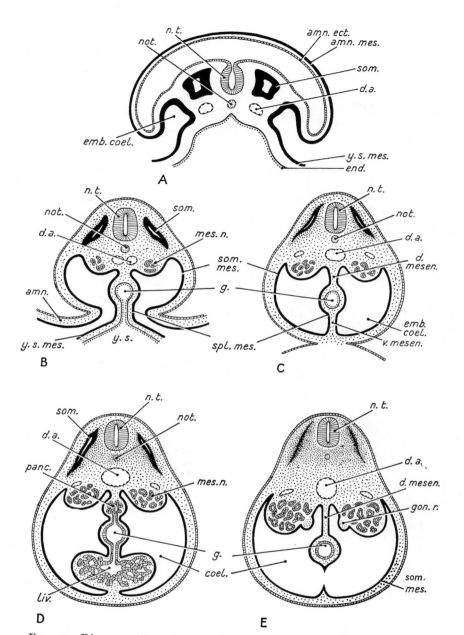

FIG. 294. Diagrammatic sections showing stages in closing off of the gut and formation of mesenteries in a mammal.

amn. amnion; *amn.ect.* amniotic ectoderm; *amn.mes.* amniotic mesoderm; *coel.* coelom; *d.a.* dorsal aorta; *d.mesen.* dorsal mesentery; *emb.coel.* embryonic coelom; *end.* endoderm; *g.* gut, *gon.r.* gonad ridge; *liv.* liver; *mes.n.* mesonephros; *n.t.* neural tube; *not.* notochord; *panc.* pancreas; *som.* somite; *som.mes.* somatic mesoderm; *spl.mes.* splanchnic mesoderm; *v.mesen.* ventral mesentery; *y.s.* yolk sac; *y.s.mes.* yolk sac mesoderm.
(Modified after Patten.)

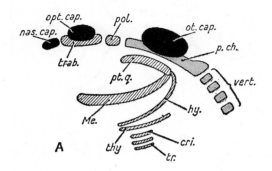

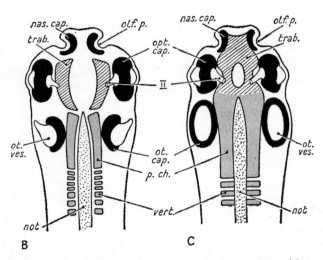

FIG. 295. The three sources of cartilage of the chondrocranium: (1) neurocranial capsules of the sense-organs (black); (2) branchial arches (crosshatched); (3) sclerotomal material (stippled).

A, Side view; B and C, dorsal views of an early and a later stage.

II. optic nerve; *cri.* cricoid; *hy.* hyoid; *Me.* Meckel's cartilage; *nas.cap.* nasal capsule; *not.* notochord; *olf.p.* olfactory pit; *opt.cap.* optic capsule; *ot.cap.* otic capsule; *ot.ves.* otic vesicle; *p.ch.* parachordal; *pol.* polar cartilage; *pt.q.* pterygoquadrate; *thy.* thyroid; *tr.* tracheal; *trab.* trabecula; *vert.* vertebrae.

replaced by endochondral bone (p. 70). The other elements of the axial skeleton also develop as condensations in mesenchyme, forming the ribs and sternum.

5. Segmentation of the head

The development of the skeleton of the head has been much modified during evolution to produce the special systems present there for the support of the sense organs, brain, and feeding apparatus (see p. 733). Nevertheless, the developmental processes at work are modifications of the fundamental segmental ones found in the rest of the body. Even in a mammal the head is essentially a segmented structure and this appears in its muscles, skeletal elements, and nerves. Added to these fundamental elements of the axial skeleton are the branchial or visceral arches, produced by modification of the processes that gave rise to the gill apparatus of earlier vertebrates.

6. The skull

The first outline of the skull is formed of cartilage, which may be regarded as produced by three sets of morphogenetic processes: (1) those that form cartilaginous capsules around the special sense organs; (2) the modified processes for the formation of the branchial arches; (3) those producing material corresponding to the sclerotomes (Fig. 295, see de Beer, 1937).

The material corresponding to the sclerotomes lies on either side of the notochord. In the occipital region it shows signs of segmentation but around the front of the notochord it forms a pair of unsegmented rods, the *parachordal cartilages*, which later join to make a parachordal plate. The segmented region of the head may be said to end at the front end of the notochord. The floor of the developing skull in front of this level is formed at first by a pair of rods known as the *trabeculae cranii*. There is reason to think that these and a pair of small polar cartilages represent the first of the series of visceral arches, lying in front of the mouth (p. 733). They become united with each other and with the parachordals, forming the front part of the floor of the neurocranium. The walls and roof appear somewhat later and the cartilaginous neurocranium is completed by the cartilage around the sense capsules (Figs. 296 on p. 724 and 297 on p. 725). The mesoderm around the olfactory pit forms the olfactory capsule, which soon fuses with the trabeculae. The optic capsule is little developed in mammals. It becomes the sclera, which is not cartilaginous. The mesoderm around the otic sac forms the otic capsule. This fuses with the

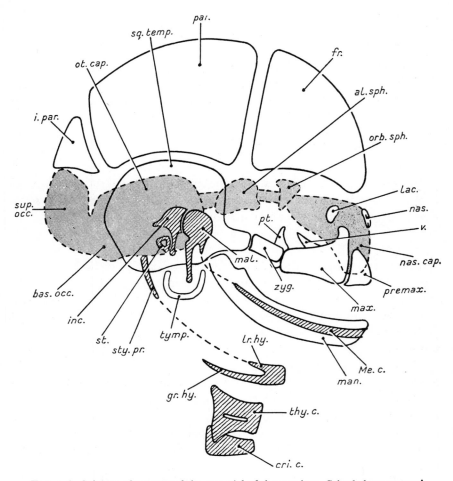

FIG. 296. Scheme of sources of the material of the cranium. Stippled areas: cartilaginous neurocranium, hatched areas: visceral arches, white areas: membrane bone.

al.sph. alisphenoid; *bas.occ.* basioccipital; *cri.c.* cricoid cartilage; *fr.* frontal; *gr.hy.* greater cornu of hyoid; *inc.* incus; *i.par.* inter parietal; *lac.* lacrimal; *lr.hy.* lesser cornu of hyoid; *mal.* malleus; *man.* mandible; *max.* maxilla; *Me.c.* Meckel's cartilage; *nas.* nasal; *nas.cap.* nasal capsule; *orb.sph.* orbito-sphenoid; *ot.cap.* otic capsule; *par.* parietal; *premax.* premaxilla; *pt.* pterygoid; *sq.temp.* squamous temporal; *st.* stapes; *sty.pr.* styloid process; *sup.occ.* supraoccipital; *thy.c.* thyroid cartilage; *tymp.* tympanic; *v.* vomer; *zyg.* zygomatic.

(After Hamilton, Boyd, and Mossman.)

parachordal plate, leaving, however, a gap, which becomes the jugular foramen.

The cartilaginous neurocranium gradually becomes converted into the bony skull, partly by the laying down of bone within the cartilage

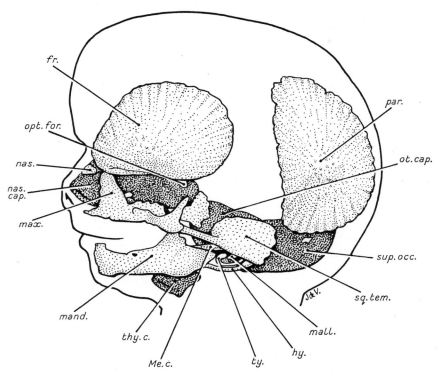

FIG. 297. Side view of skull of 80 mm. human embryo showing chondrocranium (darkly stippled) and membrane bones (lightly stippled).

fr. frontal; *hy.* hyoid cartilage; *mall.* malleus; *mand.* mandible; *max.* maxilla; *Me.c.* Meckel's cartilage; *nas.* nasal; *nas.cap.* nasal capsule; *opt.for.* optic foramen; *ot.cap.* otic capsule; *par.* parietal; *sq.tem.* squamous temporal; *sup.occ.* supra occipital; *thy.c.* thyroid cartilage; *ty.* tympanic. (After Hertwig.)

already formed (*endochondral bone*) and partly by the addition of *membrane bones* outside the original neurocranium (Fig. 297).

The bone first appears at numerous discrete centres, which then join up to make the definitive 'bones' of the adult skull. The membrane bones are the products of morphogenetic processes similar to those that form the scales of a fish. In the earliest land vertebrates the skull was therefore covered by a large number of small bones. As evolution has proceeded the number of dermal skull bones has become reduced, the rudiments fusing or being suppressed earlier and earlier in development. In mammals the adult skull consists of relatively few large bones; in man even these tend to fuse towards the end of life.

The skull grows in size mainly by the addition of new bone in the

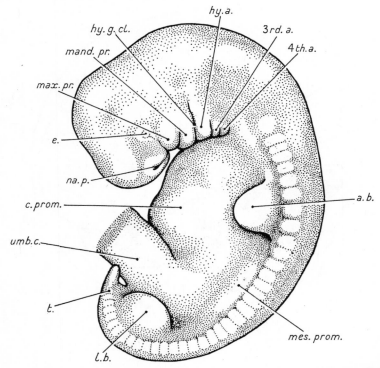

FIG. 298. Side view of human embryo five weeks after fertilization showing branchial arches.

3rd a. third arch; *4th a.* fourth arch; *a.b.* arm bud; *c.prom.* cardiac prominence; *e.* eye; *hy.a.* hyoid arch; *hy.g.cl.* hyoid gill cleft; *l.b.* leg bud; *mand.pr.* mandibular process; *max.pr.* maxillary process; *mes.prom.* mesonephric prominence; *na.p.* nasal pit; *t.* tail; *umb.c.* umbilical cord.

sutures but also by addition of material from the periosteum of the outer surface and its removal by osteoclastic action on the inside.

7. Branchial arches

The pharynx of all vertebrates is formed as a tube, whose walls show endodermal pouches and ectodermal gill clefts. It is 200 million years since the ancestors of the mammals respired by gills but embryological processes change only very slowly and the pharynx still develops on a plan based upon a series of branchial arches.

The *viscerocranium* consists of cartilaginous bars supporting the pharyngeal arches that separated the gill slits. These bars become partly ossified in the adult and are supplemented by membrane bones formed outside them (see Goodrich, 1930). The fishes from which land vertebrates are derived probably had seven gill slits and traces of these can be found in mammals (Fig. 298). The first slit has joined

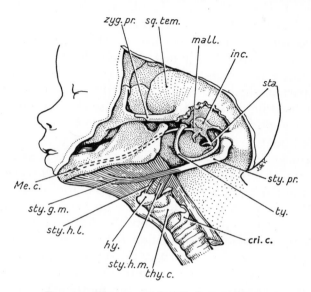

FIG. 299. The ear ossicles of a human foetus.

cri.c. cricoid cartilage; *hy.* hyoid; *inc.* incus; *mall.* malleus; *Me.c.* Meckel's cartilage; *sq.tem.* squamous temporal, *sta.* stapes; *sty.g.m.* styloglossus muscle; *sty.h.l.* stylohyoid ligament; *sty.h.m.* stylohyoid muscle; *sty.pr.* styloid process; *thy.c.* thyroid cartilage; *ty.* tympanic; *zyg.pr.* zygomatic process. (After Kollmann.)

the mouth; the second forms the hyoid gill cleft; and the remainder the branchial clefts. There are therefore six pharyngeal arches separating the pouches and clefts and the trabeculae cranii probably represent cartilaginous bars lying in front of the slit that has joined the mouth (p. 723).

The second cartilaginous bar of the whole series is thus that of the first or mandibular arch. Its upper portion grows forwards to form the *maxillary process*, the rudimentary upper jaw. The arch forms a sharp angle behind the mouth and its ventral portion again runs forward as the *mandibular process*, the rudimentary lower jaw. Each of these processes contains a cartilage, the pterygoquadrate bar in the upper and the Meckel's cartilage in the lower jaw. The jaws of the adult are formed by membrane bones developing outside these cartilages, the premaxilla (where present), maxilla, zygomatic, and squamous temporal above, and mandible (dentary) in the lower jaw (Fig. 297). The hinder portions of the cartilages of the first arch become incorporated in the ear (Fig. 299). The end of the pterygoquadrate ossifies to form the *incus* and of Meckel's cartilage to form the *malleus*.

The second of the original series of pharyngeal pouches, the spiracular or hyoidean, becomes the pharyngo-tympanic (Eustachian) tube, closed externally by the tympanic membrane (p. 510). It is reckoned as the first of the series of apparent pharyngeal pouches, excluding the slit that has joined the mouth. The second (hyoid) pharyngeal arch, lying behind this pouch, contains *Reichert's cartilage*, the upper part of which forms the third of the chain of ear ossicles, the *stapes*. The middle portion of this arch ossifies as the *styloid process* and its ventral portion becomes the *lesser cornu* and part of the body of the hyoid bone.

The cartilages of the 3rd branchial arches fuse with those of the ventral part of that of the 2nd and become the *greater cornua* and part of the body of the hyoid bone. The cartilages of the 4th and 5th arches form the *thyroid cartilage* and that of the 6th the *cricoid*. The remaining cartilages of the larynx are probably also derived from these hinder arches. There is no sharp distinction between the cartilages of the larynx and of the trachea. The latter develops as an outpushing from the pharynx (p. 736) and the formation of cartilages in its walls is the result of an extension backwards of the morphogenetic process by which the branchial arch cartilages are produced.

8. Development of the limbs and their skeleton

The paired fins of fishes, from which the limbs have evolved, were folds of the body-wall, containing a segmental series of radial cartilages, muscles, and nerves (p. 152). In the course of their change into limbs the base became narrowed and the segmental structure less obvious. The earliest limb-buds of a mammal are lateral folds with a broad base and they are not unlike fins (Fig. 298). The cranial or pre-axial borders become the pollex and hallux. The adult position of the limbs is reached by flexures at the joints (p. 152). The segmental nature of the limbs is shown by the fact that each is supplied by a series of nerves, the more cephalad of which innervate the preaxial borders (p. 152).

The development of the skeleton of the limbs of a mammal shows no trace of segmental origin (unless it be in repetition of the digits) and the limb muscles do not develop in continuity with the myotomes.

The bones of the girdles and limbs are all endochondral in origin, except the clavicle, which is a membrane bone.

9. Factors controlling development of the skeleton

The differentiation of the mesenchyme cells before they 'condense' to form the rudiments of a cartilage must be the result of some evocator action. Jacobson and Fell have shown that in the chick the cells below the epithelium of the lower jaw are already determined at the third day and that they will produce the cartilage if they are transplanted.

Soon after this evocation has occurred the tissues of each part become self-determining. This is well shown by transplantation of portions of limb-buds of the chick, which will produce whole isolated bones (p. 76). The general outline of the shape of the bones is therefore determined by the hereditary information, after appropriate evocator action. The detailed form depends upon the strains that are later placed upon the bone (p. 99), 'double dependence' (see p. 22). The muscles, bones, joints, and ligaments only maintain an effective functional state when they are provided with appropriate stimulation by the environment.

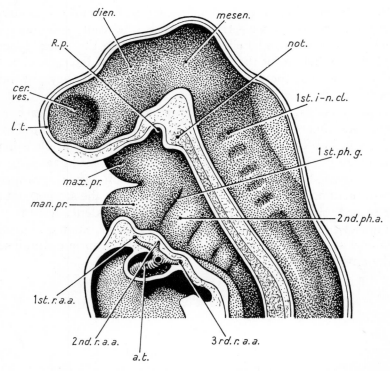

F IG. 300. Diagram of sagittal section of head and pharynx of human embryo.

a.t. aortic trunk; *cer.ves.* cerebral vesicle; *dien.* diencephalon; *1st i-n.cl.* first inter-neuromeric cleft; *l.t.* lamina terminalis; *man.pr.* mandibular process; *max.pr.* maxillary process; *mesen.* mesencephalon; *not.* notochord; *2nd ph.a.* second pharyngeal arch; *1st ph.g.* first pharyngeal groove; *1st (2nd and 3rd) r.a.a.* first (second and third) right aortic arch; *R.p.* Rathke's pouch. (Modified after His.)

XLIV

DEVELOPMENT OF THE GUT AND RESPIRATORY SYSTEM

1. Origin of the Gut

THE tubular gut is first formed from the endoderm of the yolk sac when the embryonic disc is lifted up by head and tail folds (Fig. 293). In this way head- and tail-guts become delimited, communicating by the anterior and posterior intestinal portals with the region that will form the rest of the gut. The latter is at first widely open to the yolk sac but the stalk gradually narrows and the embryonic and extra-embryonic regions become sharply separated. The gut is conventionally divided into fore-, mid-, and hind-guts. The first includes the mouth, pharynx, oesophagus, and stomach. The mid-gut includes the whole small intestine, and the hind-gut the large intestine and rectum.

The whole gut is lined by endoderm, covered with splanchnic mesoderm. By the formation of buds and pouches the endoderm gives rise to the various glands attached to the gut, and to the lungs. The splanchnic mesoderm produces the muscular coats of these organs and their mesothelial coverings (pleura and peritoneum). The gut and organs derived from it mostly lie in coelomic spaces, the pleural and peritoneal cavities. In the pharyngeal region no coelomic space is present.

2. Stomodaeum

The head-gut ends anteriorly in the bucco-pharyngeal membrane. Where this comes into contact with the ectoderm the latter forms a pit, the stomodaeum (Fig. 293), from the roof of which a diverticulum, *Rathke's pouch*, grows towards the floor of the brain. It has the effect of inducing a down-growth of the latter, the *infundibulum*, and from the two together the pituitary body develops (p. 552).

The buccopharyngeal membrane breaks down early in development and thereafter there is no sharp dividing line between the ectoderm and endoderm of the mouth. This leads to uncertainty as to the layer from which structures in the mouth are derived.

3. Nasal cavities

These first appear as thickenings of the ectoderm, the *nasal placodes* (Fig. 301), which then sink in to form *olfactory pits*, with rather large

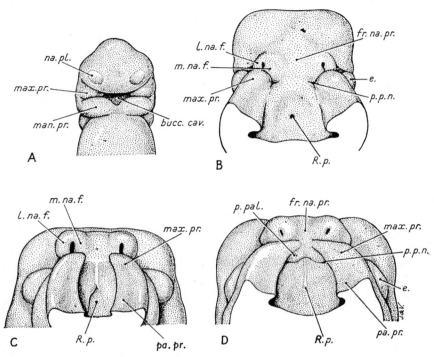

FIG. 301. Diagrams showing stages in the development of the mouth and nose. *bucc.cav.* buccal cavity; *e.* eye; *fr.na.pr.* fronto-nasal process; *l.na.f.* lateral nasal fold; *man.pr.* mandibular process; *max.pr.* maxillary process; *m.na.f.* median nasal fold; *na.pl.* nasal placode; *pa.pr.* palatal process; *p.pal.* primitive palate; *p.p.n.* primitive posterior nares; *R.p.* Rathke's pouch.

slit-like openings, lying just above the mouth. The maxillary processes, developing from the first pharyngeal arches, grow forward and medially below the openings of the olfactory pits, which become the anterior (external) *nares*. The posterior (internal) nares form as passages between the olfactory sac and the oral cavity. The *palate* forms by a backward growth from the region between the olfactory pits, the fronto-nasal process, together with medial maxillary palatal processes. The posterior nares thus come to open farther and farther back and the hard and soft palates are formed.

The whole of the nasal cavity is produced by expansion of the olfactory pits, but the nasal placodes form only the olfactory epithelium of the upper regions (p. 521). The *paranasal sinuses* of the maxilla, frontal, ethmoid, and sphenoid bones develop as pouches of the wall of the nasal cavity.

4. Mouth and pharynx

The tissue around the pharynx soon shows condensations that are the rudiments of the branchial (pharyngeal) cartilaginous arches. This

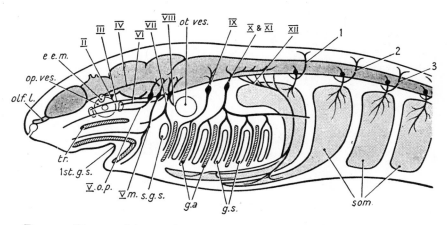

FIG. 302. Diagram of the anterior end of an early vertebrate showing the branchial arches and their nerves.

Cranial nerves: II, optic; III, oculomotor; IV, trochlear; *Vm.* trigeminal, maxillo-mandibular; *V.o.p.* trigeminal ophthalmic; VI, abducent; VII, facial; VIII, acoustic; IX, glossopharyngeal; X and XI, vagus and accessory; XII. hypoglossal; *1–3*, spinal nerves; *e.e.m.* extrinsic eye muscles; *g.a.* gill arch; *g.s.* gill slit; *olf.l.* olfactory lobe; *op.ves.* optic vesicle; *ot.ves.* otic vesicle; *s.g.s.* spiracular gill slit; *som.* somite; *tr.* trabecula.

tissue is usually referred to as mesoderm but it is formed by migration downwards of material of the neural crest (p. 769). The differentiation of this material to form cartilage presumably depends upon the position in which it finds itself rather than on its origin.

The pharyngeal arches are separated by depressions of the ectoderm and by grooves of the endoderm of the pharynx (Fig. 300) but in man these never meet to form open gill slits. Each pharyngeal arch contains, besides its cartilage, some lateral plate musculature, one of the aortic branchial arches and branches of the corresponding segmental cranial nerve. Thus the trigeminal is the main nerve of the first arch, the facial of the second, glossopharyngeal of the third, and vagus branches of the remaining arches.

The first pharyngeal pouch of the whole series is probably represented by a gill slit in front of the first pharyngeal arch that becomes incorporated in the sides of the mouth (Fig. 302). The first of the actual series, that can be seen in the human embryo lies between the maxillo-mandibular and hyoid arches (Fig. 300). It becomes the *pharyngo-tympanic (Eustachian) tube* and the corresponding ecto-dermal cleft becomes the *external auditory meatus*. The *tympanic membrane* is thus covered on its outer side by ectoderm and inner side by endoderm, while its centre contains part of the mesoderm sur-

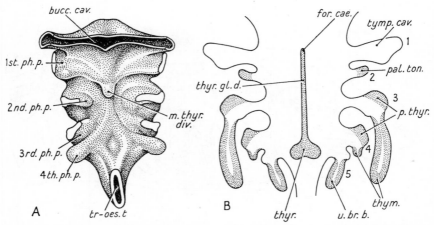

FIG. 303. A, Pharyngeal endoderm of 4 mm. human embryo; B, Diagram of pharynx of 10 mm. embryo to show the fates of its parts.

bucc.cav. buccal cavity; *for.cae.* foramen caecum; *m.thyr.div.* median thyroid diverticulum; *pal.ton.* palatal tonsil; (*1st, 2nd, 3rd, 4th*) *ph.p.* (first, second, third, and fourth) pharyngeal pouch, *p.thyr.* parathyroid; *thym.* thymus; *thyr.* thyroid; *thyr.gl.d.* thyroglossal duct; *tr-oes.t.* tracheo-oesophageal tube; *tymp.cav.* tympanic cavity; *u.br.b.* ultimobranchial body. (After Weller.)

rounding the pharynx. As development proceeds the tympanic cavity comes into relation with the structures of the inner ear that have differentiated from a separately invaginated ectodermal sac, the *otocyst*.

The second of the actual pharyngeal pouches becomes invaded by mesoderm, which differentiates into the lymphoid tissue of the *tonsil* (p. 265). The wall of the third pharyngeal pouch becomes thickened and part of it and of the fourth pouch differentiates to make the *thymus* (Fig. 303, p. 535), the remainder forms the first of the pairs of *parathyroid glands* (p 534). The second pair is formed from the walls of the fourth pharyngeal pouch, with perhaps a contribution from the fifth and last pouch, which is shallow and transient.

The floor of the mouth and pharynx gives rise to the tongue, the salivary glands, and thyroid gland. The *tongue* is formed in the central

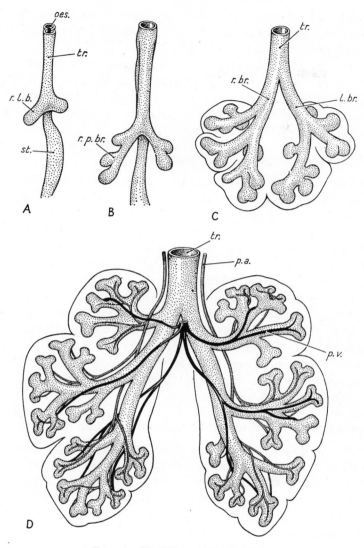

FIG. 304. Development of the lungs.

l.br. left bronchus; *oes.* oesophagus; *p.a.* pulmonary artery; *p.v.* pulmonary vein; *r.br.* right
bronchus; *r.l.b.* right lung bud; *r.p.br.* right primary bronchus; *st.* stomach; *tr.* trachea.
(After Patten.)

line of the mid-ventral portions of the mandibular, hyoid, and second
pharyngeal arches. The greater part of its musculature is derived by
ventral migration of three or more of the occipital myotomes and this
explains the course of the hypoglossal nerve, representing the ventral
roots of that region. The tongue is therefore covered with pharyngeal

endoderm and contains branchial mesoderm from these arches, as well as somitic mesoderm. Accordingly it receives nerves from several dorsal and ventral roots (V, VII, IX, X, and XII).

The *thyroid gland* develops as a thickening of the floor of the pharynx near its front end. This outgrowth elongates, making the thyroglossal duct, with the gland as a swelling on its lower end. There may possibly be a contribution to the gland from the wall of the fourth pharyngeal pouch (see Boyd, 1950).

5. Development of the trachea and lungs

The first rudiment of the respiratory apparatus appears very early as a groove in the floor of the pharynx, which deepens and finally closes over to separate the larynx from the oesophagus. The caudal end of the groove then divides into two diverticula, the *lung-buds*, which grow backwards into the pericardio-peritoneal canals (Fig. 304). The resulting endodermal tubes, the bronchi, then divide as many as eighteen times to form the adult bronchial tree. The splanchnic mesoderm covering the outgrowing lung-buds gives rise to the cartilage of the tracheal rings and to the musculature and connective tissue of the lungs. The epithelium lining the bronchial tree is cuboidal and ciliated during foetal life. At birth, when air enters the lungs, the terminal portions of the bronchi expand to form the alveoli (p. 301). The epithelium ceases to be cuboidal and becomes very thin in the adult lung (p. 302).

6. Development of the oesophagus, stomach, and duodenum

The oesophagus lies embedded in splanchnic mesoderm but is not surrounded by a coelomic space and therefore has no mesentery. Its endodermal lining is at first columnar and ciliated but later becomes stratified and squamous. It is not known whether this is a change in the oesophageal epithelium itself or whether squamous cells migrate from the epithelium of the mouth.

The stomach is at first a spindle-shaped tube but its wall expands faster on the left than on the right, so that it soon comes to have greater and lesser curvatures (Fig. 305). The dorsal mesentery (dorsal mesogastrium) is attached to the greater curvature and comes to form a sac-like fold, the *greater omentum*, allowing the stomach to expand (Fig. 306). This fold thus lies on the left side and contains a cavity the *lesser sac*, opening on the right side to the general peritoneal cavity, *greater sac*. The ventral mesogastrium is attached to the transverse septum, which contains the developing liver. It becomes the *gastro-*

hepatic (*lesser*) *omentum* and the portion between the liver and the ventral body-wall forms the *falciform ligament*. The rest of the ventral mesentery disappears.

The duodenum elongates to make a loop, suspended in a mesentery so short that the caudal portion of the duodenum is fixed to the body-

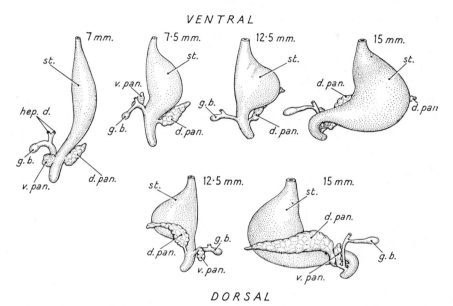

FIG. 305. Diagrams showing the development of the stomach of man.
d.pan. dorsal pancreas; *g.b.* gall-bladder; *hep.d.* hepatic ducts; *st.* stomach; *v.pan.* ventral pancreas. (After Pernkopf, *Zeits. f. Anat. u. Ent.* **64,** 1922.)

wall behind a sheet of mesothelium and is therefore said to be retro-peritoneal.

The *liver* develops as a bud from the duodenum, extending into the ventral mesentery and septum transversum. The cavity of the original diverticulum remains as the *bile-duct*, which runs along the free caudal edge of the lesser omentum (Fig. 306).

The *pancreas* in man arises from the duodenum as two buds, a dorsal and a ventral, the former lies cranial to the hepatic diverticulum, the latter opens with it. The two portions later fuse and their ducts usually join forming a single tube, opening with the bile-duct into the duodenum.

7. Derivation of mid- and hind-gut

The intestine caudal to the duodenum develops from the mid-gut. At first it is a short tube but quickly grows in length and forms loops (Fig. 306). The dorsal mesentery also grows but remains fixed to the posterior abdominal wall by two strong ligaments (retention bands).

The hind-gut gives rise to the lower part of the colon, the rectum, and upper part of the anal canal. The terminal portion at first consists of a single chamber, the *cloaca*, into which open the hind-gut, the common excretory duct (p. 742), and the allantois (p. 705), whose proximal portion becomes expanded to make the bladder. The *urorectal septum* then divides this into a dorsal *rectum* and ventral *urogenital sinus*. The rectum is at first closed by an anal membrane and opposite this there develops an ectodermal depression, the *proctodaeum*. The anal membrane breaks down and the terminal portion of the anal canal is formed by the ectoderm of the proctodaeum.

8. Differentiation in the wall of the gut

The lining of the gut and its derivatives provide a set of cells specialized to respond to the presence of food substances in such a way that the latter are broken down and absorbed. These special developments of the digestive powers that are present in all living cells have become more and more marked in the course of evolution. In the lampreys, which are not far from the ancestry of all vertebrates, there is no stomach and the cells that produce trypsin and insulin are still partly incorporated in the wall of the intestine (p. 241). Presumably as evolution has proceeded the part of the hereditary system that ensures that cells shall digest has become modified in such a way that the various special digestive organs are formed during development. Nothing is known of the underlying developmental processes by which the parts of the gut and its glands acquire their particular characters. There must be a system of evocators and responses by which the stomach develops peptic and enzymic cells, the duodenum, Brunner's glands, the pancreas its acini and islets and so on. Probably these differentiations result from quantitative differences in a single set of processes. When we come to understand them further we should be better able to control digestive activities in health and disease. Comparative anatomy and embryology should provide clues as to the common factors that underlie the activity of the many different parts of the gut.

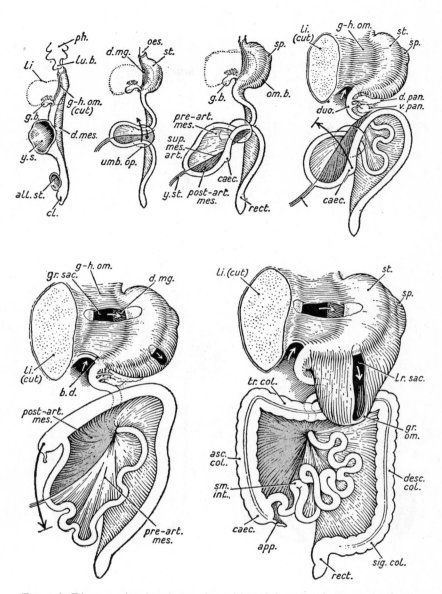

FIG. 306. Diagrams showing changes in position of the gut and mesenteries during development.

all.st. allantoic stalk; *app.* appendix; *asc.col.* ascending colon; *b.d.* bile duct; *caec.* caecum; *cl.* cloaca; *desc.col.* descending colon; *d.mes.* dorsal mesentery; *d.mg.* dorsal mesogastrium; *d.pan.* dorsal pancreas; *duo.* duodenum; *g.b.* gall bladder; *g-h.om.* gastrohepatic omentum; *gr.om.* greater omentum; *gr. sac.* greater sac; *li.* liver (in outline); *li. (cut).* liver (cut surface); *lu.b.* lung bud; *lr.sac.* lesser sac; *oes.* oesophagus; *om.b.* omental bursa; *ph.* pharynx; *post-art.mes.* post-arterial mesentery; *pre-art.mes.* pre-arterial mesentery; *rect.* rectum; *sig.col.* sigmoid colon; *sm.int.* small intestine; *sp.* spleen; *st.* stomach; *sup.mes.art.* superior mesenteric artery; *tr.col.* transverse colon; *umb.op.* umbilical opening; *v.pan.* ventral pancreas; *y.s.* yolk sac; *y.st.* yolk stalk.

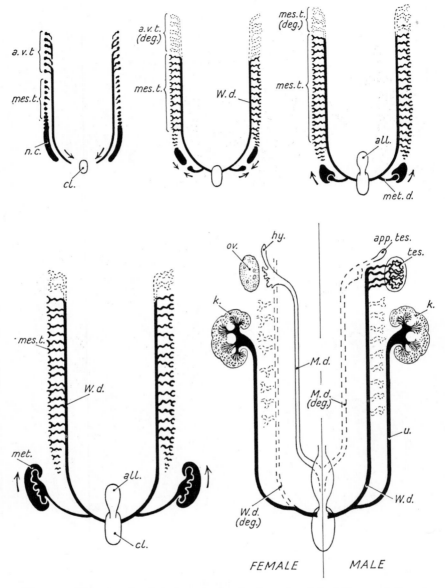

Fig. 307. Diagrams showing stages in the development of the kidney and ducts
of the urino-genital system in a male and female mammal.

all. allantois; *app.tes.* appendicular testis; *a.v.t.* anterior vestigial tubules; *a.v.t.(deg.).*
anterior vestigial tubules (degenerated); *cl.* cloaca; *hy.* hydatis; *k.* kidney; *M.d.* Mullerian
duct; *M.d.(deg.).* Mullerian duct (degenerated); *mes.t.* mesonephric tubules; *mes.t.(deg.).*
mesonephric tubules (degenerated); *met.* metanephros; *met.d.* metanephric duct; *n.c.*
nephrogenic cord; *ov.* ovary; *tes.* testis; *u.* ureter; *W.d.* Wolffian duct; *W.d.(deg.).* Wolffian
duct (degenerated). (From data supplied by Dr. E. A. Fraser.)

XLV

DEVELOPMENT OF THE UROGENITAL SYSTEM

1. The coelom and genital and excretory ducts

THE urinary and genital systems are derived from the intermediate mesoderm and adjacent coelomic wall and they show considerable traces of segmental origin. The excretory system in particular develops as a series of organs, the pro-, meso-, and metanephros, arising in that order along the length of the body (see Fraser, 1950).

The intermediate mesoderm forms a solid cord of cells, joining the somites to the dorsal wall of the coelom (Fig. 291). In many vertebrates it contains cavities opening by a series of funnels to the coelom. The fundamental method of excretion was thus to allow escape of coelomic fluid and this or a similar channel also provided for escape of the genital products. In mammals this situation no longer exists, no open nephric funnels remain, and the urinary and genital systems are mainly separate in the adult. Nevertheless we see in this, as in other systems, signs of the conservatism of organisms. In mammals the kidney develops as it did in earlier vertebrates by the formation of pro-, meso-, and metanephros.

In lampreys the genital products of both sexes are shed into the main coelomic cavity and this is still the condition in the female mammal. The coelomic cavity can indeed be regarded as the much expanded genital sac (see Goodrich, 1935). The system of nephric funnels and ducts may have served to carry away genital products before it became excretory. In modern mammals derivatives of the mesonephros, the Wolffian ducts, provide for the transmission of the genital products in the male and in the female this function is performed by a funnel and tube, the Mullerian ducts, which develop nearby.

Both the Wolffian and the Mullerian systems of ducts make their appearance during development in every individual irrespective of sex, and it is only at a relatively late stage that one or the other becomes definitively developed as a result of the influence of the hormones proceeding from the developing gonad. The gonad itself is at first of bisexual nature but the particular combination of X and Y chromosomes then ensures that either an ovary or a testis develops (p. 744).

The secretions of the gonad in turn produce further development of either the Wolffian or the Mullerian duct. Castration can be performed *in utero* and it is then found that male embryos become feminized; the Wolffian duct system fails to develop but the Mullerian system continues. Female castrates, however, develop nearly normally. The hereditary make-up of the tissues thus ensures development of female characteristics in the ducts and derivatives of the urinogenital sinus. The effect of male hormones is to suppress the female and promote the male tendencies, but probably female hormones play little part at this stage of development. In birds the situation is reversed and this is perhaps correlated with the fact that the female is hetero-gametic (XY) in birds, the male in mammals.

2. Pronephros and mesonephros

The *pronephros* of man consists of a series of cell masses between the levels of the fourth and fourteenth somites, joined by a back-wardly growing cord, the rudiment of the pronephric duct (Fig. 307). The only sign of excretory capacity in the pronephros is the formation of glomeruli protruding into the coelom, but it is not known that any excretory products are formed. The pronephric duct grows back to the cloaca and as it passes through the more posterior regions it pro-vides the stimulus for the differentiation of the meso- and meta-nephros. Waddington (1938) has shown that if the pronephros is removed from chicks the remaining portions of the urogenital system do not develop.

The *mesonephros* (Figs. 307 and 314a) forms a prominent ridge behind the pronephros, containing a number of tubules with walls invaginated to form glomeruli. The tubules open into the pronephric duct, now known as the Wolffian duct, and they probably secrete urine, especially in mammals where there are several layers between foetal and maternal blood and there is a large allantoic bladder (p. 706).

The pro- and mesonephros begin to degenerate early, so that the whole series is not to be found at any one time. The pronephros dis-appears completely, the mesonephros gives rise to the vasa efferentia of the testis and the paradidymis in the male, and to the epoöphoron in the female.

3. The metanephros

The adult kidney or *metanephros* develops from the intermediate mesoderm behind the mesonephros. Tubules and glomeruli dif-ferentiate within a solid nephrogenic ridge. The *ureter* forms as an outgrowth from the lower end of the Wolffian duct, which grows forward into the metanephros and divides to form the collecting tubules (Fig. 307).

4. The gonads

The gonads develop from two distinct sources, which are at first widely separate. The genital ridges of the coelomic epithelium, lying

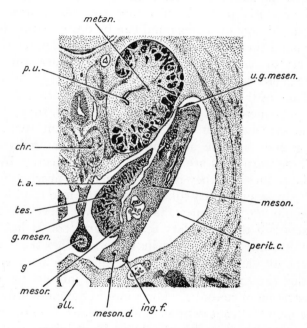

FIG. 308. Diagram of the developing gonad.

all. allantois; *chr.* chromaffin tissue; *g.* gut; *g.mesen.* gut mesentery; *ing.f.* inguinal fold; *meson.* mesonephros; *meson.d.* mesonephric duct; *mesor.* mesorchium; *metan.* metanephros; *perit.c.* peritoneal cavity; *p.u.* pelvis and ureter; *t.a.* tunica albuginea; *tes.* testis; *u.g. mesen.* urinogenital mesentery. (After Hamilton, Boyd, and Mossman.)

medial to the mesonephros, provide what may be called the *structural elements* of the gonad. The *primordial germ cells*, which ultimately give rise to the ova or spermatozoa, arise in the endoderm of the yolk sac and later migrate to the genital ridges.

The developing gonad has a bisexual composition, the outer cortex (germinal epithelium) being the female part, the central medulla (sex cords) the male part. In fishes and amphibians both parts may remain well-developed to quite a late stage, so that the gonad is visibly bisexual, but in amniotes the bisexual stage is passed through rapidly.

In a normal male the medulla suppresses the cortex and in the female vice versa. Sex is primarily determined by a balance between the actions of the sex chromosomes and autosomes within the nucleus. Every cell thus contains factors tending to development both of maleness and femaleness. Presumably the conditions in the cortical region of the gonad favour the enzymatic processes leading to femaleness, those in the medullary region to maleness.

The sex of the gonad is determined by the structural elements. In the frog the material that will form the germ cells is already localized near the vegetal pole of the egg and can be destroyed by irradiation. A sterile gonad then develops, yet acquires the characteristic structure of ovary or testis. Moreover, by suitable transplantation, germ cells of one genotypic sex can be made to grow in a gonad with structural elements of the opposite sex; the latter will then determine the nature of the gametes that result (see Willier *et al.*, 1955).

There is evidence that in normal development the cortex and medulla produce specific sex hormones with mutually inhibitory effects. These hormones are probably at first effective by diffusion through the tissues and they may also reach the nearby ducts in this way. Later, these or related substances escape into the blood-stream as the specific sex hormones that control the development of the genital ducts and the secondary sexual characters. It has long been known that in cattle if there are twins of opposite sex the female member develops into an intersexual animal known as a *freemartin*. This confirms that the male element of the gonad inhibits the female.

Administration of steroid sex hormones to the mother during pregnancy in a mammal causes signs of sex reversal or hermaphroditism both in the gonad itself and in the ducts. Thus injection of male hormones causes development of the medulla of the gonad and of the Wolffian duct system in genetic females. There is therefore good reason to suppose that the differentiation of the gonad in normal development is controlled by sex-differentiating substances that are related to the sex hormones of the adult.

Reversal of the genetically determined sex can be produced in various ways. Thus in male toads a portion of the cortex of the gonad persists attached to the testis and is known as Bidder's organ. If the testis is removed from an adult toad the Bidder's organ develops into an ovary. Sex reversal as a result of conditions of nutrition, parasitism, disease, and even temperature has been reported from many vertebrates. Gonads containing both eggs and sperms are occasionally reported in adult mammals and their occurrence is to be expected as a deviation, given a mechanism that depends upon a balance of male and female tendencies.

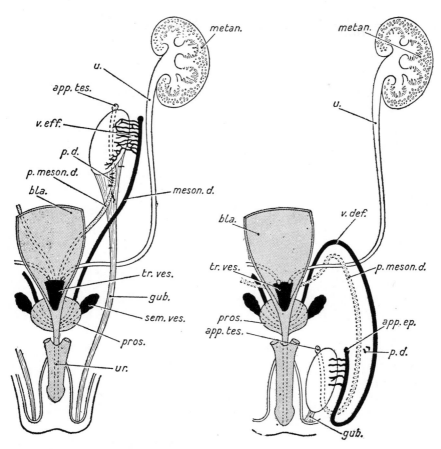

FIG. 309. Diagrams showing the development of the male genital ducts.

app.ep. appendix of epididymis; *app.tes.* appendix of testis; *bla.* bladder; *gub.* gubernaculum; *meson.d.* mesonephric duct; *metan.* metanephros; *p.d.* paradidymis; *p.meson.d.* para-mesonephric (Mullerian) duct; *pros.* prostate; *sem.ves.* seminal vesicle; *tr. ves.* trigonum vesicae; *u.* ureter; *ur.* urethra; *v.def.* vas deferens; *v.eff.* vasa efferentia.
(After Hamilton, Boyd, and Mossman.)

5. The testis and male ducts

The sex cords of the testis are separated from the germinal epithelium by a fibrous layer, the *tunica albuginea*. Since there is reason from experiments on other animals to think that the centre (medulla) of the gonad has male tendencies, it is interesting that the definitive male cells of mammals are thus formed at the centre, whereas in the female the cortex remains active throughout life (p. 671). The sex cords of the testis form a network of cellular strands, the *rete testis*, which become hollowed out to form the *seminiferous tubules*. The walls of these form the spermatocytes and supporting Sertoli cells (p. 666).

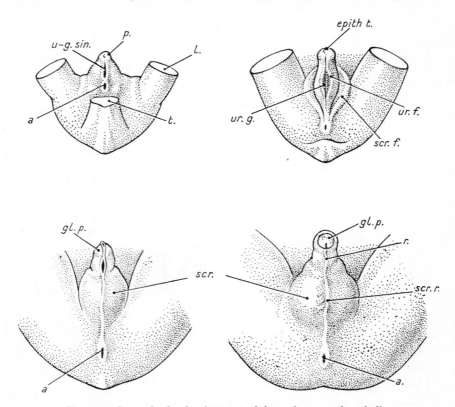

FIG. 310. Stages in the development of the male external genitalia.

a. anus; *epith.t.* epithelial tag; *gl.p.* glans penis; *l.* leg (cut); *p.* penis; *r.* raphe; *scr.* scrotum; *scr.f.* scrotal fold (genital swelling); *scr.r.* scrotal raphe; *t.* tail (cut); *u-g.sin.* urinogenital sinus; *ur.f.* urethral fold (genital fold); *ur.g.* urethral groove. (After Patten, from various sources.)

The interstitial cells are formed from the mesenchyme between the sex cords.

The developing testis has meanwhile become attached to the meso-nephros, which lies lateral to it. The seminiferous tubules make connexion with some of the mesonephric tubules to form the *vasa efferentia* (Fig. 309). The portion of the mesonephric duct into which these tubules lead becomes greatly coiled as the epididymis. The lower portion of the duct forms the muscular *vas deferens* and a diverticulum from the lower end of this makes the *seminal vesicle*. The vas opens to the urethra by a short ejaculatory duct. The male embryo shows at early stages a Mullerian duct similar to that of the female but this retrogresses in later stages. Rudiments of it persist as the *hydatid* attached to the testis, and the prostatic utricle. The *prostate gland* is formed as numerous buds from the endodermic wall of the urethra.

The *penis* has evolved in phylogeny from the vascular cloacal lips (p. 671). In development it forms from an elevation, the genital tubercle, in front of the urogenital aperture (Fig. 310). This becomes elongated and a urethral groove forms and finally closes over in such a manner as to provide a continuation of the urethra to the tip of the penis.

The testis descends from its original position on the posterior wall of the abdomen into the scrotum, preceded by the *processus vaginalis*, a diverticulum of the coelom, surrounded by muscle layers corresponding to those of the body-wall. The testis is attached to the scrotal wall by a cord, the *gubernaculum*; when elongation of the whole body takes place this cord fails to lengthen and the testis is thus drawn down into the scrotum. The *inguinal canal* through which it passes becomes constricted in man, but remains open to the coelom in the rabbit.

6. The ovary and female ducts

The problem of whether ova are continually formed throughout life is considered on p. 680. The germinal epithelium certainly remains conspicuous and there is no outer fibrous coat corresponding to the tunica albuginea of the testis. The interstitial cells that form the walls of the ovarian follicles are produced by the mesenchymal stroma of the ovary.

The female genital duct system develops not from the mesonephric duct but from an independent *Mullerian duct*, which forms in the mesoderm alongside the Wolffian duct and grows back to reach the urogenital sinus (Fig. 311). The more anterior (cephalic) portions of the Mullerian ducts remain paired and differentiate into the *uterine tubes* and their funnels, opening to the coelom near to the ovaries. The lower sections of the Mullerian ducts fuse in man to form the *uterus* and *vagina*. In most other mammals they remain separate, providing paired uteri. The uterine epithelium of the foetus undergoes considerable differentiation towards the end of pregnancy, presumably stimulated by maternal hormones passing through the placenta.

The caudal end of the utero-vaginal canal forms a solid cord of cells,

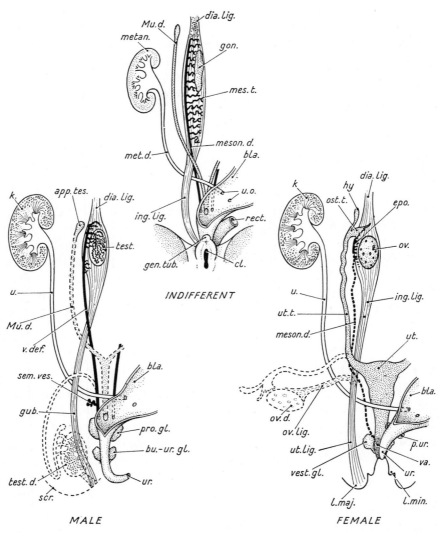

FIG. 311. Diagrams showing the development of the male and female genital ducts from the early indifferent stage. The testis and ovary are outlined by broken lines in their final positions.

app.tes. appendix of testis; *bla.* bladder; *bu.-ur.gl.* bulbo-urethral gland; *cl.* cloaca; *dia.lig.* diaphragmatic ligament; *epo.* epo-ophoron; *gen.tub.* genital tubercle; *gon.* gonad; *gub.* gubernaculum; *hy.* hydatid; *ing.lig.* inguinal ligament; *k.* kidney; *l.maj.* labium majus; *l.min.* labium minus; *meson.d.* mesonephric duct; *mes.t.* mesonephric tubule; *metan.* metanephros; *met.d.* metanephric duct; *Mu.d.* Mullerian duct; *ost.t.* ostium tubae; *ov.* ovary; *ov.d.* ovary after descent; *ov.lig.* ovarian ligament; *pro.gl.* prostate gland; *p.ur.* paraurethral gland (prostate); *rect.* rectum; *scr.* scrotum; *sem.ves.* seminal vesicle; *test.* testis; *test.d.* testis after descent; *u.* ureter; *u.o.* opening of ureter; *ur.* urethra; *ut.* uterus; *ut.lig.* uterine ligament; *ut.t.* uterine (Fallopian) tube; *va.* vagina; *v.def.* vas deferens; *vest.gl.* greater vestibular gland (bulbourethral). (Partly after Patten.)

meeting a cord growing from the posterior wall of the urogenital sinus. The vagina is formed by hollowing of these strands of cells, but it is disputed how much of its wall is lined by mesodermal (Mullerian) and how much by endodermal (urogenital sinus) epithelium.

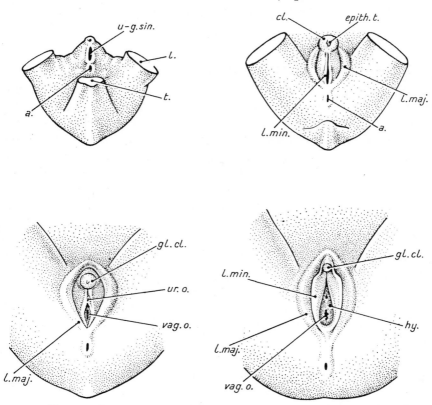

FIG. 312. Stages in the development of the female external genitalia.
a. anus; *cl.* clitoris; *epith.t.* epithelial tag; *gl.cl.* glans clitoridis; *hy.* hymen; *l.* leg (cut); *l.maj.* labia majora (genital swellings); *l.min.* labia minora (genital folds); *t.* tail (cut); *u-g.sin.* urinogenital sinus; *ur.o.* urethral orifice; *vag.o.* vaginal orifice.
(After Patten, from various sources.)

The genital tubercle is formed in the same position in the female as in the male but fails to become grooved and joined to the urethra (Fig. 312). It develops, however, into the clitoris, with sensitive skin and erectile tissue corresponding to those of the penis.

The mesonephric duct, well developed in the early female embryo, later retrogresses, but a part remains in the adult as the epoöphoron, a body of unknown function attached to the ovary.

XLVI

DEVELOPMENT OF THE BLOOD VASCULAR SYSTEM

1. Differentiation of blood islands

THE heart- and blood-vessels develop from the mesoderm. In mammals the first vessels appear as isolated blood islands in the splanchnopleur of the yolk sac. Some of the cells of these islands become flattened to form endothelial cells, which arrange themselves to make tubes. Other cells, at the centre of the tubes, become the first haemocytoblasts, from which the cellular elements of the blood are derived (p. 274). At first all the corpuscles are nucleated but as development proceeds an increasing proportion lose their nuclei.

Further blood islands form in the mesenchyme throughout the developing embryo, partly from new centres and partly by spreading of vessels from those already formed. The main vessels are thus formed separately and later become linked up and extended to provide a circulation for each part as it develops. The later vessels arise by outgrowth from the endothelium of existing vessels.

The differentiation of mesenchymal cells to haemocytoblasts is presumably an evoked response, but it is not known what stimulus is responsible. The course of the main vessels is determined by heredity but the stimulus of the demand made by developing tissues has a powerful influence on the blood-system. Actively growing centres come to have a large blood-supply and the vessels leading to them become enlarged. The responsiveness of these vessels to the amount of blood flowing through them is thus a major factor in determining the vascular pattern (double dependence).

2. The development of the heart

The heart of the earliest chordates was a simple tube below the gut, pumping blood forwards from the intestine to the gills. In the development of a mammal this same plan can be seen. The first signs of the heart are collections of mesenchymal cells between endoderm and splanchnic mesoderm below the foregut (Fig. 313). These cells associate to form a pair of endocardial tubes, which soon approach the midline and join to make a single tube. This union is the result of a folding up of the splanchnic mesoderm, which forms the myocardium and epicardium. The embryonic heart thus projects into the pericardium, attached to the foregut by a dorsal mesocardium. The endocardial tubes lead in front to a short *ventral aorta* and this by the *first aortic arches* to *dorsal aortae*. From the dorsal aorta branches communicate

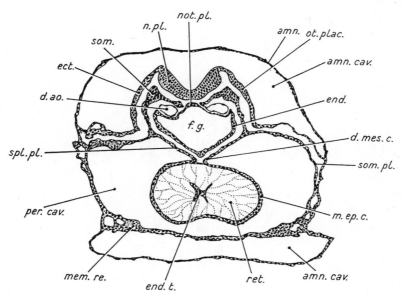

FIG. 313. Transverse section of a 7-somite human embryo showing the developing heart.

amn. amnion; *amn.cav.* amniotic cavity; *d.ao.* lateral dorsal aorta; *d.mes.c.* dorsal meso-cardium; *ect.* ectoderm; *end.* endoderm; *end.t.* endocardial tubes (fused); *f.g.* fore-gut; *mem.re.* membrana reuniens; *m.ep.c.* myoepicardium; *mes.* mesoderm; *not.pl.* notochordal plate; *n.pl.* neural plate; *ot.plac.* otic placode; *per. cav.* pericardial cavity; *ret.* reticulum; *som.* somite; *som.pl.* somatopleur; *spl.pl.* splanchnopleur. (After Payne, 1925.)

with the networks on the yolk sac and in the chorio-allantoic placenta, becoming the *vitelline* and *umbilical arteries* (Fig. 314). The corre-sponding veins lead to the hind end of the heart (Fig. 319). The vitelline arteries become the superior mesenteric arteries and the umbilical arteries represent the vessels of the precociously developed bladder (allantois).

The heart thus arises as a continuous tube, which then increases in length and is first bent to the right and then twisted to form a loop (the dorsal mesocardium disappearing) (Fig. 315). The region where the veins enter at the hind end becomes the *sinus venosus*. The part in front of this forms the first undivided *atrium*, with a ventricle cranial to it. The right-hand loop of the heart forms the conus and truncus arteriosus. By a further bend the originally caudal end of the heart (the sinus and atrium) comes to its adult position cranial to the ventricle. The determination of tissue to form cardiac muscle occurs in the early gastrula stage of amphibians or early blastoderm of the

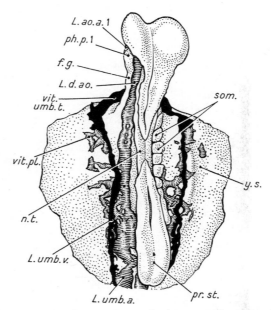

FIG. 314. Diagram of dorsal view of 7 somite human embryo showing the early blood-vessels of the yolk sac circulation. The somites have been removed from the left side.

f.g. foregut; *L.ao.a.*1. left first aortic arch; *L.d.ao.* left dorsal aorta; *L.umb.a.* left umbilical artery; *L.umb.v.* left umbilical vein; *n.t.* neural tube; *ph.p.*1. first pharyngeal pouch; *pr.st.* primitive streak; *som.* somite; *vit.pl.* vitelline plexus; *vit.umb.t.* vitello-umbilical trunk; *y.s.* yolk sac. (After Payne.)

chick, probably through an inductive action of the endoderm. Pieces of the presumptive heart tissue cultivated *in vitro* undergo self-differentiation to form a tube, with characteristic coiling whose contractions proceed in an orderly way moving it about in its dish like a worm. The presence of blood is therefore not necessary for early differentiation but the streams of blood determine the details of later development.

Continuation of Key to Fig. 314 a.

    aff.gl.a. afferent glomerular artery; *coll.v.* collateral vein; *cap.pl.* capillary plexus; *caps.* Bowman's capsule; *d.a.* dorsal aorta; *eff.gl.v.* efferent glomerular vessel; *emb.coel.* embryonic coelom; *g.* gut; *gl.* glomerulus; *gl.caps.* glomerular capsule; *mesen.* mesentery; *meson.d.* mesonephric duct; *meson.t.* mesonephric tubule; *myo.* myotome; *myoc.* myocoel; *n.* neck; *n.c.* neural canal; *n.cr.* neural crest; *not.* notochord; *p.c.v.* posterior cardinal vein; *pron.d.* pronephric duct; *s.c.v.* subcardinal vein; *scl.* sclerotome; *som.* somite; *t.* tubule; *y.s.* yolk sac.

(After Patten.)

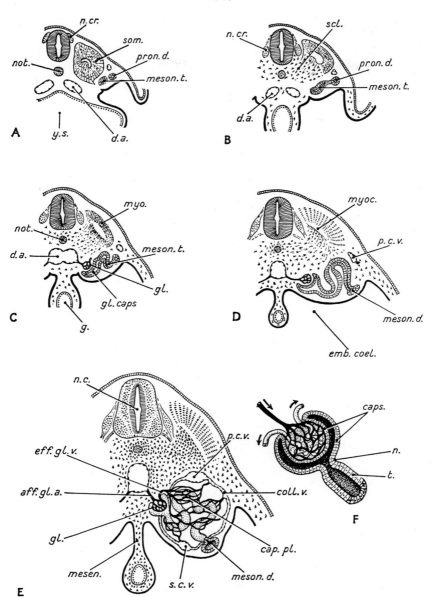

FIG. 314 *a*. Development of mammalian mesonephric tubules and their vascular relations.

A, Tubule primordium still independent of duct; B, union of tubule with primary nephric duct; C, early stage in development of glomerulus and capsule; D, further development of capsule and lengthening of tubule; E, relations of blood-vessels to well-developed mesonephric tubule; F, glomerulus and capsule, enlarged.

(*For continuation of Key see opposite page.*)

3. Development of the atria and ventricles

The sinus venosus shifts to the right and the division of the atrium begins. A ridge, the *septum primum*, grows down from the dorsal wall of the atrium towards the ventricle (Fig. 316). The atrio-ventricular

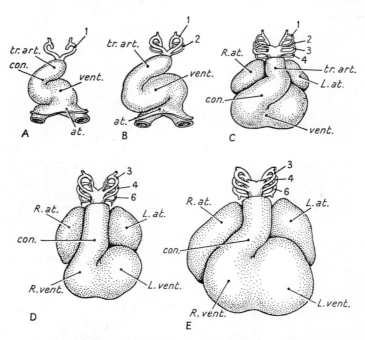

FIG. 315. External ventral views of the heart showing its development by bending of the cardiac tube.

1–4. First to fourth aortic arches; *at.* atrium; *con.* conus arteriosus; *L.at.* left atrium; *L.vent.* left ventricle; *R.at.* right atrium; *R.vent.* right ventricle; *tr.art.* truncus arteriosus; *vent.* ventricle. (After Kramer, *Amer. J. Anat.*, **71**.)

canal becomes divided into two by the outgrowth of *endocardial cushions* of connective tissue. The septum primum does not at first reach as far as the cushions but leaves an opening, the *ostium primum*, between the two atria. Later, as this ostium closes, a second aperture, the ostium secundum appears in the septum primum, maintaining the continuity between the atria *foramen ovale*. A fold of tissue, the *septum secundum*, grows from the atrial wall to the right of the septum primum and thus lies across the opening of the ostium secundum. At birth the apposition of the septa closes the foramen (p. 764).

Meanwhile the ventricle also becomes divided, by an interventricular septum growing from the base towards the atrio-ventricular cushion,

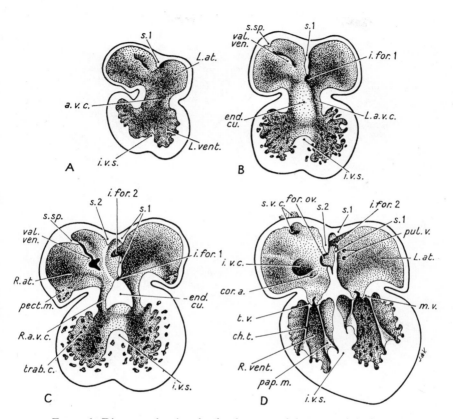

FIG. 316. Diagrams showing the development of the septa of the heart.

a.v.c. atrio-ventricular canal; *ch.t.* chordae tendinae; *cor.a.* coronary artery; *end.cu.* endo-cardial cushion; *for.ov.* foramen ovale; *i.for.1(2)* inter-atrial ostium primum (secundum); *i.v.c.* inferior vena cava; *i.v.s.* inter-ventricular septum; *L.(R.) at.* left (right) atrium; *L.(R.)a.v.c.* left (right) atrio-ventricular canal; *L.(R.)vent.* left (right) ventricle; *m.v.* mitral valve; *pap.m.* papillary muscle; *pect.m.* pectinate muscle; *pul.v.* pulmonary vein; *s.1(2)* inter-atrial septum primum (secundum); *s.sp.* septum spurium; *s.v.c.* superior vena cava; *trab.c.* trabeculae carneae; *t.v.* tricuspid valve; *val.ven.* valvulae venosae.

(After Patten.)

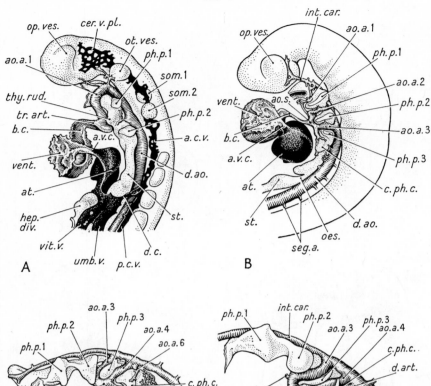

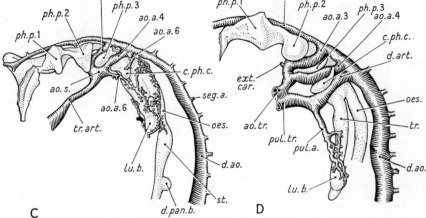

FIG. 317. Views of the left side of A, 22 somite; B, 4 mm.; C, 5 mm.; and D, 11 mm. human embryos showing the principal blood-vessels.

a.c.v. anterior cardinal vein; *ao.a. 1,2,3,4,6* aortic arches one to six; *ao.s.* aortic sac; *ao.tr.* aortic trunk; *at.* atrium; *a.v.c.* atrioventricular canal; *b.c.* bulbus cordis; *cer.v.pl.* cerebral venous plexus; *c.ph.c.* caudal pharyngeal complex; *d.ao.* dorsal aorta; *d.art.* ductus arteriosus; *d.c.* duct of Cuvier; *d.pan.b.* dorsal pancreatic bud; *ext.car.* external carotid; *hep.div.* hepatic diverticulum; *int.car.* internal carotid; *lu.b.* lung bud; *oes.* oesophagus; *op.ves.* optic vesicle; *ot.ves.* otic vesicle; *p.c.v.* posterior cardinal vein; *ph.p. 1,2,3,* pharyngeal pouches one to three; *pul.a., tr.* pulmonary artery and trunk; *seg.a.* segmental artery; *som.1,2,* somites one and two; *st.* stomach; *thy.rud.* thyroid rudiment; *tr.* trachea; *tr.art.* truncus arteriosus; *umb.v.* umbilical vein; *vent.* ventricle; *vit.v.* vitelline vein. (After Congdon.)

which it reaches at the end of the second month in man. The truncus arteriosus becomes divided by a spiral fold in such a manner that the right ventricle communicates with the pulmonary, the left with the systemic arch.

4. The aortic arches and arterial system

The arterial system of a mammal is based upon a plan fundamentally similar to that of a fish in that it consists of a ventral aorta, a series of six pharyngeal (branchial) arches, and paired dorsal aortae (see Goodrich, 1930). The morphogenetic processes that gave rise to the arterial system in the fish-like ancestors of the mammals are still retained, producing the appearance of 'recapitulation', which has so often puzzled zoologists. Evidently this formation of branchial arches is a fundamental feature of the process of vertebrate embryogenesis; its occurrence in all members of the group leads to the apparent 'recapitulation'. In mammals there are considerable modifications from the arrangement found in fishes. The aortic arches appear in a cranio-caudal series and the anterior ones quickly disappear. The whole series of six cannot therefore be seen at any one time. Moreover, the fifth is at best a transient and incomplete vessel and hardly appears in the figures given by even the most careful investigators.

In a human embryo with twenty-two somites we can recognize on each side a short ventral aorta, a first (mandibular) arch and a dorsal aorta (Fig. 317). The latter is not at first a continuous vessel but a series of intercommunicating channels, from which vessels proceed to the somites and yolk sac and to a large umbilical artery to the placenta.

The ventral aortae proceed to fuse to make the short truncus arteriosus (aortic sac). The dorsal aortae fuse in their caudal portions, but remain separate above the pharynx. Meanwhile arterial arches differentiate and disappear in series. As the third becomes complete the first disappears and so on. Yet considerable traces of the original branchial arches remain even in the adult. The first and second probably disappear completely but have been held to contribute to the maxillary and stapedial arteries. The front parts of the ventral aortae become the external carotids and of the dorsal aortae the internal carotids. The dorsal aortae disappear between the third and fourth arches, the internal carotids being thus fed through the remains of the third arches (Fig. 317). The left fourth arch becomes the aorta, while the right fourth remains only as the base of the right subclavian artery (Fig. 318).

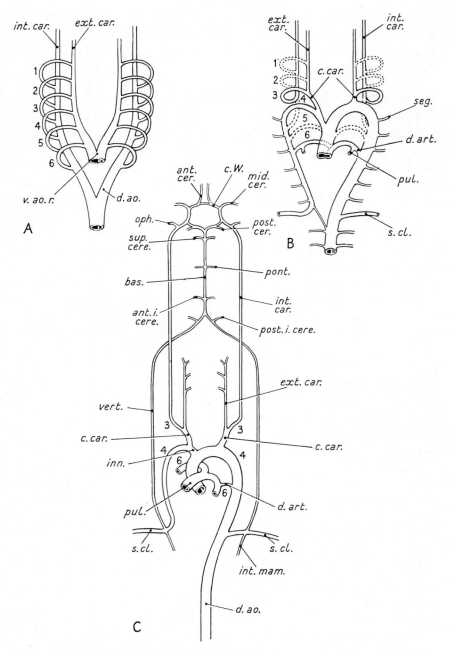

FIG. 318. Diagrams of the developmental changes in the mammalian aortic arch system.

(*For Key see opposite.*)

The fifth and sixth pharyngeal arches appear when the embryo is about 5 mm. long, the fifth being incomplete and very shortlived. From the sixth arches vessels accompany the developing lung buds. The ventral portions of the sixth arches thus become the pulmonary arteries. The dorsal portion of the left sixth arch remains connected

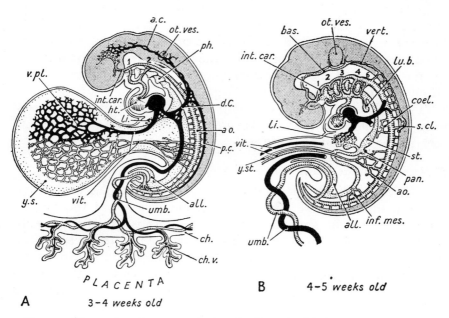

FIG. 319. The aortic arch system and other blood-vessels of the human embryo seen from the left side. A, 3–4 weeks old; B, 4–5 weeks old.

1–6, first to sixth aortic arches; *a.c.* anterior cardinal; *all.* allantois; *ao.* aorta; *bas.* basilar artery; *ch.* chorion; *ch.v.* chorionic villi; *coel.* coeliac; *d.C.* duct of Cuvier; *ht.* heart; *inf.mes.* inferior mesenteric; *int.car.* internal carotid; *li.* liver; *lu.b.* lung bud; *ot.ves.* otic vesicle; *pan.* pancreas; *p.c.* posterior cardinal; *ph.* pharynx; *s.cl.* subclavian; *st.* stomach; *umb.* umbilical; *vert.* vertebral; *vit.* vitelline artery; *v.pl.* vitelline plexus; *y.s.* yolk sac; *y.st.* yolk stalk.
(After Congdon.)

with the dorsal aorta as the *ductus arteriosus*, which provides a channel short circuiting the lungs during intra-uterine life. Blood reaching the right ventricle is passed through the ductus to the aorta. This channel

Key to Fig. 318.

A, Aortic arches: complete set as in a fish; B, early changes in embryo; C, adult condition. *1,2,3,4,5,&6*, aortic arches; *ant.cer.* anterior cerebral; *ant.i.cere.* anterior inferior cerebellar; *bas.* basilar; *c.car.* common carotid; *c.W.* circle of Willis; *d.ao.* dorsal aorta; *d.art.* ductus arteriosus; *ext.car.* external carotid; *inn.* innominate; *int.car.* internal carotid; *int.mam.* internal mammary; *mid.cer.* middle cerebral; *oph.* ophthalmic; *pont.* pontine; *post.cer.* posterior cerebral; *post.i.cere.* posterior inferior cerebellar; *pul.* pulmonary; *s.cl.* subclavian; *seg.* segmental; *sup.cere.* superior cerebellar; *v.ao.r.* ventral aortic root; *vert.* vertebral (laterally displaced). (After Patten.)

closes at birth, when the full circulation of the lungs becomes established (p. 764).

The branches given off from the dorsal aorta are at first segmental vessels passing to the somites, viscera and limb-buds. As development proceeds only the somatic intersegmental arteries retain the segmental plan. The coeliac and superior and inferior mesenteric arteries are splanchnic vessels that were originally connected with the seventh cervical and third and fifth thoracic segments; later they make anastomosis more posteriorly. The umbilical arteries can be regarded as the arteries of the allantois (p. 706) and they move back to open from the common iliac arteries (Fig. 319).

The arteries of the limbs develop as four or five segmental vessels, which are later reduced to single arteries arising at about the seventh cervical and fifth lumbar levels.

5. Development of the venous system

The veins, like the arteries, are formed upon the plan of development found in fishes, but with great modification of the time of appearance of the various vessels. The heart is essentially a sub-intestinal vessel receiving blood from the gut. The *vitelline veins* form very early in the splanchnopleur of the yolk sac and join the sinus venosus (Figs. 319, 320). Later, as the liver develops in the septum transversum, they contribute to make parts of the portal vein and inferior vena cava.

The circulation in the yolk sac is of far less importance in most mammals than that of the chorio-allantoic placenta, which can be regarded fundamentally as derived from the vessels of the allantois (p. 706). The *umbilical veins* are therefore developed very early, passing around the yolk-sac stalk to the sinus venosus. As the liver develops, the blood from the umbilical veins passes to it, joining that from the vitelline veins. The right umbilical vein disappears at about 7 mm., all the placental blood then returning in the left umbilical vein. As development proceeds a direct channel, the *ductus venosus,* appears so that most of the blood from the umbilical and vitelline veins proceeds direct to the right atrium. Some passes by *venae advehentes* to the developing liver, returning by *venae revehentes.*

The main venous drainage channels of the body of the embryo are at first the anterior and posterior cardinal veins, lying in the dorsal body-wall, lateral to the aortae (Fig. 319). These return blood to the heart by paired *ducts of Cuvier*, lying in the septum transversum and entering the sinus venosus.

The venous drainage of the front part of the body comes to be concentrated on the right anterior cardinal and duct of Cuvier, which
becomes the *superior vena cava*. In the hind part of the body the
original dorsal venous channels provided by the posterior cardinals
are replaced by a series of more ventral vessels, leading directly to the

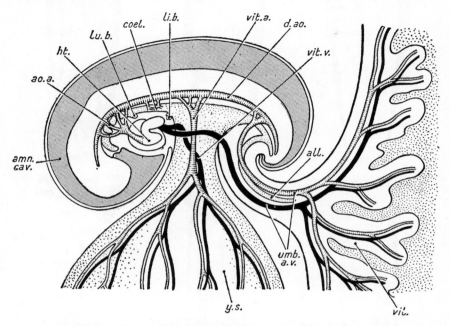

Fig. 320. Diagram showing the early embryonic blood-vessels and their relations with
the maternal tissues.

all. allantois; *amn.cav.* amniotic cavity; *ao.a.* aortic arches; *coel.* coeliac artery; *d.ao.* dorsal
aorta; *ht.* heart; *li.b.* liver bud; *lu.b.* lung bud; *umb.a.v.* umbilical artery and vein; *vil.* villi;
vit.a. vitelline artery (superior mesenteric); *vit.v.* vitelline vein; *y.s.* yolk sac.
(After Hamilton, Boyd, and Mossman.)

heart through the inferior vena cava. A series of *subcardinal* and *supracardinal* vessels is formed draining the meso- and metanephros and
the thorax (Fig. 321). From these there is developed a median vessel,
the inferior vena cava, which comes to receive the blood from the hind
limbs. It passes down through the mesentery, receiving the hepatic
veins and proceeding to the right atrium. This is thus a more ɗ ͻct
pathway from the hind part of the body to the heart than was provided
by the posterior cardinals. The dorsal portion of the thorax is drained
by the *azygos* and *hemiazygos* veins, derived from the supracardinals
(Fig. 321).

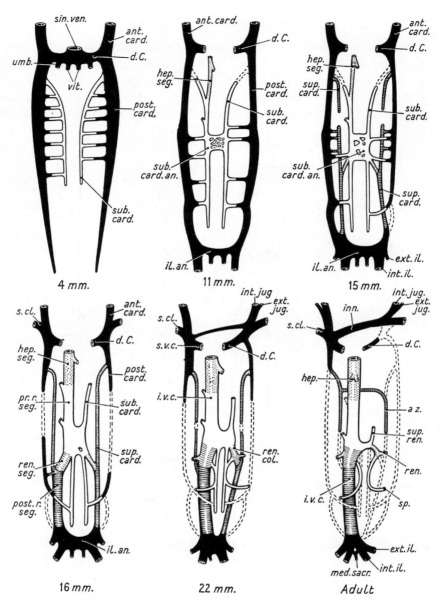

Fig. 321. Diagrams of the venous system of man at various stages of development showing the origin of the adult veins.

ant.card. anterior cardinal; *az.* azygos; *d.C.* duct of Cuvier; *ext.il.* external iliac; *ext.jug.* external jugular; *hep.* hepatic; *hep.seg.* hepatic segment of i.v.c.; *il.an.* iliac anastomosis; *inn.* innominate; *int.il.* internal iliac; *int.jug.* internal jugular; *i.v.c.* inferior vena cava; *med. sacr.* median sacral; *post.card.* postcardinal; *post.r.seg.* postrenal segment; *pr.r.seg.* prerenal segment; *ren.* renal; *ren.col.* renal collar; *ren.seg.* renal segment; *s.cl.* subclavian; *sin.ven.* sinus venosus; *sp.* spermatic; *subcard.* subcardinal, *subcard.an.* subcardinal anastomosis; *sup.card.* supracardinal; *sup.ren.* suprarenal, *s.v.c.* superior vena cava; *umb.* umbilical; *vit.* vitelline. (After McClure and Butler, *Am. J. Anat.* **35**, 338, 1925.)

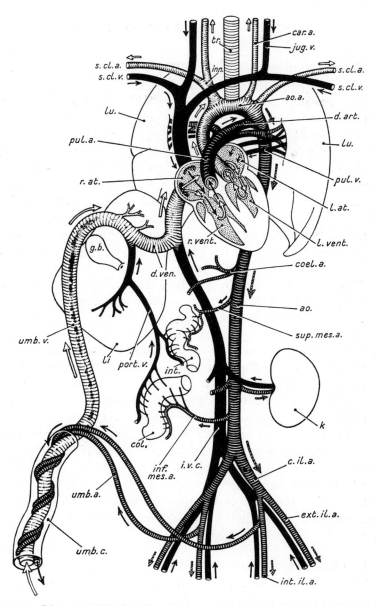

FIG. 322. Diagram of the foetal circulation. De-oxygenated blood shown black, oxygenated blood light cross hatching, mixed blood dark hatching.

ao. aorta; *ao.a.* aortic arch; *car.a.* carotid artery; *c.il.a.* common iliac artery; *coel.a.* coeliac artery; *col.* colon; *d.art.* ductus arteriosus; *d.ven.* ductus venosus; *ext.il.a.* external iliac artery; *g.b.* gall bladder; *inf.mes.a.* inferior mesenteric artery; *inn.* innominate artery; *int.* intestine; *int.il.a.* internal iliac artery; *i.v.c.* inferior vena cava; *jug.v.* jugular vein; *k.* kidney; *li.* liver; *l.at.* left atrium; *lu.* lung; *l.vent.* left ventricle; *port.v.* portal vein; *pul.a.* pulmonary artery; *pul.v.* pulmonary vein; *r.at.* right atrium; *r.vent.* right ventricle; *s.cl.a.* subclavian artery; *s.cl.v.* subclavian vein; *sup.mes.a.* superior mesenteric artery; *tr.* trachea; *umb.a.* umbilical artery; *umb.c.* umbilical cord; *umb.v.* umbilical vein.

(Based on Hamilton, Boyd, and Mossman.)

6. Course of circulation in the foetus

The placenta provides the foetal blood with oxygen and other raw materials. The blood returning in the umbilical vein to the right atrium is therefore sent mainly direct to the developing tissues of the body, only a small part of it passing through the lungs. Conversely the blood returning in the venae cavae, being poor in oxygen and rich in excretory products, requires to be sent as directly as possible to the placenta.

The mammals have developed a special series of foetal conditions by which the required separation of the streams of blood is achieved (Fig. 322). The oxygenated blood returning in the ductus venosus to the right atrium is directed by a valve at the opening of the inferior vena cava towards the foramen ovale and thus to the left side of the heart. From the left ventricle the blood passes mainly to the carotids and subclavians, the remainder down the dorsal aortae to the rest of the body (see Barclay and others, 1944).

The blood returning in the superior vena cava is deoxygenated and the opening of this vessel is so directed that all its blood passes into the right ventricle and thence to the pulmonary artery. Most of this blood passes through the ductus arteriosus into the aorta and thence by the umbilical arteries to the placenta, bye-passing the lungs.

By this means a separation of the venous and arterial circulations quite different from that of the adult is achieved. The separation is not complete because venous blood in the caudal part of the inferior vena cava is mixed with oxygenated blood returning in the umbilical vein. No doubt there is also some mixing of the streams within the right atrium, but X-ray studies of foetal sheep after suitable injections of opaque material show that a considerable degree of separation is achieved.

7. Changes in the circulation at birth

At birth a series of changes in the walls of the vessels leads to a rapid alteration of the circulation to its adult condition. The umbilical arteries contract so that no further blood leaves the body. The umbilical vein closes some minutes later than the arteries and therefore blood may actually be drawn back from the placenta. As the child becomes anoxic by deprivation of maternal oxygen the receptors controlling its own respiratory system begin to operate and respiratory movements begin. Air enters the lungs and the circulation of blood through them increases. Large quantities of blood begin to return to the left atrium and the pressure there becomes greater than in the right atrium. The flow through the foramen ovale stops and the septum primum is forced against the septum secundum to close the aperture. Meanwhile the ductus arteriosus closes by sudden contraction of a special sphincter in its wall, probably as a reflex response. Blood from the right ventricle is thus directed through the lungs and the adult circulation is established. Later the foramen ovale and lumen of the ductus arteriosus become obliterated by the growth of fibrous tissue.

These changes at birth are possible because of anticipatory growth processes, preparing the body for actions that occur only on the single occasion of birth. By selection of suitable genetic mechanisms modifying previously existing morphogenetic processes the system has been brought to operate with a high degree of precision. Presumably in the early ancestors of mammals, where much yolk was present and the placenta was less developed, the changes at birth were less abrupt.

XLVII

DEVELOPMENT OF THE NERVOUS SYSTEM

1. The origin of the nervous system

THE specialization of cells to respond to external changes first occurred on the outside of the body and in mammals the entire nervous system still develops from ectodermal tissues. The receptive and conducting elements appeared many hundreds of millions of years ago by exaggeration in certain cells of the powers of responsiveness to environmental change. The 'response' that gives neurons their usefulness is not merely the setting up of a propagated action potential but also the power of outgrowth of axonal and dendritic processes. The nervous tissues today still require the stimulus of 'function' to achieve their full differentiation (p. 787). There has been a gradual elaboration of the response system during evolution so that the nervous tissues now become differentiated during development largely by response to stimuli (evocators) *within* the organism. The hereditary processes thus ensure that a nervous system is prepared during development and is ready to function at the appropriate time.

The evolution and development of the nervous system thus shows how heredity provides a recorded memory of past responses; the genes and developmental processes have been so selected as to provide a forecasting system that prepares the organism for the conditions it will meet. The activities of the nuclear materials and the differentiations that they allow after suitable evocation represent in a coded version the information received by the race during its past history (p. 23).

2. The neural plate and neural tube

In a vertebrate the first response leading to the differentiation of nervous tissue is thus not to an external but to an internal stimulus. The chordamesodermal tissue that has passed in over the lips of the blastopore of an amphibian evokes changes in the overlying ectoderm, converting it into the *neural plate* (p. 620). There is probably a similar evocation in mammals, and in chicks the chordamesoderm invaginated through the primitive streak has a similar evoking action (p. 651).

The neural plate consists of cells taller than those of the remaining

ectoderm and the plate proceeds to fold to form first a groove and then
a complete tube (Fig. 323). This folding is an active process on the
part of the cells of the neural tube and the neighbouring ectoderm, and

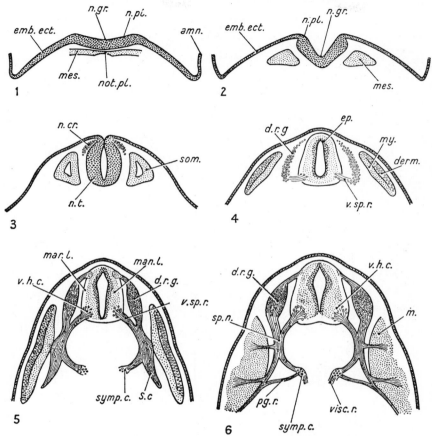

FIG. 323. Diagrams of transverse sections showing the development of the neural
tube and the segmental nerves in a human embryo.

amn. amnion; *derm.* dermatome; *d.r.g.* dorsal root ganglion; *emb.ect.* embryonic ectoderm;
ep. ependyma; *m.* muscle; *man.l.* mantle layer; *mar.l.* marginal layer; *mes.* mesoderm; *my.*
myotome; *n.cr.* neural crest; *n.gr.* neural groove; *not.pl.* notochordal plate; *n.pl.* neural plate;
n.t. neural tube; *pg.r.* postganglionic ramus; *S.c.* Schwann cells; *som.* somite; *sp.n.* spinal
nerve; *symp.c.* sympathetic cells; *v.h.c.* ventral horn cells; *visc.r.* visceral ramus; *v.sp.r.*
ventral spinal root.
(After Hamilton, Boyd, and Mossman.)

is part of the movement of convergence by which the tissues of the
embryo move dorsally (p. 609).

The margins of the neural groove meet first in the mid-region of
the body and the folds then proceed to fuse in directions forwards and
backwards from this (Fig. 284). The ends of the tube remain open

to the amniotic cavity for a while by the *anterior* and *posterior neuro-pores*. The posterior neuropore closes in such a way that the neural tube opens to the hind gut by a *neurenteric canal* (p. 604).

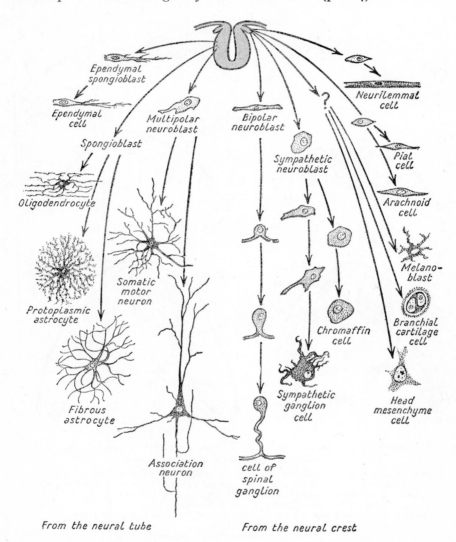

Ependymal spongioblast

Ependymal cell

Multipolar neuroblast

Bipolar neuroblast

Neurilemmal cell

Spongioblast

Sympathetic neuroblast

Pial cell

Oligodendrocyte

Arachnoid cell

Protoplasmic astrocyte

Somatic motor neuron

Melano-blast

Fibrous astrocyte

Chromaffin cell

Branchial cartilage cell

Sympathetic ganglion cell

Head mesenchyme cell

Association neuron

cell of spinal ganglion

From the neural tube   *From the neural crest*

FIG. 324. Cell types derived from the neural tube and neural crest.

All the nervous tissue throughout the body develops from cells within the neural tube and the neighbouring tissue, the neural crest. The great majority of the neurons, of course, remain within the main axis of the brain and spinal cord. The neuroblasts that will give rise to the neurons of the autonomic nervous system migrate out along certain of the nerves before they complete their differentiation. There have been reports of the formation of neurons in the wall of the gut from endoderm, but this has never been proved. The only other possible contributions to the nervous system come from the *placodes*, a series of patches of specialized ectoderm, which make contact with the cranial ganglia and may contribute cells to them (see Yntema, 1943).

The capacity to differentiate into nerve-cells is thus almost wholly restricted to the region of the ectoderm that overlies the invaginated chordamesoderm.

3. The neural crest

The ectoderm along the edges of the neural plate forms a column of cells, the neural crest, along the whole length of the axis from the level of the mesencephalon backwards. These cells migrate laterally and produce the following tissues (Fig. 324). (1) The cells of the dorsal root ganglia, which form a segmental series, including the cranial ganglia V, VII, IX, X, and XI, and all the spinal ganglia. The cells of the VIIIth nerve also belong to this series. (2) Cells of the autonomic system, which migrate to their positions in the ganglia or viscera (p. 385). (3) Cells of the adrenal medulla and other chromaffin tissue (p. 539). (4) The Schwann cells (neurilemmal cells) of all the peripheral nerves. (5) The cartilages of the branchial arches (p. 726). (6) The melanoblasts of the skin. (7) The cells of the leptomeninges (pia and arachnoid) may perhaps also arise from the neural crest.

The neural crest cells evidently have special powers of movement and differentiation, which are presumably the result of their position at the margin of the region of influence of the chordamesoderm upon the ectoderm (see Horstadius, 1950).

4. Development within the nervous system

The elaborate organization of the nervous tissue is arrived at by a series of processes:

1. Proliferation.
2. Cell death.
3. Migration.
4. Differentiation.
5. Outgrowth.
6. Functional differentiation.
7. Learning.

The earlier of these processes take place mainly under the influence of heredity, the later of the environment. Together they lead to the production of a nervous system that is able to produce actions that are accurate forecasts because they are based upon the memories provided both by the hereditary system and by the experience of the individual.

Proliferation occurs by mitosis in the region of the neural tube near to the central canal and the resultant cells migrate outwards towards the surface, so that layers of cells are formed. In the wall of the tube it is possible to recognize three layers: an inner *ependymal layer*, middle *mantle layer*, and outer *marginal layer*. The ependyma becomes the lining of the ventricles. The mantle layer contains the *neuroblasts*, which become neurons, and the *spongioblasts*, which become glia cells (Fig. 324). The marginal layer develops into the white matter.

The shape of the developing nervous system is determined by the fact that proliferation and migration do not occur uniformly throughout. Moreover, some of the early neuroblasts fail to complete their differentiation, they undergo cytolysis, and disappear. Local aggregations of cells are therefore not necessarily the result of local proliferation; they may be formed by migration, or by differential cytolysis and cell death.

The thickness of the wall thus comes to differ from place to place and bulges and foldings follow. Unfortunately we do not know in detail what determines the pattern of migration, proliferation, and cell death. At an early stage in its differentiation the neural tube shows some sign of segmental structure. In the mouse grooves divide the brain first into a series of six *proneuromeres*, which are then replaced by twice that number of *neuromeres* (Bergquist and Källen, 1953). These in turn disappear and later a series of 'transversal-bands' divides the neuraxis. The significance of this segmentation of the neural tube is uncertain (Källen, 1953). The 'segments' do not obviously correspond to those of the mesoderm or nerve roots. The grooves and bulges are the result of unequal cell proliferation, cell migration, and cytolysis, and this difference along the body axis is another sign of the tendency to repetitive or rhythmic processes, which is so characteristic of vertebrate development.

5. Development of the neuroglia

The spongioblasts remain attached for a time by processes to the inner and outer membranes of the neural tube. Some of them, the *ependymal cells*, remain attached throughout life to the inner layer and thus form the lining of the central canal. Others lose both attachments and become *astrocytoblasts*, differentiating into astrocytes or oligo-

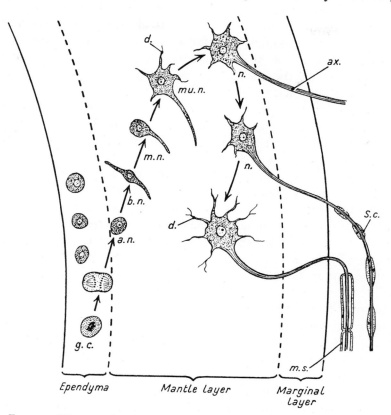

FIG. 325. Diagrams showing stages in the development of a motor neuron.

Mitosis of a germinal cell (*g.c.*) in the ependymal layer produces an apolar neuroblast (*a.n.*), which migrates into the mantle layer, and a daughter germinal cell. The former cell becomes a bipolar neuroblast (*b.n.*) by the growth of two processes one of which is then absorbed while the other becomes the axon (*ax.*) making the cell a monopolar neuroblast (*m.n.*). Dendrites (*d.*) grow out, forming a multipolar neuroblast (*mu.n.*). The axon grows into the marginal layer and beyond, establishing the cell as a neuron (*n.*). Schwann cells (*S.c.*) become attached to the axon and a myelin sheath (*m.s.*) is secreted.

(After Hamilton *et al.*)

dendrocytes (p. 379). The *microglia* cells are probably phagocytes of mesodermal origin (p. 380).

6. Development of the nerve-cells

The characteristic feature of the neurons is the presence of long conducting processes. The factors that control the growth and branching of the axoplasm to form the axons and dendrites are responsible for the whole organization of the nervous system. New nervous material is synthesized only within the nerve-cell body and the large amount of ribosenucleotides (Nissl substance) in the cytoplasm is connected with this activity. A characteristic of the differentiating nerve-cell is that the new material tends to flow out in the form of fibres. Studies in tissue culture and during regeneration of nerves (p. 333) show that the free end of a nerve-fibre behaves as an amoeboid system, probably with a more viscous outer gel-layer and more fluid central endoplasm. Changes of form are produced by local increases and decreases of viscosity and/or thickness of the gel-layer. Cinematograph films of fibres growing in tissue culture show continual changes of shape. The terminal processes are either very fine filaments or membranous pseudopodia. As the axons elongate they cross one another making a plexus pattern, which continually changes as the axons pull upon each other. No doubt similar changes take place during normal development within the body. Even in the adult we should not assume that the finer nerve plexuses are anatomically or functionally fixed. After injury to some of the fibres rapid readjustments occur in the remainder and it may be that there are changes with function, especially in the parts that are capable of learning.

In contact with suitable surfaces the axoplasmic material 'spins out' to form nerve-fibres. Its power to do this presumably depends on the type of proteins it contains. The fact that these tend to form elongated fibrous systems is responsible for the tendency of the axoplasm to show neurofibrils.

The neuroblasts pass through the stages shown in Fig. 325. After a multipolar phase one process becomes the axon and others the dendrites. The factors controlling the direction and course of outgrowth of nerve-fibres have been much debated. Three possible guiding influences have been considered (see Willier, Weiss et al., 1955).

(1) Chemical attraction of the fibres (*Chemotaxis*—Cajal).
(2) Orientation of the fibres by electrical potential fields (Ingvar).
(3) Orientation by contact with structures already formed or by 'ultrastructural' molecular characteristics of the medium (*contact guidance*—Weiss).

No definite proof of chemical attraction or repulsion of nerve-fibres has ever been given, but it cannot be excluded. Fibres grow towards centres of active proliferation, but this is not necessarily evidence of a chemical influence. Electrical potential fields can influence direction of nerve-fibre growth in tissue culture (Marsh and Beams, 1946) but it is not certain that they do so *in vivo*.

There are abundant signs that growing nerve-fibres align themselves along nerve-fibres already formed, and along other structures. Contact guidance is therefore undoubtedly one of the main means by which the arrangement of fibres within the nervous system is produced. In a developing embryo the stresses set up by unequal rates of growth produce many surface boundaries within the nervous system and among the tissues. In addition the large molecules of the materials in the intercellular spaces may become aligned by the forces to which they are subjected. Such ultrastructural organization would provide an orientating factor for the outgrowing nerve-fibre.

The organization of the various tissues of the embryo that is provided by the hereditary system thus determines to a considerable extent the pathways along which the nerve-fibres grow, both in the central and peripheral nervous systems. Pioneering fibres grow by contact guidance along surfaces provided within the tissues. Later fibres follow these pioneers and innervate the developing tissues. Completion of the differentiation only proceeds, however, after effective connexions are formed (p. 338). There is some evidence that when a nerve-fibre has made connexion with a muscle it becomes specifically changed in a fashion characteristic only for that muscle. If a limb muscle of an amphibian larva is transplanted close to a normal limb, so that it receives nerves from the limb-nerves, it is found always to contract at the same time as the muscle of the same name in the normal limb. If a whole limb is transplanted its actions will exactly copy those of the normal limb. This must mean that when a nerve-fibre enters a given muscle its ganglion cell becomes specified by that muscle and functionally linked with other neurons supplying similar muscles, an effect known as *modulation* (Willier, Weiss *et al.*, 1955).

The patterns in which the nerve-cells are made active are, however, developed mainly under hereditary influences. A piece of spinal cord from the brachial region if isolated with a limb will produce co-ordinated movements, whereas with a piece of trunk cord the limb will make only irregular movements. The factors controlling the development of such *central action systems* appropriate to each region are unknown They must be especially important in the brain.

7. Control of differentiation in the nervous system

Much of the differentiation during early stages depends upon a pattern of regional differences imposed upon the nervous system during the first stages of its evocation. Thus a portion of the spinal cord of a chick that would normally develop into the brachial region retains the characteristics of that part of the cord even if it is transplanted to other regions. In amphibians similar experiments show, however, that considerable regulation may occur.

During the later stages of development the mutual influences of neurons upon each other and of other tissues upon them play an increasingly important part (see Detwiler, 1936). As in the case of so many other tissues the early development takes place under the control of the instructions of heredity, but the later stages of differentiation of the details of structure depend upon interaction of the cells with each other and with the environment. Thus after removal of the developing limb-bud from a chick embryo the somatic motor-cells of the ventral horn of the spinal cord are greatly reduced in size and number. Evidently when the outgrowing nerve-fibres make contact with the muscles, they receive some 'stimulus' causing them to differentiate. Indeed, this contact with the periphery is necessary for the maintenance of the structure of the nerve-fibre throughout life (p. 338). Conversely, overloading of a portion of the nervous system, for example by implantation of extra limbs in a developing chick, may lead to the presence of increased numbers of neurons in the spinal ganglia. An interesting example of such a response is seen during regeneration of the tail of a lizard that has been thrown off (*autotomy*). The new tail is innervated entirely from the remaining proximal portion of the spinal cord and spinal ganglia; whose cells then grow to an exceptionally large size (Terni, 1920).

These effects of the periphery operate to different degrees in different parts of the nervous system. After the removal of a limb-bud of a chick the cells of the corresponding spinal ganglion begin their differentiation, but in the later stages of incubation they degenerate and many of them disappear. If the primordium of the superior oblique muscle of a chick is removed the cells of the trochlear nucleus form normally, but later undergo atrophy and disappear (Hamburger, 1952; and Levi–Montalcini, 1952).

As the nervous system develops the formation of each tract and centre influences the growth of others, but there is still no full understanding of these influences. Nerve-fibres growing into a region of the brain or cord may stimulate cell proliferation there. Yet much differentiation is possible without such influences. Isolated portions of the spinal cord of chickens pass through the initial stages of differentiation normally, although deprived of the stimuli that they would receive from the ingrowth of tracts. Probably most of the early differentiation is under hereditary control, although cell and tract interactions and functional influences are necessary for the development and maintenance of the details of neuronal structure on which the working of the system depends.

An elaborate system of influences by chemical substances, by contact and by electrical factors may be at work. An experiment showing one aspect of these is to graft tumour-cells to the extra-embryonic membranes of the chick. Following this operation there is excessive development of the sympathetic ganglia of the host; organs such as the mesonephros, which normally have few nerve-fibres, become packed with them (Levi–Montalcini, 1952). It is presumed that the tumour produces a blood-borne hormonal substance that stimulates development of sympathetic cells and fibres.

8. Maturation of nerve-fibres

The axons that grow out from nerve-cells are at first thin and without myelin sheaths. After connexion with the periphery each nerve-fibre proceeds to increase until it reaches a diameter specific to its function. Thus somatic motor fibres are up to 20μ in diameter in a mammal and are medullated, whilst sympathetic postganglionics are 1μ or less in diameter and without myelin sheath (p. 385). Little is known of the developmental factors that produce this arrangement. Myelin is formed on peripheral nerve-fibres by collaboration between the axon and the Schwann cells that migrate along the nerves from the neural crest (p. 769), but this does not tell us how it is determined that only some fibres become large and have thick myelin sheaths. Probably all peripheral nerve-fibres lie within the protoplasm of Schwann cells or the related Remak cells. The myelin sheath is a series of layers of phosphatide and protein produced by collaboration between the surfaces of the nerve-fibre and sheath-cell. When these layers are thick enough to be visible after staining with osmic acid the fibre is said to be 'myelinated'. Very small nerve-fibres such as the postganglionics of the autonomic nervous system are said to be non-myelinated, but even these have distinct lipo-protein sheaths.

The diameter increase of a growing fibre is a function of the connexion it makes peripherally and the amount of stimulation falling upon the dendrites of its cell: the relation of double dependence (p. 22). Thus once again we see that differentiation is a result of the interaction between certain powers possessed by the cell and stimuli

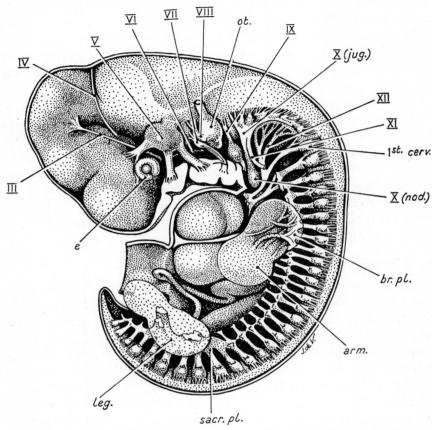

FIG. 326. Drawing of a reconstruction of the nervous system of a 10 mm. human embryo.

III, Oculomotor; IV, trochlear; V, trigeminal; VI, abducent; VII, facial; VIII, auditory; IX, glossopharyngeal; X (*jug.*), jugular ganglion of vagus; X (*nod.*), nodose ganglion of vagus; XI, accessory; XII, hypoglossal; *br.pl.* brachial plexus; *1st cerv.* first cervical; *e.* eye; *ot.* otic vesicle; *sacr.pl.* sacral plexus. (After Streeter, *Am. J. Anat.* 1908.)

provided by the surroundings. The nerve-cell body, with its hereditary equipment, is able to synthesize new material; the extent to which this material accumulates is determined by the amount of stimulation received by the cell. The factors controlling the sizes of the various types of nerve-fibre are discussed on p. 345. An important influence is the formation of the inelastic connective tissue-sheaths of the endo-, peri-, and epineurium.

Even less is known about the determination of cell and fibre size in the central nervous system. The oligodendrocytes are similar to the peripheral Schwann cells in that they wrap around the fibres

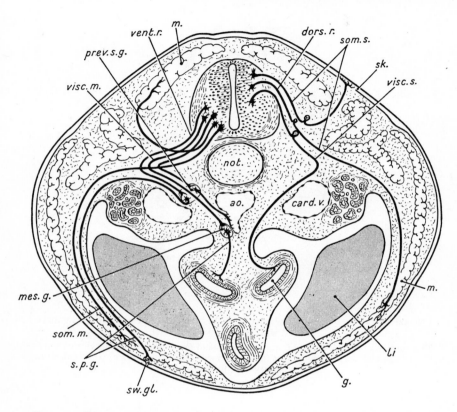

FIG. 327. Diagram showing the arrangement of the component fibres of spinal nerves.

ao. aorta; *card.v.* cardinal vein; *dors.r.* dorsal root; *g.* gut; *li.* liver; *m.* muscle; *mes.g.* mesenteric ganglion; *not.* notochord; *prev.s.g.* prevertebral sympathetic ganglion; *sk.* skin; *som.m.* somatic motor fibre; *som.s.* somatic sensory fibre; *s.p.g.* sympathetic postganglionic fibre; *sw.gl.* sweat gland; *vent.r.* ventral root; *visc.m.* visceral motor fibre (preganglionic); *visc.s.* visceral sensory fibre. (After Froriep.)

and presumably assist in myelin production. Myelination occurs at different times in the various tracts. It begins at about the fourth month in man, in the ventral roots. The dorsal roots follow later and then the fibres of the dorsal columns. Of the descending motor tracts the phylogenetically older vestibulo- and rubro-spinal become myelinated before the pyramidal (cortico-spinal), whose sheaths are not developed until the second year or later.

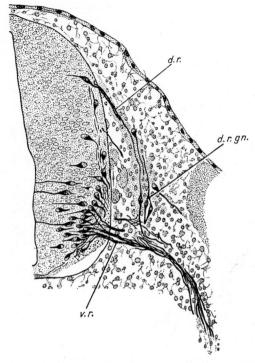

FIG. 328. Drawing of a transverse section of the neural tube of a 10 mm. pig embryo
(stained with silver to show axons).

The dorsal root (*d.r.*) is formed from the processes of neuroblasts in the dorsal root ganglion (*d.r.gn.*) whilst the ventral root (*v.r.*) is formed from the processes of neuroblasts in
the cord. (After Held.)

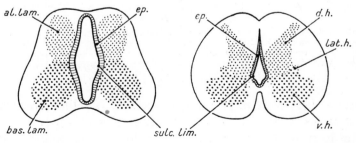

FIG. 329. Diagrammatic transverse sections of the spinal cord showing differentiation of the dorsal, ventral, and lateral horns.

al. lam. alar lamina; *bas. lam.* basal lamina; *d.h.* dorsal horn; *ep.* ependyma; *lat.h.* lateral
horn; *sulc.lim.* sulcus limitans; *v.h.* ventral horn.

9. Development of peripheral nerves

The nerve-trunks thus develop by outgrowth of processes from the ventral horn cells, spinal root ganglia and preganglionic autonomic fibres. The outgrowing fibres become aggregated into nerve-trunks under hereditary influences. The pattern is essentially segmental and even in a mammal it is rather regular along the whole length of the body (Fig. 326). In each segment there can be recognized a dorsal and a ventral root (Figs. 327 and 328). The former contains afferent fibres, processes of the cells of the dorsal root ganglion, and in the head region also some special visceral motor and autonomic preganglionic fibres. The ventral roots contain somatic motor fibres and in the thoraco-lumbar region preganglionic sympathetic fibres (p. 385). Afferent fibres do not usually pass in ventral roots, except in those of the eye-muscle nerves and in the hypoglossal nerve. The dorsal and ventral roots join in the spinal region, but not in the head (p. 206).

10. Development of the spinal cord

When the cells of the mantle layer differentiate the spinal cord comes to have thick walls and the narrow central canal is elongated vertically. Two distinct groups of cells can be recognized in the cord, the *alar plate* dorsally and the *basal plate* ventrally (Fig. 329). A groove, the *sulcus limitans*, marks the boundary between them. The dorsal and ventral midline tissues constitute the roof-plate and floor-plate of non-nervous tissue. The dorsal cells of the alar lamina receive the endings of the somatic afferent nerve-fibres of the dorsal roots and thus constitute the *somatic sensory column* of the cord. Visceral afferent fibres end somewhat more ventrally, in the *visceral sensory column*. The cells of the basal plate constitute the motor columns, the *visceral motor*, lying more dorsally and the *somatic motor* ventral to it.

These four functional columns can be traced throughout the length of the nervous system (p. 363) but it is not yet clear what developmental factors produce their segregation.

11. Development of the brain

The brain can be regarded as essentially a forward continuation of the spinal cord. The processes of differentiation are modified to produce large aggregations of neurons, the so-called suprasegmental structures, such as the cerebrum and cerebellum. Although we do not know in detail what stimuli produce aggregations of nerve-cells in the brain there is no reason to suppose that they differ fundamentally from those operating elsewhere in the nervous system.

The developing brain is at first a simple tube (Fig. 330) but the

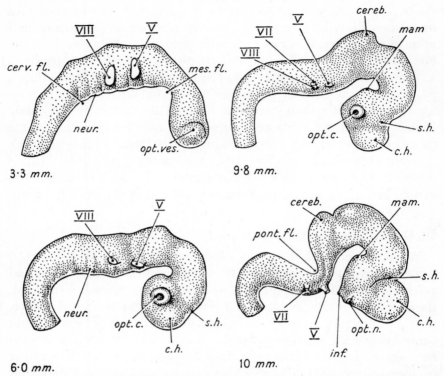

FIG. 330. Stages in the development of the brain of man. Redrawn from figures of models reconstructed from sections by Hochstetter.

IV, Trochlear nerve; V, trigeminal nerve; VII, facial nerve; VIII, auditory nerve; IX, glosso-pharyngeal nerve; X, vagus nerve.

a.c. anterior commissure; *al.lam.* alar lamina; *bas.lam.* basal lamina; *cereb.* cerebellum; *cerv.fl.* cervical flexure; *c.h.* cerebral hemisphere; *epi.* epithalamus; *e.v.cereb.* extraventricular cerebellum; *h.p.* hypophysis; *hyp.* hypothalamus; *inf.* infundibulum; *i.v.cereb.* intraventricular cerebellum; *i.v.f.* interventricular foramen; *lam.term.* lamina terminalis; *lat.vent.* lateral ventricle; *mam.* mammillary body; *med.ob.* medulla oblongata; *mes.* mesencephalon; *mes.fl.* mesencephalic flexure; *neur.* neuromere; *olf.b.* olfactory bulb; *olf.n.* olfactory nerve; *opt.c.* optic cup; *opt.ch.* optic chiasma; *opt.lu.* lumen of optic stalk; *opt.n.* optic nerve; *opt. ves.* optic vesicle; *pin.* pineal body; *pont.fl.* pontine flexure; *s.h.* sulcus hemisphericus; *sulc. lim.* sulcus limitans; *teg.* tegmentum; *thal.* thalamus; *IV.vent.r.* roof of fourth ventricle (cut edge).

walls do not thicken to the same extent throughout and thus the various flexures and outpushings are produced. At the front end of the spinal cord the central canal widens, the two sides of the mantle layer being as it were folded outwards, the roof-plate extending to form a thin non-nervous roof. This change of structure produces a sharp *cervical flexure* of the developing tube. A *mesencephalic flexure* in the same direction occurs in front of the future midbrain, at a point opposite to the front end of the notochord. This region corresponds

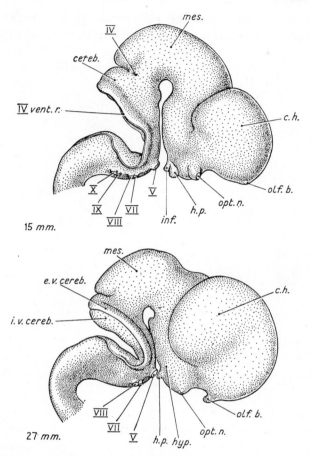

FIG. 331. Stages in the development of the brain of man (*cont.*).
(*For Key see Fig. 330.*)

to the front end of the series of segmental structures: it is the morphological front end of the body (p. 411). The first somite lies at about this level and near here arise the trigeminal and oculomotor nerves, the dorsal and ventral roots of the first segment. The somatic motor column of the basal plate therefore ends near here and the whole of the forebrain can be regarded as an extension of the afferent centres of the alar plate. This excessive growth of the dorsal region of the tube produces the marked mesencephalic flexure.

As the cerebellum develops at the front end of the hind brain a further *pontine flexure* occurs in this region (Fig. 333). With the appearance of the cerebral hemispheres there is a marked *telencephalic flexure*.

The uneven thickenings of the walls produced by unequal cell proliferation and cell migration, and perhaps also by changes of cell shape,

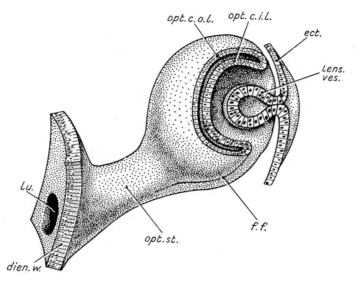

FIG. 332. Diagram of the optic cup and stalk of a 7·5 mm. human embryo.

dien.w. diencephalic wall; *ect.* ectoderm; *f.f.* foetal fissure; *lens ves.* lens vesicle; *lu.* lumen of optic stalk; *opt.c.i.l.* inner layer of optic cup; *opt.c.o.l.* outer layer of optic cup; *opt.st.* optic stalk. (After a reconstruction by Mann, 1928. *The Development of the Human Eye*, Cambridge University Press.)

lead to development of the characteristic form of the brain and ventricles. The *optic vesicle* forms very early as a lateral pouch of what is at that time nearly the front end of the tube (Figs. 330 and 331) but will become the diencephalon. The end of the optic vesicle rapidly becomes pushed in to make the optic cup and the lens differentiates from the overlying ectoderm (Fig. 332). The retina is thus morphologically a part of the lateral wall of the brain and the optic nerve represents a cerebral tract and not a true peripheral nerve.

The *cerebral (telencephalic) vesicles* appear later, in front of the optic cup. The hemispheres at first bulge forwards and remain open by a wide interventricular foramen to the unpaired between-brain (diencephalon) Fig. 333. The lateral wall of the diencephalon becomes the thalamus, receiving the pathways from the optic, auditory, and other

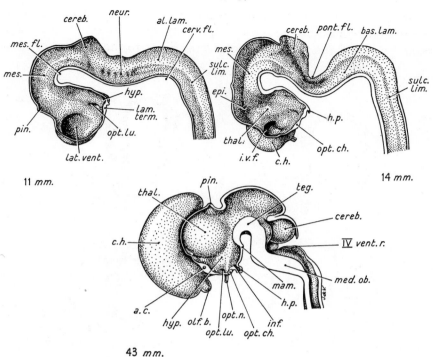

FIG. 333. Stages in development of human brain seen in models from the medial sagittal plane. Not to the same scale. Lettering as for Fig. 330.

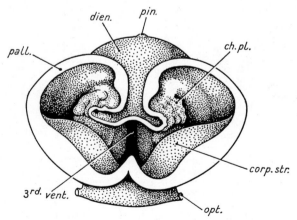

FIG. 334. Drawing of a model of the forebrain of a 17 mm. human embryo. A cut has been made across the hemispheres and the view is from the front.

ch.pl. choroid plexus of lateral ventricle; *corp.str.* corpus striatum; *dien.* diencephalon; *opt.* optic nerve; *pall.* pallium; *pin.* pineal body; *3rd vent.* third ventricle. (After Hochstetter.)

afferent systems. This thalamic region is seen during development to be in direct continuity with the lateral wall of the cerebral hemisphere (Fig. 334) and the thalamic nuclei send fibres to the hemisphere and

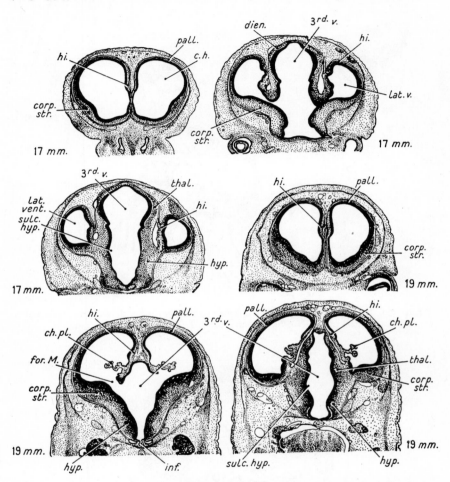

FIG. 335. Transverse sections at different levels through the forebrains of 17 and 19 mm. human embryos.

c.h. cerebral hemisphere; *ch.pl.* choroid plexus of lateral ventricle; *corp.str.* corpus striatum; *dien.* diencephalon; *for.M.* foramen of Monroe; *hi.* hippocampus; *hyp.* hypothalamus; *inf.* infundibulum; *lat.v.* lateral ventricle; *pall.* pallium; *sulc.hyp.* sulcus hypothalamicus; *thal.* thalamus; *3rd v.* third ventricle. (After Hochstetter.)

vice versa. The whole lateral wall of the forebrain, the original front end of the somatic sensory column thus becomes developed into an elaborate memory system providing forecasts that control much of behaviour (p. 457).

The ventral portion of the diencephalic region differentiates to form the hypothalamus (Fig. 335), perhaps representing the extreme anterior end of the visceral afferent and efferent columns (p. 779). The thalamus and hypothalamus are separated by a *hypothalamic sulcus* (Fig. 335), the forward extension of the sulcus limitans. The hypothalamus later acquires connexions with the overlying thalamus and with the cerebral hemispheres (hippocampus) and plays an important part in determining the basic 'emotional' features of the action pattern of the forebrain (p. 433).

The most ventral portion of the hypothalamus forms the infundibulum and this, with the invagination of Rathke's pouch, makes the *pituitary body*. The fact that this gland develops at the point representing morphologically the extreme front end of the body is interesting in view of the dominant part it plays in the chemical signalling system that regulates development and adult life. The whole of the front region is evidently highly developed as a linked system of nervous and glandular tissue dominating the rest of the body.

12. Further development of the cerebral hemispheres

The evaginated cerebral vesicles extend both forwards and backwards and thus come to lie on either side of the unevaginated portion, the diencephalon. Where the medial wall of the hemisphere meets the lateral wall of the diencephalon the choroid plexus is formed, projecting into the lateral ventricle (Fig. 334). The interventricular foramina now become narrowed and the walls of the hemispheres proceed to differentiate. The more ventral portion becomes thickened early to form the *corpus striatum*. This is morphologically a direct forward continuation of the thalamus, but as the hemisphere grows backwards the corpus striatum comes to lie lateral to the thalamus (Fig. 334). It becomes continuous with the wall of the latter and fibres passing between the thalamus and the cortex grow through the corpus striatum as the *internal capsule*.

The dorsal portion of the wall of the hemisphere is the *pallium*, within which the cerebral cortex develops. The greater part of this becomes the *neocortex* (*neopallium*), by migration of the cells away from the ventricle to give the characteristically layered structure. The differentiation first appears in the parietal region, concurrently with the arrival of the first thalamo-cortical fibres. The medio-dorsal wall of each hemisphere develops into a distinct type of cortex, the *hippocampus* (p. 432). The most lateral portion of the pallium also develops into the characteristic *pyriform cortex*, so called because this region is large and pear-shaped in mammals that have a well-developed olfactory system.

The *olfactory nerves* develop by outgrowth of processes of the cells of the olfactory epithelium of the nasal sac. These grow into the extreme front end of the developing cerebral hemispheres, where the

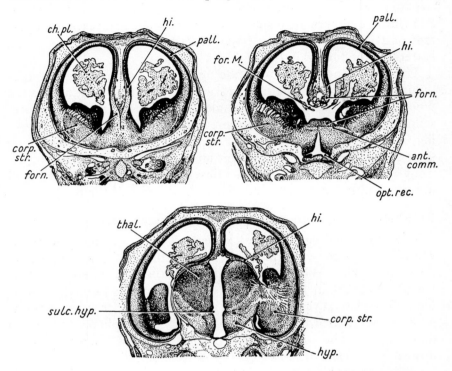

FIG. 336. Transverse sections at different levels through the forebrain of a 46 mm. human embryo.

ant.comm. anterior commissure; *forn.* fornix; *opt.rec.* optic recess. (Other abbreviations as in Fig. 335.) After Hochstetter.

olfactory bulbs then differentiate. The *olfactory tracts* join each bulb to the front part of the pyriform cortex, which is thus the part of the cortex most directly related to the olfactory function that originally dominated all forebrain activities (p. 432).

13. Cerebral commissures

The anterior end of the original neural tube (*lamina terminalis*) remains after the evagination of the cerebral hemispheres as the front wall of the diencephalon. In this lamina are formed the commissures between the two hemispheres. The *anterior commissure* is the more ventral and first to be formed (Fig. 336) and is followed by the *hippocampal commissure* above it. With the development of the neo-pallium there is a great further extension of commissural fibres, cross-ing in the *corpus callosum* and extending forwards and backwards far beyond the limits of the lamina terminalis. These crossing fibres may be said to unite the medial walls of the two hemispheres and they largely replace the hippocampus in the anterior region.

14. Later differentiation in the nervous system

The time at which the parts of the brain differentiate varies greatly; in general the control systems that are produced by heredity alone are laid down first. The parts responsible for acquiring memories during the lifetime of the individual differentiate later. At birth the mam-malian infant already possesses mechanisms for the regulation of digestion, respiration, and other functions. Even these basic regula-tion systems become markedly changed later. Temperature regula-tion, for instance, is imperfect in the new-born child (p. 40) and the operations of digestion later come under higher nervous control to a considerable extent (p. 237).

Little is known about the factors that control the laying down of the detailed connexions within the nervous system. The fibres and cells certainly greatly influence each other and probably these influences depend upon the patterns in which the various cells are thrown into action by the stimuli they receive from the environment. In a chick after removal of the otocyst the cochlear centres differentiate normally up to eleven days, but the cells then undergo atrophy and mostly dis-appear. On the other hand, the vestibular nuclei differentiate almost normally (Hamburger, 1952). The difference probably depends on the fact that the cochlear nuclei receive all their fibres from the ear, whereas the cells of the vestibular nucleus are influenced from many other sources.

There is further evidence from adults that cells whose input comes only from one source undergo atrophy if that source is removed. A most striking example of this *transneuronal degeneration* is the dis-appearance of the cells of the lateral geniculate body after removal of an eye or severance of the optic nerve.

It is probable, therefore, that the size reached by nerve-cells and their processes depends upon the stimulation that they receive from the action of neighbouring nerve-fibres. This stimulation may well be the factor that determines the details of axonal and dendritic branching and therefore of the synaptic relationship. There is much reason to think that such influences provide the basis for the learning process within the nervous system. Even in the adult cutting off the input to a nerve-cell may lead to its atrophy. It is plausible to suppose that during development changes in the amount of stimulation received lead to metabolic changes and to increase or decrease in dendritic ramifications and extent of synaptic contact. Every time that one

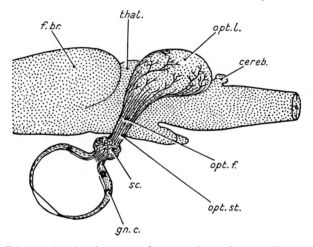

FIG. 337. Diagram showing the course of regenerating optic nerve-fibres after section of the optic nerve of an amphibian.

The optic nerve-fibres (*opt.f.*) grow out from ganglion cells (*gn.c.*) in the ganglion cell layer of the retina. They grow towards the brain in the optic stalk (*opt.st.*) becoming tangled at the region of section, the scar (*sc.*) and finally cross completely in the chiasma to the optic lobe (*opt.l.*) of the opposite side. *cereb.* cerebellum; *f.br.* forebrain; *thal.* thalamus.
(After Sperry, *Growth Symposium*, **10**, 1951.)

neuron excites another some small change may be made in the metabolic processes of the latter, leading to increased synthesis or retention of protein or other material, and hence to growth.

Power to retain a memory record as a result of past functioning is one of the most characteristic functions of the higher nervous centres, especially the cerebral cortex. Evidently differentiation within this tissue depends on the setting up of some form of link between sets of neurons that have previously been excited together, so constituting an engram or representation of that pattern of excitation. The nature of the significant relations between cortical cells is not known and it is therefore impossible as yet to investigate the means by which it is set up. Some of the histological differences between the cortical areas are present at birth in man and cannot therefore depend upon functional influences. Yet in people suffering from hereditary blindness or lack of one of the other main receptors, reductions have been observed in the numbers of cells in the corresponding primary cortical areas The detailed arrangements of the axons and dendrites have not been investigated in these conditions.

When nerve-cells and fibres have come under the influence of particular connexions they become as it were specified or 'stamped' and often have only limited powers of later readjustment. Remarkable instances of this specification of nerve-cells have been shown by

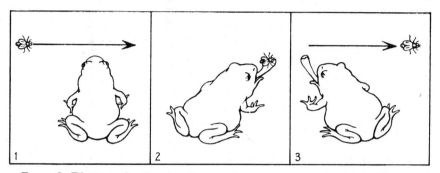

FIG. 338. Diagrams showing the effect on visuomotor responses of rotation of the eyes of a toad through 180° and severance of the optic nerve with subsequent regeneration.

1 and 2 show the capture of a fly moving from left to right in front of a toad with normal vision. 3 shows the toad, whose eyes have been rotated 180°, failing to capture the fly because the movement made is appropriate to the retinal image of the fly prior to rotation of the eyes. (Data from Sperry, *Growth Symposium*, **10**, 1951.)

studies of the regeneration of the nervous system, especially in amphibians, where the fibres of the optic nerve are able to regenerate after severance (Fig. 337) and the animals recover their normal power of snapping in the direction of an object moving in the visual field. During regeneration nerve-fibres become much intermingled at the point of union of the two cut stumps (p. 335) and it is remarkable that sufficiently 'correct' connexions can be re-formed to allow of such precise snapping movements.

If the eyes are rotated through 180° an amphibian will make reversed or 'incorrect' snapping movements (Fig. 338). If after such rotation the optic nerves are severed and regeneration is allowed the movements still take place in the reversed direction and continue to do so even after months of 'practice'.

The explanation of these remarkable results is not clear. The regenerating nerve-fibres can be shown to be chaotically interwoven at the point of union of the nerves, nevertheless they seem to make connexions in the midbrain similar to those of a normal animal. Sperry

(1951) interprets this result as showing that the nerve-fibres from the different parts of the retina differ in 'quality' and that each makes appropriate connexions in the brain. It is difficult to believe that such exact reconnexion is achieved and it may be rather that each fibre makes widespread connexions but that only certain sets of them are effective. If this is so the 'specificity' lies in the patterns of activity that are possible among the cells of the brain. It is not known whether such patterns develop as a result of hereditary processes or of learning, but once established they are very persistent. There is evidence that this is true also in mammals, except perhaps in the cerebral cortex, which is able to readjust its activities even relatively late in life. If nerves that normally produce flexion in a rat are made by transplantation and regeneration to have connexion with extensor muscles there will be a persistent reversal of function, and this is not corrected even by years of training. The motor neurons continue to discharge in their original action phase, without adjustment to the reversed anatomical arrangement. After similar operations in man some readjustment is possible because of the great plasticity provided by the cerebral cortex.

BIBLIOGRAPHY

GENERAL WORKS

BARCROFT, J. (1934). *Features in the Architecture of Physiological Function.* Cambridge: Cambridge University Press.

CAMERON, G. R. (1952). *Pathology of the Cell.* Edinburgh: Oliver & Boyd.

CLARK, W. E., LE GROS, and MEDAWAR, P. B. (1945). *Essays on Growth and Form,* presented to D'Arcy Wentworth Thompson. Edited by W. E. Le Gros Clark and P. B. Medawar. Oxford: Clarendon Press.

CUNNINGHAM, D. J. (1951). *Cunningham's Text-book of Anatomy.* Edited by J. C. Brash. 9th edition. London: Oxford University Press.

FULTON, J. F. (1951). *Physiology of the Nervous System.* 3rd edition, revised. New York: Oxford University Press.

GRASSÉ, P. (1955). *Traité de Zoologie. Mammifères.* Tome XVII. Masson, Paris.

GRAY, H. (1954). *Gray's Anatomy Descriptive and Applied.* Edited by T. B. Johnston and J. Whillis. 31st edition. London: Longmans, Green.

HAM, A. W. (1953). *Histology.* 2nd edition. London: J. B. Lippincott.

MAXIMOW, A. A., and BLOOM, W. (1952). *A Textbook of Histology.* 6th edition. London: W. B. Saunders.

RANSON, S. W. (1953). *The Anatomy of the Nervous System.* Revised by S. L. Clark. 9th edition. Philadelphia and London: W. B. Saunders.

ROMER, A. S. (1949). *The Vertebrate Body.* Philadelphia and London: W. B. Saunders.

SHERRINGTON, C. S. (1947). *Integrative Action of the Nervous System.* Cambridge: Cambridge University Press.

SINGER, C. (1928). *A Short History of Medicine.* Oxford: Clarendon Press.

STEVENS, S. S. (1951). *Handbook of Experimental Psychology.* London: Chapman & Hall.

YOUNG, J. Z. (1950). *The Life of Vertebrates.* Oxford: Clarendon Press.

CHAPTER I

ASHBY, W. ROSS (1952). *Design for a Brain.* London: Chapman & Hall.

BALDWIN, E. (1952). *Dynamic Aspects of Biochemistry.* 2nd edition. Cambridge: Cambridge University Press.

CANNON, W. B. (1932). *The Wisdom of the Body.* New York: W. W. Norton.

HALDANE, J. B. S., and SPURWAY, H. (1954). A statistical analysis of communication in 'Apis mellifera' and a comparison with communication in other animals. *Insectes Sociaux,* **1,** 247–83.

JACKSON, W. (1953). *Communication Theory.* Papers read at a Symposium on 'Applications of Communication Theory', 22–26 September 1952. Edited by Willis Jackson. London: Butterworth's Scientific Publications.

JÓHANNESSON, A. (1949). *Origin of Language.* Reykjavík: H. F. Leiftur.

MACKAY, D. M. (1950). The nomenclature of information theory. *Proceedings of Symposium on Information Theory,* Ministry of Supply, London. September 1950.

RUCH, T. C. (1951). *Motor Systems* in *Handbook of Experimental Psychology.* Edited by S. S. Stevens. London: Chapman & Hall.

SCHOENHEIMER, R. (1946). *The Dynamic State of Body Constituents.* 2nd edition. Cambridge, Mass.: Harvard University Press.

SOMMERHOFF, G. (1950). *Analytical Biology*. London: Oxford University Press.
YOUNG, J. Z. (1946). 'Effects of use and disuse on nerve and muscle.' (Sydney Ringer Memorial Lecture, University College Hospital Medical School.) *Lancet*, **2**, 109.

CHAPTER II

BILLINGHAM, R. E., and MEDAWAR, P. B. (1948). 'Pigment spread and cell heredity in guinea-pigs' skin.' *Heredity*, **2**, 29–47.
MARTIN, C. J. (1902). 'Thermal adjustment and respiratory exchange in Monotremes and Marsupials; a study in the development of homoeothermism.' *Philos. Trans.*, B. **195**, 1–37.
PORTMANN, A. (1952). *Animal Forms and Patterns: a Study of the Appearance of Animals*. (Translated by Hella Czech.) London: Faber & Faber.
ROBINSON, S. (1952). 'Physiological effects of heat and cold.' *Ann. Rev. Physiol.* **14**, 73–96.

CHAPTER III

ASBOE-HANSEN, G. (1954). 'The mast cell.' *Int. Rev. Cytol.* **3**, 399–435.
BEAR, R. S. (1952). 'The structure of collagen fibrils.' *Advanc. Protein Chem.* **7**, 69–160.
CHÈVREMONT, M. (1948). 'Le système histiocytaire ou réticulo-endothélial.' *Biol. Rev.* **23**, 267–95.
DEMPSEY, E. W., and LANSING, A. I. (1954). 'Elastic tissue.' *Int. Rev. Cytol.* **3**, 437–53.
FITTON JACKSON, SYLVIA (1954). 'The formation of connective and skeletal tissues.' *Proc. roy. Soc.*, B. **142**, 536–48.
RANDALL, J. T. (1953). *Nature and Structure of Collagen*. London: Butterworth.

CHAPTER IV

APPLETON, A. B. (1934). 'Postural deformities and bone growth.' *Lancet*, **1**, 451–4.
DALLEMAGNE, M. J. (1950). 'The physiology of supporting tissue.' *Ann. Rev. Physiol.* **12**, 101–18.
FELTS, W. J. L. (1954). 'The prenatal development of the human femur.' *Amer. J. Anat.* **94**, 1–44.
GARDNER, E. (1950). 'Physiology of movable joints.' *Physiol. Rev.* **30**, 127–76.
GLUCKSMANN, A. (1942). 'The role of mechanical stresses in bone formation in vitro.' *J. Anat., Lond.* **76**, 231–9.
HANCOX, N. M. (1949). 'The osteoclast.' *Biol. Rev.* **24**, 448–71.

CHAPTER V

EVANS, F. GAYNOR (1953). 'Methods of studying the biomechanical significance of bone form.' *Amer. J. phys. Anthrop.* N.S. **11**, 413–35.
KOCH, J. C. (1917). 'The laws of bone architecture.' *Amer. J. Anat.* **21**, 177–298.
MURRAY, P. D. F. (1936). *Bones*. Cambridge: Cambridge University Press.
PAUWELS, F. (1948). 'Die Bedeutung der Bauprinzipien des Stütz- und Bewegungsapparates für die Beanspruchung der Röhrenknochen.' *Z. Anat. EntwGesch.* **114**, 129–80.

CHAPTER VI

ASTBURY, W. T. (1933). *Fundamentals of Fibre Structure*. London: Oxford University Press.
COUTEAUX, R., and TAXI, J. (1952). 'Recherches histochimiques sur la distribution

des activités cholinestérasiques au niveau de la synapse myoneurale.' *Arch. Anat. micr.* **41**, 352–92.

ELFTMAN, H. (1941). 'The action of muscles in the body.' *Biol. Symp.* **3**, 191–209.

FATT, P., and KATZ, B. (1951). 'An analysis of the end-plate potential recorded with an intra-cellular electrode.' *J. Physiol.* **115**, 320–70.

—— —— (1953). 'Chemo-receptor activity at the motor end-plate.' *Acta. physiol. scand.*, **29**, 117–25.

HANSON, J., and HUXLEY, H. E. (1955). 'The structural basis of contraction in striated muscle.' *Symp. Soc. exp. Biol.* **9**, 228–70.

HILL, A. V. (1927). *Living Machinery.* London: G. Bell.

—— (1950). 'The dimensions of animals and their muscular dynamics.' *Proc. roy. Instn G.B.*, **34**, 450–71.

HUNT, C. C., and KUFFLER, S. W. (1954). 'Motor innervation of skeletal muscle: multiple innervation of individual muscle fibres and motor unit function.' *J. Physiol.* **126**, 293–303.

HUXLEY, A. F., and NIEDERGERKE, R. (1954). 'Interference microscopy of living muscle fibres.' *Nature, Lond.* **173**, 971–3.

HUXLEY, H., and HANSON, JEAN (1954). 'Changes in the cross-striations of muscle during contraction and stretch and their structural interpretation.' *Nature, Lond.* **173**, 973–6.

JONES, W. M., and BARER, R. (1948). 'Electron microscopy of the sarcolemma.' *Nature, Lond.* **161**, 1012.

MUNRO FOX, H., GILCHRIST, B. M., and PHEAR, E. A. (1951). 'Functions of haemoglobin in *Daphnia.*' *Proc. roy. Soc.*, B. **138**, 514–28.

CHAPTER VII

GRAY, J. (1944). 'Studies in the mechanics of the tetrapod skeleton.' *J. exp. Biol.* **20**, 88–116.

THOMPSON, D'ARCY W. (1942). *On Growth and Form.* Cambridge: Cambridge University Press.

CHAPTER VIII

DARCUS, H. D. (1951). 'The maximum torques developed in pronation and supination of the right hand.' *J. Anat., Lond.* **85**, 55–67.

CHAPTER IX

BARNETT, C. H., and NAPIER, J. R. (1953). 'The form and mobility of the fibula in metatherian mammals.' *J. Anat., Lond.* **87**, 207–13.

ELFTMAN, H. (1944). 'The bipedal walking of the chimpanzee.' *J. Mammal.* **25**, 67–71.

HAINES, R. WHEELER (1953). 'The early development of the femoro-tibial and tibio-fibular joints.' *J. Anat., Lond.* **87**, 192–206.

HICKS, J. H. (1953). 'The mechanics of the foot. I. The joints.' *J. Anat., Lond.* **87**, 345–57.

HOWELL, A. B. (1938). 'Morphogenesis of the architecture of the hip and thigh.' *J. Morph.* **62**, 177–218.

JOSEPH, J., and NIGHTINGALE, A. (1954). 'Electromyography of muscles of posture: thigh muscles in males.' *J. Physiol.* **126**, 81–85.

CHAPTER X

De BEER, G. R. (1937). *The Development of the Vertebrate Skull.* Oxford: Clarendon Press.

CHAPTER XI

GREGORY, W. K. (1934). 'A half century of trituberculy, the Cope-Osborn theory of dental evolution.' *Proc. Amer. phil. Soc.* **73**, 169–317.

KUTUZOV, HELEN, and SICHER, H. (1952). 'Anatomy and function of the palate in the white rat.' *Anat. Rec.* **114**, 67–84.

ORBAN, B. (1953). *Oral Histology and Embryology.* 3rd edition. London: Henry Kimpton.

ROMER, A. S. (1947). *Vertebrate Paleontology.* 2nd edition. Chicago: University of Chicago Press.

CHAPTER XII

DALTON, A. J. (1951). 'Electron micrography of epithelial cells of the gastro-intestinal tract and pancreas.' *Amer. J. Anat.* **89**, 109–33.

GREGORY, R. A. (1954). 'The digestive system.' *Ann. Rev. Physiol.* **16**, 155–74.

JACOBSON, L. F., and NOER, R. J. (1952). 'The vascular pattern of the intestinal villi in various laboratory animals and man.' *Anat. Rec.* **114**, 85–101.

CHAPTER XIII

BARTLEY, W., DAVIES, R. E., and KREBS, H. A. (1954). 'Active transport in animal tissues and subcellular particles.' *Proc. roy. Soc.*, B. **142**, 187–96.

DOUGHERTY, T. F., and DOUGHERTY, JEAN H. (1953). 'Blood: formed elements.' *Ann. Rev. Physiol.* **15**, 195–212.

FARR, R. S. (1951). 'Experiments on the fate of the lymphocyte.' *Anat. Rec.* **109**, 515–33.

JAQUES, L. B. (1954). 'Blood clotting and hemostasis.' *Ann. Rev. Physiol.* **16**, 175–214.

MANERY, J. F. (1954). 'Water and electrolyte metabolism.' *Physiol. Rev.* **34**, 334–417.

PANTIN, C. F. A. (1931). 'The origin of the composition of the body fluids of animals.' *Biol. Rev.* **6**, 459–82.

RADVIN, I. S., WALKER, J. M., and RHOADS, J. E. (1953). 'Blood volume maintenance and regulation.' *Ann. Rev. Physiol.* **15**, 165–94.

YOFFEY, J. M. (1950). 'The mammalian lymphocyte.' *Biol. Rev.* **25**, 314–43.

CHAPTER XIV

BARCROFT, H. (1954). 'Peripheral circulation.' *Ann. Rev. Physiol.* **16**, 215–42.

BURTON, A. C. (1953). 'Peripheral circulation.' *Ann. Rev. Physiol.* **15**, 213–46.

SOULIÉ, P. (1954). 'Heart.' *Ann. Rev. Physiol.* **16**, 243–68.

CHAPTER XV

COMROE, J. H. (1954). 'Respiration.' *Ann. Rev. Physiol.* **16**, 135–54.

LOW, F. N. (1952). 'Electron microscopy of the rat lung.' *Anat. Rec.* **113**, 437–49.

SWIGART, R. H., and KANE, D. J. (1954). 'Electron microscopic observations of pulmonary alveoli.' *Anat. Rec.* **118**, 57–71.

CHAPTER XVI

BERLINER, R. W. (1954). 'The kidney.' *Ann. Rev. Physiol.* **16**, 269–304.

KEITH, N. M. (1953). 'Water metabolism.' *Ann. Rev. Physiol.* **15**, 63–84.

SELKURT, E. E. (1954). 'Sodium excretion by the mammalian kidney.' *Physiol. Rev.* **34**, 287–333.

SJÖSTRAND, F. S., and RHODIN, J. (1953). 'The ultrastructure of the proximal convoluted tubules of the mouse kidney as revealed by high resolution electron microscopy. *Exp. Cell Res.* **4**, 426–56.

SMITH, HOMER W. (1953). *From Fish to Philosopher*. Boston: Little, Brown & Co.

CHAPTER XVII

ARIËNS KAPPERS, C. U., HUBER, G. C., and CROSBY, E. C. (1936). *The comparative anatomy of the nervous system of vertebrates, including man.* Macmillan, New York.

Cold Spr. Harb. Symp. quant. Biol. XVII (1952). The neuron.

CREED, R. S., DENNY-BROWN, D., ECCLES, J. C., LIDDELL, E. G. T., and SHER-RINGTON, C. S. (1932). *Reflex Activity of the Spinal Cord.* Oxford: The Clarendon Press.

FATT, P. (1954). 'Biophysics of junctional transmission.' *Physiol. Rev.* **34**, 674–710.

GEREN, B. B. (1954). 'The formation from the Schwann cell surface of myelin in the peripheral nerves of chick embryos.' *Exp. Cell. Res.* **7**, 558–62.

HESS, A., and YOUNG, J. Z. (1952). 'The nodes of Ranvier.' *Proc. roy. Soc.*, B. **140**, 301–20.

HODGKIN, A. L. (1951). 'The ionic basis of electrical activity in nerve and muscle.' *Biol. Rev.* **26**, 339–409.

—— HUXLEY, A. F., and KATZ, B. (1952). 'Measurement of current-voltage relations in the membrane of the giant axon of *Loligo*.' *J. Physiol.* **116**, 424–48.

KATZ, B. (1939). *Electric Excitation of Nerve.* London: Oxford University Press.

MURALT, A. v. (1954). 'Excitation and conduction in peripheral nerves.' *Ann. Rev. Physiol.* **16**, 305–24.

YOUNG, J. Z. (1945). 'The history of the shape of a nerve fibre.' In *Essays on Growth and Form* presented to D'Arcy W. Thompson, p. 41. Edited by W. E. Le Gros Clark and P. B. Medawar. Oxford: Clarendon Press.

CHAPTER XVIII

BARKER, D. (1948). 'The innervation of the muscle-spindle.' *Quart. J. micr. Sci.* **89**, 143–86.

FERNAND, V. S. V., and YOUNG, J. Z. (1951). 'The size of the nerve fibres of muscle nerves.' *Proc. roy. Soc.*, B. **139**, 38–58.

CHAPTER XIX

BROOKHART, J. M. (1954). 'Somatic functions of the central nervous system.' *Ann. Rev. Physiol.* **16**, 325–48.

CHAPTER XX

BEST, C. H., and TAYLOR, N. B. (1955). *The Physiological Basis of Medical Practice* (6th edition). London: Baillière, Tindall, & Cox.

BROWN, G. L., and PASCOE, J. E. (1952). 'Conduction through the inferior mesenteric ganglion of the rabbit.' *J. Physiol.* **118**, 113–23.

DALE, H. H. (1933). 'Nomenclature of fibres in the autonomic system and their effects.' *J. Physiol.* **80**, 10–11P.

KUNTZ, A. (1946). *The Autonomic Nervous System.* 3rd edition. London: Baillière, Tindall, & Cox.

LANGLEY, J. N. (1921). *The Autonomic Nervous System.* Part I. Cambridge: W. Heffer.

MCLENNAN, H., and PASCOE, J. B. (1954). 'The origin of certain non-medullated nerve-fibres which form synapses in the inferior mesenteric ganglion of the rabbit.' *J. Physiol.* **124**, 145–56.

MITCHELL, G. A. G. (1953). *Anatomy of the Autonomic Nervous System.* Edinburgh, London: Livingstone.

CHAPTER XXI

JANSEN, J., and BRODAL, A. (1954). *Aspects of Cerebellar Anatomy*. Oslo: J. G. Tanum.

CHAPTER XXII

EULER, U. S. v. (1954). 'Visceral functions of the nervous system.' *Ann. Rev. Physiol.* **16**, 349–70.

HESS, W. R. (1948). *Die funktionelle Organisation des vegetativen Nervensystems*. Basel: Schwabe.

—— (1954). *Diencephalon*. London: W. Heinemann.

CHAPTER XXIII

BONIN, G. v. (1950). *Essay on the Cerebral Cortex*. Springfield: Thomas.

BURNS, B. D. (1955). 'The mechanism of after-bursts in cerebral cortex.' *J. Physiol.* **127**, 168–88.

CRAGG, B. G. (1954). 'The electrical responses of mammalian cerebral cortex.' *J. Physiol.* **124**, 254–68.

—— TEMPERLEY, H. N. V. (1954). 'The organisation of neurones: a co-operative analogy.' *Electroenceph. clin. Neurophysiol.* **6**, 85–92.

HEBB, D. O. (1949). *The Organization of Behavior. A Neuro-psychological Theory*. London: Chapman & Hall.

KAADA, B. R., JANSEN, J., and ANDERSEN, P. (1953). 'Stimulation of the hippocampus and medial cortical areas in unanesthetized cats.' *Neurology*, Minneapolis, **3**, 844–57.

KLÜVER, H. (1951). 'Functional differences between the occipital and temporal lobes.' In *Cerebral Mechanisms in Behavior*, p. 147. Edited by L. A. Jeffress. New York: John Wiley.

LASHLEY, K. S. (1950). 'In search of the engram.' *Symp. Soc. exp. Biol.* **4**, 454–82.

MALMO, R. B. (1954). 'Higher functions of the nervous system.' *Ann. Rev. Physiol.* **16**, 371–90.

PAPEZ, J. W. (1929). *Comparative Neurology*. New York: T. Y. Crowell.

PENFIELD, W., and RASMUSSEN, T. (1950). *The Cerebral Cortex of Man*. New York: Macmillan.

SHOLL, D. A. (1956). *The Organization of the Cerebral Cortex*. Methuen.

—— UTTLEY, A. M. (1953). 'Pattern discrimination and the visual cortex.' *Nature*, Lond. **171**, 387–8.

CHAPTER XXIV

ADRIAN, E. D. (1947). *The physical background of perception*. Waynflete lectures, 1946. Oxford: Clarendon Press.

FATT, P., and KATZ, B. (1951). An analysis of the end-plate potential recorded with an intra-cellular electrode. *J. Physiol.* **115**, 320–70.

GRANIT, R. (1955). *Receptors and sensory perception*. New Haven: Yale University Press.

JENNINGS, H. S. (1906). *Behaviour of the Lower Organisms*. New York: Columbia University Press.

TINBERGEN, N. (1951). *The Study of Instinct*. Oxford: Clarendon Press.

YOUNG, J. Z. (1938). 'The evolution of the nervous system and of the relationship of organism and environment.' In *Evolution, essays presented to E. S. Goodrich*. Edited by G. R. de Beer, 179–204. Oxford: Clarendon Press.

CHAPTER XXV

Bishop, G. H. (1946). 'Neural mechanisms of cutaneous sense.' *Physiol. Rev.* **26**, 77–102.

Cauna, N. (1954). 'Nature and functions of the papillary ridges of the digital skin.' *Anat. Rec.* **119**, 449–68.

Hagen, E., Knoche, H., Sinclair, D. C., and Weddell, G. (1953). 'The role of specialised nerve terminals in cutaneous sensibility.' *Proc. roy. Soc.*, B. **141**, 279–87.

Lele, P. P. (1954). 'Relationship between cutaneous thermal thresholds, skin temperature and cross-sectional area of the stimulus.' *J. Physiol.* **126**, 191–205.

Sanders, F. K. (1947). 'Special senses, cutaneous sensation.' *Ann. Rev. Physiol.* **9**, 553–68.

Sinclair, D. C., Weddell, G., and Zander, E. (1952). 'The relationship of cutaneous sensibility to neurohistology in the human pinna.' *J. Anat., Lond.* **86**, 402–11.

Weddell, G., and Sinclair, D. C. (1953). 'The anatomy of pain sensibility.' *Acta neuroveg. Wien*, **7**, 135–46.

Zotterman, Y. (1953). 'Special senses: thermal receptors.' *Ann. Rev. Physiol.* **15**, 357–72.

CHAPTER XXVI

Chang, Hsiang-Tung (1953). 'Physiology of vision.' *Ann. Rev. Physiol.* **15**, 373–96.

Granit, R. (1947). *Sensory Mechanisms of the Retina.* London: Oxford University Press.

Hecht, S., Shlaer, S., and Pirenne, M. H. (1942). 'Energy, quanta, and vision.' *J. gen. Physiol.* **25**, 819–40.

Motokawa, K. (1949). 'Retinal processes and their role in color vision.' *J. Neurophysiol.* **12**, 291–303.

Pirenne, M. H. (1948). *Vision and the Eye.* London: Pilot Press.

—— (1956). Physiological mechanisms of vision and the quantum nature of light. *Biol. Rev.* **31**, 194–241.

Walls, G. L. (1942). 'The vertebrate eye and its adaptive radiation.' *Cranbrook Institute of Science Bulletin*, **19**.

Willmer, E. N. (1946). *Retinal Structure and Colour Vision.* Cambridge: Cambridge University Press.

CHAPTER XXVII

Ades, H. W. (1954). 'Hearing.' *Ann. Rev. Physiol.* **16**, 391–402.

Békésy, G., and Rosenblith, W. A. (1951). 'The mechanical properties of the ear.' In *Handbook of Experimental Psychology.* Edited by S. S. Stevens, p. 1075. London: Chapman & Hall.

Galambos, R. (1954). 'Neural mechanisms of audition.' *Physiol. Rev.* **34**, 497–528.

Lowenstein, O. (1950). 'Labyrinth and equilibrium.' *Symp. Soc. exp. Biol.* **4**, 60–82.

CHAPTER XXVIII

Adrian, E. D. (1942). 'Olfactory reactions in the brain of the hedgehog.' *J. Physiol.* **100**, 459–73.

—— (1951). 'Differential sensitivity of olfactory receptors.' *J. Physiol.* **115**, 42P.

Allison, A. C. (1953). 'The structure of the olfactory bulb and its relationship to the olfactory pathways in the rabbit and the rat.' *J. comp. Neurol.* **98**, 309–53.

—— (1953). 'The morphology of the olfactory system in the vertebrates.' *Biol. Rev.* **28**, 195–244.

BARADI, A. F., and BOURNE, G. H. (1953). 'Gustatory and olfactory epithelia.' *Int. Rev. of Cytol.*, **2**, 289–330.

GASSER, H. S. (1956). Olfactory nerve fibers. *J. gen. Physiol.*, **39**, 473–96.

HENNING, H. (1926). 'Psychologie der chemischen Sinne.' In *Handbuch der normalen und pathologischen Physiologie* ed. Bethe, A. *et al.* **11**, Receptionsorgane I, pp. 393–405. Berlin: Springer.

PATTON, H. D. (1950). 'Physiology of smell and taste.' *Ann. Rev. Physiol.* **12**, 469–84.

PFAFFMANN, C. (1951). 'Taste and smell.' In *Handbook of Experimental Psychology*, pp. 1143–71. Edited by S. S. Stevens. London: Chapman & Hall.

CHAPTER XXIX

BARTTER, F. C. (1954). 'The parathyroids.' *Ann. Rev. Physiol.* **16**, 429–44.

BRAUNSTEINER, H., FELLINGER, K., and PAKESCH, F. (1953). 'Electron microscopic observations on the thyroid.' *Endocrinology*, **53**, 123–33.

GROSS, J., and PITT-RIVERS, R. (1953). 'Recent knowledge of the biochemistry of the thyroid gland.' *Vitam. and Horm.* **11**, 159–72.

KEYNES, G. (1953). 'Thymus.' *Ann. roy. Coll. Surg. Engl.* **12**, 88.

LYNN, W. GARDNER, and WACHOWSKI, H. E. (1951). 'The thyroid gland and its functions in cold-blooded vertebrates.' *Quart. Rev. Biol.* **26**, 123–68.

MAQSOOD, M. (1952). 'Thyroid functions in relation to reproduction of mammals and birds.' *Biol. Rev.* **27**, 281–319.

WILSON, A. (1952). 'Myasthenia gravis.' *Glasg. med. J.* **33**, 381.

CHAPTER XXX

EULER, U. S. v. (1951). 'Hormones of the sympathetic nervous system and the adrenal medulla.' *Brit. med. J.*, **1**, 105–8.

SAYERS, G. (1950). 'The adrenal cortex and homeostasis.' *Physiol. Rev.* **30**, 241–320.

SELYE, H. (1950). *The Physiology and Pathology of Exposure to Stress.* Montreal: Acta.

VERZÁR, F. (1952). 'The influence of corticoids on enzymes of carbohydrate metabolism.' *Vitam. and Horm.* **10**, 297–330.

ZUCKERMAN, S., BOURNE, G., and LEWES, D. (1938). 'Cyclical changes in the adrenal glands of spayed rats.' *Nature, Lond.* **142**, 754.

CHAPTER XXXI

BARGMANN, W., and SCHARRER, E. (1951). 'The site of origin of the hormones of the posterior pituitary.' *Amer. Sci.* **39**, 255–9.

GREEN, J. D. (1951). 'The comparative anatomy of the hypophysis, with special reference to its blood supply and innervation.' *Amer. J. Anat.* **88**, 225–311.

HARRIS, G. W. (1948). 'Neural control of the pituitary gland.' *Physiol. Rev.* **28**, 139–79.

—— (1955). *Neural control of the pituitary gland.* Edward Arnold, London.

VAN OORDT, P. G. W. J. *et al.* (1952). 'Spermatogenesis in normal and hypophysectomized frogs (*Rana temporaria*), following gonadotrophin administration.' *Acta endocr., Kbh.* **9**, 155–60.

YOUNG, F. G. (1953). 'The growth hormone and diabetes.' *Recent Progr. Hormone Res.* **8**, 471–510.

CHAPTER XXXII

STADIE, W. C. (1954). 'Current concepts of the action of insulin.' *Physiol. Rev.* **34**, 52–100.

YOUNG, F. G. (1945). 'Growth and diabetes in normal animals treated with pituitary (anterior lobe) diabetogenic extract.' *Biochem. J.* **39**, 515–36.

CHAPTER XXXIII

HUXLEY, J. S. (1935). 'Chemical regulation and the hormone concept.' *Biol. Rev.* **10**, 427–41.

LOEWI, O. (1921). 'Über humorale Übertragbarkeit der Herznervenwirkung.' *Pflüg. Arch. ges. Physiol.* **189**, 239–42.

PARKER, G. H. (1932). *Humoral Agents in Nervous Activity*. Cambridge: University Press.

STARLING, E. H. (1905). 'The Croonian lectures on the chemical correlation of the functions of the body.' *Lancet* II. 339.

WITSCHI, E. (1939). In *Sex and Internal Secretions*. Ed. E. Allen. London: Baillière, Tindall, & Cox.

YOUNG, J. Z. (1934). 'Hormones and chemical correlation.' *Sch. Sci. Rev.* **60**, 502–8.

—— (1956). 'The organization within nerve cells.' *Endeavour*, **15**, 57, 5–19.

EMBRYOLOGICAL WORKS

AREY, L. B. (1954). *Developmental Anatomy*. 6th edition, revised. London: W. B. Saunders.

BRACHET, J. (1950). *Chemical Embryology*. London: Interscience Publishers, Ltd.

CORNER, G. W. (1946). *The hormones in Human Reproduction*. Princeton: Princeton University Press.

—— (1944). *Ourselves Unborn*. New Haven: Yale University Press.

DALCQ, A. M. (1938). *Form and Causality in Early Development*. Cambridge: Cambridge University Press.

GRASSÉ, P. (1954). *Traité de Zoologie*. Tome XII. Masson, Paris.

HAMILTON, W. J., BOYD, J. D., and MOSSMAN, H. W. (1952). *Human Embryology*. 2nd edition. Cambridge: W. Heffer.

NEEDHAM, J. (1931). *Chemical Embryology*. Cambridge University Press.

—— (1950). *Biochemistry and Morphogenesis*. Cambridge: Cambridge University Press.

NELSEN, O. E. (1953). *Comparative embryology of the Vertebrates*. New York, Toronto: The Blakiston Co. Inc.

PATTEN, B. M. (1953). *Human Embryology* (2nd edition). London: J. & A. Churchill.

RAVEN, CHR. P. (1954). *An Outline of Developmental Physiology*. London: Pergamon Press.

SPRATT, N. T. (1954). 'Physiological mechanisms in development.' *Physiol. Rev.* **34**, 1–24.

WADDINGTON, C. H. (1956). *Principles of Embryology*. London: Allen & Unwin.

WILLIER, B. H., WEISS, P. A., and HAMBURGER, V. (1955). *Analysis of development*. W. B. Saunders, London.

WITSCHI, E. (1956). *Development of Vertebrates*. Saunders, Philadelphia and London.

CHAPTER XXXIV

BRACHET, J. (1952). 'The role of the nucleus and the cytoplasm in synthesis and morphogenesis.' *Symp. Soc. exp. Biol.* **6**, 173–200.

GLÜCKSMANN, A. (1951). Cell deaths in normal vertebrate ontogeny.' *Biol. Rev.* **26**, 59–86.

GUSTAFSON, T. (1954). 'Enzymatic aspects of embryonic differentiation.' *Int. Rev. Cytol.* **3**, 277–327.

HOLTFRETER, J. (1948). 'Significance of the cell membrane in embryonic processes.' *Ann. N.Y. Acad. Sci.* **49**, 709–60.

REEVE, E. C. R., and HUXLEY, J. S. (1945). 'Some problems in the study of allometric growth.' *Growth and Form*. Essays presented to D'Arcy Wentworth

Thompson. Ed. W. E. Le Gros Clark & P. B. Medawar. Oxford: Clarendon Press.

WEISS, P. A. (1953). 'Some introductory remarks on the cellular basis of differentiation.' *J. Embryol. exp. Morph.* **1**, 181–211.

CHAPTER XXXV

ANCEL, P., and VINTEMBERGER, P. (1948). 'Recherches sur le déterminisme de la symétrie bilatérale dans l'œuf des amphibiens.' *Bull. biol.* Supplement 31.

CONKLIN, E. G. (1905). 'The organization and cell-lineage of the Ascidian egg.' *J. Acad. Nat. Sc., Philad.* **13**, 1–119.

DALCQ, A. (1935). *L'Organisation de l'œuf chez les Chordés*. Paris: Gauthier-Villars.

ROMANOFF, A. L., and ROMANOFF, A. J. (1949). *The avian egg*. Chapman & Hall, London.

ROTHSCHILD, LORD (1956). *Fertilization*. London: Methuen.

SWANN, M. M. (1952). 'The nucleus in fertilisation, mitosis and cell-division.' *Symp. Soc. exp. Biol.* **6**, 89–104.

CHAPTER XXXVI

BALLARD, W. W. (1955). Cortical ingression during cleavage of amphibian eggs by means of vital dyes. *J. exp. Zool.* **129**, 77–98.

BARTH, Lester G. and Barth, Lucena J. (1954), *The energetics of development.* New York: Columbia University Press.

DERRICK, G. E. (1937). An analysis of the early development of the chick by means of the mitotic index. *J. Morphol.* **61**, 257–84.

FANKHAUSER, G. (1952). 'Nucleo-cytoplasmic relations in amphibian development.' *Int. Rev. Cytol.* **1**, 165–93.

HOLTFRETER, J., and TOWNES, P. L. (1955). 'Directed movements and selective adhesion of embryonic amphibian cells.' *J. exp. Zool.* **128**, 53–120.

PASTEELS, J. (1936). 'Études sur la gastrulation des vertébrés méroblastiques. I. Téléostéens.' *Arch. Biol., Paris.* **47**, 205–308.

—— (1937). 'Études sur la gastrulation des vertébrés méroblastiques. III. Oiseaux. IV. Conclusions générales.' *Arch. Biol. Paris.* **48**, 381–488.

VOGT, W. (1925). 'Gestaltungsanalyse am Amphibienkeim mit örtlicher Vitalfärbung. Vorwort über Wege und Ziele. I. Teil: Methodik und Wirkungsweise der örtlichen Vitalfärbung mit Agar als Farbträger.' *Arch. Entw. Mech.* **106**, 542–610.

—— (1929). 'Gestaltungsanalyse am Amphibienkeim mit örtlicher Vitalfärbung. II. Teil. Gastrulation und Mesodermbildung bei Urodelen und Anuren.' *Arch. Entw. Mech.* **120**, 384–706.

CHAPTER XXXVII

CHILD, C. M. (1915). *Individuality in Organisms*. Chicago: University of Chicago Press.

—— (1941). *Patterns and Problems of Development*. Chicago: University of Chicago Press.

HOLTFRETER, J. (1934). 'Der Einfluß thermischer, mechanischer und chemischer Eingriffe auf die Induzierfähigkeit von Triton-Keimteilen.' *Arch. Entw. Mech.* **132**, 225–306.

—— (1934). 'Über die Verbreitung induzierender Substanzen und ihre Leistungen im Triton-Keim.' *Arch. Entw. Mech.* **132**, 307–83.

HUXLEY, J. S., and DE BEER, G. R. (1934). *The Elements of Experimental Embryology*. Cambridge: Cambridge University Press.

MUCHMORE, WILLIAM B. (1951). 'Differentiation of the trunk mesoderm in *Amblystoma maculatum.' J. exp. Zool.* **118**, 137–86.

NEEDHAM, J., WADDINGTON, C. H., and NEEDHAM, D. M. (1934). 'Physico-chemical experiments on the amphibian organizer.' *Proc. roy. Soc.*, B. **114**, 393–422.

NIEUWKOOP, P. D., and OTHERS (1952). 'Activation and organization of the central nervous system in Amphibians. Part I. Induction and activation. Part II. Differentiation and organization. Part III. Synthesis of a new working hypothesis.' *J. exp. Zool.* **120**, 1–108.

NIU, M. C., and TWITTY, V. C. (1953). 'The differentiation of gastrula ectoderm in medium conditioned by axial mesoderm.' *Proc. nat. Acad. Sci., Wash.* **39**, 985–9.

PASTEELS, J. (1951). 'Centre organisateur et potentiel morphogénétique chez les Batraciens.' *Bull. Soc. Zool., France*, **76**, 231–70.

SPEMANN, H. (1924). 'Die Erzeugung tierischer Chimären durch heteroplastische embryonale Transplantation zwischen Triton cristatus und taeniatus.' *Arch. Entw.Mech.* **48**, 533–70.

—— (1938). *Embryonic Development and Induction.* New Haven: Yale University Press.

WEISS, P. A. (1939). *Principles of Development.* New York: Henry Holt.

CHAPTER XXXVIII

BERRILL, N. J. (1955). *The origin of Vertebrates.* Oxford: Clarendon Press.

CONKLIN, E. G. (1932). 'The Embryology of Amphioxus.' *J. Morph.* **54**, 69–151.

DALCQ, A. (1932). 'Étude des localisations germinales dans l'œuf vierge d'ascidie par des expériences de mérogonie.' *Arch. Anat. micr.* **28**, 223–333.

FLYNN, T. T., and HILL, J. P. (1947). 'The development of the Monotremata. IV. The later stages of cleavage and the formation of the primary germ layers.' *Trans. zool. Soc. Lond.* **26**, 1–151.

PASTEELS, J. (1937). 'Études sur la gastrulation des vertébrés méroblastique. II. Reptiles.' *Arch. Biol., Paris.* **48**, 105–84.

SPRATT, N. T. (1947). 'Regression and shortening of the primitive streak in the explanted chick blastoderm.' *J. exp. Zool.* **104**, 69–100.

TRINKAUS, J. P. (1951). 'A study of the mechanism of epiboly in the egg of *Fundulus heteroclitus.' J. exp. Zool.* **118**, 269–320.

WADDINGTON, C. H. (1952). *The Epigenetics of Birds.* Cambridge: Cambridge University Press.

CHAPTER XXXIX

NEEDHAM, J. (1931). *Chemical embryology.* Vol. III. Epilegomena, 1613–64. Cambridge: Cambridge University Press.

CHAPTER XL

Ann. N.Y. Acad. Sci. **55**, 543–742 (1952). Biology of the Testes.

CIBA HANDBOOK IV. (1950). *The Sex Hormones.* Ciba Laboratories Ltd., Horsham, Sussex.

KROHN, P. L., and ZUCKERMAN, S. (1953). 'Reproduction.' *Ann. Rev. Physiol.* **15**, 429–56.

RANDALL, J. T., and FRIEDLAENDER, M. H. G. (1950). 'The microstructure of ram spermatozoa.' *Exp. Cell Res.* **1**, 1–32.

ROTHSCHILD, LORD (1952). 'Spermatozoa.' *Sci. Progr.* **40**, 1–10.

CHAPTER XLI

ASDELL, S. A. (1946). *Patterns of mammalian reproduction*. Constable, London.

BRADFIELD, J. R. G. (1955). Fibre patterns in animal flagella and cilia. *Symp. Soc. Exp. Biol.* **9**, 306–32.

BULLOUGH, W. S. (1951). *Vertebrate Sexual Cycles*. London: Methuen & Co. Ltd.

HARRISON, R. J. (1948). 'The development and fate of the corpus luteum in the vertebrate series.' *Biol. Rev.* **23**, 296–331.

MANDL, A. M., and ZUCKERMAN, S. (1951). 'The relation of age to numbers of oocytes.' *J. Endocrin.* **7**, 190–3.

MARKEE, J. E. (1940). 'Menstruation in intraocular endometrial transplants in the Rhesus monkey.' *Contrib. Embryol., Carnegie Inst. Wash.* **28**, 219. In G. W. Corner, *The Hormones in Human Reproduction*, pp. 151–308.

Marshall's Physiology of Reproduction (1952). 3rd ed. Ed. A. S. Parkes. London: Longmans, Green & Co.

PHELPS, D. (1946). 'Endometrial vascular reactions and the mechanism of nidation.' *Amer. J. Anat.* **79**, 167–97.

ROBSON, J. M. (1947). *Recent Advances in Sex and Reproductive Physiology*. 3rd edition. London: J. & A. Churchill.

YOUNG, J. Z., and BELLERBY, C. W. (1935). 'The response of the lamprey to injection of anterior lobe pituitary extract.' *J. exp. Biol.* **12**, 246–53.

ZUCKERMAN, S. (1932). *The Social Life of Monkeys and Apes*. London: Kegan Paul.

—— (1951). 'The number of oocytes in the mature ovary.' *Recent Progr. Hormone Res.* **6**, 63–109.

CHAPTER XLII

AMOROSO, E. C. (1952). 'Placentation' in *Marshall's Physiology of Reproduction*. 3rd edition: chapter 15. Ed. A. S. Parkes. London: Longmans, Green & Co.

BRAMBELL, F. W. R., HEMMINGS, W. A., and HENDERSON, M. (1951). *Antibodies and embryos*. Athlone Press, University of London.

GLADSTONE, R. J., and HAMILTON, W. J. (1941). 'A presomite human embryo (Shaw).' *J. Anat., Lond.* **76**, 9–44 and 187–203.

HERTIG, A. T., and ROCK, J. (1941). 'Two human ova of the pre-villous stage, having an ovulation age of about eleven and twelve days respectively.' *Contrib. Embryol., Carnegie Inst. Wash.* **29**, 127.

—— —— (1945). 'Two human ova of the pre-villous stage, having a developmental age of about seven and nine days respectively.' *Contrib. Embryol., Carnegie Inst. Wash.* **31**, 65.

HUGGETT, A. ST. G., and HAMMOND, J. (1952). 'Physiology of the placenta' in *Marshall's Physiology of Reproduction*. 3rd edition: chapter 16. Ed. A. S. Parkes. London: Longmans, Green & Co.

LEWIS, W. H., and WRIGHT, E. S. (1935). 'On the early development of the mouse egg.' *Carnegie Inst. Wash. Pub.* No. 459, 113–43.

RUNNER, M. N. (1947). 'Development of mouse eggs in the anterior chamber of the eye.' *Anat. Rec.* **98**, 1–17.

STREETER, G. L. (1942) and (1945). 'Developmental horizons in human embryos.' *Contrib. Embryol., Carnegie Inst. Wash.* **30**, 211; **31**, 29; **32**, 135.

CHAPTER XLIII

GILBERT, P. W. (1952). 'The origin and development of the head cavities in the human embryo.' *J. Morph.* **90**, 149–87.

GOODRICH, E. S. (1930). *Studies on the Structure and Development of Vertebrates*. London: Macmillan & Co. Ltd.

JACOBSON, W., and FELL, H. B. (1941). 'The developmental mechanics and potencies of the undifferentiated mesenchyme of the mandible.' *Quart. J. micr. Sci.* **82,** 563–86.

CHAPTER XLIV

BOYD, J. D. (1950). 'Development of thyroid and parathyroid glands and the thymus.' *Annals of the Royal College of Surgeons of England*, **7,** 455–71.

CHAPTER XLV

EVERETT, N. B. (1945). 'The present status of the germ-cell problem in vertebrates.' *Biol. Rev.* **20,** 45–55.

FRASER, ELIZABETH A. (1950). 'The development of the vertebrate excretory system.' *Biol. Rev.* **25,** 159–87.

GOODRICH, E. S. (1935). 'The study of nephridia and genital ducts since 1895.' *Quart. J. micr. Sci.* **86,** 113–392.

WADDINGTON, C. H. (1938). 'The morphogenetic function of a vestigial organ in the chick.' *J. exp. Biol.* **15,** 371–76.

CHAPTER XLVI

BARCLAY, A. E., FRANKLIN, K. J., and PRICHARD, M. M. L. (1944). *The Foetal Circulation and Cardiovascular System, and the Changes that they undergo at Birth.* Oxford: Blackwell Scientific Publications Ltd.

GOODRICH, E. S. (1930). *Studies on the Structure and Development of Vertebrates.* London: Macmillan & Co. Ltd.

CHAPTER XLVII

BERGQUIST, H., and KÄLLÉN, B. (1953). 'On the development of neuromeres to migration areas in the vertebrate cerebral tube.' *Acta anat. Basel*, **18,** 65–73.

DETWILER, S. R. (1936). *Neuroembryology.* New York: Macmillan.

HAMBURGER, V. (1952). 'Development of the nervous system.' *Ann. N.Y. Acad. Sci.* **55,** 117–32.

HÖRSTADIUS, S. (1950). *The Neural Crest.* London: Oxford University Press.

KÄLLÉN, B. (1953). 'On the significance of the neuromeres and similar structures in vertebrate embryos.' *J. Embryol. exp. Morph.* **1,** 387–92.

LEVI-MONTALCINI, R. (1952). 'Effects of mouse tumour transplantation on the nervous system.' *Ann. N.Y. Acad. Sci.* **55,** 330–43.

MARSH, G., and BEAMS, H. W. (1946). 'In vitro control of growing chick nerve fibres by applied electric currents.' *J. cell. comp. Physiol.* **27,** 139–57.

SPERRY, R. W. (1951). 'Regulative factors in the orderly growth of neural circuits.' *Growth*, **15,** 63–87.

TERNI, T. (1920). 'Sulla correlazione fra ampiezza del territorio di innervazione e grandezza delle cellule gangliari. 2. Ricerche sui gangli spinali che innervano la coda rigenerata, nei Sauri. (*Gongylus ocellatus*).' *Arch. ital. Anat.* **17,** 507–43.

YNTEMA, C. L. (1943). 'An experimental study on the origin of the sensory neurones and sheath cells of the IXth and Xth cranial nerves in Amblystona punctatum.' *J. exp. Zool.* **92,** 93–119.

INDEX